HUDSON'S DIRECTORY
HISTORIC HOUSES AND GARDENS
and OTHER PROPERTIES OF INTEREST

Harewood House, Yorkshire.

Published by

NORMAN HUDSON & COMPANY

High Wardington House, Upper Wardington, Banbury, Oxon OX17 1SP
Tel: 01295 750750   Fax: 01295 750800

Project Co-ordination: Jan Bowman and Joyce Binns
Design and Typesetting: K.C Graphics
Colour Origination by Riverline Reprographics Ltd.
Printed in Great Britain by BPC (Waterlow) Ltd.

Cover Picture: Dorney Court, Nr. Windsor, Berks.

Cottesbrooke, Northamptonshire

ABOUT THIS DIRECTORY

This Directory is in **three** sections:

1.   Introductory section including:
- The National Trust - a Centenary Celebration of Heritage
- Gallery of Family Portraits
- A Family at Ease - the Duke of Devonshire at Chatsworth.

2.   Main Section
- Houses open to the public and those offering facilities for corporate functions and special events, listed under County headings in alphabetical order.

3.   Accommodation Section
- includes principally houses occupied as family homes but where accommodation is on the basis of previous booking.

Prices and opening times quoted are those that we have been given , and to the best of our knowledge are expected to be those in force during 1995 .

Symbols used denote either ownership, responsibility or ownership, as below:

Property owned by Member of the Historic Houses Association

Property owned by the National Trust

Property in the care of English Heritage

Property owned by The National Trust for Scotland

Property in the care of Historic Scotland

Property in the care of CADW - Welsh Historic Monuments

Travel Trade Secret
Now Fully in Public Domain

This annual Directory was first published nine years ago with backing from the British Tourist Authority and encouragement from the Historic Houses Association. They recognised that the travel trade needed to be provided with detailed information about houses open to the public. This was not readily available elsewhere. The then Minister for Tourism, David Trippier, launched the first issue at the newly opened British Travel Centre in Lower Regent Street. Since then the Directory has grown apace. What was once distributed exclusively to the travel trade has now, through widespread demand, been made available to everyone.

This year the National Trust celebrates its centenary and details of most of their houses and gardens can be found in these pages. I have watched the growth of the National Trust with much interest both as a member of its Council for fifteen years and of a Regional Management Committee for six years. There is no doubt that but for the work of the Trust many important historic houses and their collections would not be here for us to see today.

Norman Hudson

In recent years English Heritage has made enormous strides forward in the presentation of their properties, the majority of which are now listed in this Directory. Many have a programme of events throughout the year.

The majority of historic houses still remain in private ownership. Private owners are generally regarded as the most cost effective guardians of this part of the national heritage. They have a strongly developed sense of trust, of indebtedness to their ancestors, of a duty to their heirs and of responsibility to the community at large. They also keep historic houses alive as living entities enabling them to continue to evolve as they always have done. But theirs is not an easy task. In my role as retained Adviser to the Historic Houses Association, which with its 1,300 members embraces most of the major privately owned houses and gardens in the country, I am able to see behind what might appear to the casual house visitor to be a privileged, comfortable and enviable way of life. Owning and occupying a historic house is not without its rewards but nearly always it involves a huge amount of work, energy and very substantial expenditure on upkeep which is almost always far in excess of any revenue that may be earned from public opening or other reasonable commercial use.

I have often been struck by how visitors to private houses, including fine art experts, are first drawn to any family photographs on display rather than to works of art. So often one hears the comment "I like this house because it is a lived in family home". For that reason I have in this edition included a "Gallery of Family Portraits". In this way readers will be able to put faces to names and match some families (and their pets) with their houses.

Norman Hudson

Derwentwater in the Lake District, from the lower slopes of Catbells.

The National Trust was not quite eighty years old when I was first elected as a member of its Council. Membership was barely 250,000. Most of the staff knew each other. Today in its centenary year membership stands at 2.2 million - it has grown enormously. Management both of the Trust and its properties has become much more complicated. It is one of the largest and most successful conservation charities in the world with a huge accumulation of conservation expertise.

In the case of historic houses the Trust has provided a valuable safety net when, for a variety of reasons, an owner has been unable to continue.

I hope that in the future the fiscal, political and economic climate will make it easier for private owners of Britain's historic houses, to continue to maintain them, not only for themselves but for the benefit of the nation and for future generations. This will mean that there will be less need for the National Trust to act as a safety net which it can now do only with the greatest difficulty and rarely without a substantial subvention of public funds. The Trust could then devote more of its energy and resources to its admirable work conserving our finest stretches of coastline and countryside.

Norman Hudson

A Centenary Celebration of Heritage

This year, 1995, the National Trust, Britain's largest conservation charity, is 100 years old.

Many special events and activities are planned for the year, with a series of concerts, plays and lectures taking place throughout the country. There will also be major centenary art exhibition, *In Trust for the Nation.* at the National Gallery from November 22 until March 1996, which will feature paintings from National Trust houses including unseen works by Titian, Velazquez, Van Dyck, Jan Steen, Turner, Hogarth and Chardin.

While the National Trust's 100th birthday is certainly a time for celebration of a century of achievement in the protection of Britain's coat, countryside and historic buildings, it is also set to be an opportunity to reflect on the value of the charity's conservation work and the need for it to continue. Man-made pressures on the environment continue to threaten beautiful and historically valuable sites, and the National Trust's original mission to preserve places of beauty and historic interest for the benefit of the nation, seems even more important and relevant in today's world one hundred years on.

The National Trust has played an increasingly important role in the conservation of heritage in all its diverse forms since the acquisition of its first property in 1895. This first property - Dinas Oleu in North Wales - was a gift by Fanny Talbot and consisted of four and a half acres of steep, gorse-clad, rock fell above Barmouth, which offered magnificent views over Cardigan Bay. By giving this fragment of land, Mrs Talbot prevented the spread of development along the coast.

Wallington, Northumberland

The Trust's second property and its first historic house was the 14th century timber-framed Clergy House at Alfriston in East Sussex, bought for £10. The Trust spent £150 on restoring it, around half its annual income at that time!

Further acquisitions continued, reflecting the commitment, vision and enthusiasm of the Trust's three founders - Octavia Hill, a social worker renowned for her pioneering work in housing reform; Sir Robert Hunter, a solicitor whose special concern was for the maintenance of open spaces in Surrey, and Canon Hardwicke Rawnsley, a person who lived in and loved the Lake District.

While the initial emphasis of the Trust's work was on countryside conservation, in 1937 the introduction by Parliament of The National Trust Act allowed owners to donate their historic homes and contents to the National Trust in lieu of tax. The Act enabled the launch of the National Trust's successful; "Country Houses Scheme" whereby the donor and their family continue to live in the house, with an agreement on public access.

Since then, many country houses which would otherwise have been sold for development or demolished, have been saved for the nation. The National Trust now cares for a diverse range of over 200 historic houses, and over

Continued …

150 gardens. Inside them, the Trust's collections include an estimated 8,000 paintings, 100,000 drawings, watercolours, prints and engravings, 1,000 sculptures, 30,000 ceramic and glass items and one million books.

Alfriston Clergy House, East Sussex.

Along with this impressive collection of historic homes and estates, the National Trust also now has responsibility for over 590,000 acres of the country's most beautiful countryside and 548 miles of outstanding coast. It all adds up to a costly but valuable conservation responsibility, particularly as the pressures on sensitive sites mount due to growing visitor numbers. More than 10 million people visit the Trust's houses and gardens in a year, and millions more enjoy its open spaces. One of the greatest achievements, and continuing challenges for the National Trust, is to maintain the delicate balance between preservation and presentation. While giving access to the public, it must at the same time not allow the character of its properties to be undermined or damaged by the pressure of visitors, for all heritage sites should be managed on the assumption that they are held in trust to be passed on intact and undamaged to the next and succeeding generations. This is what the concept of heritage means.

The Trust, fortunately, has some unique powers to assist it in its conservation concern. It is governed by a 1907 Act of Parliament which enables it (along with the National Trust for Scotland) to declare its properties 'inalienable'. This means that although they may be leased with the approval of the Charity Commission, they cannot be sold or mortgaged or compulsorily purchased against the wishes of the National Trust without the approval of Parliament. Nearly all Trust properties are held inalienably, in perpetuity, for the benefit of the nation. This special power helps ensure that preservation is forever.

The Trust has a part to play in showing the way forward, as heritage management becomes ever more complicated in a fast-changing world. By the careful use of resources and making sure that it does not exploit the places in its care, the Trust can provide, in the most practical terms a direct response to local, national and international concerns about sustainable growth.

1895-1995
The restoration period

The splendour of the British landscape is celebrated the world over. Our country homes and historic places attract admirers in their millions each year.

It's hard to imagine otherwise.

Yet, in 1895, our national assets - unique and irreplaceable - were under threat. And were it not for the labours of three visionary Victorians, the Britain we know and love might be a very different place indeed.

Powis Castle.

Together they founded the National Trust to preserve places of historic interest and natural beauty for ever, for everyone.

One hundred years later, as Britain's leading conservation charity, we care for some 400 historic properties and gardens, 547 miles of breathtaking coastline and over half a million acres of magnificent countryside.

National treasures painstakingly restored, lovingly maintained, and preserved, for generations more to enjoy.

For a free Centenary Map Guide and information on any National Trust properties, events or for membership details telephone:

0181- 464 1111.

Alternatively write to: The National Trust, Centenary Information Office, P.O. Box 39, Bromley, Kent BR1 1NH.

THE NATIONAL TRUST CENTENARY

Elisabeth Vigee Lebrun, self-portrait 1791.

▲ *Mr & Mrs Nicholas Charrington, **Layer Marney Tower**, Essex, with Lottie, an Essex Saddleback Pig. Their medieval barn now houses some of the Home Farm collection of rare breed farm animals. Layer Marney is a building of startling originality and the tallest and most flamboyant of a select group of Tudor Gate Houses.*

▲ *Lord Somerleyton, **Somerleyton Hall**, Suffolk. Lord Somerleyton as Master of the Horse holds one of the four great Offices of State. Somerleyton was bought in 1863 by Sir Francis Crossley whose family fortune came from their carpet making mills in Halifax where they were also responsible for some of the finest Victorian buildings remaining in Halifax today. Lord Somerleyton has done a great deal to further enhance the Somerleyton estate. The 12 acres of gardens are maintained to the highest standard.*

▲ *The Duke and Duchess of Marlborough, **Blenheim Palace**, Oxfordshire. Blenheim is the greatest of English palaces; that it is an architectural masterpiece rather than an extravagant pile is due to the imagination of John Vanbrugh the heroic genius of English Baroque who had recently at Castle Howard designed his first house.*

▲ *Mr and Mrs Peter Duff together with their son Simon, who organises the catering, and daughter Helena in the Gardens of **Ilsington**, Dorset which have an unusual collection of peonies and irises.*

▲ *The Earl and Countess of Arundel and Surrey with their family in front of the keep at **Arundel Castle**, Sussex. Lord Arundel is heir to the Dukedom of Norfolk created in 1483. The Dukedom carries the hereditary office of Earl Marshal of England. The Fitzalan Howard family is one of the most illustrious in English history. Lord Arundel includes among his brothers-in-law, Sir David Frost the broadcaster.*

▲ *Mr Martin Drury, Director General Designate of the National Trust. As Historic Buildings Secretary of the Trust he has influenced the way in which the Trust's buildings are managed and decisions about those that have been taken on. In 1978 he and Norman Hudson were part of a small team led by Lord Tavistock of Woburn Abbey on a British Tourist Authority Heritage Study Mission to the USA to see what lessons could be learned and applied to properties in Britain. At that time in the USA, certain aspects of presentation, interpretation; visitor control; staff training and retail sales were generally more advanced than in the UK. Now it is more usual for people from elsewhere to learn from the accumulated experience of the National Trust here.*

▲ *Viscount and Viscountess De Lisle in the gardens at **Penshurst Place**, Kent. The 14th century Great Hall at Penshurst is breathtaking and unrivalled in any private house. The gardens first laid out in the 14th century have been diversified over successive years and, in particular, recently to provide a succession of colour as the seasons change.*

▲ *Mr and Mrs John Makepeace, **Parnham House**, Dorset. John Makepeace is well known for his design and manufacture of furniture, many pieces of which are already in public collections. Less well known is the work done by Jennie Makepeace since 1980 in the extensive restoration and replanting of the 14 acre garden surrounding the Elizabethan manor house enlarged by John Nash in 1810.*

Richard Greenly

▲ *Mr Somerset and Lady Juliet de Chair and their daughter Helena at **St Osyth's Priory**, Essex. Mr de Chair bought St Osyth's in 1954 and first restored the Gatehouse for occupation. The 18th Century range now contains his art collection and outstanding paintings inherited by his wife from her father the 8th Earl FitzWilliam including celebrated Stubbs's.*

As seen in Country Living – Peter Ranter

▲ *Mr James and the Hon Mrs Hervey Bathurst and their daughters, Imogen and Isabella, at* **Eastnor Castle***, Herefordshire. Over the last few years the princely and imposing Eastnor Castle has undergone a triumphant renaissance so that it now looks better than it probably ever has. Many of the Castle's treasures hidden away in attics and cellars since the War have been brought into the stunning and newly enlivened interiors.*

▲ *Lord and Lady Palmer, the Hon Hugo Palmer, the Hon Edwina Palmer and the Hon George Palmer with their Dalmatian, Stripey and Lakeland Terrier, Archie, at* **Manderston***, Berwickshire the most sumptuous Edwardian house in Britain. Lord Palmer's ancestor Sir James Miller who had inherited a fortune from trading in hemp and herrings married the Hon Eveline Curzon a daughter of Lord Scarsdale who had been brought up at Kedleston Hall, Derbyshire, the masterpiece by Robert Adam. To impress his father-in-law Sir James commissioned, in 1903, the remodelling of Manderston with no expense spared. The result was a beautiful and impressive blend of Georgian elegance and Edwardian comfort. The house, luxurious stables, marbled dairy, formal garden, lake and woodland gardens are an immaculately maintained ensemble equally as impressive today as had been intended.*

▲ *Lord and Lady Feversham and their family,* **Duncombe Park***, Yorkshire. For many years Duncombe Park was leased as a girls school until ten years ago Lord and Lady Feversham decided to restore it to a family home. Lord Feversham who takes an active interest in the Arts and Local Government is a keen gardener. The 18th Century landscape garden at Duncombe is a masterpiece.*

▲ *The Duke and Duchess of Rutland in the long gallery at* **Haddon Hall***, Derbyshire, together with their dog "Belvoir" having the same name as their principal seat* **Belvoir Castle** *also featured in this Directory. Haddon Hall won the Christie's/HHA Garden of the Year Award 1994.*

▲ *Mr James Hunter Blair, whose home **Blairquhan**, Ayrshire is one of the finest houses by the architect William Burn. James Hunter Blair renowned for his insatiable zest for life and fun, retired last year as Chairman of the HHA in Scotland. This welcoming house with its original furniture is open to the public for a month each summer but more extensively available for small conferences, corporate hospitality and accommodation.*

▼ *Mrs Dundas Bekker and her younger daughter Henrietta looking at the shell of the dining room in the west wing of **Arniston House**, Midlothian prior to its restoration.*

◄ *The Hon Mrs Cunliffe-Lister, her son Simon and dogs Tessa, Tito and Towler at **Burton Agnes Hall**, Yorkshire. This out-standing late Elizabethan house has many surprises. Notable paintings inlcude many fine modern paintings by Gaugin, Renoir, Pissaro, Utrillo and others.*

▶ *Lord and Lady Montagu outside **Palace House, Beaulieu** together with the Hon Jonathan, the Hon Mary and the Hon Ralph Douglas-Scott-Montagu and the springer spaniels Bobby and Sika. Lord Montagu was the founding President of the Historic Houses Association and the first Chairman of English Heritage.*

▲ *Mrs Clare McLaren Throckmorton photographed at **Coughton Court**, Warwickshire with her husband Mr Andrew McLaren, daughter Christina Williams, sons, Charles and Guy Tritton, son-in-law Benedict Williams, and dogs Toffee and Beluga. Coughton Court has been the home of the Throckmortons since the 15th Century. In 1992 a new formal garden with designs based on an Elizabethan Knot garden was constructed in the courtyard.*

▲ *The Duke of Northumberland, **Alnwick Castle**, Northumberland, and **Syon Park**, Middlesex. Alnwick Castle which houses an exquisite collection of art treasures is the second largest inhabited castle in England after Windsor and has been in the possession of the Percys, Earls and Dukes of Northumberland since 1309. The State rooms in Syon Park are probably the finest work of Robert Adam who was retained by the first Duke in 1762 to re-model the house.*

▲ *The Earl and Countess of Strathmore and Kinghorne with their children the Hon George Norman Bowes Lyon (left); Simon Patrick Lord Glamis (right) and in front the Hon John Fergus Bowes Lyon. Their family home **Glamis Castle,** Angus is the childhood home of HM Queen Elizabeth the Queen Mother, the birthplace of HRH The Princess Margaret and the legendary setting of Shakespeare's play "Macbeth".*

▲ *Mr and Mrs Edward Hulse, **Breamore House**, Hampshire. Mr Hulse's 84 year old father, Sir Westrow Hulse Bt, was in the news last Christmas when he escaped almost certain death in his blazing house nearby by tying sheets together and climbing from a first floor window.*

▲ *The Earl and Countess of Normanton with their children , Lady Portia Agar, Lady Marisa Agar and Lord Somerton at* **Somerley***, Hampshire. The house is tucked away 1¹/₂ miles from the nearest road amidst a huge park. It is not generally open to the public but its privacy has made it popular as a film location and as a place for top level meetings and corporate hospitality for which it is made available.*

▲ *The Earl and Countess of Mansfield,* **Scone Palace***, Perthshire. It was at Scone where Kenneth MacAlpine united Scotland and in 838AD placed the stone of Scone upon the Moot Hill which became the crowning place of Scottish kings. Edward I moved the Coronation Stone to Westminster in 1296. One of Lord Mansfield's most distinguished ancestors was William Murray. He was twice Lord Chief Justice and Chancellor of the Exchequer. Such was his eloquence that it was said of him, "One might have heard a pin fall when he was speaking" in the House of Commons. By a judgement in favour of a run-away negro slave in 1771 he played a decisive role in the beginnings of the anti-slavery movement. He became Earl of Mansfield in 1776.*

▲ *Mr and Mrs Oliver Russell,* **Ballindalloch Castle***, Nr Grantown-on-Spey. Only recently opened to the public Ballindalloch is one of the very few privately owned castles to be lived in continuously by its original family, the Macpherson Grants, since 1546. It exemplifies the transition from the stark tower house necessary for survival in 16th century Scotland to the elegant and comfortable country house so beloved of Victorians in the Highlands. The Castle has a magnificent setting surrounded by hills with the rivers Spey and Avon flowing through the grounds.*

▲ *Sir Lachlan and Lady Maclean,* **Duart Castle***, Isle of Mull. Duart Castle has been the Maclean stronghold since the 12th century. The keep was built by a Lachlan Lubanach 5th Chief in 1360. It was burnt by the English in 1758 but restored in 1912 by Sir Fitzroy Maclean the 26th Chief of the Clan who fought as a Hussar in the Crimea and lived to be 100. The Castle which has a spectacular position overlooking the Sound of Mull contains regular reminders of stirring deeds by Macleans.*

▲ *Lord and Lady Courtenay and, coming down the stairs, the Hon Charles Courtenay, Mr Jeremy Wharton, the Hon Mrs Wharton, the Hon Camilla Courtenay, and seated, the Hon Eleanora Courtenay in the Staircase Hall at **Powderham Castle**, Devon. Lord Courtenay is the son of the Earl of Devon, the direct descendent of Sir Philip Courtenay who built Powderham between 1390 and 1420. The castle contains a large collection of portraits by many famous artists including Reynolds, Kneller and Hudson.*

Photograph by Derry Moore - (0171) 229 5950

▲ Major Tony Hibbert as photographed by a French visitor to the 26 acre **Trebah Garden** which the Hibbert family have restored and donated to the Trebah Garden Trust, a registered charity. In 1994 Trebah received 65,000 visitors.

▲ Mr and Mrs William Proby and their four daughters. **Elton Hall**, Cambridgeshire has been the home of the Proby family for over 300 years. Mr Proby is currently President of the Historic Houses Association which represents over 1,300 private owners of historic houses. Elton has a good collection of paintings but the visitor is afforded particular pleasure from the gardens which have been restored and expanded in recent years under the direction of Mrs Proby. The fragrance of 1,000 roses is memorable.

▲ Three generations of Lowsley Williams' at **Chavenage**, Gloucestershire: Mr David Lowsley Williams with his son George and grandson James (aged 2). Chavenage has often been used as a location for TV and film productions and as a venue for small conferences and functions.

◄ Sir Bernard de Hoghton lives at **Hoghton Tower**, Lancashire built by his ancestor in 1562. It was here that in 1617 King James I visited the house and knighted the loin of beef, hence "Sirloin".

▲ Lord and Lady Cavendish in the gardens at **Holker Hall**, Cumbria. Both are passionate gardeners and the gardens at Holker extending to 24 acres with a spectacular limestone cascade won the Christie's/HHA Garden of the Year Award 1991.

▲ The late Lord Methuen of **Corsham Court**, Wiltshire who sadly died as this edition was being prepared. He is seen here on a happy occasion with Anne one of his nieces, Mark a nephew by marriage and five of his great-nieces. Lord Methuen had an arboretum of 350 rare trees planted in the 1980s. Also over the years he had 75,000 daffodils and narcissi planted in the arboretum. In 1994 he commissioned a ha-ha on the east lawn which has greatly enhanced the view over the park to the lake.

▲ The Viscount and Viscountess Daventry at **Arbury Hall**, Warwickshire which has been the seat of the Newdegate family for over 400 years. This Tudor/Elizabethan house was "gothicised" to become the Gothick gem of the Midlands. The saloon and dining room ceilings are especially spectacular.

▲ *The Earl and Countess of Shelburne in the gardens at* **Bowood**, *Wiltshire. Lord Shelburne, the elder son of the Marquess of Landsdowne was formerly President of the Historic Houses Association and a Commissioner of English Heritage. He has recently constructed and successfully integrated a superb golf course in the western corner of the 2,000 acre park designed by Capability Brown.*

▲ *Mr John Chichester Constable with his daughter Rodrica Straker and her husband James, pictured in the Staircase Hall,* **Burton Constable**, *Yorkshire, after the christening of John's grand-daughter Isabel. Jack his grandson is now four.*

▲ *Dr Philip Mansel at* **Smedmore**, *Dorset which nestles at the foot of the Purbeck Hills looking across the sea to Portland Bill and has been the home of the Mansel family for nearly 400 years. The house is also a popular venue made available for weddings, business and private functions.*

◄ *Mr and Mrs James More-Molyneux with their son Michael More-Molyneux together with his wife, their children and pets (note the ferret) in front of* **Loseley Park**, *Surrey. The Loseley name is widely known because of the Jersey herd of cows and the ice cream that is now sold nationwide. The huge 17th Century tithebarn beside the house has been converted to form a comfortable and stylish venue for business and corporate hospitality events.*

▲ Mr Andrew de Candole who recently acquired **Groombridge Place**, Kent now opens the garden to the public.

▲ The Hon Arthur and Mrs Hazlerigg, **Noseley Hall**, Leciestershire, with their son William, twin daughters Eliza and Amelia, Viola and dog Magpie. Noseley Hall is not open to the public but being centrally located in the Midlands is a popular venue for corporate events, conferences and private parties.

▲ Mr and Mrs Richard Burnett with their Border Collie, Bo, at **Finchcocks**, Kent, a fine Georgian Baroque Manor with outstanding brickwork. Richard is a leading exponent of the early piano and Finchcocks which is the scene of many musical events now contains his magnificent collection of some 80 historic keyboard instruments.

▲ Mr and Mrs Richard Reynolds of **Leighton Hall**, Lancashire with their daughters Katherine and Lucy looking at a recent edition to their large collection of birds of prey which is on display.

▲ *Captain the Hon Gerald and Mrs Maitland Carew with Emma, Peter and Edward in the drawing room at* **Thirlestane Castle***, Berwickshire. "Bunny" Maitland Carew has secured a future for Thirlestane, one of Scotland's oldest and finest castles, by giving the main part of the Castle, with its unsurpassed 17th century ceilings, to a charitable trust.*

▲ *Mr and Mrs Charles Gooch and their daughters at* **Boughton Monchelsea Place***, Kent. The view from the house which stands 310 feet above sea level is one of the finest over the weald of Kent.*

◀ *Mr and Mrs Harry Bott with their eldest son Richard in the splendid gardens surrounding their house at* **Benington Lordship***, Hertfordshire. A particular feature of the gardens is the double herbaceous borders and kitchen garden with unusual vegetables grown in raised beds.*

◀ *Mr Noel Boxall examining some of the armour in the 14th century Gatehouse at* **Bickleigh Castle***, Devon. The great hall and picturesque moated garden make Bickleigh Castle a favourite venue for functions, particularly wedding receptions.*

The Marquess and Marchioness of Bath with ▶ *their son Viscount Weymouth and daughter Lady Lenka Thynne. Lord Bath has decorated the walls of his private apartments at* **Longleat,** *Wiltshire with his Neo-Expressionist murals and is creating a series of mazes in the grounds so as to trade under the slogan of "The Lions and Labyrinths of Longleat".*

▲ *Mr William Bromley Davenport of **Capesthorne**, Cheshire, his son Nicholas and (front row) daughter-in-law, Emma, wife Lizzie and daughter Liberty together with dogs Pickle, Topoo and Tomo. Mr William Bromley Davenport and his wife have recently re-furbished many of the rooms at Capesthorne.*

▲ *Dr and Mrs Robin Odgers and their daughters Susannah and Emma Jane at **Hatch Court**, Somerset. Over the last few years Dr Odgers has totally re-vitalised the walled garden. At the back of the house is a well laid out museum to Princess Patricia's Canadian Infantry and a charming 18th century China room where the family collection of porcelain is displayed.*

▲ *Lord and Lady Ivar Mountbatten at **Moyns Park**, Essex. Lord Ivar, youngest son of the third Marquess of Milford Haven does not open his house to the public but makes it available on an exclusive use basis for guests seeking complete privacy in relaxed elegant and traditional surroundings.*

*The Earl and Countess of ▶ Yarmouth with their daughter Gabriella aged 2 and son William aged 7 months at **Ragley Hall**, Warwickshire.*
Lord Yarmouth's father the Marquess of Hertford saved Ragley from near destruction after the war and not only restored it but by commissioning Graham Rust to paint a mural covering the staircase hall has made an exceptional and notable 20th century contribution to a fine house.

▲ *John McLeod of McLeod with his sons Hugh and Stephan and daughter Eleana on the occasion of Hugh's coming of age party in 1994 at **Dunvegan Castle**, Isle of Skye. Inhabited by the Chiefs of the Clan Mcleod for over 750 years, Dunvegan has a magical position and is steeped in distant history and romantic relics.*

▲ The Marquess and Marchioness of Tavistock in the courtyard at **Woburn Abbey**, Bedfordshire together with their sons Lord James Russell, Lord Robin Russell and Lord Howland. Lord Tavistock's father, the Duke of Bedford, was one of the first to open his house on a commercial basis following the War. Woburn, richly decorated and furnished, has one of the most important private art collections in the world.

▲ The Marquess and Marchioness of Zetland at **Aske**, Yorkshire. In 1995 the house with its fine collection of pictures, furniture and porcelain will be open for the first time to groups of 15 or more by appointment. It is otherwise available for a variety of functions and events.

▲ Mr and Mrs Mark Roper in their award winning garden at **Forde Abbey**. Mrs Roper is no stranger to fine gardens having been brought up at Levens Hall, Cumberland, now the home of her brother Mr Hal Bagot.

▲ Mr and Mrs John Ward and their children Charlotte, a pony called Catkin, Charles and Henry in the newly restored formal garden at **Squerryes Court**, Kent which has been their family home for over 250 years.

Iain the 10th Duke of Atholl, lives at ▶ **Blair Castle**, Perthshire the ancient home and fortress of his family for over 725 years. He has the unique distinction of having the only remaining private army in Europe - the Atholl Highlanders.

▲ *The Earl and Countess of Bradford with their children Alexander, Viscount Newport, the Hon Harry Bridgeman, the Hon Benjamin Bridgman and the Lady Alicia Bridgeman at* **Weston Park***, Shropshire which having been their family home since 12th century has recently been transferred to the Weston Park Foundation. Lord Bradford is well known as a restaurateur and writer.*

Roger Allston

▲ *Lady Victoria and Mr Simon Leatham in front of the great Elizabethan Treasure House of* **Burghley***, Lincolnshire. Lady Victoria, a daughter of the late Marquess of Exeter, has revitalised the presentation of the immense collection of art treasures.*

▲ *Mr and Mrs Patrick Gordon Duff Pennington together with Mr and Mrs Peter Frost Pennington and their children Isla, Fraser and Ewan at* **Muncaster Castle***, Cumbria which has been owned by the Pennington family since 1208. Apart from the Castle and its treasures; gardens which from March to June have wonderful rhododendrons, azaleas, camellias and magnolias, there is an owl centre which has a fine collection of owls from all over the world.*

▲ *Major and Mrs Martin Gibbs with their family at* **Sheldon Manor***, Wiltshire. Sadly Major Gibbs died shortly after this photograph was taken and before he had learned that this captivating house, noted for its welcoming ambiance and quality of food served had received yet another accolade, as outright winner of the AA/NPI Historic House Awards. Houses were judged on their character and authenticity as well as the occupants enthusiasm for showing the house to the public.*

Elsie Gibbs said of the award, "It is a great tribute to the work of my husband and dedication of all who have helped us over 25 years. My son and I look forward to continuing as usual in 1995".

▲ Mr and the Hon Mrs Algy Heber-Percy with labrador Snipe and Norwich Terrier, Toby, in the Gardens at **Hodnet Hall**, Shropshire. From the glorious daffodils of spring to the magnificent roses of summer each season brings fresh delights to these award winning lakeside gardens which extend over 60 acres.

▲ The Duke and Duchess of Wellington at their home **Stratfield Saye**, Berkshire. After Waterloo the first Duke of Wellington, or the Great Duke as he was universally known, was regarded as the saviour of his country and of Europe. Visitors to the house can see the 18 ton funeral hearse constructed from the metal of French cannons captured at Waterloo for the Great Duke's funeral in 1852 which was a major national occasion.

▲ Mr and Mrs Robin Compton in the gardens at **Newby Hall**, Yorkshire which the late 17th century connoisseur of country houses Celia Fiennes thought "the finest I saw in Yorkshire". In recent years Mrs Compton has painstakingly restored the fine Adam interiors of the house. The 25 acres of gardens have received even more attention and it is now truly a "garden for all seasons". The view from the house down the 300 yard double herbaceous border is one of England's finest garden vistas.

▲ Sir Thomas and Lady Ingleby with their children Eleanor, Jack, James and Joslan at **Ripley Castle**, Yorkshire. 28 generations of the Ingleby family have lived at Ripley and the current generation are respected for being one of the hardest working historic house owners in their efforts to make a commercial success of the Castle and Estate as a place to visit and as a Stately Home venue. Sir Thomas also founded the Stately Homes Hotline, a scheme to combat theft from historic houses.

▲ Mr and Mrs Lawrence Banks with their dogs Rogue and Halo Jones in their gardens at **Hergest Croft**, Herefordshire which have been developed over 130 years by four generations of the Banks family. Lawrence Banks, a banker, was formerly treasurer of the Royal Horticultural Society. Elizabeth Banks is widely know as a landscape architect and historian who has advised in connection with numerous great gardens throughout Britain.

▲ Lord and Lady Cobbold at **Knebworth House**, Hertfordshire which for over 500 years has been the home of the talented and versatile Lytton family. The Victorian romantic novelist Edward Bulwer-Lytton and Constance Lytton the suffragette are not now generally known about, but the splendours of Lord Lytton's Viceroyalty of India and the Great Delhi Durbar of 1877 are commemorated in a splendid exhibition that can be see by visitors to Knebworth.

▲ Mr and Mrs John Fryer-Spedding in the Bee Garden at **Mirebouse**, Cumbria. The latin inscription in front of the hives comes from Virgil's fourth Georgic which is about beekeeping. It says: "The first thing must be to find a suitable position for the bees". The Bee Garden is an important feature for visitors.

◄ Lord and Lady Hastings at **Seaton Delaval**, Northumberland. Many find Seaton Delaval the most exciting of Vanbrugh's houses. Ducal magnificence in miniature - sheer theatre. For many years the central block which had been gutted by fire stood a gaunt ruin but in recent years Lord Hastings has carried out partial restoration.

◄ *The Earl and Countess Spencer with their Children, Lady Kitty Spencer and twins Lady Amelia Spencer and Lady Eliza Spencer and dogs Arthur (Spaniel), Delia (Rhodesian Ridgeback), Flossie (Border Terrier) and Bertie (Labrador) on the grand staircase dating from 1650 at **Althorp**, Northamptonshire. Althorp's picture gallery - 115 feet of panelling covered with masterpieces culminating in van Dycks celebrated double portrait "War and Peace" - is breathtaking. The quality of the picture collection is almost matched by that of the 18th century furniture and porcelain. Like many other owners Lord Spencer is going further than merely opening the house to the public and will make it and the 450 acres of surrounding parkland, available for a variety of events.*

▲ *Sir Reresby and Lady Sitwell in front of the Georgian stables at **Renishaw Hall**, Derbyshire. Renishaw has a beautiful Italian garden, park and lake which were the creation of the eccentric Sir George Sitwell (1860-1943) father of the literary "trio" (Edith, Osbert and Sacheverell) and grandfather of Sir Reresby. They have made a new museum on the Sitwells in the stables*

◄ *Mr and Mrs Robert Wright and their children Timothy, Felicity and Jeremy with dogs Meg and Jake photographed in the main hall at **Eyam Hall**, Derbyshire, in front of the picture of Major John Wright who fought in the American War of Independence as Aide-de-Camp to General Burgogne. The Wright family have lived at Eyam Hall since 1671. The house, only a few miles from palatial Chatsworth, retains a small scale intimacy with a succession of rooms full of interest, but never imposing.*

The Duke of Roxburghe with his dogs ▶
*Barley and Sandy, in front of **Floors
Castle**, Roxburghshire, designed by
William Adam and the largest inhabit-
ed castle in Scotland. The Castle has
been seen on cinema screens worldwide
in the film "Greystoke" as the home of
Tarzan, The Earl of Greystoke.*

◀ *Capt and Mrs Nigel Hadden-Paton
of **Rossway Park**, Hertfordshire with
their children Harry, Alice, Polly and
Clementine. Among those companies
who entertained their families at
Rossway Park last year were Mercury
One to One, The Toy Trust, Kleinwort
Benson and Gartmore Asset
Management. Jardine Thompson
Graham used the facilities to run a
series of mini MBA courses
throughout the summer and the house
and gardens were used to provide
the backdrop to several weddings
and dances.*

▶ *Mr Ian Chance of **Wingfield College**, Suffolk, with his wife Hilary,
baby daughter Alice and son James. Having restored its medieval
college and planted a topiary garden Ian Chance founded an Arts and
Music Festival which takes place at Wingfield and throughout
East Anglia.*

▲ *The Earl and Countess of Pembroke with William, Lord Herbert, Lady Jemima Herbert and Lady Alice Herbert at* **Wilton House**, *Wiltshire. The Abbey and lands of Wilton were given in 1544 by Henry VIII to William Herbert who had married Anne Parr, sister of Catherine, sixth wife of King Henry. The house not only contains one of the finest art collections in Europe but is particularly well known for its magnificent state apartments including the famous Single and Double Cube rooms.*

▲ *Capt and Mrs Martin Busk whose garden at* **Houghton Lodge**, *Hampshire was this last year used as one of the settings for the BBC series "Buccaneers". Houghton Lodge is one of the most picturesque of 18th century gothic "cottages ornees". In their kitchen garden they have a hydroponicum, a living exhibition of horticulture without soil demonstrating its application worldwide and in space.*

◄ *Mr and Mrs William Cash,* **Upton Cresset Hall**, *Shropshire. Bill Cash is perhaps better known as a member of Parliament with strong views on Europe rather than as someone with a long standing interest in historic buildings who has restored this Elizabethan manor house with a magnificent Gatehouse.*

▲ *Sir John Ropner in his arboretum at* **Thorp Perrow**, *Yorkshire. The arboretum comprises over 1,000 trees and shrubs set in 85 acres and provides some spectacular sights in spring and autumn.*

▲ Mr and Mrs James Lonsdale and their daughters at **Kingstone Lisle Park**, Oxfordshire. James Lonsdale has a forestry business and in the walled garden produces 250,000 oak trees from acorns under glass each year. Kingstone Lisle is a modest sized house with great style which on occasions the Lonsdales allow to be used on a commercial basis for exclusive parties.

▲ Mr and Mrs Peter Prideaux-Brune with Nicholas and William Prideaux-Brune and dogs Paddington and Lightbulb at **Prideaux Place**, Cornwall, the home of their family for 400 years. In recent years the house and gardens have been the subject of extensive and impressive restoration. Many of the thousands of visitors to Rock, Polzeath, Daymer Bay and Padstow are not always aware that this Elizabethan gem surrounded by its deer park overlooking the sea, is on their doorstep. They should resolve not to miss it next time.

▼ The Earl of Countess of Harewood whose home **Harewood House**, Yorkshire, is particularly noted not only for its superb Robert Adam interiors and ceilings but for its furniture much of which was made especially for Harewood by Thomas Chippendale.
Lord Harewood, a grandson of King George V, has for many years been eminent in the musical world, particularly Opera.

▲ Commander and Mrs Michael Saunders Watson with their daughter Fiona, son and daughter-in-law, James and Elizabeth, and son David (seated) with dogs Dido and Scorpion in the gardens of **Rockingham Castle**, Northamptonshire. Following his naval career Cdr Saunders Watson has been President of the HHA and Chairman of the British Library. Rockingham Castle, built by William the Conqueror was a Royal castle until 1530 and since then has been the home of the Watson family. Almost every century has contributed something of note to Rockingham. More recently some good 20th century paintings were introduced by Cdr Saunders Watson's uncle, Sir Michael Culme-Seymour.

A Family At Ease

RICHARD GREENLY.

Above: The Duke and Duchess of Devonshire continue a 400 year -old family tradition of welcoming visitors to their magnificent home and gardens.

The Dukes of Devonshire have lived at Chatsworth for over 400 years …

Siân Ellis visits a stately home with a long tradition of hospitality.

This article first appeared in **Heritage** magazine also published as **Realm** in the USA.

Facing page: The great glory of Chatsworth is its situation. The house, seen here from the west, is surrounded by rolling trees, whilst the River Derwent flows through the park.

Photographs by: Richard Greenly, Charnham Lane, Hungerford, Berkshire RG17 0EY.
Telephone: (01488) 685256

RICHARD GREENLY.

DAVID OAKES/SWIFT.

RICHARD GREENLY.

THE approach to Chatsworth, near Bakewell in Derbyshire, is like the joyous climax of an opera. Climbing and dipping over the rolling peaks, past the charming village of Edensor where many of the Chatsworth estate employees live, one anticipates with impatience the first glimpse of this grandest of English country houses. Then, above the trees in the distance, one spies the awesome white jet of the Emperor Fountain, created by Joseph Paxton in 1844, gushing some 280 feet into the air. The road winds and the house suddenly appears, stately and imposing, framed on all sides by a landscape of extraordinary splendour.

"The great glory of Chatsworth is its situation," says Andrew Cavendish, 11th Duke of Devonshire, "the beauty of its park and the way the house stands in it." His favourite room is his private study on the ground floor, which provides breathtaking views of the hills rising up to the north-west of the house. "Someone asked me why I often call this my sitting-room and not my study," he remarks. "It is because I do more sitting here than studying!"

Strolling onto the steps of the South Front, facing the Sea-Horse Fountain carved by Caius Gabriel Cibber (1630-1700), with the Emperor Fountain towering from its canal beyond, further confirms the beauty of Chatsworth. Up towards the east stands the Cascade House which feeds the Sea-Horse Fountain; to the west are gardens and the River Derwent. And all around are hills and trees. "We can thank Bess for all that," says the Duke with a broad sweep of his arm to the skyline.

It was "Bess of Hardwick" (c.1527-1608) and her second husband, Sir William Cavendish (1505-57), who built the first house at Chatsworth from 1552. The Hunting Tower, still standing today on the escarpment to the east of the house, dates from the 1580s.

Sir William hailed from Cavendish in

Main picture: The Emperor Fountain arcs into the sky. Left: The Devonshire family crest is the serpent. Top left: The Duke in the Sculpture Gallery.

Suffolk and had prospered as one of King Henry VIII's commissioners for the Dissolution of the Monasteries. But Bess persuaded him to sell the former monastery lands that he owned in Hertfordshire and move to her native Derbyshire, where they created a large house on the site of the square block that is Chatsworth today.

Little changed at Chatsworth until William Cavendish (1640-1707) was created 1st Duke of Devonshire in 1694 for his part in bringing William of Orange to the English throne. The 1st Duke pulled down the South Front of the old house and altered the East Front; he also had a formal garden laid out and the Cascade and its House created by Grillet and Thomas Archer. Later he rebuilt the West and North Fronts, probably to his own design, and had the Canal Pond dug, all this before his death in 1707.

The 4th Duke (1720-64), who was one of our shortest-serving Prime Ministers, from November 1756 until May 1757, also wrought great changes at Chatsworth, enclosing land which became the present park and engaging "Capability" Brown to destroy the formal garden and replace it with the then fashionable "natural" style. He also decided that the house should be approached from the west and set about clearing this aspect of buildings which obstructed the view.

But the greatest era for Chatsworth occurred during the time of the 6th or "Bachelor" Duke (1790-1858), who engaged Sir Jeffry Wyatville to create a new long North Wing. "The 6th Duke was very rich, tax was low, work was cheap and he could do a lot," says the present Duke. "And he was extravagant, too! I feel, though, that architecturally the wing spoilt Chatsworth, yet it is good as it separates what are now the private quarters from the rest of the house."

The 6th Duke also had a mind for comfort, enclosing the North corridor, originally an open and no doubt draughty colonnade, and laying a coloured ▶

Right: Park Top, the 11th Duke's most successful racehorse, sculpted in bronze by Angela Conner. Top right: The Duke admires a favourite painting.

marble pavement to divert attention from the irregularities of its architecture. He added further corridors and the Sketch Galleries to make it easier to proceed around the house.

After meeting Joseph Paxton, the 6th Duke developed a passionate interest in gardening. Paxton became head gardener at Chatsworth in 1826 when he was just 23, and with the Duke he transformed the gardens into those so greatly admired today.

Paxton's colossal rockeries, Emperor Fountain and stepped "Conservative Wall" glasshouse astounded visitors. But it was his Great Conservatory made of wood, iron and glass, and extending over three-quarters of an acre, which was to be his most famous achievement, a precursor of his magnificent Crystal Palace constructed for the Great Exhibition of 1851 in Hyde Park. Sadly, the Great Conservatory does not survive, demolished soon after the First World War, but the splendour of Paxton's gardens flourishes.

This is in no small part thanks to the present Duke and Duchess, both of whom have a keen interest in the gardens. "When you share an interest, it can become contentious," says the Duke, "but fortunately we like different things. My wife likes grand scale gardening and I like spring and autumn bulbs, of which I have planted thousands. So we do not clash."

When the Duke succeeded to the title in 1950 he was, he admits, "not at all prepared." His elder brother, William, had been killed in the Second World War whilst serving with the Coldstream Guards in Belgium; Andrew also served with the Coldstream Guards and was awarded the Military Cross. He then pursued a career in politics, holding office in the Conservative Government as Parliamentary Under-Secretary of State for Commonwealth Relations (1960-62), Minister of State, Commonwealth Relations Office (1962-64) and for Colonial Affairs (1963-64).

"I would like to have done more," he says, wise with hindsight. "When the Tory Government fell and we had four years of Opposition in prospect, I was offered a job as a Steward of the Jockey Club. It was a real job, but I would have waited if I had known we would be back in Government by 1970!"

Throughout this time the Duke had pressing matters to consider at Chats-

worth as a result of his father's unexpected death in 1950, at the age of only 55. Death duties at the maximum rate of 80 per cent needed to be paid. "But I had good fortune," says the Duke. "I had the most brilliant and sympathetic legal advisors, and I was young — just 30. All I had to do was listen to good advice."

That advice led him to the realisation that Chatsworth and its garden and park must be a self-supporting enterprise. He sold many important works of art and thousands of acres of land, and it took 17 years finally to resolve the affairs.

Losing some of the family's treasured paintings was painful, but the Duke takes a philosophical view. "It was the lesser of two evils, like so many decisions in life. I am very lucky that we had the resources and I could sell paintings. Others would not be able to do that."

Fortunately, too, the Dukes of Devonshire have a great tradition of collecting and connoisseurship. ▶

Main picture: Sir Jeffry Wyatville designed the bookcases in the Library for the 6th Duke. Today there are over 17,000 volumes at Chatsworth. Above: The magnificent Cascade, created at the end of the 17th century by Grillet and Thomas Archer. Top: The Rose Garden and the 1st Duke's greenhouse.

▶ After its glorious aspect, Chatsworth is admired above all for its beautiful collections of paintings, drawings, books and furniture.

The 2nd Duke (1673-1729) was the first great collector: of paintings, drawings, prints, coins and carved Greek and Roman gems. The 3rd Duke (1698-1755) commissioned much William Kent furniture which is now displayed at Chatsworth.

The extravagant 6th Duke collected all manner of objects, including two complete libraries; he and Wyatville then designed the bookcases in the sumptuous Library to accommodate them. He also built the Sculpture Gallery in order to display his marvellous collection of stone and sculpted figures.

The present Duke is no exception to the family tradition. His study is a magpie's nest of treasures. He has a wonderful mineral collection and a fine collection of 20th century books. He is also fond of paintings and sculptures by contemporary artists, and Lucian Freud has painted all his family: his wife Deborah, son Peregrine and daughters Emma and Sophia. "But my scale of collecting is modest compared with that of the 6th Duke," he insists. "The economic situation is different today."

To the question of whether public visitors to his home are an intrusion, the Duke replies that he welcomes them. Indeed, throughout the history of Chatsworth it is apparent that the Dukes of Devonshire have always been remarkably enlightened in respect of public visitors, in eras when one would not have expected such consideration. Not only did most entertain in lavish style, with many a royal visitor (including an unwilling one in Mary Queen of Scots, who was imprisoned in the house at various times from 1569-84), but they also opened Chatsworth to visitors from its very beginning.

Celia Fiennes and Daniel Defoe both wrote about the house in the 17th and 18th centuries, and an inn was even built at Edensor in 1775 to accommodate sightseers. When the family was away, the housekeeper would show visitors around and the 5th Duke had "open days" when dinner was provided.

Paxton's endeavours for the 6th Duke attracted great crowds and *The Mirror of Literature and Amusement* of February 1844 gave a glowing report of the Duke's welcome. "The humblest individual is not only shown the whole, but the Duke has expressly ordered the waterworks to be played for everyone without exception. This is acting in the true spirit of great wealth and enlightened liberality; let us add, also, in the spirit of wisdom." Not for nothing is the family crest a serpent, the symbol of wisdom!

Today's visitors to Chatsworth are maintaining a great tradition, and like their predecessors they will find a magnificent home and a gracious welcome. ●

Main picture: The ornate State Drawing Room. The portrait over the fireplace is of the 1st Duke of Devonshire (1640-1707). Above: The present Duke ensconced in his private study, surrounded by his books and minerals.

Top: Splendid tableware in the Great Dining Room.

Westbury Court Garden, Gloucestershire

1 ROYAL CRESCENT
Bath

NUMBER 1 was the first house to be built in the Royal Crescent, John Wood the Younger's fine example of Palladian architecture. The Crescent was begun in 1767 and completed by 1774.

The House was given to the Bath Preservation Trust in 1968 and both the exterior and interior have been accurately restored.

Visitors can see a grand town house of the late 18th Century with authentic furniture, paintings and carpets.

On the ground floor are the Study and Dining Room and on the first floor a Lady's Bedroom and Drawing Room. A series of maps of Bath are on the second floor landing. In the Basement is a Kitchen and a Museum Shop.

❖

ADVICE TO COURIERS & DRIVERS
Please make sure you are familiar with restrictions in The Royal Crescent and parking regulations in the centre of Bath.

FACILITIES FOR THE DISABLED
The house is not suitable for the disabled.

CATERING
There is no restaurant or tea room, but there are many facilities in Bath.

GUIDED TOURS
There are guides in every room. Tours in French and Italian are available on request. Average time taken is 45 minutes.

GIFT SHOP
The Gift Shop is open at the same time as the house, and sells such items as classical creamware and books.

GUIDE BOOKS
A full-colour guide book is available, French, German, Spanish, Italian, Japanese, Chinese, Danish and Dutch translations available on request.

SCHOOL VISITS/CHILDREN
School visits are welcome. The cost per child is £2.00 and guides can be provided. New Education Officer.

CONTACT

Mrs Elizabeth Grant
Curator/Administrator
1 Royal Crescent
Bath
Avon
BA1 2LR

Tel: (01225) 428126
Fax: (01225) 481850

LOCATION

Exit 18 from the M4,
then the A46
to Bath
$2^{1}/_{2}$ hours

Rail: Bath Spa
Railway Station
(1hr, 20 mins
from London)

Taxi: Streamline

OPENING TIMES

Summer
1 March - 29 October
Daily except Mondays.
10.30am - 5.00pm
Closed Good Friday.
Open Bank Hols and Bath
Festival Mondays.

Winter
31 Oct - 10 Dec
Daily except Mondays.
10.30am - 4.00pm

Closed Jan & Feb

Last admissions 30 mins before closing. Special tours by arrangement with the administrator.

ADMISSION

All Year
Adult £3.50
Child* £2.50
Student £2.50
OAP £2.50
Family £8.00
Groups
Adult £2.50
School* £2.00
Student £2.50

*Aged 5 - 16yrs.

BATH ABBEY
Tel: 01225 464930 **Fax**: 01225 429990

Bath, Avon, BA2 6RP.
Owner: — **Contact:** Canon Askew
England's last great medieval church, begun 1499 as monastery, dissolved 1539. Now a parish church. Fine perpendicular architecture, fan vaulting, windows. On site of Saxon monastery and Norman Cathedral.
Location: Centre of Bath, adjacent to Roman Baths.
Opening Times: Easter - 31 Oct: 9.00am - 4.30pm, 8.00 Holy Communion, 9.15am Parish Communion, 11.00am Choral Matins, 12.15pm Holy Communion, 3.15pm Choral Evensong, 6.30pm Evening Service.
Admission: Adult £1.00 (Voluntary contribution)

BECKFORD'S TOWER
Tel: 01225 422212/338727 **Fax**: 01225 481 850

Lansdown Road, Bath, Avon.
Owner: Bath Preservation Trust **Contact:** Ms Vicky Yarham
Location: Lansdown Road.
Opening Times: April - Oct; Sat, Sun & Bank Holiday Monday; 2.00 -5.00pm.
Admission: Adult £1.50, Child under 17 75p, Child under 10 free. Groups at discretion of administrator.

BLAISE CASTLE HOUSE MUSEUM
Tel: 01179 506789 **Fax**: 01179 593475

Henbury Road, Henbury, Bristol, Avon, BS10 7QS.
Owner: Bristol City Council **Contact:** The Curator
18th century mansion, now Bristol's Museum of Social History.
Location: 5 miles NW of Bristol city centre, off B4057
Opening Times: All Year. Tues - Sun, 10.00am - 1.00pm & 2.00 - 5.00pm. Also Bank Holiday Mondays.
Admission: Free.

BRISTOL CATHEDRAL
Tel: 01179 264879 **Fax**: 01179 263678

College Green, Bristol, Avon, BS1 5TJ.
Contact: Mrs J Coupe
Founded in 1140 as an Augustinian monastery, the building has developed in a variety of styles over the centuries and became a Cathedral in 1542. The Norman Chapter House and colourful early English Lady Chapel should not be missed.
Location: Central Bristol.
Opening Times: All Year. 8.00am - 6.00pm. Sunday services: 8.00am, 10.00am and 3.30pm. Weekday services: 8.40am, 12.30pm, 3.30pm and 5.15pm.
Admission: Donation.

CLAVERTON MANOR

OPEN
25 Mar - 5 Nov
Grounds: 1 - 6.00pm
Museum: 2 - 5.00pm
(except Mondays)
Bank Hol Weekends,
Suns & Mons.
11.00am - 5.00pm
5 Nov - 10 Dec
Sats & Suns only.
House & New Gallery
1.00 - 4.00pm
Grounds &
Folk Gallery closed.

Tel: 01225 460503
Fax: 01225 480726

THE AMERICAN MUSEUM, BATH, AVON BA2 7BD
Owner: The Trustees of the American Museum in Britain **Contact:** *Mrs. S Ford*
Situated overlooking the valley of the River Avon and housed in a Georgian mansion, the Museum has 18 period furnished rooms from the 17th to 19th centuries. Special sections devoted to the American Indian, the Pennsylvania Germans, the Shakers etc. New Gallery with seasonal exhibitions. Many exhibits in beautiful gardens. A replica of George Washington's garden at Mount Vernon. American arboretum.
Location: Off the A36 (not suitable for coaches) other route via Bathwick Hill, Bath.
Admission: Adult £5.00, OAP £4.50, Child £2.50 (1994 prices).

CLEVEDON COURT
Tel: 01275 872257

Tickenham Road, Clevedon, Avon, BS21 6QU
Owner: The National Trust **Contact:** The Administrator
Home of the Elton family, this 14th century manor house, once partly fortified, has a 12th century tower and 13th century hall. Collection of Nailsea glass and Eltonware. Beautiful terraced garden.
Location: 1¹/₂m E of Clevedon, on B3130, signposted from exit 20 of M5.
Opening Times: 2 Apr-28 Sep:Wed, Thur, Sun & BH Mon, 2.30 - 5.30pm. Last adm: 5.00pm.
Admission: Adult £3.40, Child £1.60. Children under 17 must be accompanied by an adult. Parties of 20+ by prior arrangement, no reduction.

DYRHAM PARK
Tel: 01179 372501

Nr Chippenham, Avon, SN14 8ER.
Owner: The National Trust **Contact:** The Administrator
Late 17th century house set in ancient deer park. Original furniture and Dutch paintings in a fine series of panelled rooms.
Location: 8M N of Bath, 12m E of Bristol, approach from Bath/Stroud road (A46), 2m S of Tormarton interchange with M4.
Opening Times: Park: All Year. Daily, 12 Noon - 5.30pm (or dusk if earlier). Last admission 5.00pm. Closed Christmas Day. House and Garden: 1 Apr-29 Oct, Daily, except Thur & Fri, 12 Noon - 5.30pm. Last admission 5.00pm (or dusk if earlier).
Admission: House, Garden & Park: Adult £5, Child £2.50. Park only: Adult £1.60, Child 80p. Parties must book.

GATCOMBE COURT
Tel: 01275 393141 **Fax**: 01275 394274

Flax Bourton, Bristol, Avon, BS19 1PX.
Owner: Charles Clarke Esq **Contact:** Charles Clarke Esq
A Somerset Manor House, dating from early 13th century, which has evolved over the centuries since, it is on the site of a large Roman Village, traces of which are apparent. There is a garden terraced by old stone walls, with many climbing roses, yew hedges and a herb garden.
Location: 5m W of Bristol.
Opening Times: By written appointment.

HORTON COURT
Tel: 01985 843600

Horton, Near Chipping Sodbury, Bristol, Avon, B17 6QR.
Owner: The National Trust **Contact:** The Administrator
A Cotswold manor house with 12th century Norman hall and early Renaissance features. Of particular interest is the late perpendicular ambulatory, detached from the house. Norman hall and ambulatory only shown.
Location: 3m NE of Chipping Sodbury, ³/₄m N of Horton, 1m W of A46.
Opening Times: 1 Apr - 28 Oct: Wed & Sat, 2.00 - 6.00pm or dusk if earlier.
Admission: Adult £1.50, Child 80p

JOHN WESLEY'S CHAPEL
Tel: 01179 264740

36 The Horsefair, Broadmead, Bristol, Avon, BS1 3JE.
Contact: Rev A R George
The oldest Methodist chapel in the world.
Location: 36 The Horsefair.
Opening Times: Summer; Mon - Sat, 10.00am - 4.00pm, Living Rooms closed 1.00 - 2.00pm but the chapel remains open. Winter; same as summer except closed on Wednesdays. Closed Bank Holidays.
Admission: Groups £2 ea. (includes talk by warden). Others free - donations appreciated.

LEIGH COURT
Tel: 01275 373393 **Fax**: 01275 374681

Abbots Leigh, Bristol, Avon, BS8 3RA.
Owner: J T Group **Contact:** Mrs Sally Barker
The style of the building is Greek Revival and it stands in 25 acres of parkland.
Location: 2 m from J18 on M5.
Opening Times: As Leigh Court is used as a conference centre prior booking to view is advised.

1 ROYAL CRESCENT, BATH
See Page 1 for full page entry.

ROMAN BATHS AND PUMP ROOM
Tel: 01225 461111 **Fax**: 01225 448521

Stall Street, Bath, Avon, BA1 1LZ.
Owner: Bath City Council **Contact:** Mr S Clews
Location: Central Bath.
Opening Times: Oct - Mar; Mon - Sat 9.30am - 5.00pm. April - Sept; Mon - Sat 9.00am - 6.00pm, Sun 10.30am - 5.00pm. Aug; Also Open 8.00 - 10.00pm. Not open Christmas and Boxing Day. Last admission 30 minutes before closing.
Admission: Adult £5, under 18 £3, under 8 free, Family (2 adults + up to 4 children) £13, Group (20 or more), Adults £4, Child in summer £2, Child in winter £1.50. Prices after 31 March are unconfirmed.

SHERBOURNE GARDENS
Tel: 01761 241 220

Litton, Bath, Avon, BA3 4PP.
Owner: John Southwell Esq **Contact:** John Southwell Esq
Location: 7m N of Wells on B3114, off A39.
Opening Times: 2 April, 7 May; 4 June - 1 Oct; Sun & Mon, 11.00am - 6.00pm.
Admission: Adult £1.50, Child free, Groups of 12 plus £1.25.

THE BUILDINGS OF BATH MUSEUM

Tel: 01225 333895

The Paragon, Bath, Avon, BA1 5NA.
Owner: Bath Preservation Trust   **Contact:** Christopher Woodward Esq
Location: The Paragon, Central Bath.
Opening Times: Throughout The Year; Tues - Sat, 10.30am - 5.00pm.
Admission: Adult £2.50, Group (10 or more)/OAP/Student/UB40 £1.50 Under 16 £1.00.

THE MANOR HOUSE

Tel: 01275 872067

Walton-in- Gordano, Clevedon, Avon, BS21 7AN.
Owner: Simon M Wills Esq   **Contact:** Simon M Wills Esq
4 acre garden, including shrubs and trees.
Location: 2m NE of Clevedon on B3124.
Opening Times: Garden only: 19 April - 14 Sept, Wed & Thurs; 9 April , 29 May, 18 June, 20 Aug, 10.00am - 4.00pm.
Admission: Adult £1.50, accompanied children under 14 free.

VINE HOUSE

Tel: 01275 872067

Henbury, Bristol, Avon.
Owner: Professor T F Hewer   **Contact:** Professor T F Hewer
2 acre garden.
Location: 4 m NW of Bristol centre.
Opening Times: By Appointment Only.
Admission: Adult £1.00, Concessions 50p, prices not confirmed.

WESTBURY COLLEGE GATEHOUSE

Tel: 01985 843600

College Road, Westbury-on- Trym, Bristol, Avon.
Owner: The National Trust   **Contact:** Rev G M Collins
The 15th century gatehouse of the College of Priests (founded in the 13th century) of which John Wyclif was a prebend.
Location: 3m N of the centre of Bristol.
Opening Times: Visitors to collect the key by prior written arrangement.
Admission: Adult £1.00, Child 50p.

SPECIAL EVENTS DIARY

- **25th March to 5th November**
  The American Museum, Claverton Manor
  Two Exhibitions in the New Gallery
  Lyn Le Grice "The Cutting Edge of Style" and "Monsters, Myths and Misconceptions" 15th/16th century maps and engravings.

- **13th - 14th May**
  The American Museum, Claverton Manor
  American Civil War Camp Life and Drill Displays showing daily life of a soldier during the Civil War.

- **10th - 11th June**
  The American Museum, Claverton Manor
  American Indian Weekend - exhibition in the Lecture Hall and dancing in the grounds.

- **30th June**
  Dyrham Park Festival
  100 Years of Jazz and Dance Tickets £10.00

- **1st July**
  Dyrham Park Festival
  100 Years of Jazz and Dance Tickets £10.00

- **1st - 2nd July**
  The American Museum, Claverton Manor
  American Independence Day Displays - small camp in grounds and drill displays.

- **16th - 17th September**
  The American Museum, Claverton Manor
  American Civil War Weekend - battle re-enactment in grounds and exhibition in Lecture Hall.

LUTON HOO
Luton

LUTON HOO is famous for housing the world famous Wernher Collection, formed primarily by Sir Julius Wernher, who purchased the mansion in 1900, and altered the House with opulent Edwardian interiors, by the designers of the Ritz Hotel in London.

There is also a large collection of Russian Fabergé jewellery and jewelled objects in addition to mementoes of the Russian Imperial family. This is the only collection of work by Carl Fabergé on public view in the country.

Recent additions to the collection included memorabilia of the Tsarevitch, which are displayed in the beautifully restored Chapel, which is now consecrated as a Russian Orthodox Church to the memory of Tsar Nicholas II, and the Imperial Family.

Visitors can view the full splendour of the 18th Century Capability Brown landscape from the terraces, together with the formal gardens by Romayne Walker from earlier this century. In addition the most peaceful area is the Rock Garden, a quiet retreat, always with some colour and a variety of most interesting plants.

❖

SUITABILITY FOR OTHER EVENTS
Fashion shows, archery, clay pigeon shooting, garden parties, shows, rallies, filming, product launches and still photography. Meetings, conferences, luncheons and dinners.

ADVICE TO COURIERS & DRIVERS
No dogs or photography. There is a picnic area.

FACILITIES FOR THE DISABLED
Parking and cloakroom facilities provided.

PARKING FOR COACHES & CARS
There is unlimited parking for coaches and cars.

CATERING
The restaurant seats up to 90 people, plus an additional 45 in the annexe. The latter is normally used for groups booking in advance. Menu suggestions are available on request. Catering facilities are offered for special functions and conferences.

GUIDE BOOKS
New colour guide book.

GUIDED TOURS
Only available for pre-booked groups. Average time 2 hours. fee payable. Special viewing can be arranged for morning or evening visits with or without supper. Details on request.

GIFT SHOP
Open at the same time as the House

CONFERENCE/FUNCTIONS
All modern conference facilities and services can be provided. Banqueting facilities include the Pillared Hall, Dining Room, Ballroom, Drawing Room and Small Conference Room, and can be booked all year round.

CONTACT

The Administrator
Luton Hoo
Luton
Bedfordshire
LU1 3TQ

Tel: (01582)22955

Fax: (01582)34437

LOCATION

M1, Exit 10.
London 30 miles
Birmingham 85 miles.

Rail: Kings X Thames link to Luton/ Harpenden.

Bus: Green Line 747 Jet Link. London Country 321 from Watford. United Counties X1, X2 or X3 from Bedford.

Air: Luton Airport 1 mile.

OPENING TIMES

Summer
11 April - 15 October '95

Bank Holiday Mondays only 10.30am - 5.45pm

Tues, Wed & Thurs. Open for Coaches and Groups only by prior arrangement.

Fris, Sats & Suns. Gardens & Restaurant open 12 noon. House 1.30pm - 5.45pm

Winter
17 October - 10 April '94 Closed.

Conference/Function Facilities available all year.

ADMISSION

Summer
HOUSE & GARDEN
Adult £5.50
Child* £2.50
OAP/Student . . .£5.00
Groups (min 25)
Adult £5.00
Child* £2.00
OAP £4.50
** Min. 25 persons pre-paid within 14 days.

GARDEN ONLY
Adult £2.50
Child* £1.00
OAP/Student . . .£2.25
*Must be of school age

Winter
Closed

CONFERENCE AND FUNCTION FACILITIES

ROOM	DIMENSIONS	CAPACITY	LAYOUT	POWER POINTS	SUITABLE FOR A/V
Ballroom	24' x 69'	200	Theatre	3	3
Dining Room	38' x 24'	50	Any Function	3	3
Pillared Hall	57' x 37'		Any Function	3	3
Conference Hall	25' x 25'	35	Any Function	3	3
Sitting Room		50	Any Function	3	3

MENTMORE TOWERS
Nr. Leighton Buzzard

MENTMORE TOWERS is an example of the Victorian 'Jacobethan' revival at its best. Built in 1855 for Baron Meyer Amschel de Rothschild, this grand romantic house is a reminder of the enormous wealth and power of the Rothschilds in the 19th Century.

The architect was Sir Joseph Paxton, designer of the Crystal Palace, whose early experience designing greenhouses is reflected in the liberal use of glass to open up Mentmore's glittering interior. The main rooms of the House are grouped around the vast Entrance Hall dominated by the magnificent white marble Grand Staircase. The use of marble in the reception rooms contrasts with the ornate gilded style of the living rooms. De Rothschild plundered Europe for his great house, the gilded boiseries in the Dining Room were from the early 18th Century Hotel de Villars in Paris and the striking black and white marble fireplace in the Hall is reputed to have been designed by Rubens for his home in Antwerp.

The House is now the administrative Headquarters of Maharishi University of Natural Law.

❖

SUITABILITY FOR OTHER EVENTS
Corporate hospitality, archery, shows, filming, sales exhibitions, fairs, concerts, conferences, product launches.

EXTRA FACILITIES
Parkland. Tables for 100 and chairs for 200 people. Lectures can be given on the property, contents, gardens and history. The Lecture Room has a max. capacity of 250 people. Cost of hire of the room and lecture negotiable. Projector and screen can be provided.

VIDEO FACILITIES
We can now offer 3 machine high-band editing, including time-coded computer list editing. Cameras (Sony DXC3000PK), a prompter, and portable and studio high-band recorders are also available for hire.

Standard conversion and VHS duplication from low-band, high-band and one inch are also available at very competitive rates.

ADVICE TO COURIERS & DRIVERS
Do not enter grounds through front gates. Use trade entrance by Church or South Entrance. No dogs except guide dogs. No smoking. No unaccompanied children.

FACILITIES FOR THE DISABLED
Disabled and elderly visitors may alight at the entrance to the property. Vehicles can then be parked in the allocated area. There are no toilet facilities for the disabled.

PARKING FOR COACHES & CARS
Capacity of the car park - 100 cars and 10 coaches, near to the House.

GUIDED TOURS
Up to 40 people per tour. Average time taken is 45 minutes.

GIFT SHOP
Postcards are available.

SCHOOL VISITS/CHILDREN
Groups of children are welcome. A guide can be provided on request.

CONTACT

The Events Manager
Mentmore Towers
Mentmore
Nr Leighton Buzzard
Bedfordshire
LU7 0QH

Tel: (01296) 662183
(01296) 661881

Fax: (01296) 662049

LOCATION

M1 Junction 9 Join A5, past Whipsnade Zoo then turn left, following signs for Ivinghoe, Cheddington and Mentmore. London: 1hr (40 miles)

Rail: Cheddington Station 2 miles, Leighton Buzzard 4 miles

Taxi: Valcars (01296) 661666

OPENING TIMES

Summer
April - October
Bank Hol Mons
1.45pm - 4.00 pm.
Last tour 3.15

Tues to Sat Groups by appointment only.

Sun. 1.45pm-4pm
last tour 3.15

Winter
November - March
Closed

ADMISSION

Adult £3.00
Child* £1.50
OAP £2.00
Student £2.00
GROUPS**
Adult £2.50
Child* £1.00
OAP £2.50

* Aged under 14
** Min. 20 People

CONFERENCE AND FUNCTION FACILITIES

ROOM	DIMENSIONS	CAPACITY	LAYOUT	POWER POINTS	SUITABLE FOR A/V
Grand Hall	34' x 43'	35 - 250	Various	8	✓
Dining Room	36' x 27'	35 - 125	Various	6	✓
Gold Room	22' x 30'	26 - 110	Various	18	✓
Conservatory	21' x 55'	35 - 150	Various	6	✓

WOBURN ABBEY
Woburn

THE ABBEY, home of the Dukes of Bedford for over 350 years, was built on the site of a Cistercian Monastery, founded in 1145. During the 17th Century, it was restored, with further re-designing and rebuilding by Henry Flitcroft and later Henry Holland in the 18th Century. Today the house is more or less as Flitcroft and Holland left it, with the exception of the East Wing which was demolished in 1950 along with the huge Indoor Riding School and the Real Tennis building.

The interior is richly decorated and furnished and has one of the most important private art collections in the world, with English and French furniture; paintings by many of the world's famous artists, including 21 views of Venice by Antonio Canale in the Canaletto Room; English, Continental and Oriental porcelain and silver by some of the famous Huguenot silversmiths.

Within the 3,000 acre Deer Park landscaped by Humphrey Repton there are nine species of deer, including the Milu, better known as Pere David, which was saved from extinction by the 11th Duke of Bedford. Nearby is the 350 acre drive-through Safari Park.

— ❖ —

CONTACT

Peter A Gregory
Woburn Abbey
Woburn
Bedfordshire
MK43 0TP

Tel: (01525) 290666
Fax: (01525) 290271

LOCATION

From London, either M1 exit 12/13 or A5, turn off at Hockliffe (1¼ hrs).

Rail: Euston-Leighton-Buzzard, Bletchley or Milton Keynes.

Air: Luton 14 mls
Heathrow 39 mls

Taxi: Farmer, Milton Keynes (01908) 583484

SUITABILITY FOR OTHER EVENTS
Fashion shows, product launches, wedding receptions and filming. Company 'days out' can also be arranged.

EXTRA FACILITIES
Use of parkland and garden. Lectures on the property, its contents, gardens and history can be arranged.

ADVICE TO COURIERS & DRIVERS
No unaccompanied children. No photography in House. Dogs in park on leashes. Guide dogs only in House. Special 'out of hours' tours can be pre-booked during either summer or winter - special rates apply.

FACILITIES FOR THE DISABLED
Wheelchairs can be accommodated in the Abbey by prior arrangement There are toilet facilities for the disabled.

PARKING FOR COACHES & CARS
There is a very large hardstanding and grass area for coaches and cars.

CATERING
Day to day catering in the Flying Duchess Pavilion Coffee Shop, whenever the Abbey is open to the public. Conferences, banqueting, luncheons, dinners etc may be arranged in the Sculpture Gallery, Lantern and Long Harness Rooms.

GUIDED TOURS
Parties are taken round in groups of 15. Tours can be conducted in French, German and Dutch. There is an additional charge of £7.50 per guide.

GIFT SHOP
There are two gift shops, one in the Abbey, the other in the grounds. Both offer a wide variety of attractive and useful gifts.

GUIDE BOOKS
Colour, 48 page guide book, £2.00.

SCHOOL VISITS/CHILDREN
Groups are welcome. Special schools programme is available on request. Cost per child £2.50 (group rate). A guide (extra charge) can be made available if required. Particular interests for children include: Study Trail and Woburn Safari Park

OPENING TIMES

Summer
26 March - 29 October
Daily 11.00am - 4.00pm
NB: Bank Hols Abbey closes 5.00pm

Winter
30 Oct - Mid-March.
Open weekdays by appointment only.

Open Saturdays, Sundays and Bank Hols from the first Saturday after Christmas.

ADMISSION

All year
HOUSE
(including Private Apts)
Adult £6.50
Child* £3.00
OAP £5.50
Groups (15 persons min.)
Adult £5.50
Child** £2.50
OAP £4.50

* 12 - 16 years
**7 - 16

Reduced rates apply if private apartments not available. 11.00am-4.00pm.

CONFERENCE AND FUNCTION FACILITIES

ROOM	DIMENSIONS	CAPACITY	LAYOUT	POWER POINTS	SUITABLE FOR A/V
Sculpture Gallery	130' x 25'	400	Reception	3	3
		300	Theatre		
		250	Dinner/Dance		
Lantern Room	24' x 21'	100	Reception	3	3
		80	Theatre/Dinner		
		20	Boardroom		

WREST PARK & GARDENS ⊞
Silsoe

Set in 150 acres of ornate parkland which were first laid out early in the 18th century, Wrest Park offers a unique insight into the history of gardening styles from 1700 - 1850.

The Great Garden, with its splendid half mile vista down the Long Water, recalls the grounds of the Palace of Versailles. Treasures abound, including the Bath House, built as a classical ruin, and the exquisite Bowling Green House.

Wrest Park House itself, inspired by 18th century French chateaux, was built in 1839 and several rooms, including the grand staircase, are open to the public.

❖

OPENING TIMES

1 April - 30 September

10.00am - 6.00pm

Weekends and
Bank Holidays only.

CONTACT

The Administrator
Wrest Park
Silsoe
Luton
Bedfordshire
MK45 4HS

Tel: (01525) 860152

ADMISSION

Adults £2.30
Child* £1.20
OAP/Student/UB40
holders £1.70

15% discount or. groups
of 11 or more

* 5 - 15 years.
Under 5's free

LOCATION

Wrest Park House is
3/4 mile east of Silsoe
off the A6, 10 miles
south of Bedford.

Rail: Flitwick

Bus: United Counties
X1,X2, X5

ADVICE TO COURIERS & DRIVERS
Tour leader and Coach driver have free entry. 1 extra place for every 20 additional people.

PARKING FOR COACHES & CARS
There are free coach parking facilities

CATERING
Refreshments are available.

GUIDED TOURS
Personal stereo tours are included in the admission price.

SCHOOL VISIT/CHILDREN
School visits are free if booked in advance. Contact the Administrator.

BUSHMEAD PRIORY ⌗

Tel: 01230 62614

Colmworth, Bedford, Bedfordshire.
Owner: English Heritage **Contact:** Mr Stimpson
A rare Survival of the medieval refectory of an Augustinian priory, with its original timber-framed roof almost intact and containing interesting wall paintings and stained glass.
Location: On unclassified road near Colmworth, 2 m E of B660.
Opening Times: 1 Apr - 30 Sept. 10.00am - 6.00pm. Jul - Aug weekends only.
Admission: Adult £1.30, Child 70p, Conc £1.00.

CECIL HIGGINS ART GALLERY

Tel: 01234 211222

Castle Close, Bedford, Bedfordshire, MK40 3NY.
Owner: Bedford Borough Council & The Trustees of the Cecil Higgins Art Gallery
Contact: Halina Graham
Original home of Cecil Higgins this award winning Victorian mansion has rooms displayed to give a lived in atmosphere. Gardens leading down to the river embankment.
Location: Centre of Bedford, just off the river embankment
Opening Times: Open throughout the year; Tues - Sat 11.00am - 5.00pm. Sun and BH Mon 2.00 - 5.00pm; except 23, 24, 25, 26 Dec.

CHICKSANDS PRIORY

Tel: 01234 824195

Shefford, Bedford, Bedfordshire.
Owner: Ministry of Defence **Contact:** Mr R Ward
The Priory was founded in 1150 for Nuns and Canons of the English Order of Gilbertines.
Location: In RAF Chicksands, $1^1/4$ m from Shefford, 8 m S of Bedford, off and A600.
Opening Times: April - Oct, first and third Sundays, 2.00 - 4.30pm. Also parties out of season by contacting Mr Ward.
Admission: Free.

DE GREY MAUSOLEUM ⌗

Tel: 01536 402840

Flitton, Bedford, Bedfordshire.
Owner: English Heritage **Contact:** Mr Stimpson
A remarkable treasure-house of sculpted tombs and monuments from the 16th to 19th centuries dedicated to the de Grey family of nearby Wrest Park.
Location: Attached to the church on unclassified road $1^1/2$ m W of A6 at Silsoe.
Opening Times: Weekends only.

HOUGHTON HOUSE ⌗

Tel: 01234 824195

Ampthill, Bedford, Bedfordshire.
Owner: English Heritage
Reputedly the inspiration for "House Beautiful" in Bunyan's "Pilgrims's Progress", the remains of this early 17th century mansion still convey elements which justify the description, including work attributed to Inigo Jones.
Location: 1m NE of Ampthill off A421, 8m S of Bedford.
Opening Times: Any reasonable time.

LUTON HOO 🏛

See Page 4 for full-page entry.

MENTMORE TOWERS 🏛

See Page 5 for full-page entry.

WOBURN ABBEY 🏛

See Page 6 for full-page entry.

WREST PARK ⌗

See Page 7 for full-page entry.

SPECIAL EVENTS DIARY

- **11th - 12th March: Luton Hoo**
  Craft Fair.
- **12th March: Woburn Abbey**
  East Midlands Doll Fair.
- **17th - 19th March: Luton Hoo**
  Antique Fair.
- **16th - 17th April: Mentmore Towers**
  Antique Fair.
- **6th - 8th May: Woburn Abbey**
  Bedfordshire Spring Craft Fair.
- **21st May: Woburn Abbey**
  Action Research Charity Cycle Ride.
- **3rd - 4th June: Woburn Abbey**
  Woburn Angling Fair.
- **10th-11th June: Woburn Abbey**
  The Woburn Abbey Flower and Garden Show.
- **18th June: Woburn Abbey**
  Large Models Association - 10th annual meeting with demonstration flying of $^1/5$th scale models.
- **2nd July: Woburn Abbey**
  Corvette Club National Car Rally.
- **7th July: Mentmore Towers**
  V E Day Jazz Tribute with The Glen Miller Sound. Concert with Fireworks.
- **8th July: Mentmore Towers**
  "Last Night of the Fireworks Proms". Concert with Fireworks
- **8th July: Woburn Abbey**
  Royal British Legion Annual Day Out
- **8th - 9th July: Woburn Abbey**
  National Riley Car Club Rally Weekend

- **16th July: Woburn Abbey**
  Reliant Scimitar & Sabre Car Club Rally.
- **23rd July: Woburn Abbey**
  Chiltern Jaguar Drivers Club Car Rally.
- **6th August: Woburn Abbey**
  Radio Society of Great Britain - Annual Spares Sale.
- **17th - 20th August: Woburn Abbey**
  The Weetabix British Womens Open (Golf Tournament).
- **19th - 20th August: Woburn Abbey**
  De Havilland Moth Club - Annual Fly In (15th year). Commemorating the Flying Duchess of Bedford (wife of the 11th Duke). Demonstrations and competitions on these nostalgic "plus" days.
- **20th August: Woburn Abbey**
  Woburn Commercial Vehicle Rally and Road Run.
- **26th - 28th August: Mentmore Towers**
  Craft Fair.
- **2nd - 3rd September: Woburn Abbey**
  Bedfordshire Autumn Craft Show.
- **28th Sept- 1st October: Woburn Abbey**
  Dunhill British Masters (Golf Tournament)
- **29th Sept - 30th Sept   Mentmore Towers**
  Antique Fair.
- **28th Sept - 1st Oct: Woburn Abbey**
  Dunhill British Masters (Golf Tournament).
- **6th - 8th October: Woburn Abbey**
  Annual Woburn Abbey Antiques Fair.
- **22nd October: Woburn Abbey**
  East Midlands Doll Fair.
- **20th - 22nd October: Luton Hoo**
  Interior Design Exhibition.
- **10th - 11th November: Woburn Abbey**
  Christmas Craft Fair.

DORNEY COURT
Windsor

"One of the finest Tudor Manor Houses in England." Dorney Court is an enchanting, many gabled pink brick and timbered manor house with more than just a taste of history.

The Grade 1 listed Dorney Court offers a most welcome, refreshing and fascinating experience. Built about 1440 and lived in by the present family for over 400 years.

The rooms are full of the atmosphere of history: early fifteenth and sixteenth century oak, beautiful seventeenth century lacquer furniture, eighteenth and nineteenth century tables, 400 years of family portraits, stained glass and needlework. Here Charles II once came to seek the charms of Barbara Palmer, Countess of Castlemaine, the most intelligent, beautiful and influential of ladies. St James' Church, next door, is a lovely cool, cheerful and very English village church.

"The approach to the house is through ancient Buckinghamshire woodland which transports the visitor into a dreamland. Suddenly the early Tudor house, a ravishing half timbered vision in gabled pinkish brick, comes into view, prettily grouped with a church. This is Dorney Court, a surprisingly little known manor house ... happily genuine...an idyllic image." *Daily Telegraph*

❖

CORPORATE HOSPITALITY
Dorney Court is a privately owned and lived in family house and because it is in no way a 'tourist attraction' hotel or commercial banqueting hall, is the perfect place for an 'upmarket' group visit or for exclusive private functions for companies and tourist groups from overseas.

Dorney offers exclusivity and privacy combined with a superbly convenient rural location, only 25mls west of London.

The house is ideal for private dinners etc., often matched into conferences held elsewhere, and makes a complete change from the work environment.

Catering can either be done by the best of outside caterers or by ourselves. We farm the surrounding land as we have for centuries, producing some of the best of England's lamb, growing strawberries, raspberries and other delicious fruit and vegetables. As far as possible we use fresh home produced food such as lamb and asparagus in spring but if not appropriate then the best available fresh ingredients such as summer salmon, grouse or partridge in autumn with venison or beef in winter.

On a cold and dark winter's night, the Great Hall flickers in candlelight and the large wood fires glow with warmth. In summer you can stroll the lawns with a cooling cocktail. The cocktail might be the famous Palmer cocktail, winner of the Grand Prix in Paris in 1934, the secret recipe given to the family by an Hungarian barman in Budapest, the only recognisable ingredient being the topping up champagne, cooling and refreshing.

SUITABILITY FOR OTHER EVENTS
Activity and family fun days, product launches, spouses programmes and garden parties, overseas tourist groups, filming, photography. No private family parties, weddings or dancing.

GENERAL ADVICE
No facilities for disabled, unaccompanied children, dogs or photography in the house.

SCHOOL VISITS
£2.00 per child plus £16 per guide required. No charge for accompanying adults.

PICK-YOUR-OWN FRUIT
June - August everyday. 10% discount Mons - Weds 10.00am - 5.00pm.

GIFT SHOP
Open for visitors to the House. Guide Book £2.00.

GUIDED TOURS
Are available for private visits: one and a half hours.

CONTACT

Peregrine & Jill Palmer
Dorney Court
Windsor
Berkshire
SL4 6QP

Tel: (01628) 604638

Fax: (01628) 604638

LOCATION

25 miles west of London via M4, 40 mins. depending on traffic.

Rail: Windsor 5 miles, Burnham 2 miles.

Air: London Airport (Heathrow) 20 minutes

OPENING TIMES

Summer
Easter - September
Mon, Tue and Bank Holiday Mons
2.00 - 5.30pm
Suns: May - Sept only
2.00 -5.30pm

Wed - Sat. by appointment only

NB. Open at other times for booked groups by appointment. Open all Easter weekend: 2 - 5.30pm.
Last admission 5pm

Winter
October - Easter
Pre-booked tours only.
(1996 dates will change)

ADMISSION

HOUSE & GARDEN
  Adult £4.00
  Child** £2.00
  OAP £3.60
Groups*
  Adult £3.60
  Child £2.00

Private Visits £5.50
10% discount NT, NADFAS and OAP's

* Minimum 10 people
**Age 10-16 years

CONFERENCE AND FUNCTION FACILITIES

ROOM	DIMENSIONS	CAPACITY	LAYOUT	POWER POINTS	SUITABLE FOR A/V
Great Hall	33' x 24'	65	Various	3	✓
Dining Room	20' x 20'	18	Various	3	✓

BASILDON PARK

OPEN
1 April - October
Wed - Sat
2.00 - 6.00pm
Sun and Bank
Hol Mons
12 Noon - 6.00pm
(closed Good Fri and
Wed after Bank Hol)
Grounds: as house
but open 12 Noon -
6.00 on Sats
Last adm: 5.30pm.

Tel: 01734 843040

LOWER BASILDON, NR. PANGBOURNE, READING RG8 9NR

Owner: The National Trust   *Contact:* The Administrator

A fine Georgian house overlooking the Thames Valley, with important pictures, furniture and plasterwork. Attractive Octagon Room and Decorative Shell Room, garden and woodland walks. Home-made teas in house; shop in stable-yard. Free car park.

Location: 2^1/$_2$ miles north-west of Pangbourne on the A329, 7 miles from M4 junction 12.

Admission: Adult £3.60, Child £1.80, Family Ticket £9.00. Grounds only £1.50

THE SAVILL GARDEN

OPEN
Mar - Oct
10.00am - 6.00pm

Nov - Feb
10.00am - 4.00pm

Tel: 01753 860222

Fax: 01753 859617

WINDSOR GREAT PARK, BERKSHIRE SL4 2HT

Owner: Crown Property   *Contact:* Mr. J. Bond

World renowned woodland garden of 35 acres, providing a wealth of beauty and interest at all seasons. Spring is heralded by hosts of daffodils, masses of rhododendrons, azaleas, camellias, magnolias and much more. Roses, herbaceous borders and countless alpines are the great features of summer, and the leaf colours and fruits of autumn rival the other seasons with a great display.

Location: Wick Lane, Englefield Green. Clearly signposted from Ascot, Bagshot, Egham and Windsor. Nearest station: Egham.

Admission: Adult £3.30, OAP £2.80, Parties of 20+ £2.80. Under 16's free. Accom.

DONNINGTON CASTLE

Newbury, Berkshire.

Owner: English Heritage   **Contact:** The Administrator

Built in the late 14th century, the twin towered gatehouse of this heroic castle survives amidst some impressive earthworks. The remainder was destroyed during one of the longest sieges of the Civil War, lasting nearly two years.

Location: 1 m N of Newbury off B4494.

Opening Times: Any reasonable time.

DORNEY COURT

See Page 9 for full page entry.

ENGLEFIELD HOUSE   **Tel:** 01734 302221   **Fax:** 01734 323748

Englefield, Theale, Reading, Berkshire, RG7 5EN.

Owner: Sir W Benyon   **Contact:** Sir W Benyon

A 7 acre garden, herbaceous and rose borders, fountain, stone balustrades and staircases, woodland and water garden, set in Deer Park. Large variety of trees, plants and shrubs, children's garden, plant sales.

Location: 4m W of Reading off A4.

Opening Times: Garden only: all year, Mon 10.00am till dusk. Apr - Jun: Mon, Tues, Wed and Thur 10.00am till dusk. Sun, 14 May: 2.00 - 6.00pm.

Admission: £1.00.

ST GEORGE'S CHAPEL, WINDSOR   **Tel:** 01753 865538   **Fax:** 01753 620165

Windsor, Berkshire, SL4 1NJ.

Owner: The Dean & Canons of Windsor   **Contact:** Lt Colonel N J Newman

Opening Times: Mon - Sat, 10.00 - 4.00pm, Suns 2.00am - 4.00pm.

Admission: Free admission on payment of entry charge into Windsor Castle.

SWALLOWFIELD PARK   **Tel:** 01734 883815

Swallowfield, Reading, Berkshire, RG7 1TG.

Owner: Country Houses Association   **Contact:** Mrs Glaister

Built in 1678 by the second Earl of Clarendon.

Location: In Swallowfield, 6 m SE of Reading. 4m S of J11/M4.

Opening Times: 1 May - 30 Sept, Wed and Thur, 2.00 - 5.00pm.

Admission: Adult £2.50, Child £1.50, Groups by arrangement.

WELFORD PARK   **Tel:** 01488 608203

Newbury, Berkshire, RG16 8HU.

Owner: Ms A C Puxley   **Contact:** Ms A C Puxley

A Queen Anne house, with attractive gardens and grounds.

Location: On Lambourn Valley Road. 6 miles from Newbury West.

Opening Times: 2 Aug - 28 Aug and 29 May, 2.30 - 5.00pm by prior arrangement.

Admission: House by prior arrangement; Adult £3.00, Child Free, Conc £2.00. Grounds free but by arrangement.

WINDSOR CASTLE   **Tel:** 01753 868286

Windsor, Berkshire, SL4 1NJ.

Owner: H M The Queen   **Contact:** The Administrator

Windsor Castle has belonged to the Sovereigns of England for over 900 years. Enquiries for the Castle tel: 01753 831118, for St George's Chapel Tel: 01753 865538.

Location: 3 m off J6 of M4.

Opening Times: All year 10.00am - 4.00pm, last admissions one hour before closing.

Admission: Adult £8.00, Child under 17 £4.00, Conc £5.50, Family (2+2) £18.00. Additional charges for Queen Mary's Dolls' House, The Exhibition of The Queen's Presents and Royal Carriages. Group rates available.

SPECIAL EVENTS DIARY

- **13th May**
  The Savill Garden Spring Plant Fair - 10.00am-5.30pm
  Free admittance to Plant Fair. Car Parking £1.30. Many small specialist nurseries, garden crafts and old gardening books. Enquiries 01753-860222.

- **27th - 29th May**
  Stratfield Saye House
  Craft Fair.

- **4th June**
  Basildon Park
  Children's Day.

- **19th August**
  Basildon Park
  Jazz Concert with Fireworks.

- **20th August**
  Basildon Park
  Gilbert and Sullivan Lantern light Gala.

- **26th August**
  The Savill Garden Autumn Plant Fair - 10.00am-5.30pm
  Free admittance to Plant Fair. Car Parking £1.30. Many small specialist nurseries, garden crafts and old gardening books. Enquiries 01753-860222.

- **26th August**
  Stratfield Saye House
  Wellington Prom - Open Air Concert

STOWE SCHOOL
Buckingham

STOWE owes its pre-eminence to the vision and wealth of two owners. From 1715 to 1749 Viscount Cobham, one of Marlborough's Generals, continuously improved his estate, calling in the leading designers of the day to lay out the gardens, and commissioning several leading architects - Vanbrugh, Gibbs, Kent and Leoni - to decorate them with garden temples. From 1750 to 1779 Earl Temple, his nephew and successor continued to expand and embellish both Gardens and House. The House has now become a major public school.

Around the mansion is one of Britain's most magnificent landscape gardens. now in the ownership of the National Trust. Covering 250 acres and containing no fewer than 6 lakes and 32 garden temples, it is of the greatest historic importance. During the 1730's William Kent laid out in the Elysian Fields at Stowe, one of the first 'natural' landscapes and initiated the style known as 'the English Garden'. Capability Brown worked there for 10 years, not as a consultant but as head gardener, and in 1744 was married in the little church hidden in the trees.

❖

CONTACT

The Commercial Manager
Stowe School
Buckingham
MK18 5EH

Tel: (01280)6 813650
House only
or (01280) 822850
Gardens

LOCATION

From London, M1 to
Milton Keynes, 1¹/₂ hrs
or Banbury 1¹/₄ hrs

Bus: from Buckingham
4 miles

Rail: Milton Keynes
15 miles

Air: Heathrow 50 miles

SUITABILITY FOR OTHER EVENTS
Venue for International Conferences, prestige exhibitions and private functions.

EXTRA FACILITIES
Indoor swimming pool, sports hall, tennis court, squash courts parkland, cricket pitches and golf course.

FACILITIES FOR THE DISABLED
Disabled and elderly visitors may alight at the entrance to the property. Vehicles can then be parked in the allocated areas. There are toilet facilities for the disabled in the gardens. 'Batricars' are available.

PARKING FOR COACHES & CARS
There is extensive parking for coaches and cars.

CATERING
The National Trust Restaurant /Tea Room can cater for up to 100 people. Parties should book in advance.

GUIDED TOURS
At an additional cost, parties can be given a guided tour in groups of 30. Average time taken for a tour of the house and garden 2¹/₂ hours. House only - 30 minutes.

GIFT SHOP
During term time, open Monday - Friday 9.00am - 12 noon, 12.50pm - 5.00pm; Saturdays 1.00pm - 5.00pm. During school holidays, open Monday - Friday 9.00am - 5.00pm; Saturday and Sunday 11.00am - 5.00pm; Items include postcards, books, gifts, souvenirs and prints.

GUIDE BOOKS
Guide book £1.20 and £6.00. There is also a guide to the gardens.

OPENING TIMES

Summer
HOUSE
Sundays only
12 Noon - 5.00pm
25 March - 11 April
4 July - 1 Sept

GARDENS
Daily
10.00am - Dusk
25 March - 16 April and
3 July - 3 Sept

17 April - 2 July and
4 Sept - 29 Oct
Mon, Wed, Fri & Sun.

Winter
GARDENS
Daily   10.00am - Dusk
27 Dec - 7 Jan 1996

NB: It may be necessary to close the house at times when it is being used for private functions. Please telephone first to check.

ADMISSION

Summer
HOUSE ONLY
   Adult £2.00
   Child £1.00
   OAP £2.00
   Student £2.00
10% discount for
parties of more than 30

GARDENS ONLY
   Adult £3.80
   Child £1.90
   OAP £3.80

Winter
House closed (Sundays by appointment only).
Gardens as above

CONFERENCE AND FUNCTION FACILITIES

ROOM	DIMENSIONS	CAPACITY	LAYOUT	POWER POINTS	SUITABLE FOR A/V
Roxburgh Hall	–	460	Theatre	✓	✓
Audio Visual Room	–	50	Theatre	✓	✓
Music Room	–	120	Various	✓	✓
Marble Hall	–	150	Various	✓	✓
State Dining Room	–	180	Various	✓	✓
Garter Room	–	200	Various	✓	✓
Memorial Theatre	–	120	Theatre	✓	✓

WADDESDON MANOR
The Rothschild Collection, Waddesdon

WADDESDON MANOR was designed by the French architect Destailleur in the 1870's for Baron Ferdinand Rothschild from the Austrian branch of the family. The Renaissance style chateau was conceived as a showcase for the Baron's prodigious collection of works of art, which includes French Royal furniture, Savonnerie carpets and Sévres porcelain as well as important portraits by Gainsborough and Reynolds and works by Dutch and Flemish masters of the 17th century.

In 1986 a far reaching programme of maintenance and conservation work was undertaken by the Rothschild family. The Collection on the ground floor was re-opened last year and the newly remodelled Wine Cellars containing an exceptional 'library' of Rothschild vintages, were put on public view for the first time. This year the restoration will be complete with the inauguration of newly created rooms on the first floor. These include a magnificent suite of French 18th century panelled rooms, an exhibition of Sévres porcelain, and the paintings of leon Bakst showing the Rothschild family in the story of Sleeping Beauty. In addition, a number of works of art from Lord Rothschild's family are being put on loan. Restoration work in the Garden has included repairs to the fountains and garden sculpture, reinstated of the 19th century Parterre and extensive replanting of shrubs and trees.

---❖---

CONTACT

Bookings and Special Events Officer,
Waddesdon Manor
near Aylesbury
Buckinghamshire
HP18 OJH

Tel: (01296) 651282

Recorded message:
(01296) 651211

Fax:(01296) 651293

LOCATION

Waddesdon Manor lies at the west end of Waddesdon village, 6 miles north west of Aylesbury on the Bicester road (A41).

From London 1 hour 20 minutes, M40 Junct. 7

Rail: nearest station Aylesbury BR.

Buses: 1,15, 16 from Aylesbury Bus Station.

SUITABILITY FOR OTHER EVENTS
Private tours of the House may be arranged. In addition, facilities are available for lunches, dinners, wine-tastings lectures and business meetings. Film location use may also be possible.

EXTRA FACILITIES
Aviary, formal gardens, children's play area. Watergarden open to the public on certain days throughout the year.

ADVICE TO COURIERS & DRIVERS
Coaches are advised to book in advance.

FACILITIES FOR THE DISABLED
Wheelchairs and ramp access. Limited access to House. Guide dogs in grounds only.

PARKING FOR COACHES & CARS
Car and coach park within short walking distance of the House.

CATERING
Licensed restaurant and Stables Tearoom. Large groups encouraged to book in advance. Catering for special events and private parties can be discussed with the Head of Banqueting.

GUIDED TOURS
Entry to the House is strictly by timed ticket , sold on a first come first served basis. Visitors may not gain immediate entry to the House as early slots are filled quickly.

GIFT SHOP
Gift Shop and Wine Shop open 1st March-22and Dec, Wed - Sun, 11am to 6pm (5pm when house is closed). A large range of high quality gifts and a unique selection of Rothschild wines from the most reasonable of vintages to a Grand Cru. The plant centre is open from 10am -5pm daily.

GUIDE BOOKS
Garden leaflet, Aviary leaflet £1.00. Garden Guide £4.95. House Guide approx. £3.00

OPENING TIMES

HOUSE
6 April - 15 October

Thurs to Sat   1 - 6.00pm

Sundays, Bank Holiday Monday and Good Friday 11.00am - 6.00pm

July & August Wednesdays 1 - 6.00pm

Last admission 5.00pm

GROUNDS, AVIARY, SHOPS, LICENSED RESTAURANT
1 March - 22 December

Wed to Sun and Bank Holiday Mondays 11.00am - 6.00pm

Private Tours of the house by special arrangement.

ADMISSION

GROUNDS, AVIARY, SHOPS, LICENSED RESTAURANT AND PARKING
Adult £3.00
Child £1.00

HOUSE, STATE RECEPTION ROOMS
Adult £6.00
Child (over 5 only) . .£4.50

FIRST FLOOR EXHIBITION ROOMS
Adult £6.00
Child (over 5 only) . .£4.50

Combined ticket
Adult £8.00
Child (over 5 only) . .£6.50

Additional charge to House on Sun, Bank Holiday Mon and Good Friday
Per person £1.00

ASCOTT

Tel: 01296 688242

Wing, Leighton Buzzard, Buckinghamshire, LU7 0PS.
Owner: The National Trust   **Contact:** The Administrator
Anthony de Rothschild collection of fine pictures, French and English furniture and exceptional oriental porcelain. The garden contains unusual trees, flower borders, naturalised bulbs, water-lilies and a topiary sundial.
Location: ¹/₂m E of Wing, 2m SW of Leighton Buzzard, on A418.
Opening Times: House & Garden: 5 Apr - 7 May and 1 - 30 SeptSep, Tue - Sun, 2.00pm - 6.00pm (open Good Friday but closed BH Mon) last admission 5.00pm. Garden only: 10 May - 30 Aug, every Wed and last Sun in month, 2.00pm - 6.00pm.
Admission: House & Garden: £5.00. Grounds only: £3.00. No reduction for parties, which must book.

BOARSTALL TOWER

Boarstall, Aylesbury, Buckinghamshire, HP18 9QX.
Owner: The National Trust   **Contact:** The Administrator
The stone gatehouse of a fortified house long since demolished. It dates from the 14th century, and was altered in the 16th and 17th centuries, but retains its crossloops for bows. The tower is almost surrounded by a moat.
Location: Midway between Bicester and Thame, 2m W of Brill.
Opening Times: By written appointment with tenant. May - end Sept: Wed, 2.- 6.00pm.
Admission: £1.00, no reduction for parties.

BUCKINGHAM CHANTRY CHAPEL

Market Hill, Buckingham, Buckinghamshire.
Owner: The National Trust   **Contact:** The Administrator
Rebuilt in 1475 and retaining a fine Norman doorway. The chapel was restored by Gilbert Scott in 1875, at which time it was used as a Latin or Grammar School.
Location: On Market Hill.
Opening Times: Apr - end Oct: by written appointment with the Buckingham Heritage Trust, c/o The Book Barn, Church Way, Whittlebury, Northants, NN12 8SX..
Admission: £1.00, no reduction for parties.

CHENIES MANOR HOUSE

Tel: 01494 762888

Chenies, Buckinghamshire, WD3 6ER.
Owner: Lt. Col. A A MacLeod Matthews   **Contact:** Lt. Col. A A MacLeod Matthews
Early Tudor Manor House with contemporary furniture, tapestries, secret passages and hiding places. Lovely gardens.
Location: Off A404 between Amersham and Rickmansworth.
Opening Times: 2 April - 31 Oct.
Admission: Adult £3.50, Child £1.75.

CHICHELEY HALL

Tel: 01234 391252   Fax: 01234 391388

Newport Pagnell, Buckinghamshire, MK16 9JJ.
Owner: The Hon Nicholas Beatty   **Contact:** J N Robertson Esq
The house is one of the finest and least altered 18th century houses in the country, built between 1719 - 23. Conference facilities.
Location: 10 m from Milton Keynes, ³/₄ hour from J14 M1.

CHILTERN OPEN AIR MUSEUM

Tel: 01494 871117   Fax: 01494 872163

Gorelands Lane, Chalfont St Giles, Buckinghamshire, HP8 4AD.
Owner: Chiltern Open Air Museum Trust.   **Contact:** Mrs M Moir
A museum of historic buildings showing their original uses including a blacksmith's forge, stables, barns etc.
Location: At Newland Park, Chalfont St Giles, 4¹/₂ m from Amersham. 3m from J17/M25.
Opening Times: 1 April - 29 Oct, Wed - Sun, 2.00pm - 6.00pm, plus Tues in Aug.
Admission: Adult £3.00, Child 5-16yrs/Conc £2.50, Family £10, under 5 free, 10% discount for groups of 30 plus.

THE COURTHOUSE

Tel: 01753 671 177

Long Crendon, Aylesbury, Buckinghamshire, HP18 9AN.
Owner: The National Trust   **Contact:** The Administrator
A 14th century building of two storeys partly half-timbered probably first used as a wool store. The manorial courts were held here from the reign of Henry V until recent times. The ground floor re-arranged as a flat is let.
Location: 2m N of Thame, via B4011.
Opening Times: Upper floor only: Apr - end Sept. Wednesdays 2.00 - 6.00pm, Sats, Suns & BH Mon 11.00am - 6.00pm.
Admission: £1.00. No reduction for parties.

CLAYDON HOUSE

OPEN

1 Apr - end of Oct
Sat - Wed
1.00 - 5.00pm

Last admission
4.30pm

Tel: 01296 730349
or 01296 730693

MIDDLE CLAYDON, NR. BUCKINGHAM MK18 2EY

Owner: The National Trust   *Contact: Custodian*

A fine 18th Century house with splendid rococo carvings in the state rooms. Florence Nightingale often visited Claydon. Her bedroom and museum with mementoes of her life are on show. Home-made teas available. Free car park.

Location: In Middle Claydon 13 miles north-west of Aylesbury, signposted from A413, A421 and A41.
Admission: Adult £3.60, Child £1.80, Family ticket £9.00.

COWPER & NEWTON MUSEUM

Tel: 01234 711516

Orchard Side, Market Place, Olney, Buckinghamshire, MK46 4AB.
Owner: Board of Trustees   **Contact:** Mrs E Knight
Georgian home of Poet, William Cowper, containing his personal possessions and those of Rev. John Newton (author of "Amazing Grace"). Lace collection and gardens with Cowper's summer house.
Location: On A509, 5m N of Newport Pagnell.
Opening Times: Apr - Oct: Tues - Sats, 10.00am - 1.00pm and 2.00 - 5.00pm. Nov - Mar 1.00 - 4.00pm. Closed 15 Dec to 1 Feb and Good Fri. Open Bank Hol Mons.
Admission: Adult £1.50, Child 50p, OAP £1.00.

DORNEYWOOD GARDEN

Dorneywood, Burnham, Buckinghamshire, SL1 8PY.
Owner: The National Trust   **Contact:** The Administrator
The house was given to the National Trust as an official residence for either a Secretary of State or Minister of the Crown. Garden only open.
Location: SW of Burnham Beeches. 2m E of Cliveden.
Opening Times: Wed 5 & 9 Jul & Sept, 5 & 12 Aug. 2 - 5.30pm. **By written appointment only to Dorneywood Trust.**
Admission: £2.50. No reduction for parities..

ETON COLLEGE

Tel: 01753 671177

Windsor, Buckinghamshire, SL4 6DB.
Owner: Eton College   **Contact:** Mr Howard Eaton
Location: Off J5 / M4
Opening Times: 1 Apr - 1 Oct. Times vary, best to check with the Visits Manager.
Admission: Adult £2.30-£6.20, Child £1.80-£6.20 -varies according to whether tour taken.

HUGHENDEN MANOR

OPEN

4 - 26 March
Sat and Sun only
1 Apr - 1 Oct
Wed - Sat
2.00 - 6.00pm

Sun & Bank Hol Mon
(closed good Fri)
Last adm: 5.30pm

4 Oct - 30 Oct
Wed - Sat:
2.00 - 5.00pm,
Sun 12 - 5.00pm
Last adm: 4.30pm

Tel: 01494 532580

HIGH WYCOMBE, HP14 4LA

Owner: The National Trust   *Contact: The Property Manager*

Victorian Gothic home of Disraeli from 1847 until his death in 1881. The house contains much of his furniture, pictures, books and other relics. Shop in stable yard. Free car parking.

Location: 1¹/₂ miles north of High Wycombe on the A4128..
Admission: Adult £3.60, Child £1.80, Family ticket £9.00.

JOHN MILTON'S COTTAGE

Tel: 01494 872313

21 Deanway, Chalfont St Giles, Buckinghamshire, HP8 4JH.
Owner: Milton Cottage Trust   **Contact:** Mr E A Dawson
Contains many Milton relics and a library. Two museum rooms and charming cottage garden open to the public.
Location: ½ m W of A413. 3m N of J2 / M40.
Opening Times: 1 Mar - 31 Oct, Wed - Sun, 10.00am - 1.00pm & 2.00pm - 6.00pm. Closed Mon / Tues except BH Mons.
Admission: £2 entry except; under 15's 60p, Groups of 20 plus £1.50.

NETHER WINCHENDON HOUSE

Tel: 01844 290101

Aylesbury, Buckinghamshire, HP18 ODY.
Owner: Robert Spencer Bernard Esq   **Contact:** Mr R Spencer Bernard
Medieval and Tudor manor house with 18th century additions.
Location: 2m N of A418 equidistant between Thame & Aylesbury.
Opening Times: 1 - 29 Aug and 27 / 28 Aug. 2.30 - 5.30pm (last party at about 4.45pm).
Admission: Adult £2.50 (HHA members free), Child £1.50, Senior citizens £1.50 (not w/es or BHs). Groups by prior arrangement.

PITSTONE WINDMILL

Ivinghoe, Buckinghamshire.
Owner: The National Trust   **Contact:** The Administrator
One of the oldest post mills in Britain; in view from Ivinghoe Beacon.
Location: ½m S of Ivinghoe, 3m NE of Tring. Just W of B488.
Opening Times: May - end Sept: Sun & BH Mon. 2.30 - 6.00pm, last admission 5.30pm.
Admission: £1.00.

PRINCES RISBOROUGH MANOR HOUSE

Princes Risborough, Aylesbury, Buckinghamshire, HP17 9AW.
Owner: The National Trust   **Contact:** The Administrator
A 17th century red-brick house with Jacobean oak staircase.
Location: Opposite church off market square
Opening Times: House and front garden by written arrangement only with tenant. Wed 2.30 - 4.30pm last admission 4.00pm. Drawing room and staircase shown.
Admission: £1.00. No reduction for parties..

STOWE LANDSCAPE GARDENS

OPEN
25 Mar - 16 Apr
Daily
17 Apr - 2 Jul
Mon, Wed, Fri, Sun.
3 July - 3 Sept.
Daily
4 Sept - 29 Oct
Mon, Wed, Fri, Sun.
Closed Christmas
Eve, Christmas Day
and Boxing Day.
27 Dec - 7 Jan (1996)
Daily
10.00am - 5.00pm or
dusk if earlier.
Last admission one
hour before closing.
Tel: 01280 822850

NR. BUCKINGHAM MK18 5EH
Owner: The National Trust   Contact: The Administrator
Splendid landscaped gardens with buildings and temples by Vanbrugh, Kent and Gibbs. One of the supreme creations of the Georgian era (NB the main house is in the ownership of Stowe School). Morning coffee, light lunches and tea available. Shop in Menagerie.
Location: 3 miles north west of Buckingham.
Admission: Adult £3.80, Child £1.90, Family ticket £9.50.

STOWE SCHOOL

See page 11 for full page entry.

WADDESDON MANOR

See page 12 for full page entry.

WEST WYCOMBE PARK

Tel: 01494 524411

West Wycombe, High Wycombe, Buckinghamshire, HP14 3AJ.
Owner: The National Trust   **Contact:** The Administrator
A Palladian house with frescos and painted ceilings fashioned for Sir Francis Dashwood in the mid 18th century. The landscape garden and lake were laid out at the same time as the house with various classical temples including some by Nicholas Revett.
Location: At W end of West Wycombe S of the A40.
Opening Times: Grounds only: April & May, Sun & Wed.
2.00pm - 6.00pm Easter May & Spring BH Sun & Mon 2.00pm - 6.00pm. House & Grounds: Jun Jul & Aug Sun - Thur, 2.00pm - 6.00pm. Last admission 5.15pm.
Admission: The West Wycombe Caves and adjacent cafe are privately owned and NT members are liable to admission fees. House & Grounds £4.00, Family £10.00. Grounds only £2.50.

WINSLOW HALL

Tel: 01296 712323

Winslow, Buckinghamshire, MK18 3HL.
Owner: Sir Edward Tomkins   **Contact:** Sir Edward Tomkins
William and Mary house generally attributed to Wren. Virtually unchanged structurally and mostly original interiors. Good period furniture, pictures and Chinese objets d'art. Attractive garden with unusual trees and shrubs.
Location: In the town of Winslow on the A413.
Opening Times: Any time by appointment . Bank Hols (except Christmas) and Weds and Thurs in Jul and Aug. 2.30pm - 5.30pm.
Admission: £4.50. Children under 12 free.

SPECIAL EVENTS DIARY

- **22nd May - 4th June**
  Cowper & Newton Museum
  June "Cowper's Summerhouse Restored".

- **4th June**
  Claydon House
  Family Gamelan Concert.

- **4th June**
  Waddesdon Manor
  Children's Day.

- **4th June**
  Stowe Landscape Gardens
  Children's Day.

- **17th June**
  Claydon House
  Centenary Lanternlight Concert - The English Chamber Orchestra.

- **15th July**
  Stowe Landscape Gardens
  Military Band Concert with Fireworks.

- **29th July**
  Waddesdon Manor
  The National Trust/Waddesdon Centenary Lecture.

- **1st - 31st August**
  Cowper & Newton Museum
  "Through The Lens of a Victorian Camera."

- **25th September - 8th October**
  Cowper & Newton Museum
  "Putting Cowper & Friends in the Picture".

- **1st - 15th September**
  Cowper & Newton Museum
  "Toys of Yesterday".

ELTON HALL
Peterborough

ELTON HALL, the home of the Proby family for over 300 years, stands in the midst of unspoilt landscaped parkland on a site where there has been a house since the Norman Conquest. Sir Peter Proby, Lord Mayor of London and Comptroller of the Royal Household, was granted land and property at Elton by Queen Elizabeth I. His grandson, Sir Thomas Proby, completed the main House in 1666. In the 18th Century John Proby was created the first Earl of Carysfort. He and his successors enlarged it to the 18th Century character that it has today.

Elton is a fascinating mixture of styles. Every room contains treasures - magnificent furniture from many countries and fine paintings from early 15th Century Old Masters to the remarkable Pre-Raphaelite work of Alma Tadema and Millais. Great British artists are well represented by Gainsborough, Constable and Reynolds. The Library is one of the finest in private hands containing some 12,000 books. The collection includes the unique Henry VIII's Prayer Book in which can be seen the writing of the Tudor King and two of his wives.

GARDENS

The formal gardens have been carefully restored in recent years. The Victorian Rose Garden contains some 1,000 roses including many old fashioned varieties whose fragrance in the summer months is quite memorable.

New herbaceous borders provide great interest to gardeners and non-gardeners alike. An arboretum has recently been planted. Picnics may also be taken in this pleasant area.

EXTRA FACILITIES
Parkland for rallies etc. Clay Pigeon shoots can be arranged. Special lecture-tours of Hall. Please apply for details.

ADVICE TO COURIERS & DRIVERS
Elton Hall is not suitable for disabled visitors because of the steps. It is, however, of great interest to art lovers. No dogs in Hall or formal gardens. No photography in Hall. Ploughmans suppers and buffet suppers are available for parties being taken on a guided tour. Parking for 200 cars and 10 coaches, 50 yards from the house.

FACILITIES FOR THE DISABLED
Disabled and elderly visitors may alight close to the entrance. Vehicles can then be parked in the allocated areas. There are no toilet facilities for the disabled and steps at the entrance and in the Hall.

CATERING
The State Dining Room is available for Banquets, Receptions etc. Up to 70 can be seated or 100 for buffet-type functions. Menus and prices on application. The Billiard Room seats 50 people. Prices on application. Meals can be booked in advance and menus are available on request.

GUIDED TOURS
Parties of up to 100 people can be split into groups of 20, except on Bank Holidays. Average time taken for a tour ³/₄ hour.

SCHOOL VISITS/CHILDREN
Elton Hall is suitable mainly for 5th and 6th forms. There is a special question sheet with a competition for younger children. Grassed picnic area available. Guided tours available; please apply to House Manager for costs.

CONTACT

The House Manager
Estate Office
Elton Hall
Elton
Peterborough
PE8 6SH

Tel: (01832) 280468
Fax: (01832) 280584

LOCATION

From London, A1(M), A605 to Elton. 86 mls. From Leicester, A47, B671, A605 to Elton.

Bus: Peterborough Kettering bus passes the Hall.

Rail: P'borough 8mls.

Air: Private Airport 3mls.

Taxi: Norwood, Oundle 273585.

SUITABILITY FOR OTHER EVENTS
Corporate Entertaining, product launches, promotions, photographic and film location work

CONFERENCE AND FUNCTION FACILITIES

ROOM	DIMENSIONS	CAPACITY	LAYOUT	POWER POINTS	SUITABLE FOR A/V
Billiard Room	38' x 28'	60	Buffet Lunch/Dinner	3	3
State Dining Room	38'6" x 23'6"	100	Banquets/Receptions Product Launches	3	3
Old Laundry	21' x 20'	40	Product Launches Receptions	3	3
Conference Room	21' x 20'	20	Conferences	3	3

OPENING TIMES

Summer

Easter, May & August Bank Holidays, Sun & Mon   2 -5.00pm

July
Wed & Sun   2 - 5.00pm

August
Wed, Thurs & Sun   2 - 5.00pm

Winter

Private parties by appointment.

ADMISSION

Summer

HOUSE & GARDEN
Adult £3.80
Child* £1.90
OAP £3.80
Student £1.90

GARDEN ONLY
Adult £1.90
Child* £0.95
OAP £1.90
Student £0.95

Groups**
Adult £3.80
Child* £1.90

Free ticket to all party organisers

* Aged 5-15

** Over 20 people.
Over 50 people gain additional 10% discount.

Winter

Private Parties by appointment only

ANGLESEY ABBEY

Tel: 01223 811200

Lode, Cambridge, Cambridgeshire, CB5 9EJ.

Owner: The National Trust   **Contact:** The Administrator

The house, dating from 1600, is built on the site of an Augustinian abbey, and contains the famous Fairhaven collection of paintings and furniture. It is surrounded by an outstanding 100 acre garden and arboretum with a wonderful display of hyacinths in spring and magnificent herbaceous borders and a dahlia garden in summer. A watermill in the grounds is in full working order and the machinery is demonstrated on the first Sunday in each month.

Location: 6 m NE of Cambridge on B1102.

Opening Times: House: 29 Mar - 15 Oct, Wed to Sun & BH Mon, 1.00pm - 5.00pm. Garden: 29 Mar - 9 Jul, Wed to Sun & BH Mon 11.00am - 5.30pm, 10 Jul to 5 Sept, daily 11.00am - 5.30pm. Last admission to House & Garden 4.30pm. Closed Good Fri. Lode Mill: 29 Mar - 29 Oct, Wed to Sun & BH Mon 1.00pm - 5.00pm.

Admission: House & Garden: Adult £4.80, Sun & BH Mon Adult £5.80, Parties £3.80. Garden only: £3.00, Sun & BH Mon £3.50. Lode Mill: free.

DENNY ABBEY

Tel:01223 860489

Cambridge, Cambridgeshire.

Owner: English Heritage   **Contact:** The Administrator

What at first appears to be an attractive stone-built farmhouse is actually the remains of a 12th century Benedictine abbey which, at different times, also housed the Knights Templar and Franciscan nuns.

Location: 6m N of Cambridge on A10.

Opening Times: 1 Apr - 30 Sept, weekends only, 10.00am - 6.00pm.

Admission: Adult £1.30, Child 70p, Conc £1.00.

ELTON HALL

See page 15 for full page entry.

ELY CATHEDRAL

Tel: 01353 667735   **Fax**: 01353 665658

Ely, Cambridgeshire, CB7 4DL.

Contact: Jan Pye

A wonderful example of Romanesque architecture. Octagon and Lady Chapel are of special interest. Superb Medieval domestic buildings surround the Cathedral.

Location: On A10, 15m N of Cambridge.

Opening Times: Summer: 7.00am - 7.00pm. Winter: Mon - Sat, 7.30 am - 6.00pm, Sun and week after Christmas, 7.30am - 5.00pm. Sunday services: 8.15am, 10.30am and 3.45pm. Weekday services: 7.40am, 8.00am, 11.30am, 12.30pm and 5.30pm.

Admission: Adult £2.80, Child (12+) £2.00, Conc £2.00, Group concessions.

ISLAND HALL

Tel: 0171 491 3724

Godmanchester, Huntingdon, Cambridgeshire, PE18 8BA.

Owner: Christopher D Vane Percy Esq   **Contact:** Christopher D Vane Percy Esq

Location: 15m NW of Cambridge A14.

Opening Times: 2, 9, 16, 23 & 30 Jul, 2.30pm - 5pm. Last admittance 4.30pm.

Admission: Adult £2.50, Grounds only, £1.50 Child £1, Groups over 40 £2.

KIMBOLTON CASTLE

Tel: 01480 860505   **Fax**: 01480 860386

Kimbolton, Huntington, Cambridgeshire, PE18 0AE.

Owner: Governors of Kimbolton School   **Contact:** T F Hayward Esq

Location: In Downe, 5½m S of Bromley of A4233.

Opening Times: Easter, Whit and August BHs, and Suns late Jul / Aug - afternoons.

Admission: Adult £1, Child 50p, Conc 50p, Groups by arrangement.

LONGTHORPE TOWER

Tel: 01733 268482

Peterborough, Cambridgeshire.

Owner: English Heritage   **Contact:** The Administrator

The finest example of 14th century domestic wall paintings in northern Europe. The tower, with the Great Chamber that contains the paintings, is part of a fortified manor house. Special exhibitions are held in the upper floor.

Location: 2m W of Peterborough on A47.

Opening Times: 1 Apr - 30 Sept., 10.00am - 6.00pm. Jul - Aug: weekends only.

Admission: Adult £1.00, Child 50p, Conc 80p.

THE MANOR HEMINGFORD GREY

OPEN

All year
by appointment

Tel: 01480 463134

HUNTINGDON, CAMBRIDGESHIRE PE18 9BN

Owner: Mr and Mrs P.S. Boston   *Contact:* Diana Boston

Built about 1130 and made famous as Green Knowe by the author Lucy Boston. The Manor is reputedly the oldest continuously inhabited house in the country and much of the Norman house remains. Visitors are offered the unique chance to walk into the books and to see the Lucy Boston patchworks. The garden features topiary and old roses.

Location: Off A14, 3 mls south-east of Huntingdon. 12 miles north-west of Cambridgeshire

Admission: Adults £2.50, Child £1.50. Garden only: Adults £1.50, Child £1.00.

OLIVER CROMWELL'S HOUSE

Tel: 01353 662062   **Fax**: 01353 668819

29 St Mary's Street, Ely, Cambridgeshire, CB7 4HF.

Owner: Ms Michelle Green   **Contact:** Ms Michelle Green

Location: 15m NW of Cambridge A14.

Opening Times: 1 Oct - 31 Mar: Mon - Sat, 10.00am - 5.15pm. 1 Apr - 30 Sept: Daily, 10.00am - 6.00pm.

Admission: Enquire for details.

PECKOVER HOUSE & GARDEN

Tel: 01945 583463

North Brink, Wisbech, Cambridgeshire, PE13 1JR.

Owner: The National Trust   **Contact:** The Administrator

A town house, built c.1722, with fine plaster and wood rococo decoration, and a collection of the Cornwallis family portraits. The notable 2 acre Victorian garden includes an orangery and the recently restored Reed Barn.

Location: On N bank of River Nene, in Wisbech B1441.

Opening Times: House & Garden: 1 Apr - 31 Oct, Sun, Wed & BH Mon, 2.00 - 5.30pm. Garden only: as house, but also open Sat, Mon & Tues, 2.00 - 5.30pm. Parties on house open days by appointment.

Admission: Adult, £2.40 (£1.00 on garden only days), party £1.80.

PRIOR CRAUDEN'S CHAPEL

Tel: 01353 662837   **Fax**: 01353 662187

King's School, Ely, Cambridgeshire, CB7 4DB.

Owner: Kings School   **Contact:** The Bursar

Early 14th century chapel recently restored to show glimpses of coloured walls and wall paintings.

Location: The College Ely Cathedral. In Cathedral Precincts.

Opening Times: Normal working hours, 9.00am - 5.00pm on weekdays.

Admission: Free.

RAMSEY ABBEY GATEHOUSE

Tel: 01263 733471

Abbey School, Ramsey, Cambridgeshire.

Owner: The National Trust   **Contact:** The Curator

Remains of a 15th century gatehouse of the Benedictine Abbey.

Location: At SE edge of Ramsey at point where Chatteris road leaves B1096, 10m SE of Peterborough.

Opening Times: 1 Apr - end Oct: Daily 10 am - 5pm, other times by written application.

Admission: Donation.

UNIVERSITY BOTANIC GARDEN

Tel: 01223 336265   **Fax**: 01223 336278

Bateman Street, Cambridge, Cambridgeshire, LB2 1JF.

Owner: University of Cambridge   **Contact:** Mr P Orriss, Superintendent

40 acres of outstanding gardens with lake and glasshouses, near the centre of Cambridge, incorporating nine National collections, including geranium, fritillaria. Tea room and gift shop in the Gilmour Building.

Location: 1m South of Cambridge city centre, off A1309 (Trumpington Road).

Opening Times: Daily, except Christmas Day and Boxing Day, 10.00am - 6.00pm (Summer), 10.00am - 5.00pm (Spring and Autumn) 10.00am - 4.00pm (Winter).

Admission: Adult £1.50, Child / OAP £1.00.

ADLINGTON HALL
Macclesfield

ADLINGTON HALL, the home of the Leghs of Adlington from 1315 to the present day, was built on the site of a Hunting Lodge which stood in the Forest of Macclesfield in 1040. Two oaks, part of the original building, remain with their roots in the ground and support the east end of the Great Hall, which was built between 1480 and 1505.

The Hall is a Manor House, quadrangular in shape, and was once surrounded by a moat. Two sides of the Courtyard and the east wing were built in the typical 'Black and White' Cheshire style in 1581. The south front and west wing (containing the Drawing Room and Dining Room) were added between 1749 and 1757 and are built of red brick with a handsome stone portico with four Ionic columns on octagonal pedestals. Between the trees in the Great Hall stands an Organ built by 'Father' Bernard Smith (c.1670-80). Handel subsequently played on this instrument, and now fully restored, it is the largest 17th Century organ in the country.

GARDENS
The Wilderness was landscaped in the style of Capability Brown in the mid 18th century and incorporates both earlier 17th century plantings and sympathetic Victorian additions. The formal french style has given way to an apparently wild, but very carefully cultivated informality. Dotted about the circuitous paths are a number of decorative buildings.

SUITABILITY FOR OTHER EVENTS
Suitable for corporate activity events, clay pigeon shooting, product launches, business meetings, conferences, concerts, fashion shows, garden parties, shows, rallies and filming.

CONFERENCE/FUNCTION FACILITIES
The Great Hall and Dining Room available for use when the Hall is not open to the public.

ADVICE TO COURIERS & DRIVERS
Special requests are considered.

FACILITIES FOR THE DISABLED
Disabled and elderly visitors may alight at the entrance to the Hall. No toilets for the disabled.

PARKING FOR COACHES & CARS
Capacity of the car park - 100 cars and 4 coaches, 100 yards from the Hall.

CATERING
Teas and light refreshments in the Hall.

GUIDED TOURS
Tours are available.

SCHOOL VISITS/CHILDREN
School parties are welcome. Cost per child £1.50. A guide can be provided for the tour.

CONTACT

The Guide
Adlington Hall
Macclesfield
Cheshire
SK10 4LF

Tel: (01625) 829206/
(01625) 820201

LOCATION

5 miles north of Macclesfield (A523), 13 miles south of Manchester. London 178 miles.

Rail: Macclesfield and Wilmslow stations 5 miles.

Air: Manchester airport 8 miles.

OPENING TIMES

Summer
Good Friday - 30 Sept. Sundays and Bank Holidays 2pm - 5.30pm.

Parties by appointment any day or early evening.

Winter
By appointment only.

ADMISSION

Summer
HALL & GARDENS

Adult £4.00
Child £1.50
Groups: Min. 25 people
Adult £3.50
Child £1.00

Winter
Groups: Min. 25 people
Adult £3.50
Child £1.00

CONFERENCE AND FUNCTION FACILITIES

ROOM	DIMENSIONS	CAPACITY	LAYOUT	POWER POINTS	SUITABLE FOR A/V
Great Hall	37' x 26' x 38'	125	Theatre	5	✓
		60	Schoolroom		
		60 / 80	Buffet		
		80 / 100	Dinner/Dance		
Dining Room	35' x 23' x 18'	50	Theatre	3	✓
		25	U-Shape		
Hunting Lodge	60' x 30' x 28'	150	Theatre	15	✓
	40' x 30' x 20'	70/80	U-Shape		
		130	Dinner/Dance		
		150	Lunch/Dinner		

ARLEY HALL & GARDENS
Northwich

ARLEY HALL, the home of the Hon Michael and Mrs Flower, was built about 1840 by the owner's great great grandfather, Rowland Egerton-Warburton, to the design of the Nantwich architect, George Latham. An important example of the Victorian Jacobean style, it has fine plaster work and wood panelling as well as interesting furniture, pictures and other contents. Adjoining Arley Hall is a large private Chapel designed by Anthony Salvin .

An impressive range of activities can be held both in the Hall and in the grounds, from Corporate Conferences of any size to Cocktail Parties and Ambassadorial Receptions. Arley Hall offers all its visitors an elegant setting combined with the professional approach to top class management. Catering to the highest standards.

GARDENS
Overlooking beautiful parkland, and providing great variety of style and design, the Gardens extending over 12 acres rank among the finest in the country. Winner of the Christie's HHA 'Garden of the Year' award in 1987. The features include the Double Herbaceous Border, one of the earliest to be established in England 1846, unique avenue of clipped Quercus Ilex, collection of Shrub Roses, fine Yew hedges, Herb Garden, Walled Garden, Woodland Garden with exotic trees, Shrubs, Azaleas and a collection of over 200 varieties of Rhododendrons.

❖

SUITABILITY FOR OTHER EVENTS
Business Meetings & Conferences, Corporate Activity Events, Receptions & Dinner Parties, Concerts, Filming.

EXTRA FACILITIES
100 acres parkland, grass, cricket pitch. Grand piano in Gallery.

ADVICE TO COURIERS & DRIVERS
Free entry and refreshments for courier and coach driver. Photography only in the gardens.

FACILITIES FOR THE DISABLED
Disabled and elderly visitors may alight at the entrance to the Hall, before parking in the allocated areas. Toilets for the disabled.

PARKING FOR COACHES & CARS
Unlimited parking for cars, 250 yds from Hall and 6 coaches may be parked 100 yds away. Special arrangements can be made for function parking 50 yds from the Hall.

CATERING
The Restaurant/Tea Room seats up to 100 people for light refreshments, lunches and evening meals. Prices range from £1.00 to £12.00.

GUIDED TOURS
Tours of up to 25 people per guide are conducted round the Hall. Guided tours of the Gardens can be arranged for a minimum of £30 per party. Average time taken for a tour of the Hall 1 hour, and for the gardens 1½ hours.

GIFT SHOP/SPECIALIST PLANT NURSERY
Open when the Gardens are open to the public, also at other selected times.

GUIDE BOOKS
Colour Guide Books on House and Gardens.

SCHOOL VISITS/CHILDREN
New for 1995 ! Open for guided tours of Hall and Gardens, Environmental and Heritage Trails. Mondays and Fridays only.

CONTACT

Eric Ransome
Arley Hall and Gardens
Northwich
Cheshire
CW9 6NA

Tel: (01565) 777353

Fax: (01565) 777465

LOCATION

5 miles from Knutsford

5 miles from Northwich

5 miles from M6
Motorway Junct. 19/20.

5 miles from M56
Motorway Junct. 9/10.

Air: Manchester
Airport 16 mls.

OPENING TIMES

Summer
8 April - 1 October inclusive

Daily, except Mons
12 Noon - 5.00pm

Mon Bank Hols only
12 Noon - 5.00pm

Restricted opening of Hall in April & Sept - weekends and Bank Hols only.

Open to pre-booked groups, by arrangement.

Winter
Open by arrangement only for groups and on special advertised occasions.

ADMISSION

GARDENS, GROUNDS
& CHAPEL
  Adult £2.80
  Child (5 -16) £1.40
  Child (under 5) . .FREE*
Groups (min. 15 people)
  Adult £2.30
  Child £1.15
  OAP £2.10

HALL (Extra)
  Adult £1.80
  Child (5-16) £0.90
  Child (Under 5) . .FREE*
Groups (min. 15 people)
  Adult £1.50
  Child £0.75
  OAP £1.40
*When part of a family group only

FAMILY TICKETS (2 + 2)
  Gardens £7.00
  Hall £4.50
  Season . . . .£12.00 ea.

Friends of Arley Assoc.;
contact 01606 891754
Membership secretary.

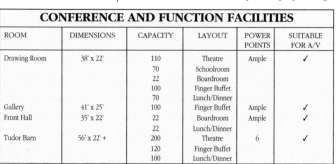

CONFERENCE AND FUNCTION FACILITIES

ROOM	DIMENSIONS	CAPACITY	LAYOUT	POWER POINTS	SUITABLE FOR A/V
Drawing Room	38' x 22'	110	Theatre	Ample	✓
		70	Schoolroom		
		22	Boardroom		
		100	Finger Buffet		
		70	Lunch/Dinner		
Gallery	41' x 25'	100	Finger Buffet	Ample	✓
Front Hall	35' x 22'	22	Boardroom	Ample	✓
		22	Lunch/Dinner		
Tudor Barn	56' x 22' +	200	Theatre	6	✓
		120	Finger Buffet		
		100	Lunch/Dinner		

CAPESTHORNE HALL
Macclesfield

CAPESTHORNE HALL has been the home of the Bromley-Davenport Family and their ancestors since Domesday times when the appointment of Chief Forester carrying the responsibility of law and order in the Forests of Macclesfield and Leek was granted to them. Since then many generations have served in Parliament, the Bromley side providing both a Chancellor and Speaker. The present owner is H.M. Lord Lieutenant for Cheshire.

The existing Hall dating from 1719 was originally designed by the Smiths of Warwick, then altered by both Blore in 1837 and Salvin in 1861, the latter rebuilding the centre section following a disastrous fire.

The Hall contains a great variety of paintings, sculptures, furniture and tapestry including a collection of Colonial furnishings brought over by the late Lady Bromley-Davenport from her former American home in Philadelphia.

The park and gardens extend to some 60 acres and feature a beautiful Georgian Chapel dating from 1720 where services are still held, a chain of man-made lakes the central one being spanned by a multi-arch brick bridge. A pair of 18th Century Milanese gates, and a nature trail and woodland walk where an old Ice House and Water Cascade can be seen.

❖

SUITABILITY FOR OTHER EVENTS
Capesthorne's situation makes it the ideal venue for functions aimed at the Manchester and North West corporate sector. Facilities are available for clay pigeon shooting, product launches, filming, still photography, shows, wedding receptions, fishing, caravanning and camping, equestrian events (own cross-country course), garden parties, rallies, barbecues, survival games, murder mystery evenings, firework displays, son et lumière etc.

EXTRA FACILITIES
The Theatre is used as a Lecture Room and seats up to 150 people. Cost of hire of the room, audio-visual facilities and lecture negotiable.

ADVICE TO COURIERS & DRIVERS
Rest Room and free meal provided for drivers. No photography in the Hall. Dogs in Park only.

FACILITIES FOR THE DISABLED
Compacted paths, ramps and toilet facilities available.

PARKING FOR COACHES & CARS
Parking for 100 cars/20 coaches on hard-standing and for 2,000 in the park, 50 yds from the house.

CATERING
Capesthorne has its own in-house catering staff providing a wide variety of meals from afternoon tea to banquets. Garden Restaurant, Bromley Room and the ornate Saloon and Queen Anne Rooms available. Special arrangements for corporate functions and weddings

GUIDED TOURS
Can be arranged for up to 50 people at any one time Also available in Italian. The owner can meet tours visiting the house. Average time taken for tour 1 hour.

GIFT SHOP/GUIDE BOOKS
Open when Hall is open and by request at other times. Various brochures on the house, park and garden are available.

CONTACT

Jacquie Caldwell
Capesthorne Hall
Siddington
Macclesfield
Cheshire
SK11 9JY
Tel: (01625) 861221
or (01625) 861779
Fax: (01625) 861619

LOCATION

30 mins South of Manchester on A34 Near M6, M63 and M62.
Airport: Manchester International 20 mins.
Helicopter: (051) 427 1609.
Rail: Macclesfield 5mls (2hrs from London).
Taxi: (01625) 533464.
Air Taxi: (061) 499 1447.

OPENING TIMES

Summer
April - September

Bank Hol Mons only
Tues: June - July only
Weds: from May
Thurs: June - July only
Sundays throughout

HOUSE, GARDENS & CHAPEL
1.30 - 3.30pm

GARDENS & CHAPEL ONLY
12noon - 6.00pm

Groups welcome by appointment.

Caravan Park also open March to October.

Corporate enquiries welcome all year.

ADMISSION

Summer

HOUSE AND GARDEN
Adult £3.00
Child* £1.00
OAP £2.50

GARDEN ONLY
Adult £2.25
Child* £1.00
OAP £2.00
Family Ticket . . . £7.00

Groups**
Please telephone for details.

* Aged 5 - 16yrs.
**Min 20 people

CONFERENCE AND FUNCTION FACILITIES

ROOM	DIMENSIONS	CAPACITY	LAYOUT	POWER POINTS	SUITABLE FOR A/V
Theatre	120' x 25'	155	Theatre	Ample	✓
Garden Restaurant	100' x 20'	100	Theatre	Ample	✓
		80	Schoolroom		
		50	Boardroom		
		100	Buffet		
		80	Lunch/Dinner		
Saloon	40' x 25'	100	Theatre	Ample	✓
		80	Schoolroom		
		50	Boardroom		
Queen Anne Room	38' x 26'	80	Schoolroom	Ample	✓
		100	Theatre		

ADLINGTON HALL

See page 17 for full page entry.

ARLEY HALL & GARDENS

See page 18 for full page entry.

BEESTON CASTLE

Tel: 01829 260464

Chester, Cheshire.
Owner: English Heritage   **Contact:** The Administrator
Standing majestically on sheer, rocky crags which fall sharply away from the castle walls, Beeston has possibly the best views of the surrounding countryside of any castle in England and the rock has a history stretching back over 2,500 years.
Location: 11m SE of Chester on minor road off A49, 2 m W of Bunbury.
Opening Times: 11m SE of Chester on minor road off A49, 2 m W of Bunbury.
Admission: Adult £2.20, Child £1.10, Conc £1.70.

CAPESTHORNE HALL

See page 19 for full page entry.

CHESTER CATHEDRAL

Tel: 01244 324756   **Fax**: 01244 341110

12 Abbey Square, Chester, Cheshire, CH1 2HU.

     Contact: Mr N Fry
Founded in 1092 as a Benedictine monastery, it became an Anglican cathedral in 1541. All styles of architecture are represented as well as spectacular medieval woodwork.
Location: Chester city centre.
Opening Times: 7am - 6.30pm daily.
Admission: Donation.

CHESTER ROMAN AMPHITHEATRE

Tel: 01244 602666

Vicars Lane, Chester, Cheshire.
Owner: English Heritage   **Contact:** The Administrator
The largest Roman amphitheatre in Britain, partially excavated. Used for entertainment and military training by the 20th Legion, based at the fortress of Deva.
Location: On Vicars Lane beyond Newgate, Chester.
Opening Times: Any reasonable time.

CHOLMONDELEY CASTLE GDNS

Tel: 01829 720383 **Fax**: 01829 720519

Malpas, Cholmondeley, Cheshire, SY14 8AH.
Owner: The Marchioness of Cholmondeley   **Contact:** Mrs Jean Grimes
Extensive pleasure gardens dominated by romantic Gothic castle.
Location: Off A49 Tarporley/Whitchurch Rd. Off A41 Chester/Whitchurch Rd.
Opening Times: 2 - 30 Apr, Suns and Bank Hol Mons only, 12 Noon - 5.30pm. May - Oct, Wed and Thur, 12 Noon - 5.00pm. Sun and Bank Hol Mon, 12 Noon - 5.30pm.
Admission: Adult £2.60, Child 75p, Senior citizens £1.80, Groups: Adult £2.50, Senior citizen £1.50, Child 75p.

DORFOLD HALL

Tel: 01270 625245   **Fax**: 01270 628723

Nantwich, Cheshire, CW5 8LD.
Owner: R C Roundell Esq   **Contact:** R C Roundell Esq
Early 17th century house with good plaster ceilings and panelling. Gardens.
Location: 1 m W of Nantwich on A534.
Opening Times: Tues afternoons 2 - 5.00pm, Apr - Oct inclusive.
Admission: Adult £3, Child £1.50. Parties on other days by appointment.

DUNHAM MASSEY HALL

Tel: 0161 9411025

Belchamp Walter, Sudbury CO10 7AT
Owner: The National Trust   **Contact:** The Administrator
Georgian house with Edwardian additions set in a 250-acre wooded deer park. Until 1976 this was the home of the 10th and last Earl of Stamford. Over 30 rooms are open, with outstanding collections of furniture, paintings and silver; also a fine library, kitchen, laundry and stables. The house is built on the site of a Tudor building whose moat provides power for a working Jacobean mill. Large garden with shrubs, herbaceous borders, mature trees and waterside plants.
Location: 3 m SW of Altrincham off A56.
Opening Times: House: 1 Apr - 29 Oct, Sat to Wed, 12 Noon - 5.00pm, last admission 4.30pm. Garden: 1 Apr - 29 Oct, daily, 11.00am - 5.30pm, last admission 5.00pm. The Mill machinery will normally operate on Wed & Sun. Park: daily throughout the year.
Admission: House & Garden: Adult £4.50, Child £2, Family £11.00. House only: Adult £3, Child £1.50. Garden only: £2.50, Child £1. Discount for pre-booked parties.

GAWSWORTH HALL

Tel: 01260 223456   **Fax**: 01260 223469

Church Lane, Gawsworth, Macclesfield, Cheshire, SK11 9RN.
Owner: Timothy Richards Esq   **Contact:** Timothy Richards Esq
Fine Tudor black and white house.
Location: 3m S of Macclesfield on A536.
Opening Times: Adult £3.40, Child £1.70. Groups of 20 plus £2.80.

HARE HILL

Tel: 01625 828981

Over Alderley, Macclesfield, Cheshire, SK10 4QB.
Owner: The National Trust   **Contact:** The Head Gardener
A woodland garden surrounding a walled garden with pergola, rhododendrons and azaleas; parkland: link path to Alderley Edge (2m).
Location: Between Alderley Edge and Prestbury, turn off N at B5087 at Greyhound Road.
Opening Times: 19 Mar - 19 Oct: Wed, Thur, Sat, Sun and BH Mon 10am - 5.30pm. Special opening to see rhododendrons and azaleas: 12 May - 2 Jun daily, 10am - 5.30pm. Closed Nov - Mar.
Admission: £2.50 ea. Entrance per car £1.50 refundable on entry to garden. Parties by written appointment c/o Garden Lodge, Oak Road, Over Alderley, Macclesfield, SK10 4QB. Not suitable for school parties.

LITTLE MORETON HALL

Tel: 01260 272018

Scholar Green, Congleton, Cheshire, CW12 4SD.
Owner: The National Trust   **Contact:** The Administrator
Begun in the 15th century, and regarded as the most perfect example of a timber-framed moated manor house in the country. A long wainscoted gallery, chapel, great hall and knot garden are of particular interest.
Location: 4 m SW of Congleton, on E side of A34.
Opening Times: 1 Apr - 30 Sep: Wed to Sun, 12 Noon - 5.30pm (closed Good Fri): BH Mon 11 - 5.30pm; Oct: Sat & Sun, 12 Noon - 5.30pm or dusk if earlier. Last adm: 5pm.
Admission: Adult £3.50, Family £8.80, pre-booked party £2.80.

LYME PARK

OPEN

House: 1 Apr - 31 Oct
Sat - Wed
1.30 - 5.00pm
Bank Hol Mons
11.00am - 5.00pm

Garden: 1 Apr - 31 Oct
Daily: 11 am - 5.00pm
Nov - 17 Dec
Sat & Sun
12 Noon - 4.00pm

Park: Daily
8.00am - 8.30pm or dusk.

Tel: 01663 762023
Fax: 01663 765035

DISLEY, STOCKPORT, CHESHIRE SK12 2NX

Owner: The National Trust   *Contact: The Property Manager*
Legh family home for 600 years. Part of the original Elizabethan house survives with 18th century and 19th century additions by Giacomo Leoni and Lewis Wyatt. Four centuries of period interiors - Mortlake tapestries, Grinling Gibbons carvings, unique collection of English clocks. Historic gardens with orangery by Wyatt, a lake and the 'Dutch' garden, 1,377 acre park, home to red and fallow deer.
Location: Off the A6 between Stockport & Buxton.
Admission: House and Garden: £3.00, Family £7.00. Park only: £3.00 per car.

NESS GARDENS

Tel: 01513 368733 **Fax**: 01513 531004

Ness, Neston, Cheshire, L64 4AY.
Owner: University of Liverpool   **Contact:** Dr. E J Sharples
Location: Off A540. 10m NW of Chester.
Opening Times: 1 Mar - 31 Oct, 9.30am - dusk. Nov - Feb, 9.30am - 4pm.
Admission: Adult £3.50, Child £2.50, Family £8, Concessions £2.50, Groups £3.

NETHER ALDERLEY MILL

Tel: 01625 523012

Congleton Road, Nether Alderley, Macclesfield, Cheshire, SK10 4TW.
Owner: The National Trust   **Contact:** The National Trust
A fascinating overshot tandem wheel watermill, dating from the 15th century, with a stone-tiled low pirched roof. The machinery was derelict for 30 years, but has now been restored to full working order, and grinds flour occasionally for demonstrations.
Location: 1½m S of Alderley Edge, on E side of A34.
Opening Times: 2 Apr - end May & Oct: Wed, Sun & BH Mon, 1 - 4.30pm. Jun - Sep, Tues to Sun & BH Mon 1 - 5.00pm.
Admission: Adult £1.80, Parties (max 20+) by prior arrangement.

NORTON PRIORY WALLED GARDEN & MUSEUM
Tel: 01928 569895

Tudor Road, Manor Park, Runcorn, Cheshire, WA7 1SX.
Owner: Norton Priory Museum   **Contact:** Norton Priory Museum
Site of Medieval priory set in beautiful woodland gardens.
Location: 3 m from J11/M56.
Opening Times: Every afternoon from 1 Mar - 31 Oct (museum open all year).
Admission: Adult £2.50, Child £1.30, Family £6.50, Concessions £1.30, Group £1.30.

PECKFORTON CASTLE

OPEN

Easter 14 Apr - 10 Sept.

Open daily

10.00am - 6.00pm

Tel: 01829 260930
Fax: 01829 261230

STONEHOUSE LANE, PECKFORTON, NR TARPORLEY, CHESHIRE CW6 9TN
Owner: Graybill Ltd.   *Contact: Mrs. E Graybill*

An intact Norman style Castle, built by Lord Tollemache 1840 and designed by Anthony Salvin. It was the setting for the Robin Hood Film in 1991. Animated tour assistants, gossiping verger, singing minstrel, original Lord Tollemache and resident ghost to entertain/licensed tea room curios/private hire - functions all year availability.

Location: Off A49, on dramatic sandstone trail. 12 miles east of Chester.
Admission: Adult £2.50, OAP £2.00. Child under 5 Free, Concessions £1.50, Parties over 20 persons £1.00. Free Parking.

QUARRY BANK MILL & STYAL COUNTRY PARK

Wilmslow, Cheshire, SK9 4LA   **Tel:** 01625 527468   **Fax:** 01625 539267
Owner: The National Trust   **Contact:** Mr S Feber
A major Georgian cotton mill restored as a working museum of the cotton industry, now running under waterpower. There are demonstrations of weaving and spinning, and galleries illustrate the millworkers' world, textile finishing processed, the Gregs as pioneers of the factory system and water as a source of energy. The original Apprentice House, as lived in by mill apprentices in 1830, is fully restored.
Location: 1½ m of Wilmslow off B5166, 2½ m from B56 exit 5.
Opening Times: Oct - Mar 11am - 5pm last admission 3.30pm. Apr - Sep 11am - 6pm last admission 4.30pm.
Admission: Mill & Apprentice House: Adult £4.50, Child/conc £3.20, Family £13.50. Mill only: Adult £3.50, Child/conc £2.50. Apprentice House & Garden only: Adult £3.00, Child/conc £2.30. Groups by prior arrangement.

STAPELEY WATER GARDENS LTD
Tel: 01270 628628   **Fax:** 01270 624188

London Road, Stapeley, Nantwich, Cheshire, CW5 7LH.
Contact: R G A Davies Esq
Location: 1 m S of Nantwich on A51 to Stone. Follow brown tourist signs from J16/M6.
Opening Times: Every day except Christmas, 10am opening.
Admission: Adult £3.15, Child £1.65, Senior citizen £2.25, Groups call for details.

TATTON PARK
Tel: 01565 750250

Knutsford, Cheshire WA16 6QN

Owner: The National Trust   **Contact:** Mr K Davies
One of the most complete historic estates open to visitors in England. The 19th century Wyatt house, set in more than 1000 acres of deer park, contains the Egerton family collection of pictures, books, china, glass, silver and specially commissioned Gillow furniture; servants' rooms and cellars depict life downstairs. The 50-acre garden contains an authentic Japanese garden, Italian garden, orangery, fernery, rose garden and pinetum. Also, a medieval old hall, an 18th century farm working as in 1930s and many varieties of wildfowl. There is a new outdoor and sailing centre for pre-booked groups, and a walk round the Landscape History Trail begins the interpretive theme 'A Story for Every Age'.
Location: 3½ m N of Knutsford, 4 m S of Altrincham, 5 m from M6, junction 19.
Opening Times: Summer opening: 1 Apr - 22 Oct. Park: 10am - 7pm every day Gardens: Tue - Sun, 10.30am - 6pm. Mansion & Farm: Tue - Sun, 12 Noon - 5pm. Old Hall: Sat, Sun & BHs 12 Noon - 5pm. Housekeeper's Store: 11.30am - 5.30pm. All open BH Mon. Winter opening: 23 Oct - 31 Mar. Park 11am - 5pm. Gardens: 11am - 4pm. Housekeeper's Store: Tue - Sun, 11.30am - 4pm.
Admission: Adult £2.50, Child £1.50, Groups £2.00, Family £7.50 for each attraction.

TABLEY HOUSE

OPEN

April - October inclusive

Thursday, Friday Saturdays, Sundays and Bank Holidays

2.00 - 5.00pm

Tel: 01565 750151

KNUTSFORD, CHESHIRE WA16 0HB
Owner: Victoria University of Manchester   *Contact: The Administrator*

Magnificent Palladian Mansion, Grade I, by John Carr of York completed 1769 for the Leicester family who lived at Tabley for over 700 years. Fine collection of English works of art, furniture, memorabilia can be seen in the State Rooms. Private chapel 1678. Tea Room, Gift Shop Access for wheelchairs.
Location: M6 junction 19, A556.
Admission: Adults £3.50. Children £1.00 Group bookings on application.

SPECIAL EVENTS DIARY

- **24th February: Adlington Hall**
  Organ Recital - "Musica Dolce" (Advance Tickets only).
- **8th - 9th April: Capesthorne Hall**
  Rainbow Craft Fair.
- **23rd April: Peckforton Castle**
  Falconry and Birds of Prey Display.
- **7th - 8th May: Adlington Hall**
  Craft Fair 10.30am-6.00pm.
- **14th May: Peckforton Castle**
  Falconry and Birds of Prey Display.
- **10th June: Capesthorne Hall**
  Fireworks & Laser Symphony Concert.
  Open Air Concert by Performing Arts Management.
- **18th June: Peckforton Castle**
  Marcher Knights Medieval Re-enactment.

- **16th July: Peckforton Castle**
  Marcher Knights Medieval Re-enactment.
- **30th July: Peckforton Castle**
  Falconry and Birds of Prey Display.
- **12th - 13th August: Adlington Hall**
  Craft Fair 10.30am - 6.00pm.
- **20th August: Peckforton Castle**
  Marcher Knights Medieval Re-enactment .
- **2nd September: Capesthorne Hall**
  Last Night of the Proms Concert" A rousing patriotic evening ending with stunning fireworks.
- **3rd September: Peckforton Castle**
  Marcher Knights Medieval Re-enactment.
- **23rd - 24th September: Capesthorne Hall**
  Rainbow Craft Fair

ANTONY HOUSE & GDN. & ANTONY WOODLAND GDN.
Torpoint

Antony House and Garden: A superb example of an early 18th century mansion. The main block is faced in lustrous silver-grey stone, flanked by mellow brick pavilions. The ancestral home of the Carew family for nearly 600 years, the house contains a wealth of paintings, tapestries, furniture and embroideries, many linking the great families of Cornwall. Set in parkland and fine gardens overlooking the Lynher river. An 18th century Bath House in the grounds can be viewed by arrangement. Tea room and shop.

Antony Woodland Garden: The woodland garden was established in the late 18th century with the assistance of Humphrey Repton. It features over 300 varieties of camellias, together with magnolias, rhododendrons, azaleas and other flowering shrubs, interspersed with many fine species of indigenous and exotic trees. A further 50 acres of natural woods bordering the tidal waters of the Lynher provide a number of delightful walks. No dogs.

❖

CONTACT

Antony House
(The National Trust)
The Adminstrator
Antony House & Gdn
Torpoint
Cornwall
PL11 2QA

Tel: (01752) 812191

Antony Woodland Garden
(Carew Pole Gdn Trust)
Torpoint
Cornwall
PL11 2QA

LOCATION

Antony House and Antony Woodland Garden:
5 mls west of Plymouth via Torpoint car ferry, 2 miles north-west of Torpoint.

OPENING TIMES

Antony House and Garden
1 Apr - 31 Oct
Tue, Wed, Thur & Bank Hol Mons
plus Suns in June, July & Aug
1.30pm - 5.30pm

Guided tours at less busy times.

Last tour 4.45pm

Antony Woodland Garden
1 Mar - 31 Oct
Daily
11.00am - 5.30pm

ADMISSION

Antony House:
Adult £3.60
Parties . . . .£2.80.

Antony Woodland Garden:
Adult £1.50
Child 50p

Joint gardens only ticket to NT owned garden and Antony Woodland Garden
Adult £2.50
Child £1.25
Parties £2.00

MOUNT EDGCUMBE
Torpoint

MOUNT EDGCUMBE HOUSE stands above its tree-lined avenue overlooking Plymouth Sound, as it has done for the past 500 years.

It was the ancestral home of the Mount Edgcumbe family, and following severe World War II damage was rebuilt by the architect Adrian Gilbert Scott. The interior follows the 16th Century design, but is light and airy, and has recently been renovated using 18th century techniques and design.

GARDENS

The garden surrounding the House is a delightful mixture of the formal, with its Victorian beds, and the informal. It includes a rare example of an 18th Century Shell Seat and several ancient trees.

The 18th century Formal Gardens designed by the family in the English, French and Italian styles have recently been complemented by New Zealand and American gardens.

———————— ❖ ————————

CONTACT

Mrs. Cynthia Gaskell-Brown
Mt Edgcumbe House
Cremyll
Torpoint
Cornwall
PL10 1HZ

Tel: (01752) 822236
Fax: (01752) 822199

LOCATION

From Plymouth via Torpoint Ferry, follow A374 to Antony then B3247. 1 hr approx. From Cornwall, A38 to Trerulefoot Roundabout, A374, From London, M4, M5 via Bristol to Exeter, then A38 to Plymouth. (3-4 hours).

Foot: From Plymouth (Royal Parade) bus to Cremyll Ferry at Admirals Hard, Durnford Street. Ferrycrossing 7 minutes

Bus: Bus from Royal Torpoint Ferry.

Air: Plymouth Airport.

Taxi: (01752) 822196.

SUITABILITY FOR OTHER EVENTS
Fashion shows, photography, archery, garden parties, shows, filming, hot air ballooning, commercial product launching. Any idea considered.

EXTRA FACILITIES
Also available for use: parkland, helipad, cricket pitch and good coastal walking. Lectures can be arranged on the property, its gardens and history for up to 60 people. A room, seating about 35, can be hired by prior arrangement. A projector and screen are available. Baby changing facility.

ADVICE TO COURIERS & DRIVERS
Grounds include Formal Gardens so allow plenty of time. Free entry to house for familiarisation visit and free meal

when accompanying party on production of appropriate identification. No unaccompanied children, no dogs - this applies to the House and Earl's Garden only. No photography in House.

FACILITIES FOR THE DISABLED
Restaurant, Formal Gardens, House and part of Park area suitable for the disabled. Disabled and elderly visitors may alight by entrance to the House. Lift in House to first floor. There are toilet facilities for the disabled in the Orangery Restaurant and in the House. Two wheelchairs are available.

PARKING FOR COACHES & CARS
Car park for 50 cars and 6 coaches 400 yds from House. Other car parks at Cremyll, Maker and Rame.

CATERING
'The Orangery' in the Formal Gardens has a capacity of 120. Parties can book in advance and special rates are given to groups of more than 25 people. Menus available on request

GUIDED TOURS
These are available, by prior arrangement for groups of up to 60 people (split into groups of 20). Room Stewards are normally on duty. Tours in other languages may be arranged. Average time taken to see the House and Earl's Garden $1^1/2$ hours.

GIFT SHOP
The Cremyll Lodge Gift Shop is open 10.30am - 5.00pm from 1st April to the end of October, and sells many locally-made souvenirs and gifts. There is also a Gift Shop in the House: House opening times apply.

GUIDE BOOKS
New colour guide book, £2.95. Souvenir booklet £1.00, text available in Japanese, French, Spanish, German, Dutch, Polish and Russian.

SCHOOL VISITS/CHILDREN
School visits welcome. A guide and schoolroom can be provided. Areas of interest: tree trail, seashore, wild deer herd, geology, fortifications.

OPENING TIMES

All Year
PARK AND FORMAL GARDENS open daily . Free

Summer
1 April - 31 October
HOUSE AND EARL'S GARDEN
Bank Hols Mons only 11.00am - 5.00pm

Tuesdays Closed

Wed, Thurs, Fri, Sat & Sun. 11.00am - 5.00pm

Winter
House open only by appointment.

ADMISSION

HOUSE AND EARL'S GARDEN
Adult £3.00
Child* £1.50
Concessions** . .£2.20
Family £7.00
Season £5.50

* Aged 5-16
**NACF members, Friends of Plymouth City Museums and Art Gallery, Unemployed, Disabled, Student, OAP.

Groups
Any booking made in advance with a value of £30.00 or more attracts a 20% discount, which can be passed to the booking agent to be used at his discretion.

Winter
Full normal admission is charged to groups visiting outside normal hours by special arrangement.

TREWITHEN
Probus

CONTACT

Mrs I Norman
Trewithen
Grampound Road
Nr Truro
Cornwall
TR2 4DD

Tel: (01726) 882763
or (01726) 882418

LOCATION

From London (4 - 5 hrs)
M4, M5, A30, A390.
Via A390, St Austell
20 mins; Truro 20 mins;
Newquay-St Mawgan
20 mins.

Taxi: (01726) 73153.

TREWITHEN means 'house of the trees', and the name truly describes this fine early Georgian House in its splendid setting of wood and parkland. Country Life described the house as "one of the outstanding West Country houses of the 18th Century."

The origins of the house go back to the 17th Century, but it was the architect Sir Robert Taylor, as well as Thomas Edwards of Greenwich who was responsible for the fine building we see today. The rebuilding was commissioned by Philip Hawkins, who bought the house in 1715, and was completed only some 40 years later. The house has been lived in by the same family for over 250 years.

Behind Trewithen's facade of quiet elegance hides a fascinating history. The Hawkins family were eminent landowners, they encouraged tin, copper and china clay mining in Cornwall and they built a railway and a harbour (Pentewan). The most notable member was Christopher Hawkins, created a baronet in 1799, who was MP for Grampound and, later, Father of the House of Commons. All Hawkins were great collectors and much of their contribution to both county and national life is reflected inside the house.

GARDENS

The gardens at Trewithen, (some 12 hectares) are outstanding and of international fame. Created since the beginning of the century by George Johnstone - a direct Hawkins descendant - they contain a wide and rare collection of flowering shrubs. Many of the plants here are unique to Trewithen: they were sent in seed form during the 1920s from Tibet, China and Nepal, and now flower spectacularly in the mild Cornish climate. Some of the Magnolias and Rhododendron species in the garden are known throughout the world. Plants and Shrubs are available for sale. The gardens, impressive throughout the year, are particularly attractive between March and the end of June, and again in the Autumn. They are one of the two attractions in this county to be awarded three stars by Michelin.

---❖---

OPENING TIMES

Summer
GARDENS
1 March - 30 September
Daily except Sundays
10.00am - 4.30pm
Suns (Apr & May only)

HOUSE
April - July & Aug Bank
Holiday Monday
Mon & Tues 2 - 4.00pm
NB. Please book

Winter
1 Oct - Last day in Feb.
Closed

All Year
NURSERY
Mon - Sat 9am - 4.30pm

ADVICE TO COURIERS & DRIVERS
Please pre-book to visit the House. No dogs or photography in the house. Dogs on leads in the garden.

FACILITIES FOR THE DISABLED
There are toilet facilities for the disabled.

PARKING FOR COACHES & CARS
Parking for 150 cars & 7 coaches 50 yards from the house.

CATERING
Tea shop at Trewithen for light refreshments.

GUIDED TOURS
These are available for groups of up to 10 people for the House only. There is no additional cost for this. Average time taken to see the House 1/2 hour. There is a new video room: a 25 minute video showing the history of the House and Garden is shown free of charge.

GARDEN SHOP
The Garden Shop is open for the same hours as the Gardens themselves. The shop sells guide books, postcards and a substantial range of plants and shrubs, many of which are rare, highly prized or famous Trewithen hybrids. There is a picnic area and exciting childrens' play corner.

GUIDE BOOKS
Colour guide books, 80p.

ADMISSION

Summer
HOUSE ONLY
  Adult £3.00
  Child £1.50
  OAP £3.00
  Student £3.00
GARDENS
March - September
  Adult £2.50
  Child* £1.50
  Group adult £2.20

* Aged 5 - 15; under 5s free

** Over 12 adults

ANTHONY HOUSE & GARDEN
ANTHONY WOODLAND GARDEN

See page 22 for full page entry.

BOSVIGO HOUSE GARDENS

Tel: 01872 75774   **Fax**: 01872 41565

Bosvigo Lane, Truro, Cornwall, TR1 3NH.
Owner: Michael Perry Esq   **Contact:** Mr Michael Perry
Walled gardens surrounding Georgian House (not open).
Location: ³/₄ mile from city centre. Turn down Dobbs Lane near Sainsbury roundabout.
Opening Times: Mar - 30 Sept, Wed - Sat, 11.00am - 6.00pm.
Admission: Adult £1.50, Child 50p, Concessions £1.50.

CAERHAYS CASTLE & GARDEN

Tel: 01872 501870   **Fax**: 01872 501310

Caerhays, Gorran, St Austell, Cornwall, PL26 6LY.
Owner: F J Williams Esq   **Contact:** F J Williams Esq
Location: South coast of Cornwall - between Mevagissery and Portloe.
Opening Times: House; 27 Mar - 5 May, Mon - Fri, 11.00am - 4.30pm excluding BHs.
Garden; 20 Mar - 5 May, Mon - Fri, 2.00pm - 4.00pm.
Admission: House; £3 - guided tours only. Gardens; Standard £2.50., Child £1.50.
Guided tours by Head Gardener can be arranged outside normal opening times £3.50ea.

CARWINION GARDENS

Tel: 01326 250258

Owner: A Rogers Esq   **Contact:** A Rogers Esq
10 acres of many varieties of Bamboo.
Location: 4m W of Falmouth.
Opening Times: DAILY, 10.00am - 5.30pm.
Admission: Adult £2, Child under 16 free, Conc / group £1.

CHYSAUSTER ANCIENT VILLAGE

Tel: 01736 61889

Gulval, Cornwall
Owner: English Heritage   **Contact:** The Administrator
On a windy hillside, overlooking the wild and spectacular coast, is this deserted Romano-Cornish village with a 'street' of eight well preserved houses, each comprising a number of rooms around an open court.
Location: 2¹/₂m NW of Gulval off B3311, near Penzance.
Opening Times: 1 Apr - 30 Sept, daily 10am - 6pm, 1 Oct - 31 Oct, daily 10am - 4pm.
Admission: Adult £1.50, Child 80p, Conc £1.10.

COTEHELE

OPEN
1 Apr - 31 Oct
House
Restaurant & Mill
11.00am - 5.30pm
Daily except Fris
(open Good Fri)
last Adm. ¹/₂hr
before closing
Garden, Shop &
Tea room, Daily
11.00am - 5.30pm
All close 5pm in
Oct.
Gallery: Daily
12 Noon - 5.00pm
Nov - Mar
Garden open daily
Tel: 01579 51346

ST. DOMINICK, NR. SALTASH, CORNWALL PL12 6TA

Owner: The National Trust   *Contact: The Property Manager*
Enchantingly remote, perched high above the wood banks of the Tamar, Cotehele was home to the Edgcumbe family for nearly six centuries. The house retains a remarkably medieval atmosphere and contains a wealth of contemporary furnishings and *objets d'art*. The large estate includes a working watermill, a river quay with restored sailing barge and miles of woodland walks.
Location: On west bank of Tamar, 1 m west of Calstock by footpath (6 mls by road), 8 mls south-west of Tavistock, 14 mls from Plymouth via Saltash Bridge.
Admission: House, Garden, Mill: £ 5.00. Garden & Mill: £2.50
Parties (by prior written arrangement only): £4.00.

GLENDURGAN

Tel: 01208 74281

Mawnan Smith, Falmouth, Cornwall, TR11 5JZ.
Owner: The National Trust   **Contact:** The Administrator
A valley garden of great beauty with fine trees, shrubs and water gardens. The laurel maze, recently restored, is an unusual and popular feature. A wooded valley runs down to the tiny village of Durgan on the river.
Location: 4m SW of Falmouth, ¹/₂m SW of Mawnan Smith, on road to Helford Passage.
Opening Times: 1 Mar - 31 Oct: Tue to Sat & BH Mon (closed Good Fri), 10.30am - 5.30pm. Last admission 4.30pm.
Admission: £2.80, no reduction for parties.

HEMERDEN HOUSE

Tel: 01752 841410 (W/days), 337350 (W/ends).

70 Fore Street, Saltash, Cornwall, PL7 5BZ.
Owner: J H G Woollcombe Esq   **Contact:** Paul Williams & Partners (Agents)
Late 18th and 19th century family house.
Location: 3m E of Plympton off A38.
Opening Times: 1 May - 31 Aug, 2.00pm - 5.30pm, including Bank Hols. Not open every day please telephone for details.
Admission: Standard £2.30. Groups by arrangement.

LANHYDROCK

OPEN
1 Apr - 31 Oct
Daily except Mons
when the house
only is closed (open
Bank Hol Mons)
11.00am - 5.30pm

Closes 5.00pm
in Oct.

Last adm: ¹/₂ hr
before closing.

Nov - end of Mar
Garden open daily

Tel: 01208 73320

BODMIN, CORNWALL PL30 5AD

Owner: The National Trust   *Contact: The Property Manager*
The grandest and most welcoming house in Cornwall, Lanhydrock is superbly set in 450 acres of woods and parkland and encircled by a garden of rare shrubs and trees, lovely in all seasons. Although dating from the 17th century, Lanhydrock was largely rebuilt after a fire in 1881 and now exemplifies the great Victorian country house.
Location: 2¹/₂ miles south east of Bodmin, follow signposts from either A38 or B3268.
Admission: House, Garden & Grounds: Adult £5.40. Garden & Grounds: £2.50
Pre-arranged parties £5.00. Family ticket £14.50.

LAUNCESTON CASTLE

Tel: 01566 772365

Launceston, Cornwall.
Owner: English Heritage   **Contact:** The Administrator
Set on the motte of the original Norman castle and commanding the town and surrounding countryside, the shell keep and tower survive of this medieval castle which controlled the main route into Cornwall.
Location: In Launceston.
Opening Times: 1 Apr - 30 Sept, daily 10.00am - 6.00pm.
Admission: Adult £1.30, Child 70p, Conc £1.00.

LAWRENCE HOUSE

Tel: 01566 773277

9 Castle Street, Launceston, Cornwall, PL15 8BA.
Owner: The National Trust   **Contact:** The Administrator
Georgian house given to the National Trust to help preserve the character of the street, and now leased to Launceston Town Council as a museum and civic centre.
Location: In Launceston.
Opening Times: Apr - early Oct: Mon - Fri, 10.30am - 4.30pm.
Admission: Donation.

THE LOST GARDEN OF HELIGAN

Tel: 01726 844157   **Fax**: 01726 843023

Pentewan, Staustell, Cornwall, PL26 6EN.
Owner: Colin Howlett Esq   **Contact:** Mr Colin Howlett
Opening Times: All year, 10.00am - 4.30pm (last admissions).
Admission: Adult £2.80, Child (5-15 years) £1.60, Family £7.80, Senior citizens £2.40. Groups by prior arrangement.

MOUNT EDGECUMBE

See page 23 for full page entry.

PENCARROW

OPEN

Easter - 15 Oct
1.30 - 5.00pm
Sun - Thurs.

1 June - 10 Sept
& Bank Holiday
Mondays
opens 11.00am.

Tel: 01208 841369

BODMIN, CORNWALL PL30 3AG

Owner: *Molesworth-St Aubyn family*   ***Contact:*** *The Administrator*

Still owned and lived in by the family. Georgian house and grade II listed gardens. Superb collection of pictures, furniture and porcelain. Marked walks through 50 acres of beautiful formal and woodland gardens, Victorian rockery, Italian gardens, lake and ice house. Craft centre, tearooms, children's play area and plant shop. Facilities for the disabled. Dogs welcome in the grounds.

Location: 4 miles north west of Bodmin off A389 and B3266 at Washaway.

Admission: Adult £3.80. Child £1.80.

PENDENNIS CASTLE

Tel: 01326 316594

Falmouth, Cornwall.

Owner: English Heritage   **Contact:** The Administrator

This castle is a testament to the quality of the coastal defences erected by Henry VIII. The well preserved granite gun fort and outer ramparts with great angled bastions defended against invasion from the sea, but it was captured from the land after a long siege during the Civil War.

Location: On Pendennis Head 1m SE of Falmouth.

Opening Times: 1 Apr - 30 Sept, daily 10am - 6pm, 1 Oct - 31 Mar, daily 10am - 4pm.

Admission: Adult £2.20, Child £1.10, Conc £1.70.

PENJERRIC GARDENS

Tel: 01872 870105

Budock, Falmouth, Cornwall, TR11 5ED.

Owner: Mrs Rachel Morin   **Contact:** Mrs Rachel Morin

Location: 3m from Falmouth between Budock and Mawnan Smith.

Opening Times: 1 Mar - 30 Sept, Wed, Fri and Sun, 1.30pm - 4.30pm.

Admission: Adult £1, Child 50p.

PRIDEAUX PLACE

OPEN

Easter - end of Sept.
Sun - Thurs
1.30pm - 5.00pm
closed Fri & Sat
Easter, Late Spring
and August
Bank Hol
11..00am - 5.00pm
1 Oct - Easter
Open by
arrangement for
groups 10+.

Tel: 01841 532945
or   01841 532411

PADSTOW, CORNWALL PL28 8RP

Owner: *Peter Prideaux Brune*   ***Contact:*** *Peter Prideaux Brune*

Tucked away in the busy port of Padstow, the family home of the Prideaux family for the past four hundred years, is surrounded by gardens and wooded grounds overlooking a deerpark and the Camel estuary to the moors beyond. The house still retains its 'E' shape Elizabethan front, contains family treasures and has a homely atmosphere. The impressive outbuildings have been restored in recent years and the 16th Century plaster ceiling in the great chamber has been uncovered for the first time since 1760.

Location: 5 miles from A39 on A389 Newquay/Wadebridge link road. Signposted by Historic House Signs.

Admission: House & Garden: Adult/OAP £4.00, Child £1.00. Grounds only: £2.00 Groups: Adult/OAP £3.50. Children by arrangement.

PROBUS GARDENS

Tel: 01208 872687

Nr. Truro, Cornwall

Owner: Alistair Rivers Esq   **Contact:** Mr Alistair Rivers

Location: 3m from Falmouth between Budock and Mawnan Smith.

Opening Times: 1 Apr - 30 Sept, daily, 10am - 5pm. 1 Oct - 31 Mar, Mon - Fri, 10am - 4pm.

Admission: Adult £2.40, Child free, Groups £1.90.

RESTORMEL CASTLE

Tel: 01726 882597   **Fax**: 01726 882597

Lostwithiel, Cornwall

Owner: English Heritage   **Contact:** The Administrator

Perched on a high mound, surrounded by a deep moat, the huge circular keep of this splendid Norman castle survives in remarkably good condition.

Location: 1½m N or Lostwithiel off A390.

Opening Times: 1 Apr - 30 Sept, daily 10am - 6pm, 1 Oct - 31 Oct, daily 10am - 4pm.

Admission: Adult £1.30, Child 70p, Conc £1.10.

ST CATHERINE'S CASTLE

Fowey, Cornwall.

Owner: English Heritage   **Contact:** The Administrator

A small fort built by Henry VIII to defend Fowey harbour, with fine views of the coastline and river estuary.

Location: ¾m SW of Fowey along footpath off A3082.

Opening Times: Any reasonable time.

ST MAWES CASTLE

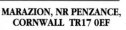

OPEN

1 April - 30 Sept
Daily
10.00am - 6.00pm

1 Oct - 31 Oct
Daily
10.00am - 4.00pm

1 Nov - 31 Mar
Weds - Suns only
10.00am - 4.00pm

Tel: 01326 270526

ST MAWES, CORNWALL TR2 3AA

Owner: *English Heritage*   ***Contact:*** *The Head Custodian*

Built by Henry VIII as a defence against invasion by France, St. Mawes Castle with its three huge circular bastions and gun ports covering every angle of approach is a fine example of Tudor military architecture. Today, still intact, it stands in delightful sub tropical gardens.

Location: In St. Mary's.

Admission: Adult £1.50, OAP/Student/UB40 £1.10, Child 80p.
15% discount on parties of 11 or more.

ST. MICHAEL'S MOUNT

MARAZION, NR PENZANCE, CORNWALL TR17 0EF

Owner: *The National Trust*
Contact: *The Administrator*

Tel: 01736 710507

This magical island is the jewel in Cornwall's crown. The great granite crag which rises from the waters of Mount's Bay is surmounted by an embattled 14th century castle, home of the St. Aubyn family for over 300 years. The Mount's flanks are softened by lush sub-tropical vegetation and on the water's edge there is a harbourside community which features shops and restaurants.

Location: At Marazion there is access on foot over causeway at low tide. In summer months there is a ferry at high tide.

OPEN

1 Apr - 31 Oct: Mon - Fri 10.30am - 5.30pm
Last admission 4.45pm

1 Nov - end of Mar: Mons, Weds & Fris guided tours or free flow as tide, weather/ circumstances permit.

Admission: £3.50,
Family Ticket £9.00,
Pre-arranged parties £3.00

TINTAGEL CASTLE

Tel: 01726 844157

Tintagel , Cornwall.
Owner: English Heritage   **Contact:** The Administrator

The spectacular setting for the legendary castle of King Arthur is the wild and windswept Cornish coast. Clinging precariously to the edge of the cliff face are the extensive ruins of a medieval royal castle built by Richard, Earl of Cornwall, younger brother of Henry III. Despite extensive excavation since the 1930s and a mass of picturesque legend, Tintagel is still an enigma, its history full of gaps and the nature of its earlier occupation quite uncertain.

Location: On Tintagel Head, 1/2m along uneven track from Tintagel
Opening Times: 1 Apr - 30 Sept, daily 10am - 6pm, 1 Oct - 31 Mar, daily 10am - 4pm.
Admission: Adult £2.20, Child £1.10, Conc £1.70

TRENGWAINTON GARDEN

Tel: 01736 68410

Front Lodge, Trengwainton, Penzance, Cornwall, TR20 8RZ.
Owner: The National Trust   **Contact:** Mr K Sansom

This large shrub garden, with views over Mount's Bay, is particularly colourful in spring and early summer. The walled garden has many tender plants which cannot be grown in the open anywhere else in England.

Location: 4m S of Truro, on both sides of B3289 above King Harry Ferry
Opening Times: Mar to end Oct, Wed - Sat, 10.30am - 5.30pm.
Admission: Adult £2.60.

TINTAGEL OLD POST OFFICE

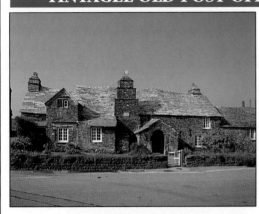

OPEN

1 Apr - 31 Oct
Daily
11.00am - 5.30pm

Closes 5.00pm in October

Tel: 01840 770024

TINTAGEL, CORNWALL PL34 0DB
Owner: The National Trust   Contact: The Administrator

One of the most characterful buildings in Cornwall, and a house of great antiquity, this small 14th century manor is full of charm and interest. Tumble roofed and weathered by the centuries, it is restored in the fashion of the Post Office it was for nearly 50 years.

Location: In the centre of Tintagel.
Admission: £2.00. Pre-arranged parties £1.50.

TRERICE

OPEN

1 Apr - 31 Oct
Daily except Tues
11.00am - 5.30pm

Closes 5.00pm in October

Last admission
1/2 hour before closing.

Tel: 01637 875404

NEWQUAY, CORNWALL TR8 4PG
Owner: The National Trust   Contact: The Administrator

Trerice is an architectural gem and something of a rarity - a small Elizabeth manor house hidden away in a web of narrow lanes and still somehow caught in the spirit of its age. An old Arundell house, it escaped the common fate of material alteration over the centuries and has what is possibly the earliest Dutch-style gabled façade in the country.

Location: 3 mls south-east of Newquay via the A392 & A3058 (turn right at Kestle Mill).
Admission: £3.60. Pre-arranged parties £3.00.

TREBAH

OPEN

Daily, all year.

10.30am - 5.00pm

Tel: 01326 250448
Fax: 01326 250781

MAWNAN SMITH, CORNWALL TR11 5JZ
Owner: Trebah Garden Trust   Contact: Mr Henry Shaw

26 acre sub-tropical ravine garden running down to Helford River. A stream winds through water gardens with waterfall and Koi Carp, flanked with carpets of Arums and candelabra primulas and two acres of blue and white hydrangeas. 100 year old rhododendrons and magnolias over-hang glades of giant Gunnera and Tree ferns. An enchanted garden for plantsmen, artists and the family.

Location: 1 mile SW of Mawnan Smith. Tourism signs from Treliever Cross roundabout on A39 approach to Falmouth.
Admission: Adult £2.80, Child and Disabled £1.00, Special group rates.

TRESCO ABBEY GARDENS

OPEN

All year

10.00am - 4.00pm

Tel: 01720 422849

ISLES OF SCILLY, CORNWALL PL28 8RP
Owner: Mr. R A and Mrs L A Dorrien-Smith   Contact: Mr. M.A Nelhams

Tresco Abbey built by Augustus Smith has been the family home since 1834. The garden here flourishes on the small island. Nowhere else in the British Isles does such an exotic collection of plants grow in the open. Agaves, Aloes, Proteas and Acacias from such places as Australia, South Africa, Mexico and the Mediterranean grow within the secure embrace of massive Holm Oak hedges. Valhall Ships Figurehead Museum.

Location: Isles of Scilly. Isles of Scilly Steamship 01720 422849. B.I.H. Helicopters 01736 463871. Details of day trips on application.
Admission: Adult £3.50, Child £1.00. Weekly ticket £6.00. Guided group tours available.

TRELISSICK GARDEN

Tel: 01872 862090

Feock, Truro, Cornwall, TR3 6Q.
Owner: The National Trust   **Contact:** The Administrator

The rare shrubs and plants make this large garden attractive in all seasons, There are also an extensive park and woodland walks beside the river and farmland, with beautiful views over the Fal Estuary and Falmouth harbour. The house is not open, but there is an Art and Craft Gallery by the Home Farm Courtyard.

Location: 4m S of Truro, on both sides of B3289 above King Harry Ferry
Opening Times: 1 Mar - 31 Oct, Mon to Sat 10.30am - 5.30pm, Sun 12.30pm - 5.30pm. Closes 5pm in Mar and Oct. Last admission 1/2 hour before closing. Woodland walks open Nov to end Feb.
Admission: £3.50, Family £8.50, Pre-arranged party rate £3.00, £1 car park fee refundable on admission.

TREWITHIN

See page 24 for full page entry.

TRURO CATHEDRAL

Tel: 01872 76782   **Fax:** 01872 77788

Truro, Cornwall, TR1 2AH.

Contact: The Dean's Secretary

19th century Gothic style Cathedral, designed by the eminent Victorian architect, John Loughborough Pearson.

Location: Truro city centre.
Opening Times: 8.30am - 5.00pm. Sun services: 8.00am, 9.00am, 10.00am and 6.00pm. Weekday services: 7.30am, 8.00am and 5.00pm. Closed occasionally for services.

SPECIAL EVENTS DIARY

- **22nd - 23rd April**
  Lanhydrock
  Cornwall Garden Society Spring Flower Show.

- **23rd July**
  Pencarrow
  Field Sports Day.

- **28th July**
  Lanhydrock
  Open Air Concert in Park - with Syd Lawrence Orchestra.

- **4th August**
  Pencarrow
  Jazz in the Garden.

- **6th August**
  St Michael's Mount/Marazion Regatta
  Contact John Britten tel: 01736 67500.

- **24th September**
  St Michael's Mount
  International Musicians Seminar Concert (IMS) - Sandor Vegh. Tickets £8.00. Complimentary glass of wine, castle and garden open free to concert goers.

- **8th December**
  Lanhydrock
  The Hilliard Ensemble.

Prideaux Place

BRANTWOOD
Coniston

BRANTWOOD is the most beautifully situated house in the Lake District. It enjoys the finest lake and mountain views in England, and no other house in the district has such diverse literary and artistic associations.

The home of John Ruskin from 1872 until 1900, Brantwood became an intellectual powerhouse and one of the foremost cultural centres in Europe. Tolstoy, Mahatma Gandhi, Proust and William Morris can all be counted amongst Ruskin's disciples.

Ruskin was one of the greatest figures of the Victorian age. Poet, artist and critic, he was also a social revolutionary who challenged the moral foundations of 19th Century Britain.

Ruskin's ideas came to shape much of our thinking today, and his words are as relevant now as ever they were in his own lifetime.

Brantwood today contains a glorious collection of Ruskin drawings and watercolours, and the house still retains that special feeling which has given inspiration to so many.

GARDENS
In the oakwoods and beside the lake-shore Ruskin created a garden which is under active and imaginative restoration. It is a special place, a true lakeland paradise. The woods in springtime are carpeted with bluebells and the heavy scent of the yellow "azalea luteum" fills the air.

SUITABILITY FOR OTHER EVENTS
The house is spectacularly situated, with magnificent lake and mountain views and lends itself particularly to photographic or film use, but is suitable for a variety of events. Ruskin's wonderful Dining Room has potential for groups of up to 12.

EXTRA FACILITIES
3/4 mile Lakeshore with large pier. 250 acre estate, woodland and moorland. Grand Piano.

ADVICE TO COURIERS & DRIVERS
Coaches have access to Brantwood but the last 1 1/2 miles are a little slow. Parties can come by water from Coniston Pier a delightful approach with good access for coaches. New Ferry service from Coniston. Dogs not allowed in the House.

FACILITIES FOR THE DISABLED
Disabled visitors may alight at the entrance to the property. There are special toilet facilities available.

PARKING FOR COACHES & CARS
75 cars and 2 coaches within 100 yards of the property.

GIFT SHOP
Bookshop and high quality craft gallery.

SCHOOL VISITS/CHILDREN
School visits are welcomed but special facilities are not yet available. Nature and Woodland Walks are of special interest.

GUIDE BOOKS
Colour guide book, £2.50.

CATERING
'Jumping Jenny' Tearooms & Restaurant seating 60. Groups can book in advance but the total capacity cannot be booked during normal opening hours. Menus available on request and prices are very flexible according to requirements, special rates available for groups. Catering facilities available for special functions, conferences etc.

GUIDED TOURS
Visitors are usually free to tour the property at leisure but guided tours can be arranged. The Administrator will meet groups visiting the House. Lectures on the property can be arranged.

LOCATION

Road: M6 Junct. 36, 25 miles, London 5 hours, Edinburgh 3 hours, Chester 2 1/2 hours.

Rail: Windermere Station 14 miles.

Water: Steam Yacht "Gondola" sails regularly to Brantwood from Coniston Pier. New Ferry Service M.V. "Ruskin" sails hourly. (30 mins past the hour).

Taxi: Coniston Taxis (015394) 41683

OPENING TIMES

Summer
Mid March - Mid Nov
Daily　11.00 - 5.30pm

Winter
Mid Nov - Mid March
Daily　11.00 - 4.00pm

ADMISSION

All Year
Adults £3.25
Child* . . . . .FREE
*Under 18
Groups
Adults £2.50

CONFERENCE AND FUNCTION FACILITIES
Rooms are available but only during the evening in Summer or all day Monday or Tuesday in Winter. The Administrator will participate in Functions and meet groups if required. Full details available upon request.

DALEMAIN
Cumbria

CONTACT

R Hasell-McCosh
Dalemain Estate Office
Dalemain
Penrith
Cumbria
CA11 0HB

Tel: (017684) 86450
or (01899) 20208

Fax: (017684) 86223

LOCATION

From London, M1, M6
exit 40: 4 hours.

From Edinburgh, A73,
A74, M6 exit 40: 2^1/$_2$ hrs

Rail: Penrith 3 miles.

Taxi: Walkers Taxis,
Penrith 62349.

DALEMAIN is a fine mixture of Medieval, Tudor and Early Georgian architecture. The imposing Georgian facade strikes the visitor immediately but in the cobbled courtyard the atmosphere of the North Country Tudor Manor is secure. The present owners family have lived at Dalemain since 1679 and have collected china, furniture and family portraits. Visitors can see the grand Drawing Rooms with 18th Century Chinese Wallpaper and fine oak panelling also the Nursery and Housekeeper's Room. The Norman Pele Tower contains the regimental collection of the Westmoreland and Cumberland Yeomanry. The House is full of the paraphernalia of a well established family House which is still very much lived in by the family.

The 16th Century Great Barn holds a collection of agricultural bygones and a Fell Pony Museum.

GARDENS

The Garden has a long history stretching back to the medieval Herb Garden. Today a Knot Garden remains with a fine early Roman fountain and box hedges enclosing herb beds.

The imposing terrace wall supports a full and colourful herbaceous border during the summer months. The late Mrs McCosh revitalised the gardens replanting many of the borders introducing rare and exotic plants. Visitors can enjoy the fine views of the park and the woodland and riverside walks.

The gardens have been featured on television's 'Gardeners World' and also in 'Country Life'.

SUITABILITY FOR OTHER EVENTS
Fashion shows, archery, clay pigeon shooting, garden parties, rallies, filming, caravan rallies, antique fairs and childrens' camps. Business Meetings and Conferences with limited numbers during closed season.

EXTRA FACILITIES
Grand piano, parkland and Lake District National Park are available for use. Lectures on the House, contents, gardens and history can be arranged for up to 60 people. Cost for hire of room and lecture on request. Deer Park

ADVICE TO COURIERS & DRIVERS
Parties of 20 or more must pre-book. Allow 2 hours to see Dalemain. No dogs. Parking for 100 cars and 30 coaches, 50 yards from the House. No photography in the House.

FACILITIES FOR THE DISABLED
Disabled or elderly visitors may alight at the entrance prior to parking in the allocated areas. There are toilet facilities for the disabled. Free admission for disabled visitors in wheelchairs

GUIDED TOURS
, German and French translations in every room. Tours take 1 hour approx. Garden Tour for parties extra.

CATERING
Licensed Restaurant/Tea Room seats 60. Prices and menus on request. Groups should pre-book for lunches and high teas. Catering available for special functions/conferences.

GIFT SHOP
Items include local crafts, house souvenirs, fine china, high quality gifts, postcards stamps etc. Surplus plants on sale in the courtyard.

GUIDE BOOK
Colour guide £2.00.

SCHOOL VISITS/CHILDREN
School groups are welcome and guides can be provided. Military, Country Life, Agricultural and Fell Pony Museums. Adventure playground.

OPENING TIMES

Summer
9 April - 8 October
Daily except Fris & Sats
11.15am - 5.00pm

NB Parties of 20 or more should pre-book.

Winter
Mid-October - Easter
Open by special arrangement.

ADMISSION

HOUSE & GARDEN
Adult £4.00
Child* £3.00
Family £11.00
Disabled** . . . . .FREE

Groups***
Adult £3.80
Child* £2.80

* Under 16 years.
**Disabled in wheelchair.
*** Min. 12 Adults

CONFERENCE AND FUNCTION FACILITIES

ROOM	DIMENSIONS	CAPACITY	LAYOUT	POWER POINTS	SUITABLE FOR A/V
Dining Room		40	Theatre	3	✓
		15	Boardroom	3	✓
Old Hall		50	Buffet	4	✓
		50	Lunch/Dinner	4	✓

HOLKER HALL
Grange-over-Sands

HOLKER HALL, home of Lord and Lady Cavendish, shows the confidence, spaciousness and prosperity of Victorian style on its grandest scale. The New Wing, built by the 7th Duke of Devonshire (1871-4), replaced a previous wing totally destroyed by fire. Workmanship throughout is of the highest quality, particularly the detailed interior carving and linenfold panelling.

Despite this grand scale, Holker is very much a family home. Visitors can wander freely throughout the New Wing. Photographs, beautiful floral displays and bowls of scented pot pourri create the warm and friendly atmosphere so often remarked upon by visitors. Varying in period and style, Louis XV pieces happily mix with the Victorian. Pictures range from an early copy of the famous triple portrait of Charles I by Van Dyck to a modern painting by Douglas Anderson.

GARDENS
Christies/HHA Garden of the Year (1991), includes formal and woodland areas covering 24 acres. Designated "amongst the best in the world in terms of design and content" by the Good Gardens Guide.   This wonderful Italianate-cum-English Garden includes a limestone cascade, a fountain, a rose garden and many rare and beautiful plants and shrubs. Holker is also home to the Great Garden and Countryside Festival held on the first weekend in June.

SUITABILITY FOR OTHER EVENTS
Filming and still photography. Promotion venues include: limestone escarpments and quarries.

EXTRA FACILITIES
Deer Park and Discovery Walks. Lakeland Motor Museum, adventure playground and exhibitions.

ADVICE TO COURIERS & DRIVERS
No dogs in Gardens or Hall. No video cameras in Hall.

FACILITIES FOR THE DISABLED
Disabled and elderly visitors may be dropped at the entrance. There are unisex toilet facilities for the disabled. Ramps where necessary.

PARKING FOR COACHES & CARS
Capacity of the car park, 50+ cars and 12 coaches, 100-150 yards from Hall. Plus grass car parking.

CATERING
The Clocktower Cafeteria (capacity 120), is a self-service café, selling salads, hot and cold sandwiches, home made cakes and beverages (including wine by the glass and canned beer and lager).

GUIDED TOURS
Tours of Hall available at additional cost of 50p per person: must be pre-booked.

GIFT SHOP
Open 10.30am - 5.30pm, same days as the Hall, wide range of gifts from toys to fine china.

GUIDE BOOKS
Colour guide book, £2.00. Translations available in French, Spanish and German. Childrens Guide 75p. Guide to the Woodland Gardens by Lord Cavendish.

SCHOOL VISITS/CHILDREN
Environmental study day for primary school children, cost per child from £2.00. Holker is the holder of two Sandford Awards for Heritage Education. Holker provides a wide range of educational opportunities for primary aged children to fit in with curriculum requirements i.e: Houses & Home; Technology & Design; Structures; Victorians.

CONTACT

Mrs Carolyn Johnson
Holker Hall & Gardens
Cark-in-Cartmel
Grange-over-Sands
Cumbria
LA11 7PL

Tel: (015395) 58328

Fax: (015395) 58776

LOCATION

From Kendal, A6, A590, B5277, B5278: 16 mls.

Motorway: M6 Junct. 36

Bus: From Grange-over-Sands

Rail: To Cark-in-Cartmel.

Taxi: Parkers Motors, Grange-over-Sands. Nelsons Garage, Cark-in-Cartmel.

OPENING TIMES

Summer
2 April - 31 October

Daily except Saturdays
10.00am - 6.00pm

NB Last admission 4.30pm

Winter
1 November - 31 March
Closed

ADMISSION

Summer   1994 prices

HOUSE & GARDEN
  Adult £4.75
  Child £2.85

Groups
  Adult £3.25
  OAP £3.00
  Child £2.35

Winter
Closed

MUCASTER CASTLE
Ravenglass

MUNCASTER CASTLE has been owned by the Pennington family since 1208. It has grown from the original pele tower built on Roman foundations to the impressive structure visible today. Outstanding features are the Great Hall and Salvin's octagonal library and the Drawing Room with its barrel ceiling.

The Castle contains many treasures including beautiful furniture, exquisite needlework panels, tapestries and oriental rugs. The family silver is mostly by Paul Storr and is accompanied in the Dining Room by the Ongley Service, the most ornamental set of porcelain ever created by the Derby factory, Florentine 16th Century bronzes and an alabaster lady by Giambologna can be seen. The Castle has 3 ghosts. All the rooms open to the public are lived in by the family who are actively involved in entertaining their many visitors.

The woodland gardens cover 77 acres and command spectacular views of the Lakeland Fells, with many delightful walks. From mid March to June the rhododendrons, azaleas, camellias and magnolias are at their best.

The Owl Centre boasts a fine collection of owls from all over the world. 'Meet the Birds' occurs daily at 2.30pm (26th March to 29th October), when a talk is given on the work of the centre. Weather permitting the birds fly.

CONTACT

Peter Frost-Pennington
Muncaster Castle
Ravenglass
Cumbria
CA18 1RQ

Tel: (01229) 717614
Fax: (01229) 717010

LOCATION

From London 6 hrs,
Chester 2 $1/2$ hrs
Edinburgh 3 $1/2$ hrs
M6 exit 36, A590,
A595 (from south).
M6 exit 40, A66, A595
(from east). Carlisle,
A595 (from north).

Rail: Ravenglass
(on Barrow-in-Furness-
Carlisle Line) 1$1/2$ mls.

SUITABILITY FOR OTHER EVENTS
Muncaster provides a backdrop for fashion shoots, garden parties, filming, clay pigeon shooting and wedding receptions.

EXTRA FACILITIES
Lectures can be arranged on the property, its contents, gardens and history. By prior arrangement a grand piano can be hired.

ADVICE TO COURIERS & DRIVERS
For groups, please apply for information pack and book in advance to qualify for discounts. No photography or filming inside castle. Free parking for 500 cars 800 yds from the House. Coaches and disabled visitors may park closer.

FACILITIES FOR THE DISABLED
Toilets, wheelchair for loan. Special tapes available for walkman tour for the partially sighted or those with learning difficulties. Disabled and elderly visitors may alight near to Castle.

OWL CENTRE
Home of the World Owl Trust run by TV naturalist Tony Warburton.

GIFT SHOPS & PLANT CENTRE
Open daily 26th March to 29th October 11am to 5pm selling a wide variety of gifts and plants. Colour guide book available.

GUIDED TOURS
All castle visitors are offered a Sony Walkman individual tour narrated by the family that lasts 40 mins included in the entry price. Private tours with a personal guide (option family member) can be organised for a small additional fee.

CATERING
The Stables Buttery caters for up to 80 with a full menu. Groups may book meals in advance (01229) 717432. Catering in the Castle can also be arranged (01229) 717614.

SCHOOL VISITS/CHILDREN
School visits are welcome and guides are provided if required. Cost per child £2.20. Historical subjects from the Romans to W.W.II. Special work sheets available.

CONFERENCE AND FUNCTION FACILITIES

ROOM	DIMENSIONS	CAPACITY	LAYOUT	POWER POINTS	SUITABLE FOR A/V
Drawing Room	–	120	Theatre	6	✓
		100	Lunch/Dinner		
Dining Room	–	30 / 70	Various	2+	✓
Family Dining Room	–	20	Boardroom/Dinner	4	
		40	Theatre		
Great Hall	–	110	Various	6	✓

OPENING TIMES

Summer
26 March - 29 October

CASTLE
Daily except Mons
Mon Bank Hols only
1.00 - 4.00pm
Last entry 4.00pm

GARDENS AND
OWL CENTRE
Daily 11.00am - 5.00pm

Winter
CASTLE Closed.
Open by appointment
for groups.

GARDENS AND OWL
CENTRE
Daily 11.00am - 5.00pm

ADMISSION

Summer

CASTLE, GARDENS &
OWL CENTRE
  Adult £4.90
  Child* £2.80
  Family (2+2) . .£13.50
Groups**
  Adult £3.90
  Child* £2.20
Season Tickets
  Adult £12.50
  Family(2+3) . . .£28.00

GARDENS & OWL
CENTRE
  Adult £3.20
  Child* £1.70
  Family (2+2) £8.50
Groups
  Adult £2.80
  Child* £1.50

* Aged 5 - 15years;
  Under fives free.
**Min payment £40.

ABBOT HALL ART GALLERY
Tel:01539 722494   **Fax**: 01539 722464

Kirkland, Kendal, Cumbria, LA9 5AL
Owner: Lake District Art Gallery & Museum Trust   **Contact:** Mr E King
Georgian house with good portraits and furniture displayed in restored rooms.
Location: Kirkland, Kendal, Cumbria, LA9 5AL
Opening Times: 11 Feb - 22 Dec daily; Apr - Oct 10.30am - 5.00pm; Feb, Nov, Dec & Mar - phone for reduced hours.
Admission: Adult £2.50, Child £1.25, Conc £1.25, Family £5.00, Groups £1.20.

ACORN BANK GARDEN
Tel: 017683 61893

Temple Sowerby, Penrith, Cumbria, CA10 1SP.
Owner: The National Trust   **Contact:** The Administrator
A 2¹/₂ acre garden protected by fine oaks under which grow a vast display of daffodils. Inside the walls there are two orchards containing a variety of fruit trees. Surrounding the orchards are mixed borders with shrubs, herbaceous plants and roses, while the impressive herb garden has the largest collection of culinary and medicinal plants in the north. A circular woodland walk runs beside the Crowdundle Beck; the mill is under restoration, but not yet open to visitors. The house is let to the Sue Ryder Foundation and is not open to the public.
Location: Just N of Temple Sowerby, 6m E of Penrith on A66.
Opening Times: 1 Apr - 31 Oct 10.00am - 5.30pm, last admission 5.00pm.
Admission: Adult £1.60, Child 80p, pre-arranged party £1.10.

APPLEBY CASTLE
Tel: 017683 51402   **Fax**: 017683 51082

Appleby In Westmorland, Cumbria, CA16 6XH.
Owner: Ferguson International Holdings Plc   **Contact:** Mrs T Edwards
27 acres of beautiful riverside grounds. Fine 11th century Norman keep and Great Hall of the house. Large collection of birds; wildfowl, parakeets, owls and rare breeds of farm animals in the grounds, also incorporating the National School of Falconry, Café & Tea room, Gift Shop.
Location: Situated on A66 Scotch Corner to Penrith trunk Road. 11 miles SE of J40.
Opening Times: 8 Apr - 29 Oct 1995 daily 10.00am - 5pm until 2 Oct and then daily 10.00am - 4.00pm to 29 Oct. Winter months by appointment only.
Admission: Adult £3.50, Child £1.50, OAP £2.00. Children under 5 years of age are free. Special reductions for pre-booked parties.

BEATRIX POTTER GALLERY
Tel: 015394 36355

Main Street, Hawkshead, Cumbria, LA22 0NS.
Owner: The National Trust   **Contact:** The Administrator
An annually changing exhibition of Beatrix Potter's original illustrations from her children's story books. The building was once the office of her husband, the solicitor William Heelis, and the interior remains largely unaltered since his day.
Location: In the Square.
Opening Times: 2 Apr - 31 Oct: Sun to Thur (closed Fri and Sat except Good Fri), 10.30am - 4.30pm. Last admission 4.00pm.
Admission: Adult £2.50, Child £1.30, no reduction for parties.

BRANTWOOD
See page 29 for full page entry.

BROUGH CASTLE
Tel: 0191261 1585

Brough, Cumbria.
Owner: English Heritage   **Contact:** The Administrator
Perched on a superb vantage point overlooking an old trade route, now the A66, this ancient site dates back to Roman Times. The 12th century keep replaced an earlier stronghold destroyed by the Scots in 1174. The castle was restored by Lady Anne Clifford in the 17th century.
Location: 8m SE of Appleby S of A66.
Opening Times: Any reasonable time.

BROUGHAM CASTLE
Tel: 01768 62488

Brougham, Cumbria.
Owner: English Heritage   **Contact:** The Administrator
These impressive ruins on the banks of the river Eamont include an early 13th century keep and later buildings. You can climb to the top of the keep and survey the domain of its eccentric one time owner Lady Anne Clifford, who restored the castle in the 17th century. There is a small exhibition of Roman tombstones from the nearby fort.
Location: 1¹/₂m SE of Penrith.
Opening Times: 1 Apr - 30 Sept, daily 10.00am - 6.00pm.
Admission: Adult £1.30, Child 70p, Conc £1.00.

CARLISLE CASTLE
Tel: 01228 591922

Carlisle, Cumbria.
Owner: English Heritage   **Contact:** The Administrator
This impressive medieval castle, where Mary Queen of Scots was once imprisoned, has a long and tortuous history of warfare and family feuds. A portcullis hangs menacingly over the gatehouse passage, there is a maze of passages and chambers, endless staircases to lofty towers and you can walk the high ramparts for stunning views. There is also a medieval manor house in miniature: a suite of medieval rooms furnished as they might have been when used by the castle's former constable. The castle is also the home of the Museum of the King's Own Border Regiment (included in the admission price).
Location: N of Carlisle town centre.
Opening Times: 1 Apr - 30 Sept, daily 10.00am - 6.00pm. 1 Oct - 31 Mar, daily 10.00am - 4.00pm. (Closed 24-26 Dec, 1 Jan).
Admission: Adult £2.20, Child £1.10, Conc £1.70.

CARLISLE CATHEDRAL
Tel: 01228 48151   **Fax**: 01228 48769

Carlisle, Cumbria, CA3 8TZ.
            Contact: Ms C Baines
Fine sandstone Cathedral, founded in 1122. Medieval stained glass. carvings and painted wall panels. Treasury with displays of silver, diocesan and cathedral treasures.
Location: Carlisle city centre, 2m from junction 43 of M6.
Opening Times: 7.45am - 6.15pm daily. Closes 4.00pm between Christmas Day and New Year. Sunday services: 8.00am, 10.30am and 3.00pm. Weekday services: 8.00am, 12.30pm and 5.30pm.
Admission: Donation.

CONISHEAD PRIORY
Tel: 01229 584029   **Fax**: 01229 580080

Ulverston, Cumbria, LA12 9QQ.
Owner: Mahjushari Mahayana Buddhist Centre   **Contact:** Mr R Tyson
Fine sandstone Cathedral, founded in 1122. Medieval stained glass. carvings and painted wall panels. Treasury with displays of silver, diocesan and cathedral treasures.
Location: 2 m S of Ulverston on Bardsea Coast Rd A5087.
Opening Times: Easter - Sept, w/e and Bank Hols only, 2.00pm - 5.00pm. Closed 22/3 Jul, 29/30 Jul, 5/6 Aug, 12/13 Aug.
Admission: House tour; Adult £1.50, Child 75p, Concessions £1.00.

DALEMAIN
See page 30 for full page entry.

DOVE COTTAGE & WORDSWORTH MUSEUM
Tel: 015394 35544/35547   **Fax:** 015394 35748

Town End, Grasmere, Cumbria, LA22 9SH.
Owner: The Wordsworth Trust   **Contact:** Mr S Wordsworth
Dove Cottage, Wordswoth's home 1799 - 1808. Guided Tours. garden open weather permitting. Award-winning Wordsworth museum houses permanent exhibition and a programme of special exhibitions. Book & Gift shop, Teashop.
Location: Town End, Grasmere, Cumbria, LA22 9SH.
Opening Times: Daily 9.30am - 5.30pm. Last ticket sales 5.00pm. Closed: mid-Jan to mid-Feb and December 24-26.
Admission: Adult £3.90, Child £1.95, Family ticket £5.85. Adult group rate £3.00.

FURNESS ABBEY
Tel: 01229 823420

Barrow-in-Furness, Cumbria.
Owner: English Heritage   **Contact:** The Administrator
Hidden in a peaceful green valley are the beautiful red sandstone remains of the wealthy abbey founded in 1123 by Stephen, later King of England. This abbey first belonged to the Order of Savigny and later to the Cistercians. There is a museum and exhibition.
Location: 1¹/₂m N of Barrow-in-Furness on minor road off A590.
Opening Times: 1 Apr - 30 Sept, daily 10.00am - 6.00pm, 1 Oct - 31 Oct, daily 10.00am - 4.00pm, 1 Nov - 31 Mar, Wed - Sun, 10.00am - 4.00pm (Closed 24 - 26 Dec, 1 Jan).
Admission: Adult £2.20, Child £1.00, Conc £1.70.

HARDKNOTT ROMAN FORT
Tel: 01229 823420

Ravenglass, Cumbria.
Owner: English Heritage   **Contact:** The Administrator
One of the most dramatic sites in Britain, with stunning views across the Lakeland fells. This fort, built between AD120 and 138, controlled the road from Ravenglass to Ambleside. There are visible remains of granaries, the headquarters buildings and the commandant's house, with a bath house and parade ground outside the fort.
Location: 9m NE of Ravenglass, at W end of Hardknott Pass.
Opening Times: Any reasonable time. Access may be hazardous in winter.

HERON CORN MILL & MUSEUM OF PAPERMAKING

Tel: 015395 63363   **Fax:** 015395 63363

c/o Henry Cooke Makin, Waterhouse Mills, Beetham, Milnthorpe, Cumbria, LA7 7AR.

Owner: Heron Corn Mill Beetham Trust   **Contact:** Mr Neil Stobbs

Location: 1m south of Milnthorpe on the A6.

Opening Times: 11am - 5pm Tues - Sun open Bank Hol Mons. Easter 1st Apr- 30th Sept.

Admission: Adult £1.25, Child 80p, Family £4 (2+2), OAPs 80p, Coach parties/Groups 10% discount if pre-booked.

HILLTOP

Tel: 015394 36269

Near Sawrey, Ambleside, Cumbria, LA22 0LF.

Owner: The National Trust   **Contact:** The Administrator

Beatrix Potter wrote many Peter Rabbit books in this little 17th century house, which contains her furniture and china.

Location: 2m S of Hawkshead, in hamlet of Near Sawrey, behind the Tower Bank Arms.

Opening Times: 1 Apr - 31 Oct: Sat to Wed & Good Fri, 11am - 5pm. Last adm: 4.30pm.

Admission: Adult £3.30, Child £1.70, no reduction for parties.

HOLEHIRD

Tel: 015394 46008

Petterdale Road, Windermere, Cumbria, LA23 1NP.

Owner: Lakeland Horticultural Society   **Contact:** Prof H R Perkins

Over 5 acres of hillside gardens overlooking Troutbeck Valley, with magnificent views of Windermere lake and fells, including a walled garden and national collection of astilbes, hydrangeas and polystichum ferns.

Location: On A592, ³/₄m North of junction with A591.

Opening Times: All year, dawn to dusk.

Admission: By donation, request of £1.00 per adult.

HOLKER HALL

See page 31 for full page entry.

HUTTON-IN-THE-FOREST

OPEN

31 Apr - 31 Sept

House:
1.00 - 4.00pm
Easter Sun & Mon.
Thurs, Fris, & Suns
Also Weds in Aug &
all Bank Hol Mons.

Grounds:
11.00am - 5.00pm
Daily except
Saturdays and
Christmas Day.

Tel: 01768 484449
Fax: 01768 484571

PENRITH, CUMBRIA CA11 9TH

Owner: The Lord Inglewood   *Contact: Edward Thompson*

The home of Lord Inglewood's family since the beginning of the 17th century. Built around a medieval pele tower with 17th, 18th and 19th century additions. Fine English furniture and pictures, ceramics and tapestries. Outstanding gardens and grounds with terraces, walled garden, dovecote, lake and woodland walk through magnificent specimen trees.

Location: 7 miles north west of Penrith and 2¹/₂ miles from exit 41 M6 on B5305

Admission: House, Gardens & Grounds: Adult £3.50, Child £1.50 .
Gardens & Grounds: Adult £2.00, Children Free.

LANERCOST PRIORY ⊞

Tel: 016977 3030

Brampton, Cumbria.

Owner: English Heritage   **Contact:** The Administrator

This Augustinian priory was founded c.1166. The nave of the church, which is intact and in use as the local parish church, contrasts with the ruined chancel, transepts and priory buildings.

Location: Off minor road S of Lanercost, 2m NE of Brampton.

Opening Times: 1 Apr - 30 Sept, daily 10.00am - 6.00pm.

Admission: Adult £1.00, Child 50p, Conc 80p.

LEVENS HALL

OPEN

2 Apr - 28 Sept.
Sun - Thurs

11.00am - 5.00pm
Last Admission
4.30pm

Steam Collection
2.00 - 5.00pm.

Tel: 01539 560321

KENDAL, CUMBRIA LA8 OPD

Owner: C H Bagot Esq.   *Contact: P. Milner*

This Elizabethan mansion contains a fine collection of Jacobean furniture, panelled interiors, plasterwork, Cordova leather wall coverings and the earliest English patchwork. The world famous topiary garden was laid out in 1694 by Monsieur Beaumont and has since remained largely unaltered. Garden lovers will appreciate the colourful spring and summer bedding together with many unusual herbaceous plants. In addition there is a working collection of model steam engines.

Location: 5 miles south of Kendal on the A6 (M6 exit 36).

Admission: House & Garden: Adult £4.20, Over 65 £3.80, Child £2.50
Garden: Adult £2.90, Over 65 £2.70, Child £1.80

LINGHOLM GARDENS

Tel: 017687 72003

Lingholm, Keswick, Cumbria, CA12 5UA.

Owner: Viscount Rochdale   **Contact:** Miss M Dymock

Formal and woodland gardens, rhododendrons, azaleas, magnificent trees and shrubs, primulas, meconopsis, herbaceous borders. Spring daffodils, autumn colours. Plant centre. Tea room. Disabled facilities.

Location: 1m S of Portinscale village, off A66 West of Keswick.

Opening Times: 1 Apr - 31 Oct daily 10.00am - 5.00pm. Tea room 11.00am - 5.00pm.

Admission: Adult £2.70, accompanied child free.

MIREHOUSE

OPEN

1 Apr - 31 Oct
Grounds, Tearoom,
Playgrounds
Daily
10.30am - 5.30pm
House: Suns, Weds
(also Fris in Aug)
2pm - last entry
at 4.30pm
Groups welcome at
other times
appointment
Tel: 01768 772287
Fax: 01768 772287

KESWICK, CUMBRIA CA12 4QE

Owner: John Spedding Esq.   *Contact: Clare Spedding*

First built in 1666, Mirehouse has only been sold once in 1688 and remains a welcoming family home. An unusually literary house with an interesting picture collection and live classical piano music. The grounds stretch to Bassenthwaite Lake and include woodland playgrounds, walled garden, wildflower meadow and access to the ancient lakeside church of Saint Bega. French, German, Spanish spoken.

Location: 3¹/₂ miles north of Keswick on A591 (Carlisle road). Regular bus service (Cumberland motor services)

Admission: Grounds:Adult £1, Child 80p. House & Grounds: Adult £3.00, Child £1.50. (Family (2 + 4) tickets available only for House & Grounds entry).

MUNCASTER CASTLE

See page 32 for full page entry.

MUNCASTER WATER MILL

Tel: 01229 717232

Ravenglass, Cumbria, CA18 1ST.

Owner: R Park Esq   **Contact:** R Park Esq

Old Manorial Mill with 13ft overshot wheel and all milling equipment.

Location: 1m S of Milnthorpe on A6.

Opening Times: Apr - Oct Daily, Jun - May 10.30am - 5.30pm, Apr - May & Sept - Oct 11.00am - 5.30pm.

Admission: Adult £1.20, Child 60p, Family £3.00.

NAWORTH CASTLE

Tel: 01697 73229

Brampton, Cumbria, CA1 2RW.
Owner: The Earl Of Carlisle **Contact:** Colleen Hall
Historic Border fortress built in 1335 and renovated by the Howard family in 1602.
Location: 12m E of Carlisle.
Opening Times: Open for groups (15+) by appointment only.
Admission: Groups £3.30 per person.

PENRITH CASTLE

Tel: 01697 73229

Penrith, Cumbria.
Owner: English Heritage **Contact:** The Administrator
This 14th century castle, set in a park on the edge of the town, was built to defend Penrith against repeated attacks by Scottish raiders.
Location: Opposite Penrith railway station.
Opening Times: Park opening hours.

RYDAL MOUNT

Tel: 015394 33002

Ambleside, Cumbria, LA22 9LU.
Owner: The Trustees of Rydal Mount **Contact:** Mr & Mrs Ilkington (Curators).
Wordsworth's home from 1813 - 1850 with gardens designed by Wordsworth.
Opening Times: Mar - Oct 9.30am - 5.00pm.
Admission: Adult £2.50, Child £1.00, Adult Group £2.00 pp (10+).

TOWNEND

Tel: 015394 32628

Troutbeck, Windermere, Cumbria, LA23 1LB.
Owner: The National Trust **Contact:** The Administrator
An exceptional relic of Lake District life of past centuries. Originally a 'statesman' (wealthy yeoman) farmer's house, built about 1626. Townend contains carved woodwork, books, papers, furniture and fascinating domestic implements of the past, accumulated by the Browne family who lived here from that date until 1943
Location: 3m SE of Ambleside at S end of Troutbeck village.
Opening Times: 2 Apr - 31 Oct: Tues - Fri, Sun & BH Mon, 1pm - 5pm or dusk if earlier.
Admission: Adult £2.50, Child £1.30, Family £7.00, no reduction for parties which must be pre-booked.

WORDSWORTH HOUSE

Tel: 01900 824805

Main Street, Cockermouth, Cumbria, CA13 9RX.
Owner: The National Trust **Contact:** The Administrator
The house where William Wordsworth was born in 1770. This north-country Georgian town house was built in 1745. Seven rooms are furnished in 18th century style, with some personal effects of the poet; his childhood garden, with terraced walk, leads down to the Derwent.
Opening Times: 3 Apr - 31 Oct: weekdays, 11.00am - 5.00pm, also Sat 15 and 29 April, 27 May and all Sats 1 Jul - 2 Sept. Closed remaining Sats and all Suns. Last admission 4.30pm.
Location: Main Street, Cockermouth.
Admission: Adult £2.40, Child £1.20, Family £6.50, pre-booked parties £1.80.

SIZERGH CASTLE

OPEN
2 Apr - 31 Oct
House:
1.30 - 5.30pm

Garden:
12.30 - 5.30pm

Tel: 01539 60070

NR. KENDAL, CUMBRIA
Owner: The National Trust *Contact:* Mr Brian Doling

The Strickland family home for more than 750 years; impressive 14th century pele tower; extended in Tudor times some of the finest Elizabethan carved overmantels in the country; good English and French furniture. Trust's largest limestone rock garden. Tea room and shop.
Location: 3½ miles south of Kendal, north west of the A590/A591 interchange.
Admission: Adult £3.30, Child £1.70, Family £9.00
Garden only: £1.70

STAGSHAW GARDEN

Tel: 015394 35599

Ambleside, Cumbria, LA22 9LU.
Owner: The National Trust **Contact:** The Administrator
This woodland garden was created by the late Cubby Acland, Regional Agent for the National Trust. It contains a fine collection of azaleas and rhododendrons, planted to give good blends of colour under the thinned oaks on the hillside; also many trees and shrubs, including magnolias, camellias and embothriums.
Location: ½m S of Ambleside on A591.
Opening Times: 1 Apr - end Jun: daily 10.00am - 6.30pm, Jul - end Oct: by appointment.
Admission: £1.00, no reduction for parties.

STOTT PARK BOBBIN MILL

Tel: 015395 31087

Finsthwaite, Cumbria.
Owner: English Heritage **Contact:** The Administrator
When this working mill was built in 1835 it was typical of the many mills in the Lake District which grew up to supply the spinning and weaving industry in Lancashire but have since disappeared. A remarkable opportunity to see a demonstration of the machinery and techniques of the Industrial Revolution.
Location: ½ m N of Finsthwaite near Newby Bridge.
Opening Times: 1 Apr - 30 Sept daily 10.00am - 6pm, 1 Oct - 31 Oct 10.00am - 4.00pm.
Admission: Adult £2.30, Child £1.70, Conc £1.20.

SPECIAL EVENTS DIARY

- **February - June**
Dove Cottage and The Wordsworth Museum
"Writers in their Place". This collection of contemporary photographs of writers' homes, from Milton to James Joyce, has returned by popular demand. The exhibition is supplemented by early editions of the writers' books, portraits and manuscripts. There are samples of writers' verse to illustrate their works.

- **2nd - 4th June: Holker Hall & Gardens**
The Great Garden & Countryside Festival. 4th year offers magnificent Horticultural Displays including Chelsea Gold Medalists. Festival Gardens; Society Countryside, WI and Floral Art Displays; Gardeners Question Time and Advice Centre. Traditional and modern crafts including the launch of the Made in Britain Craft Marquee housing the very best of British Craftsmanship. Trade stands, entertainment and much, much more. Show advice telephone 015395 58838.

- **24th June: Sizergh Castle**
Garden Party - 2pm June Ball - 8pm
Tickets contact Judith Bowles Tel: 015394 35599.

- **25th June: Sizergh Castle**
Grand Auction of Promises.
Tickets contact Judith Bowles Tel: 015394 35599.

- **July - September**
Dove Cottage and The Wordsworth Museum
Exhibition "John Keats : Bicentenary" Keats was born in 1795. The Wordsworth Trust's major Festival of Arts & Culture event will celebrate his Bicentenary.

- **27th August: Holker Hall & Gardens**
M G Rally - pre and post 1955 models, Concours and Driving Trials. Discounted admission to all M G Drivers.

CATTON HALL
Swadlincote

CATTON, first mentioned in the Domesday Book in 1085 and purchased by ancestors of the Neilson family in 1405, stands on the banks of the River Trent, surrounded by 100 acres of its own traditional and private parkland.

This classic Georgian house, which is not open to the public, has remained unspoilt since it was built in 1745 and still contains most of its original collection of antique furniture and fine 17th and 18th century paintings. It is lived in by the Neilson family as their private home and has a wonderful relaxed and friendly atmosphere which makes all visitors feel welcome whether they are guests for a formal dinner or enjoying activities in the park from a marquee.

Catton is perfectly situated in the centre of England and within 100 miles of half the population of the country, and with easy access to all the main motorways. London, Bristol, Liverpool and York are all about 2 hours by car. Birmingham or East Midlands airports, The Belfry Golfing Centre, National Exhibition Centre and the International Conference Centre are within half an hour by road.

CONTACT

Robin & Katie Neilson
Catton Hall
Catton
Swadlincote
Derbyshire
DE12 8LN

Tel: (01283) 716311

Fax: (01283) 712876

LOCATION

Catton lies $^1/_2$ hour north of Birmingham, half way between Lichfield and Burton on Trent and 5 minutes to the East of the A38.

Railway: Lichfield 10 minutes.

Rail and Airport: Birmingham $^1/_2$ hour.

SUITABILITY FOR EVENTS
Outside there are 100 acres of flat, permanent grassland ideal for clay shooting, motorised activities, ballooning, falconry, archery, shows, fairs, fireworks and marquees to suit every possible occasion.
We are specialists at arranging tailor made events in a personal and professional way. Inside we offer exclusive facilities to enjoy concerts, conferences, business meetings, lunches or dinners, whether formal or informal, or special evenings which might include murder, magic or music.

EXTRA FACILITIES
A small chapel to accommodate up to 100 people for a wedding or concert. Seven miles cross country ride with 36 optional jumps. Pheasant and partridge shooting. Fishing.

ACCOMMODATION
Extremely comfortable en suite accommodation is available in three 4 poster rooms and five twin bedded rooms.

FACILITIES FOR THE DISABLED
There is access only to the grounds and ground floor of the house but no other special facilities are available.

PARKING FOR COACHES AND CARS
Unlimited parking for cars and coaches within 50 yards of the house.

CATERING
Excellent in-house catering is arranged for most functions although outside caterers are welcome.

GUIDED TOURS
Group tours can be arranged by appointment.

CONFERENCE AND FUNCTION FACILITIES

ROOM	DIMENSIONS	CAPACITY	LAYOUT	POWER POINTS	SUITABLE FOR A/V
Dining Room	22' x 35'	22	Boardroom	✓	✓
		100	Buffet		
		40	Lunch/Dinner		
Ballroom	34' x 21'	150	Theatre	✓	✓
Hall	22' x 38'	130	Theatre	✓	✓
Drawing Room	35' x 21'	150	Theatre	✓	✓

CHATSWORTH
Bakewell

THE GREAT TREASURE HOUSE of Chatsworth is everything a palace should be but still maintains the sympathetic proportions of a family home. The first house was built by Bess of Hardwick in 1552 and it has been lived in by the Cavendish family, Dukes of Devonshire ever since. The House today owes its appearance to the 1st Duke who remodelled the building at the end of the 17th Century, while the 6th Duke added a North Wing by Sir Jeffry Wyatville 200 years later. Visitors see 24 rooms including the run of 5 virtually unaltered 17th Century State Rooms and Chapel. There are painted ceilings by Verrio, Thornhill and Laguerre, furniture by William Kent and Boulle, tapestries from Mortlake and Brussels, a library of over 17,000 volumes, sculpture by Cibber and Canova, old master paintings by Rembrandt, Hals, Van Dyck, Tintoretto, Giordano, Lely as well as Landseer and Sargent; the collection of classical sculpture, Oriental and European porcelain and the dazzling silver collection including an early English silver chandelier. The present Duke is a collector like his ancestors and the sculptures by Angela Conner and paintings by Lucien Freud bring the treasures up to date.

GARDEN
The garden was the creation of the 6th Duke and his gardener Sir Joseph Paxton, who later built the Crystal Palace. Together they devised a system of cascades, fountains and pools culminating in the 290ft jet of the Emperor Fountain. They planted rare trees and specimen shrubs and placed naturalistic rocks, buildings and statuary to enhance the design. More recent additions include the Maze and the now famous serpentine beech hedge. From bulbs in Spring to rich colours in Autumn Chatsworth's vast garden provides a worthy setting for the great House.

SPECIAL ATTRACTIONS
Maze in Garden; collection of paintings, drawings, sculpture, silver and porcelain; cascade; Capability Brown landscape; farmyard; adventure playground.

ADVICE TO COURIERS & DRIVERS
Allow a minimum of 2 hours to see Chatsworth. There is a coach drivers' rest room. Unlimited parking for cars, 100 yards from the House, and coaches, 25 yards from the House.

FACILITIES FOR THE DISABLED
Unfortunately it is not possible for people in wheelchairs to tour the House due to the number of stairs. They are most welcome in the garden and two electric wheelchairs are available at the entrance. Toilet facilities and a leaflet specially designed for our disabled visitors, on arrival.

CATERING
The Restaurant serving home-made food can cater for up to 300 for afternoon tea and other meals. Menus on request.

GUIDED TOURS
Tours of house and/or greenhouses available (extra £12 per person) by arrangement. Average time taken 1¹/₂ hrs.

GUIDE BOOKS
Two full-colour guide books for sale: Chatsworth House, avaialable in French, German and Japanese translations and Chatsworth Garden. Special guide for children.

GIFT SHOP
There are two shops open at the same time as the House. Items chosen for the shops by the Duchess of Devonshire.

AUDIO TOURS
A cassette with a tape recorded tour can be hired at the Entrance Hall. Group bookings must be made in advance.

SCHOOL VISITS/CHILDREN
Guided tours, packs, trails and schools room are now available for a school visit. Teachers are welcome to arrange a free preliminary visit and discuss their requirements with the Schools Liaison Officer, who can give talks in school. For further details telephone Simon Seligman on Baslow (01246) 582204.

CONTACT

Eric Oliver
Chatsworth
Bakewell
Derbyshire
DE45 1P

Tel: (01246) 582204
Fax: (01246) 583536

LOCATION

From London 3 hours, M1 Junction 29, signposted via Chesterfield.

Rail: Chesterfield Station, 9 miles.

Bus: Chesterfield - Bakewell, 1¹/₂ miles.

OPENING TIMES

Summer
22 March - 29 October

Daily 11.00am - 4.30pm

Winter
Closed

ADMISSION

HOUSE & GARDEN
Adult £5.75
Child £3.00
OAP/Student . . .£5.25
Family £15.00
Pre-booked parties
Adults £5.20
Schools £2.75
OAP/Student . . .£4.50
GARDEN ONLY
Adult £3.00
Child £1.50
OAP £2.50
Student £2.50
Family £8.00
SCOTS SUITE
Adult £1.00
Child £0.50
Car Park £1.00

HADDON HALL
Bakewell

THIS WONDERFULLY ROMANTIC house, the most complete surviving medieval manor house in the Country, is situated in the heart of the Peak District. Built over a period of 400 years, it's architecture progresses from Norman, through Medieval and Tudor, to Elizabethan, thereby displaying every aspect of domestic life from the past. Natural, rather than formal, Haddon is wrapped in an atmosphere of homeliness and is a truly 'understandable' house.

Since the 12th century, Haddon has been the home of the Vernon and Manners families. It was the Vernons, owners from 1170 to 1567, who were largely responsible for the construction of the house as we see it today. The House changed ownership in 1567,

through the marriage of Dorothy Vernon to John Manners, 2nd son of the 1st Earl of Rutland. In 1703, the Dukedom of Rutland was conferred upon the Manners family and Haddon was abandoned in favour of Belvoir Castle, the Ducal seat in Rutland for 200 years. Haddon was uninhabited, until the 9th Duke of Rutland returned early this century to make the house's restoration his life's work.

The terraced Rose Gardens, stepping down to the fast-flowing River Wye, are planned for year-round colour. Over 150 varieties of rose and clematis, many over 70 years old, provide colour and scent throughout the summer. Winner of the H.H.A./Christie's "Garden of the Year Award presented in 1994.

❖

SUITABILITY FOR OTHER EVENTS
Fashion shows archery, garden parties and filming. Haddon is able to provide the finest facilities for clay pigeon shooting in the North of England, with the shooting ground adjacent to the Hall which provides magnificent backdrops. A full clay pigeon shooting package, with tutoring by olympic coaches, is available, accompanied by excellent catering facilities. Please write for further details and dates.

CONFERENCE FACILITIES
This Medieval House is able to offer restricted facilities for conferences and functions in the Main Banqueting Hall and Long Gallery. Please contact the Estate Office with any enquiries, and we should be delighted to assist.

EXTRA FACILITIES
There is provision for helicopters if required. Lectures on the property, its contents, gardens and history can be arranged for up to 35 people. Projector and screen can be provided.

ADVICE TO COURIERS & DRIVERS
Owing to the age of the House, and its uneven, worn stone floors and staircases, Haddon is not entirely suitable for large groups of elderly people. No dogs are allowed in the House or Grounds, except guide dogs.

FACILITIES FOR THE DISABLED
Disabled and elderly people may alight at the entrance and vehicles then parked in the allocated area. A courtesy vehicle is available to help disabled visitors from the coach park to the Hall. Please advise us of your requirements.

PARKING FOR COACHES & CARS
Parking for 200 cars and coaches, 500 yards from the House. Charge for cars 50p.

CATERING
The Restaurant/Tea Room seats up to 75 people. Prices range from £2 - 3 for tea and other meals. For special functions, buffets lunches and dinners can be arranged.

GUIDED TOURS
£20.00 extra for groups of 20. 7 days notice required.

GUIDE BOOKS
Colour guide book, £2.00.

SCHOOL VISITS/ CHILDREN
School groups are welcome, price £2.40 per child. Schools' pack is available, enabling children to follow interesting project work. There is an in-school introductory talk by the guide who will take the children round the house on the day if their visit. Schoolroom available. Special guide books can be purchased and dressing up and talks with slides can be arranged.

CONTACT

The Comptroller
Estate Office
Haddon Hall
Bakewell
Derbyshire
DE45 1LA

Tel: (01629) 812855
Fax: (01629) 814379

LOCATION

From London 3 hours,
Sheffield $^1/_2$ hour,
Derby $^3/_4$ hour.
Haddon is on the A6,
$1^1/_2$ miles south of
Bakewell.

M1 Junct. 29/30, M6
Junct. 17/18/19, 1 hour.

From Manchester
1 hour.

OPENING TIMES

Summer
1 April - 30 September

Open daily
11.00am - 5.45pm

Last entry 5.00pm.

NB Also closed on Sundays in July & August, except 27 Aug.

Winter
October - 30 March
Closed

ADMISSION

Summer
Adult £4.50
Child* £2.80
OAP £3.50
Family Ticket . . £12.50
2 adults/2 children

GROUPS**
Adult £3.50
Child* £2.40
OAP £3.50

* Aged 5-16
** Min 20 people

ARKWRIGHT'S MILL

Mill Lane, Cromford, Derbyshire, DE4 3RQ.

Contact: Ms. Jones

The world's first successful water powered cotton spinning mill.
Location: Mill Lane, Cromford.
Opening Times: Every Day Except Christmas Day 9.00am - 5.00pm.
Admission: Free entry onto site. Guided tour, Adults £2.00, Conc £1.50.

BAKEWELL OLD HOUSE MUSEUM

Tel: (0787) 72744   **Fax:** (0787) 00000

Cunningham Place, Bakewell, Derbyshire, DE45 1DD.
Owner: Bakewell & District Historical Society   **Contact:** Dr J T Brighton
Early Tudor house, costumes and Victorian Kitchen.
Location: ¼m from Bakewell centre
Opening Times: 1 Apr - 31 Oct, daily, 2.00pm - 5.00pm.
Admission: Adult £1.80, Child 80p.

BOLSOVER CASTLE

Tel: 01246 823349

Chesterfield, Derbyshire.
Owner: English Heritage   **Contact:** The Administrator
An enchanting and romantic spectacle, situated high on a wooded hilltop dominating the surrounding landscape. Built on the site of a Norman castle, this is largely an early 17th century mansion. Most delightful is the 'Little Castle', a bewitching folly with intricate carvings, frescoes and wall painting. There is also an impressive 17th century Indoor Riding School which is still used on occasions.
Location: In Bolsover, 6m E of Chesterfield on A632.
Opening Times: 1 Apr - 30 Sept, daily 10.00am - 6.00pm, 1 Oct - 31 Oct, daily 10.00am - 4.00pm, 1 Nov - 31 Mar, Wed - Sun, 10.00am - 4.00pm.
Admission: Adult £2.20, Child £1.10, Conc £1.70.

CALKE ABBEY

Tel: 01332 863822

Ticknall, Derby, Derbyshire, DE73 1LE.
Owner: The National Trust   **Contact:** The Administrator
The house that time forgot, this Baroque mansion, built 1701 - 03 for Sir John Harpur, is virtually unaltered since the death of the last baronet in 1924. Within the house there is a Caricature Room, gold and white drawing room, Sir Vauncey's childhood bedroom, the Gardner Wilkinson Library and beer cellar. Fascinating natural history collections. Magnificent early 18th century state bed. A carriage display in the stable block, walled gardens and pleasure grounds, Portland sheep in the park, an early 19th century church.
Location: 10m S of Derby, on A514 at Ticknall between Swadlincote and Melbourne.
Opening Times: House, Garden & Church: 1 Apr to end Oct: Sat to Wed & BH Mon (closed Good Fri). House & Church: 1.00pm - 5.30pm, Garden: 11.00am - 5.30pm. Ticket Office: 11.00am - 5.00pm. Last admission 5.00pm. Park: open during daylight hours all year: Apr - Oct closed 9.00pm (or dusk if earlier): Nov - Mar closes at dusk.
Admission: All sites: Adult £4.50, Child £2.20, Family £11.20. Garden only: £2.00. Discount for pre-booked parties.

CATTON HALL

See page 36 for full page entry.

CHATSWORTH

See page 37 for full page entry.

ELVASTON CASTLE COUNTRY PARK

Tel: 01332 863822   **Fax:** 01332 863822

Broorwash Road, Elvaston, Derby, Derbyshire, DE72 3EP.
Owner: Derbyshire County Council   **Contact:** Mr M Marshall
200 acre park landscaped in 19th century. Walled kitchen garden. Estate museum with exhibitions of traditional crafts.
Location: 5m SE of Derby, A6 or A52.
Opening Times: Park; all year round, dawn - dusk. Shop/Tea Room/Exhibitions; Easter - 29 Oct, daily, 11.00am - 4.30pm. Museum; Easter - 29 Oct, Wed - Sat, 1.00pm - 4.30pm. Sun and BHs, 10.00am - 5.00pm.
Admission: All sites: Adult £4.50, Child £2.20, Family £11.20. Garden only: £2.00. Discount for pre-booked parties.

EYAM HALL

OPEN

2 Apr - 29 Oct
Weds, Thur, Suns,
Bank Hol Mons
& Bank Hol Tues.
11.00am -5.30pm,
last tour 4.30pm.
Pre-booked
parties as above.
Schools: Tuesdays
and weekdays
13 - 31 Mar
Buttery & Gift Shop
open Tues to Sun,
Bank Hol Mons.

Tel: 01433 631976

EYAM, SHEFFIELD, DERBYSHIRE S30 1QW

Owner: The Wright family   *Contact: Miss Carolyn Fooks*

Built by the Wright family in 1671 and still their family home, Eyam Hall is a cosy and intimate house, only recently opened to the public. All visitors receive a guided tour at no extra cost, including the Jacobean staircase, tapestry room "wallpapered" with tapestries and impressive old kitchen. Family portraits, furniture, china, glass, silver, embroidery, costumes and clocks.
Location: 100 yards west of Church in centre of village. Eyam is off A623 between Baslow and Chapel-en-le-Frith.
Admission: Adults £3.25, Child £2.25, Concessions £2.75. Family (2 adults + 4 children) £9.50. Party rates available, must pre-book.

HADDON HALL

See page 38 for full page entry.

HARDWICK ESTATE - STANSBY MILL

Tel: 01246 850430

Stainsby, Chesterfield, Derbyshire.
Owner: The National Trust   **Contact:** The Administrator
18th century water-powered corn mill in working order.
Location: From M1 junction 29 take A6175, signposted to Clay Cross then first left and left again to Stainsby Mill.
Opening Times: 1 Apr - end Oct: Wed, Thur, Sat, Sun & BH Mon, 12.30pm - 4.30pm, last admission 4.00pm.
Admission: Adult £1.50, Child 70p, pre-booked parties (no reduction).

HARDWICK HALL

Tel: 01246 850430

Doe Lea, Chesterfield, Derbyshire, S44 5QJ.
Owner: The National Trust   **Contact:** The Administrator
A late 16th century 'prodigy house' designed by Robert Smythson for Bess of Hardwick. The house contains outstanding contemporary furniture, tapestries and needlework, many pieces identified in an inventory of 1601; a needlework exhibition is on permanent display. Walled courtyards enclose fine gardens, orchards and a herb garden. The Country Park contains Whiteface Woodland sheep and Longhorn cattle.
Location: 6½m W of Mansfield, 9½m SE of Chesterfield: approach from M1 (exit 29) via A6175.
Opening Times: Hall: 1 Apr - end Oct: Wed, Thur, Sat, Sun & BH Mon, 12.30pm - 5.00pm or sunset if earlier (closed Good Fri). Last admission 4.30pm. Garden: 1 Apr - end Oct: daily 12.00pm - 5.30pm.
Admission: Hall & Garden: Adult £5.50, Child £2.70, Family £13.70. Garden only: £2.00. No reduction for parties.

HARDWICK OLD HALL

Tel: 01246 850430

Doe Lea, Chesterfield, Derbyshire, S44 5QJ.
Owner: English Heritage   **Contact:** The Administrator
This large ruined house, finished in 1591, still displays Bess of Hardwick's innovative planning and interesting decorative plasterwork. A joint ticket is available for the New Hall and Gardens and the Old Hall.
Location: 9½ m SE of Chesterfield, off A 6175.
Opening Times: 1 Apr - 31st Oct, open Wed, Thurs, Sat, Sun and Bank Hols (except Good Fri), 12.00pm - 6.00pm (or sunset if earlier). Last admissions 4.30pm.
Admission: Adult £1.50, Child £1.10, Conc 80p.

KEDLESTON HALL

Tel: 01332 842191

Kedleston, Derby, Derbyshire, DE22 5JH.

Owner: The National Trust   **Contact:** The Administrator

Palladian mansion set in a classical park landscape, built 1759 - 65 for Nathaniel Curzon, 1st Baron Scarsdale, whose family has lived at Kedleston since the 12th century. The house has the most complete and least altered sequence of Robert Adam interiors in England, and the rooms still contain their original great collection of family portraits, old masters, and their original furniture and other contents. The Indian Museum houses objects collected by Lord Curzon during his travels and when he was Viceroy of India (1899 - 1905). There is an exhibition of Robert Adam architectural drawings for the house and grounds, and Adam bridge and fishing pavilion in the park, a garden and pleasure grounds. The 'Peacock Dress' worn at the Delhi Coronation Durbar 1903 is on display.

Location: 5m NW of Derby, signposted from roundabout where A38 crosses A52 close to Markeaton Mark.

Opening Times: House: 1 Apr - end Oct (closed Good Fri), Sat to Wed, 1.00pm - 5.30pm, last admission 5.00pm. Garden: as house 11.00am - 6.00pm. Park: April to end Oct, daily 11.00am - 6.00pm, Nov - 17 Dec, Sat & Sun only 12.00pm - 4.00pm.

Admission: Adult £4.20, Child £2.10, Family £10.50. Reduced rate for booked parties on application.

LOSEHILL HALL

Tel: 01433 620346   **Fax**: 01433 620373

Peak National Park Centre, Castleton, Derbyshire, SB0 2WB.

Owner: Peak National Park   **Contact:** Peter Townsend Esq

Residential study centre running special interest holidays, Open only to those on courses or groups by request.

Location: On A625 between Castleton and Hope.

Opening Times: Weekend and week-long breaks and holidays throughout the year.

Admission: Weekends from £110. Week-long from £299.

MELBOURNE HALL

OPEN

Hall
August
(not first 3 Mons)
2.00 - 5.00pm

Gardens
1 April - 30 Sept.
Weds, Sats, Suns
Bank Hol Mons.
2.00 - 6.00pm

Tel: 01332 862502
Fax: 01332 862263

MELBOURNE, DERBYSHIRE DE73 1EN

Owner: Lord and Lady Ralph Kerr   *Contact: Lord and Lady Ralph Kerr*

This beautiful house of history in its picturesque poolside setting, was once the home of victorian Prime Minister William Lamb. As 2nd Viscount Melbourne, William gave his name to the famous city in Australia. The fine gardens, in the French formal style, contain Robert Bakewell's intricate wrought iron arbour and a fascinating yew tunnel.

Location: 8 miles South of Derby. M1 from London exit 24 follow signs to East
     Midlands Airport.

Admission: Hall: Adult £2.50, OAP £2.00, Child £1.00.
         Gardens: Adult £3.00, OAP & Child £1.50.
         Hall & Gardens Adult £3.50, OAP £3.00, Child £2.00.

PEVERIL CASTLE

Tel: 01433 620613

Market Place, Castleton, Sheffield, Derbyshire, SB0 2WX.

Owner: English Heritage   **Contact:** Mr G Hill

There are breathtaking views of the Peak District from this castle, perched high above the pretty village of Castleton. The great square tower stands almost to its original height.

Location: 15m W of Sheffield on A625.

Opening Times: 1 Apr - 30 Sept, daily 10.00am - 6.00pm, 1 Oct - 31 Mar, daily 10.00am - 4.00pm. (Closed 24 - 26 Dec, 1 Jan).

Admission: Adult £1.30, Child 70p, Conc £1.00.

RENISHAW HALL

OPEN

Easter Mon

June - August
Fridays, Saturdays,
& Sundays only.

1 Sept - 17 Sept

Fridays, Saturdays &
Sundays only
10.30am - 4.30pm

Tel: 01246 432042

SHEFFIELD, DERBYSHIRE S31 9WB

Owner: Sir Reresby Sitwell, Bt., DL   *Contact: Sir Reresby Sitwell, Bt., DL*

George Sitwell built in 1625 a small H-shaped manor house to which his descendant Sitwell Sitwell later 1st baronet, added vast additions, also the Georgian Stables (now containing a small museum) and various follies in and around the Park. The beautiful Italianate garden, park and lake were the creation of the eccentric Sir George Sitwell, grandfather of the present owner.

Location: 6 miles equidistant from Sheffield & Chesterfield, 3 miles junct. 30 of M1.

Admission: House: by written application only £7.00 per head.
         Garden only: Adult £3.00 OAP £2.00 Small Child £1.00
         Museum only: Adult £1.50 OAP £1.00 Small Child 50p
         Garden & Museum: Adult £4.00 OAP £3.00 Small Children £1.25

REVOLUTION HOUSE

Tel: 01246 453554/559727   **Fax**: 01246 206667

High Street, Old Whittington, Chesterfield, Derbyshire, S41 9LA.

Contact: Ms A M Knowles

Originally the Cock and Pynot ale house, now furnished in 17th century style.

Location: 3m N of Chesterfield on B6052 off A61.

Opening Times: 14 Apr - 29 Oct, daily,10.00am - 4.00pm. Special opening at Christmas.

Admission: Free.

SUDBURY HALL

Tel: 01283 585305

Ashbourne, Derbyshire, DE6 5HT.

Owner: The National Trust   **Contact:** The Administrator

One of the most individual of late 17th century houses, begun by George Vernon c.1661. The rich decoration includes wood carvings by Gibbons and Pierce, superb plasterwork, mythological decorative paintings by Laguerre. The great staircase is one of the finest of its kind in an English house.

Location: 6m E of Uttoxeter at the crossing point of A50 Derby - Stoke and A515 Lichfield - Ashbourne.

Opening Times: Hall: 3 May - 29 Oct: Wed to Sun and BH Mon (Closed Good Fri) 1.00pm - 5.30pm or sunset if earlier. Last admission 5.00pm. Grounds: 12.30pm - 6.00pm.

Admission: Hall: Adult £3.20, Child £1.60, Family £8.00, Parties by prior arrangement.

SUTTON SCARSDALE HALL

Chesterfield, Derbyshire.

Owner: English Heritage   **Contact:** The Administrator

The dramatic hilltop shell of a great early 18th century baroque mansion.

Location: Between Chesterfield and Bolsover.

Opening Times: Hall: 3 May - 29 Oct: Wed to Sun and BH Mon (Closed Good Fri) 1.00pm - 5.30pm or sunset if earlier. Last admission 5.00pm. Grounds: 12.30pm - 6.00pm.

Admission: Any reasonable time.

WINSTER MARKET HOUSE

Tel: 01335 350245

Matlock, Derbyshire.

Owner: The National Trust   **Contact:** The Administrator

A market house of the late 17th or early 18th century. The ground floor is of stone with the original five open arches filled in, while the upper storey is of brick with stone dressings. The building was bought in 1906 and restored. It is now an NT Information Room.

Location: 4m W of Matlock on S side of B5057 in main street of Winster.

Opening Times: 1 Apr - end Oct, daily.

Admission: Free.

SPECIAL EVENTS DIARY

• **29th April: Eyam Hall**
Piano Recital by Nina Vinogradova-Bick.

• **13th - 14th May: Chatsworth**
Chatsworth Angling Fair. The only specialist angling fair in the country catering for game, coarse and sea fishing enthusiasts with added family attractions. For further info tel: (01246 582204).

• **24th - 25th June: Catton Park**
Catton Park Country Fair and Horse Trials.

• **2nd - 3rd September: Chatsworth**
Country Fair - Spectacular with massed pipe and military bands, hot air balloons, free-fall parachuting and over 150 trade stands. For further information telephone (01246 582204).

KILLERTON HOUSE
Broadclyst

KILLERTON HOUSE is set in a 7,000 acre estate of rolling parkland, forest, woodland and fields. The house was built by the Acland family as a temporary residence but the permanent house was never started. Now owned by the National Trust, visitors today feel as if they have come to a comfortable country home; they are invited to play the organ or piano in the music room, tour the splendid dining room and cosy library, or visit the laundry with its 'wet' and 'drying' areas.

The first floor rooms contain displays of costumes from the last three centuries shown in room tableau and changed every year. The theme for 1995 is "Happy Anniversaries - a celebration of fashion", which includes a special display on the collector Paulise de Bush.

GARDENS

Killerton's 15 acre garden is a garden for all seasons with choice plants from around the world brought back by Victorian plant collectors who used Killerton as a trial ground. Flowering bulbs carpet the garden slopes in winter and spring, banks of rhododendrons and azaleas flare into colour in May, while the summer herbaceous borders and autumn reds and oranges are spectacular. Children are fascinated by the bear hut, a wooden summer house decorated with wicker and pine cones which was home to the Acland's pet bear, and the ice house where forty tons of ice were stored in Victorian times. Visitors to Killerton can also enjoy extensive walks around the estate, browsing around the produce and gift shops and the plant centre, and the special events organised for all ages.

❖

CONTACT

Mrs Denise Melhuish
The Administrator
Killerton House
Broadclyst
Exeter
Devon
EX5 3LE

Tel: (01392) 881345

LOCATION

On west side of B3181, entrance off B3185. From M5 northbound, exit 29 via Broadclyst and B3181. From M5 southbound, exit 28.

Rail: Pinhoe (not Sunday) 4¹/₂ miles; Exeter St. Davids and Exeter Central both 7 miles.

SUITABILITY FOR OTHER EVENTS
Business meetings, conferences, filming, concerts and plays.

EXTRA FACILITIES
Orienteering route. Special events such as activities for children, concerts and demonstrations through the year.

ADVICE TO COURIERS & DRIVERS
Pre-booking with the Administrator essential. Reductions for pre-arranged parties of 15+. No photography in the house. Dogs welcome in park only. Allow at least 2 hours for house and garden visits. Visitors should avoid wearing sharp-heeled shoes.

FACILITIES FOR THE DISABLED
Special parking. Motorised buggies with driver take visitors to the house and on a garden tour. Lavatories. Wheel chairs available.

Free admission, on request, to the necessary companion of a visitor with physical or visual disability.

PARKING FOR COACHES & CARS
Ample parking for cars. Space for 4 coaches.

CATERING
Restaurant in the house with waitress service (capacity 90). Self-service tea room in the old stables. Visitors may picnic throughout the grounds.

GUIDED TOURS
Occasionally outside opening hours. Contact the Administrator.

GIFT SHOP/GUIDE BOOK
Gift shop, plant centre with stock reflecting the plants in the garden and food shop selling local produce. Main shop £1.50.

SCHOOL VISITS/CHILDREN
Pre-booked school groups welcome. Killerton is ideal for National Curriculum studies in history, geography, environmental education, science and technology, and art. Activity room with handling collection and books, teachers' pack and environmental educational activities, including walks with the warden and pond dipping. Teachers planning a visit are encouraged to make a free preliminary visit. Entrance is free for National Trust School Corporate Members. Children's guide book available.

OPENING TIMES

Summer

18 March - 31 October
HOUSE
Daily 11.00am - 5.30pm
Last admissions 5pm
Closed Tuesdays

NB. There may be restricted access to the Drawing Room between 18 - 31 March.

GARDEN
Daily 10.30am - dusk

Winter

31 October - April 1996
HOUSE closed.

GARDEN
Daily 10.30am - dusk

Shop, plant centre and produce shop, also tea room Tel: (01392) 881912 for opening times, which vary during winter.

ADMISSION

Summer

Adult £4.60
Child £2.30
Family £11.00
Pre-booked groups
Adult £3.50
Child £1.75

GARDEN ONLY
Adult £2.80
Child £1.40

Winter

Nov. - Feb.
GARDEN ONLY
Adult £1.00
Child £0.50

CONFERENCE AND FUNCTION FACILITIES

ROOM	DIMENSIONS	CAPACITY	LAYOUT	POWER POINTS	SUITABLE FOR A/V
Study		50	Theatre	3	✓
		80	Standing		
		60	Buffet		
Restaurant		45	Lunch/Dinner		
		80	Buffet		

POWDERHAM CASTLE
Exeter

Historic family house of the Earl of Devon, Powderham Castle was built between 1390 and 1420 by Sir Philip Courtenay. The present Earl is his direct descendant. The Castle was extensively damaged during the Civil War and fell to the Parliamentary Forces after a protracted siege. When the family returned to the Castle 70 years later they embarked on a series of rebuilding and restoration which continued into the 19th Century.

The Castle contains a large collection of portraits by many famous artists, including Reynolds, Kneller and Hudson as well as some charming paintings by gifted members of the family. The 14ft high Stumbels Clock and the magnificent rosewood and brass inlaid book-cases by John Channon are particularly fine.

One of the most spectacular rooms on view to visitors is the Music Room, designed for the 3rd Viscount by James Wyatt. It contains an exceptionally Axminster Carpet upon which sits recently commissioned carved gilt wood furniture.

GARDENS
The Castle is set within an ancient deer park beside the Estuary of the River Exe and the Gardens and grounds are informally laid out. The Rose Garden is planted mostly with older sweet scented varieties and enjoys fine views from its terraces across the Park. Timothy, a 150 year old tortoise, lives here and keeps the lawns weed free.

SUITABILITY FOR OTHER EVENTS
Antique and Craft Fairs, conferences, dinners, charity balls, filming and wedding receptions, car launches including 4WD, vehicle rallies, clay pigeon shoots etc.

EXTRA FACILITIES
Grand piano in Music Room, 3800 acre Estate, Tennis Court, cricket pitch Horse Trials Course.

ADVICE TO COURIERS & DRIVERS
Commission and complimentary drinks and meals for drivers in the Courtyard Tea Rooms . Advance warning of group bookings preferred but not essential. Unlimited parking.

FACILITIES FOR THE DISABLED
Limited facilities

CATERING
Home made lunches and proper Devon Cream Teas.

GIFT SHOP
A gift and souvenir shop with a variety of quality items.

GUIDE BOOKS
Guide books are available in English with French, Dutch and German translations.

GUIDED TOURS
All visits by guided tour which lasts about 1 hour.

SCHOOL VISITS/CHILDREN
Schools and children of all ages very welcome. Guided tour is a fascinating and useful insight into the life of one of England's Great Houses over the centuries.

CONTACT

Mr Tim Faulkner
The Estate Office
Powderham Castle
Kenton
Exeter
Devon
EX6 8JQ

Tel: (01626) 890243
Fax: (01626) 890729

LOCATION

6 miles south west of Exeter, 4 miles Junct 30, M5.
Air: Exeter Airport 9 miles.
Rail: Starcross Station 2 miles.
Bus: Devon General Nos 85, 85A, 85B to Castle Gate.

OPENING TIMES

Summer
9 April - 29 October

Daily   10am -5.30pm
Except Saturdays closed to public, but available for private hire.

Winter
30 October - Easter

Available for hire for conferences, receptions and functions.

ADMISSION

Summer

Adult	£4.40
OAP	£4.25
Child	£2.95

Group Rates
Adult	£3.75
OAP	£3.55
Child	£1.95
Family	£11.75

(2 adults + 2 children or 1 adult + 3 children)

CONFERENCE AND FUNCTION FACILITIES

ROOM	DIMENSIONS	CAPACITY	LAYOUT	POWER POINTS	SUITABLE FOR A/V
Music Room	56' x 25'	130	Theatre		
		130	Seated		
		150	Buffet		
Dining Room	42' x 22'	65	Seated		
		90	Buffet		
		80	Theatre		
Ante Room	28' x 18'	25	Theatre		
Library 1	32' x 18'	50	Seated		
		75	Buffet		
		50	Theatre		
Library 2	31"x18'	As Library 1			

TAPELEY PARK & GARDENS 🏛
Bideford

The house, originally Queen Ann was recreated to its present condition, as the last century turned, by Sir John Belcher (a leading architect at the time) under the direction of Lady Rosamond Christie.

The Italian terraced gardens at Tapeley Park vie, in terms of layout, with all the great gardens in the West County. Their setting in the context of the confluence of the Taw and Torridge estuaries looking out towards Lundy Island and of Tapeley Park itself - a neo-classical house belonging to the Christies family (which founded and is responsible for Glyndebourne Opera) - vies, too, with the great gardens of this country.

GARDENS

The gardens are in the process of some imaginative restoration. Kirsty Christie, who trained as a painter, brings an artists eye to the new planting with the help of a well known gardener: Lady Mary Keen who is a writer and designer and was responsible with Lady Christie (the chatelaine of Glyndebourne) for designing the new areas at Glyndebourne.

Together they have drawn up guidelines for replanting the Italian garden layout - a layout which is Arcadian. This exciting venture will give visitors the chance to see a great garden returning to its former glory.

The terraced, formal gardens are bounded on the North by the house, the West by lawns overlooking the Atlantic, the South by agriculture and the East by a flight of shallow stone steps leading to shrubbery, a traditional ice house, a shell-house and a walled vegetable garden containing curved glass-houses. Additionally, to the North of the House, there is a woodland walk flanked by hydrangeas, rhododendrons and camellias down to a lily pond surrounded by a mid-19th century stand of Western Red Cedars (one of the earliest stands in the UK) planted as a memorial to to Archibald Clevland who ironically died in the battle of Inkerman having survived as one of three subalterns in the Charge of the Light Brigade some months earlier. (The Christies are direct descendants of the Clevlands).

❖

SUITABILITY FOR OTHER EVENTS
Wedding receptions, banquets, charity balls, filming, car launches including 4WD, vehicle rallys, clay pigeon and game shooting.

EXTRA FACILITIES
Croquet, Putting Lawns, Bowls, Pets Corner and pre-booked Seminars. Tapeley forms part of a 6.000 acre Estate, including the nearby UNESCO- designated Braunton Burrows.

ADVICE TO CARRIERS AND DRIVERS
Coach parking within the grounds and complimentary meals for coach drivers. Advance warning of group bookings preferred but not essential.

FACILITIES FOR THE DISABLED
Ramps, providing access to the majority of the garden. W.C. accommodation available.

PARKING OR COACHES AND CARS
Extensive parking

CATERING
Afternoon teas, light lunches and Devon Cream Teas. Buffet lunches for functions available, menu on request.

SHOP
A specialist plant centre provides a rare opportunity to purchase plants from Tapeley and award-winning producers. There is also a shop with a variety of merchandise.

GUIDE BOOKS
A guide book is on sale which traces the historical aspects of the property, the establishment, evolution and continued development of the gardens and grounds.

GUIDED TOURS
Guided Garden tours for pre-booked groups of 35+.

SCHOOL VISITS / CHILDREN
Schools and children of all ages are welcome. There are nature walks and a picnic area.

CONTACT

Miss M.E. Hedges,
N.D.C.I. Ltd.,
Lawn House,
1 Trafalgar Lawn,
Barnstaple,
Devon EX32 9BD

Tel: (01271) 42371

Fax: (01271) 42371

LOCATION

45 mins from Junct. 27, M5. Signposted along the A39, 1 mile from the Torridge Bridge, near Bideford Approx. 50 minutes from Exeter.

Rail: Barnstaple 8 miles.

OPENING TIMES

Summer
Easter - 30 September

Daily except Mons.*
10.00am - 5.00pm

*Open Bank Holiday Mons. Closed Saturdays when pre-booked for private functions. Phone to confirm opening.

Winter
1 October - Easter
Available for hire. Receptions and other functions. Phone for details.

ADMISSION

Adult £2.50
OAP £2.00
Child £1.50

A LA RONDE

Tel: 01395 265514

Summer Lane, Exmouth, Devon, EX8 5BD.

Owner: The National Trust   **Contact:** The Administrator

A unique 16-sided house built in 1796 for two spinsters, Jane and Mary Parminter. The fascinating interior decoration includes a shell-encrusted room, a feather frieze, and many 18th century contents and collections brought back by the two women from a European Grand Tour.

Location: 2m N of Exmouth on A376.

Opening Times: 1 Apr - 31 Oct, daily except Fri & Sat, 11.00am - 5.30pm. Last admission ¹/₂ hour before closing.

Admission: Adult £3.10, Child £1.50, no reduction for parties.

ARLINGTON COURT

Tel: 01271 850296

Arlington, Barnstaple, Devon, EX31 4LP.

Owner: The National Trust   **Contact:** The Administrator

The house, built in 1822 and set in 30 acres of park and garden, contains fascinating collections for every taste, including model ships, shells, costumes, pewter and furniture of the last century. A large array of early horse-drawn vehicles is displayed in the stables and there are carriage rides from the front of the house (party bookings of rides by prior arrangement). The park is grazed by Shetland ponies and Jacob sheep. Woodland and lakeside walks.

Location: 7m NE of Barnstaple on A39.

Opening Times: 1 Apr - 31 Oct, daily except Sat but open Sat of BH weekends, 11.00am - 5.30pm. Last admission 5.00pm.

Admission: Adult £4.60, Family £11. Garden only: £2.40. Pre-arranged parties (15+) £3.50.

BAYNARD'S COVE FORT ⊞

Dartmouth, Devon

Owner: English Heritage   **Contact:** The Administrator

Set among the picturesque gabled houses of Dartmouth, on the waterfront at the end of the quay, this is a small artillery fort built 1509 - 10 to defend the harbour entrance.

Location: In Dartmouth, on riverfront.

Opening Times: Any reasonable time.

BERRY POMEROY CASTLE ⊞

Tel: 01803 866618

Totnes, Devon.

Owner: English Heritage   **Contact:** The Administrator

A romantic late medieval castle, dramatically sited half-way up a wooded hillside, looking out over a deep ravine and stream. It is unusual in combining the remains of a large castle with a flamboyant courtier's mansion.

Location: 2¹/₂m E of Totnes off A385.

Opening Times: 1 Apr - 30 Sept, daily 10.00am - 6.00pm.

Admission: Adult £2.00, Child £1.00, Conc £1.50.

BICKLEIGH CASTLE

OPEN

Easter Week
(Good Fri to Fri.)
then Weds., Suns &
Bank Hols to late
May Bank Hol, then
to early Oct, daily.
(closed Sats.)
2.00 - 5.30pm
Groups of 20+
welcome by prior
arrangement.

Tel: 01884 855363

BICKLEIGH, TIVERTON, DEVON, EX16 8RP
Owner: O N Boxall Esq   Contact: O N Boxall Esq

Royalist stronghold: 900 years of history and architecture. 11th century detached Chapel; 14th century Gatehouse comprising Armoury (with Cromwellian arms and armour), Guard Room - tudor furniture and fine oil paintings, Great Hall - 52' long and 'Tudor' Bedroom, massive fourposter. 17th century Farmhouse: inglenook fireplaces, bread ovens, oak beams. Museum: Maritime exhibitions: 'Mary Rose', 'Titanic' and model ships, World War II spy and escape gadgets. Spooky Tower, The Great Hall and picturesque moated garden make Bickleigh Castle and Garden a favoured venue for functions, particularly wedding reception.

Location: Off the A396 Exeter-Tiverton road. Follow signs from Bickleigh Bridge.

Admission: Adult £3.50, Child (5 - 15) £1.70, Family Tickets £9.50

BICTON PARK & GARDENS

OPEN

March/October
10.00am - 4.00pm

April - September
10.00am - 6.00pm

Tel: 01395 568465

Fax: 01395 568889

BICTON PARK & GARDENS, BUDLEIGH SALTERTON, DEVON EX9 LDP
Owner: Bicton Park Charitable Trust   Contact: Jenny Stephens

Over 60 acres of Parkland and Gardens, including Italian, American, Oriental, Hermitage and Alpine Gardens: Palm House and specialist greenhouses: Countryside Museum housing nationwide collection of farm and country implements, machinery and vehicles. "Fabulous Forest". Large indoor play area for under teens plus acres of Adventure Playground. 25 minute woodland Railway Ride. Full catering facilities. Plant and Gift Shop.

Location: 2 miles north of Budleigh, Salterton on B3178.

Admission: Adult £3.75, OAP/Child £2.75, Family Ticket £12. Group & school rates.

BOWDEN HOUSE

Tel: 01803 863664

Totnes, Devon, TQ9 7PW.

Owner: Mrs Belinda Petersen   **Contact:** Mrs Belinda Petersen

Elizabethan mansion with Queen Anne facade.

Location: Follow brown signs on A381 from Totnes.

Opening Times: 7 Mar - 31 Oct, Mon - Thurs plus BH Suns. Museum Opens At 12.00pm,Tours Starts At 2.00pm. Or 1.30pm In High Season.

Admission: Adult £4.50, 10 - 13 yrs £2.50, 6 - 9 years £1.50, under 6 free, Group £3.50 pp. Tickets include Photo Museum and old film shows.

BRADLEY MANOR

Tel: 01626 54513

Newton Abbot, Devon, TQ12 6BN.

Owner: The National Trust   **Contact:** Mrs A H Woolner

A small medieval manor house set in woodland and meadows.

Location: On Totnes road A381.

Opening Times: Apr - end Sept: Wed, 2.00pm - 5.00pm: also Thur 6 & 13 Apr, 21 & 28 Sept. Last admission 4.30pm.

Admission: £2.60, no reduction for parties.

BUCKFAST ABBEY

Tel: 01364 642519   **Fax**: 01364 643891

Buckfastleigh, Devon, TQ11 0EE.

Owner: Buckfast Abbey Trustees Registered   **Contact:** Mr R Clutterbuck

The monks of Buckfast welcome visitors to their Abbey, which they rebuilt themselves on its medieval foundations. Church, medieval precinct, shops selling Buckfast Tonic wine and honey, restaurant, video, exhibition.

Location: ¹/₂m N of A38 Plymouth - Exeter dual carriageway at Buckfastleigh turnoff.

Opening Times: Church and grounds - open daily all year, 5.30pm - 9.30pm. Shops, restaurant, video - open daily 9.00am - 5.30pm (Summer) 10.00am - 4.00pm (Winter). Exhibition - Open Easter - end October 10.30am - 4.30pm (11.30am - 4.30pm Sundays). Shops closed Good Fri and Christmas Day. Restaurant closed Boxing Day.

Admission: Free. Car parking £1.00, Coaches £2.50. Exhibition - Adult 75p, Child 30p Easter to October.

BUCKLAND ABBEY

Tel: 01822 853607

Yelverton, Plymouth, Devon, PL20 6EY.

Owner: The National Trust   **Contact:** The Administrator

The spirit of Sir Francis Drake is rekindled at his home with exhibitions of his courageous adventures and achievements throughout the world. Originally a 13th century monastery, the Abbey was ingeniously transformed into a family residence by Sir Richard Grenville of Revenge fame before Drake bought it in 1581. Also of interest are monastic farm buildings, craft workshops and country walks.

Location: 6m S of Tavistock, 11m N of Plymouth, turn off A386 ¹/₄m S of Yelverton.

Opening Times: 1 Apr - 31 Oct: daily except Thur 10.30am - 5.30pm, also Nov - end Mar, Sat & Sun 2.00pm - 5.00pm. Last admission ³/₄ hour before closing. Closed 18 - 29 Dec.

Admission: Adult £4, Family £10. Grounds only: £2. Pre-arranged parties (15+) £3.20.

CADHAY

OPEN

July & Aug
Tues, Weds, Thurs

Also late Mon & Suns
spring and summer
bank holidays

2.00 - 5.30pm

Groups by
appointment only.

Tel: 01404 812432

OTTERY ST. MARY, DEVON EX11 1QT

Owner: Mr O.N.W. William Powlett   *Contact:* Lady William Powlett

Cadhay is approached by an avenue of lime-trees, and stands in a pleasant listed garden, with herbaceous borders and yew hedges, with excellent views over the original medieval fish ponds. The main part of the house was built about 1550 by John Haydon who had married the de Cadhay heiress. He retained the Great Hall of an earlier house, of which the fine timber roof (about 1420) can be seen. An Elizabethan Long Gallery was added by John's successor at the end of the 16th century, thereby forming a unique and lovely courtyard.

Location: 1 mile north west of Ottery St. Mary on B3176.

Admission: Adults £3.00, Child £1.50.

CASTLE DROGO

Tel: 01647 433306

Drewsteignton, Exeter, Devon, EX6 6PB.

Owner: The National Trust   **Contact:** The Administrator

This granite castle, built between 1910 and 1930, is one of the most remarkable works of Sir Edwin Lutyens. It stands at over 900ft overlooking the wooded gorge of the River Teign with beautiful views of Dartmoor. Spectacular walks through surrounding 600 acre estate.

Location: 4m S of A30 Exeter-Okehampton road via Crockernwell.

Opening Times: Castle: 1 Apr - 31 Oct, daily except Fri, 11.00am - 5.30pm. Garden: 1 Apr - 31 Oct, daily 10.30am - 5.30pm last admission 5.00pm.

Admission: Castle, garden & grounds: £4.60, Family £11.00. Garden & grounds only: £2.00. Pre-arranged parties £3.60.

COLETON FISHACRE GARDEN

Tel: 01803 752466

Drewsteignton, Exeter, Devon, EX6 6PB.

Owner: The National Trust   **Contact:** Mr B Howe

20 acre garden in a stream-fed valley set within the spectacular scenery of this NT Coast. The garden was created by Lady Dorothy D'Oyly Carte between 1925 and 1940, and is planted with a wide variety of uncommon trees and rare and exotic shrubs. Coleton Fishacre House is a private family home and is of special interest to people studying 20th century architecture and design. View by written appointment.

Location: 2m from Kingswear; take Lower Ferry road, turn off at toll house.

Opening Times: Mar: Sun only, 2.00pm - 5.00pm, also 1 Apr 0 31 Oct: Wed, Thur, Fri, Sun & BH Mons 10.30am - 5.30pm or dusk if earlier. Last admission ¹/₂ hour before closing.

Admission: £2.80, pre-booked parties £2.20.

COMPTON CASTLE

Tel: 01803 872112

Drewsteignton, Exeter, Devon, EX6 6PB.

Owner: The National Trust   **Contact:** The Administrator

A fortified manor house with curtain wall, built at three periods: 1340, 1450 and 1520 by the Gilbert family. It was the home of Sir Humphrey Gilbert (1539-1583), coloniser of Newfoundland and half-brother of Sir Walter Raleigh; the family still lives here.

Location: At Compton, 3m W of Torquay.

Opening Times: 1 Apr - 31 Oct: Mon, Wed & Thur, 10.00am - 12.15pm and 2 - 5.00pm, The courtyard, restored great hall, solar, chapel, rose garden and old kitchen are shown. Last admission ¹/₂ hour before closing.

Admission: £2.60, pre-arranged parties £2.00.

DARTINGTON HALL GARDENS

Tel: 01803 865551   **Tel:** 01803 866688

Dartington, Totnes, Devon, TQ9 6EL.

Owner: Dartington Hall Trust   **Contact:** Mr R Wright

28 acre gardens surrounds 14th century Hall.

Location: 30 mins from M5 at Exeter (off A38 at Buckfastleigh).

Opening Times: Open all year round.

Admission: Donations welcome.

DARTMOUTH CASTLE

Tel: 01803 833588

Dartington, Totnes, Devon, TQ9 6EL.

Owner: English Heritage   **Contact:** The Administrator

This brilliantly positioned defensive castle juts out into the narrow entrance to the Dart estuary, with the sea lapping at its foot. It was one of the first castles constructed with artillery in mind and has seen 450 years of fortification and preparation for war.

Location: 1m SE of Dartmouth off B3205, narrow approach road.

Opening Times: 1 Apr - 30 Sept, daily 10.00am - 6.00pm, 1 Oct - 31 Oct, daily 10.00am - 4.00pm. 1 Nov - 31 Mar, Wed-Sun, 10.00 - 4.00pm.

Admission: Adult £2.00, Child £1.00, Conc £1.50.

DOCTON MILL & GARDEN

Tel: 01237 441369   **Fax:** 01237 441369

Spekes Valley, Hartland, Devon, EX39 6EA.

Owner: Martin G Bourcier Esq   **Contact:** Martin G Bourcier Esq

Garden for all seasons in 8 acres of sheltered wooded valley.

Location: 3m Hartland Quay.

Opening Times: Mar - Oct, 10.00am - 5.00pm. No coaches.

Admission: Adult £2.00, Child 50p.

ESCOT

Tel: 01404 822188   **Fax:** 01404 822 903

Parklands Farm, Ottery St Mary, Devon, EX11 1LU.

Owner: Mr J M Kennaway   **Contact:** Mr J M Kennaway

2 acre walled garden planted with Victorian varieties of rose, edged with Italian style borders. Wilderness Walk includes a variety of shrubbery, trees, rhododendrons and azaleas.

Location: 9m E of Exeter on A30 at Fairmile.

Opening Times: Easter - 1 Oct, 10.00am - 6.00pm. 1 Oct - Easter, 11.00am - 4.00pm.

Admission: Adult £1.95, Child £1.65, Family of 5 £8, Senior citizens £1.65, Groups £1.50.

EXETER CATHEDRAL

Tel: 01392 55573 / 214219   **Fax:** 01392 498769

Exeter, Devon, EX1 1HS.

Contact: Mrs Juliet Dymoke Marr

Cathedral shop, refectory. Facilities for the visually impaired and disabled. Parking within ¹/₂ mile. The Exeter Rondels - 333 ft of Tapestry on the plinth around the walls of the Nave. This depicts national, local and Cathedral history from Roman times to the present day.

Location: Central to the City - between High Street and Southernhay. Groups may be put down in South Street.

Opening Times: Open all year, Mon - Fri 7.30am - 6.30pm, Sat 7.30am - 5.00pm, Sun 8.00am - 7.30pm.

Admission: No formal charge - donation requested of £2 per person.

FURSDON HOUSE

Tel: 01392 860860

Cadbury, Exeter, Devon, EX5 5JS.

Owner: E D Fursdon Esq   **Contact:** Mrs D Fursdon

Family home for 700 years with Jacobean and Regency features and museum with costume collection with fine examples from 18th and 19th centuries. Set in parkland with walled, terraced garden and tea room.

Location: On A3072 between Tiverton and Crediton, 9m North of Exeter.

Opening Times: Easter to end Sept Thurs and Bank Hols Mons tours at 2.30pm and 3.30pm.

Admission: Adult £2.90, Child under 16 £1.50, Child under 10 free, Groups of 20+ £2.70.

HARTLAND ABBEY

Tel: 012374 41264

Leigh Farm, Hartland, Bideford, Devon.

Owner: Sir Hugh Stucley Bt.   **Contact:** Mrs Mary Heard

Augustinian Abbey founded in 12th century. Victorian and Edwardian photographic exhibition. Shrub gardens and woodland walk to remote Atlantic cove.

Location: 15m W of Bideford, 4m off A39.

Opening Times: May - Sept, Wed, 2.00pm - 5.30pm. Easter - Aug, BH Sun and Mon.

Admission: Adult £3.50, Child £1.50, Group £3.

HEMYOCK CASTLE

Tel: 01823 680745

Hemyock, Cullompton, Devon, EX15 3RJ.

Owner: Capt Sheppard   **Contact:** Mrs P M Sheppard

Former medieval moated castle, displays show site's history as fortified manor house, castle and farm. Medieval, civil war and Victorian tableaux, archaeological finds, cider press and cow parlour.

Location: Exit Junction 26 M5, Blackdown Hills, Devon/Somerset border. Wellington 5m.

Opening Times: Bank Hol Mons 2.00pm - 5.00pm. Other times by appointment. Groups and private parties welcome.

Admission: Adult £1.00, Child 50p, Group rate available.

HILL HOUSE NURSERY & GARDENS

Tel: 01803 762273

Landscove, Ashburton, Devon, TQ13 7LY.
Owner: Ray Hubbard Esq **Contact:** Ray Hubbard Esq
3 acre garden featured several times on TV.
Location: A38 Ashburton .
Opening Times: 11.00am - 5.00pm every day. Tea rooms; 1 Mar - 1 Oct, 11.00am - 5.00pm.
Admission: Free. Group tours by arrangement.

HOUND TOR DESERTED MEDIEVAL VILLAGE

Ashburton Road, Manaton, Dartmoor, Devon.
Owner: English Heritage **Contact:** The Administrator
The remains of the dwelling.
Location: 1¹/₂ m S of Manaton off Ashburton road.
Opening Times: Any reasonable time.

KILLERTON HOUSE

See page 41 for full page entry.

KNIGHTSHAYES COURT

Tel: 01884 254665

Bolham, Tiverton, Devon, EX16 7RQ.
Owner: The National Trust **Contact:** The Administrator
Begun in 1869, the house, with its richly decorated Victorian interior, is a rare survival of the work of Williams Burges. It stands on the east side of the Exe valley and has one of the finest gardens in Devon, with specimen trees, rare shrubs, spring bulbs and summer flowering borders.
Location: 2m N of Tiverton off A396.
Opening Times: 1 Apr - 31 Oct: Garden, daily 11.00am - 5.30pm. House, daily, except Fri (but open Good Fri) 1.30pm - 5.30pm last admissions 5.00pm. Nov & Dec: Sun 2.00pm - 4.00pm for pre-booked parties only.
Admission: House: £4.80, Garden & grounds only: £2.80. Pre-booked parties £3.80.

LYDFORD CASTLES AND SAXTON TOWN

Lydford, Oakhampton, Devon.
Owner: English Heritage **Contact:** The Administrator
Standing above the lovely gorge of the River Lyd, this 12th century tower was notorious as a prison. The earthworks of the original Norman fort are to the south. A Saxon town once stood nearby and its layout is still discernible.
Location: In Lydford off A386 8 m S of Okehampton.
Opening Times: Any reasonable time.

MARKERS COTTAGE

Tel: 01392 461546

Broadclyst, Exeter, Devon, EX5 3HR.
Owner: The National Trust **Contact:** The Administrator
Fascinating medieval cob house which contains a cross-passage screen decorated with a painting of St Andrew and his attributes.
Location: Off B3181 in village of Broadclyst.
Opening Times: 1 Apr - 31 Oct: Sun, Mon and Tues, 2.00pm - 5.00pm.
Admission: £1.00

MARWOOD HILL

Tel: 01271 42528

Barstaple, Devon, EX31 4ER
Owner: Dr J A Smart **Contact:** Dr J A Smart
20 acre garden with 3 small lakes. Extensive collection of camellias, bog garden. National collection of astilbes.
Location: 4m North of Banstaple.
Opening Times: Dawn to dusk throughout the year.
Admission: Adult £2.00, Child free under 12, OAP £1.50.

MORWELLHAM QUAY

Tel: 01822 832766 **Fax:** 01822 833808

Tavistock, Devon, PL19 8JL.
Owner: The Morewellham & Tamar Valley Trust **Contact:** Gary Emerson
Port and cottages restored as museum.
Location: Tavistock, Devon.
Opening Times: Summer 10.00am - 5.30pm, Winter (Nov-Easter) 10.00am - 4.30pm., Last admissions 2 hours before closing.
Admission: Adult £7.50, Child £5, Family £16, Senior citizens/students £7, Groups; Adult £5.75, Child £4, Senior citizens £5.

MOUNT BATTEN TOWER

Tel: 0117 9750700

Mount Batten Point, Plymstock, Devon.
Owner: English Heritage **Contact:** The Administrator
A 17th century gun tower, 30 feet high and with original windows and vaulted roof. There are good views across Plymouth Sound from here.
Location: In Plymstock, on Mount Batten Point.
Opening Times: Summer 10.00am - 5.30pm, Winter (Nov-Easter) 10.00am - 4.30pm., Last admissions 2 hours before closing.
Admission: Contact Regional Office Tel: 01272 750700

OAKHAMPTON CASTLE

Tel: 01837 52844

Oakehampton, Devon.
Owner: English Heritage **Contact:** The Administrator
The ruins of the largest castle in Devon stand above a river surrounded by splendid woodland. There is still plenty to see, including the Norman motte and the jagged remains of the Keep. There is a picnic area and lovely woodland walks.
Location: 1m SW of Okehampton town centre.
Opening Times: 1 Apr - 30 Sept, daily 10-6.00pm, 1 Oct - 31 Oct, daily 10-4.00pm.
Admission: Adult £2.00, Child £1.00, Conc £1.50.

OVERBECKS MUSEUM & GARDEN

Tel: 01548 842893

Sharpitor, Salcombe, Devon, TQ8 8LW.
Owner: The National Trust **Contact:** The Administrator
Spectacular views over Salcombe estuary can be enjoyed from the beautiful 6 acre garden, with its many rare plants, shrubs and trees. The elegant Edwardian house contains collections of local photographs taken at the end of the last century, local ship building tools, model boats, toys, shells, birds, animals and other collections, together with a secret room for children. Also of interest is an exhibition showing the natural history of Sharpitor.
Location: 1¹/₂m S of Salcombe, signposted from Malborough and Salcombe.
Opening Times: Museum: 1 Apr - 31 Oct: daily except Sat 11.00am - 5.30pm, last admission 5.00pm. Garden: daily throughout year 10.00am - 8.00pm or sunset if earlier.
Admission: Museum & Garden: £3.40, Garden only: £2.00. No reductions for parties.

POWDERHAM CASTLE

See page 42 for full page entry.

RHS GARDEN ROSEMOOR

OPEN

Apr - Sept
10.00am - 6.00pm

Mar & Oct
10.00am - 5.00pm

Nov - Feb
10.00am - 4.00pm

Tel: 01805 624067
Fax: 01805 624717

GREAT TORRINGTON, DEVON

Owner: The Royal Horticultural Society *Contact: The Royal Horticultural Society*

The oldest part of Rosemoor, Lady Anne's garden, includes many rare plants with the accent particularly on trees and shrubs. The new garden developed by the RHS includes formal rose gardens, a cottage garden and the new walled fruit and vegetable garden. The visitors centre is open from 2 January to 24 December offering gifts and books, a plant centre and delightful restaurant facilities.

Location: Great Torrington, North Devon.
Admission: Adults £3.00, Child under 6 Free, Child (6 - 16) £1.00.
Groups of 20+ £2.50.

ROYAL CITADEL

Tel: 0117 9750700

Plymouth Hoe, Plymouth, Devon.
Owner: English Heritage **Contact:** The Administrator
A large, dramatic 17th century fortress, with walls up to 70 feet high, built to defend the coastline from the Dutch and still in use today.
Location: At E end of Plymouth Hoe.
Opening Times: By guided tour only (1¹/₂ hrs) at 12.00pm and 2.00pm, 1 May - 30 Sept. Assemble at Plymouth Dome below Smeaton's Tower on the Hoe.
Admission: Adult £2.50, Child £2, Conc £1.50.

SALTRAM

Tel: 01752 336546

Plympton, Plymouth, Devon, PL7 3UH.
Owner: National Trust   **Contact:** The Administrator
A remarkable survival of a George II mansion and its original contents, in a landscaped park. Two of the most important rooms were designed by Robert Adam, with magnificent interior plasterwork and decoration. The house contains fine period furniture, china and pictures, including many portraits by Reynolds. Also of interest are the Great Kitchen, the stables, a gallery of West Country art in the chapel and an orangery in the gardens.
Location: 2m W of Plympton, 3¹/₂m E of Plymouth city centre, between A38 and A379.
Opening Times: House: 1 Apr - 31 Oct, daily except Fri & Sat, but open Good Fri, 12.30pm - 5.30pm. Art Gallery, Garden & Great Kitchen: as house but from 10.30am. Last admission 5.00pm.
Admission: House: £5.00, Garden only £2.20.

SAND

Tel: 01395 597230

Sidbury, Sidmouth, Devon, EX10 OQN.
Owner: Lt.Col. P Huyshe   **Contact:** Lt.Col. P Huyshe
Lived in house, owned by Huyshe family from 1560, rebuilt 1592 - 94 in unspoilt valley. Screens passage, heraldry, family documents. Also Sand Lodge roof structure of late 15th century hall house.
Location: Grid Ref: SY 146925 ¹/₄m off A375 Honiton to Sidmouth.
Opening Times: Sun, Mon: Apr 16, 17, May 7, 8, 28, 29, Jul 30, 31, Aug 27, 28, 2 - 5.30pm.
Admission: Adult £2.50, Child/full time student 50p.

SHUTE BARTON

Tel: 01297 34692

Shute, Axminster, Devon, EX13 7PT.
Owner: The National Trust   **Contact:** The Administrator
One of the most important surviving non-fortified manor houses of the Middle Ages. Commenced in 1380 and completed in the last 16th century, then partly demolished in the late 18th century, the house has battlemented turrets, late Gothic windows and a Tudor gatehouse.
Location: 3m SW of Axminster, 2m N of Colyton on B3161.
Opening Times: 1 Apr - 31 Oct: Wed & Sat, 2.00 - 5.30pm. Last admission 5.00pm.
Admission: £1.60, pre-arranged parties £1.20.

TAPELEY PARK & GARDEN

See page 43 for full page entry.

THE GARDEN HOUSE

Tel: 01822 854769   **Fax:** 01822 854769

Buckland Monachorum, Yelverton, Devon, PL2 07LQ.
Owner: Fortescue Garden Trust   **Contact:** Mr K Wiley
Outstandingly beautiful garden created since 1945 on inhospitable site of an ancient monastery.
Location: 1m W off A386 at Yellerton.
Opening Times: 1 Mar - 31 Oct, daily, 10.30am - 5.00pm.
Admission: Adult £2.75, Child 50p, Conc £2.25, Group £2.25.

THE OLD BAKERY

Tel: 01297 80333

Branscombe, Seaton, Devon, EX12 3DB.
Owner: National Trust   **Contact:** The Administrator
A traditional stone built and partially rendered building beneath a slate roof which was, until 1987, the last traditional bakery in use in Devon. The baking room has been preserved and houses traditional baking equipment. The remainder of the building is used as tea-rooms.
Location: In Branscombe off A3052.
Opening Times: Daily Easter to Oct and weekends in winter 11.00 - 5.00pm.

TIVERTON CASTLE

Tel: 01884 253200

Tiverton, Devon, EX16 6RP.
Owner: A K Gordon Esq   **Contact:** A K Gordon Esq
Grade I listed historic medieval castle, now a peaceful, private house containing important Civil War armoury, New World tapestry, clock collection.
Location: Tiverton
Opening Times: 16 Apr - 24 Sept, Suns and Thurs and Bank Hol Mons. Aug, Sun - Thurs. 2.30pm - 5.30pm.
Admission: Adult £3.00, Child (7-16) £2.00, under 7 free.

TORRE ABBEY

Tel: 01803 293593

The Kings Drive, Torquay, Devon, TQ2 5NX.
Owner: Torbay Borough Council   **Contact:** L Retallick
Torbay's most historic building. Over 20 rooms, including Victorian tea room open. Medieval remains are extensive. Gardens.
Location: Torquay Sea Front, behind Torre Abbey Sands and next to the Riviera Centre.
Opening Times: 9.30am - 6.00pm (last admissions 5.00pm).
Admission: Adult £2.50, Child £1.50, Family £5.95, Conc £2.00, Group £1.80.

TOTNES CASTLE

Tel: 01803 864406

Totnes, Plymouth, Devon.
Owner: English Heritage   **Contact:** The Administrator
By the North Gate of the hill town of Totnes you will find a superb motte and bailey castle, with splendid views across the roof tops and down to the River Dart. It is a symbol of lordly feudal life and a fine example of Norman fortification.
Location: In Totnes, on hill overlooking the town.
Opening Times: 1 Apr - 30 Sept, daily 10.00am - 6.00pm, 1 Oct - 31 Oct, daily 10.00am - 4.00pm, 1 Nov - 31 Mar, Wed - Sun, 10.00am - 4.00pm.
Admission: Adult £1.50, Child 80p, Conc £1.10.

YARDE MEDIEVAL FARMHOUSE

Tel: 01548 842367

Malborough, Kingsbridge, Devon, TQ7 3BY.
Owner: John R Ayres Esq   **Contact:** John R Ayres Esq
Location: 5m S of Kingsbridge off A381.
Opening Times: Easter - 30 Sept, 2.00 - 5.00pm Wed, Fri, Sun.
Admission: Adult £2, Child 50p, Child under 5 free, Groups by appointment only.

SPECIAL EVENTS DIARY

- **26th March: Bicton Park**
  Mothering Sunday Special Luncheon.

- **16th April: Bicton Park**
  Aladin Treasure Trail - Prizes Fancy Dress etc.

- **8th May: Bicton Park**
  V E Celebration Street Party - Stalls, Bands, Red Arrows Simulator - Fashions Shows, Dinner Dance.

- **4th June: Bicton Park**
  4th Great West Jaguar Day.

- **8th June: Bicton Park**
  Special Fathers Day Luncheon.

- **1st - 2nd July: Powderham Castle**
  Powderham Horse Trials.

- **8th - 9th July: Powderham Castle**
  Historic Vehicle Gathering.

- **15th July: Killerton**
  Exeter Festival Jazz Concert.

- **16th July: Killerton**
  Exeter Festival 'Proms" Concert with fireworks.

- **26th August: Bicton Park**
  It's A Knockout - As seen on TV.

ABBOTSBURY
Weymouth

SHELTERED from the sea by the mighty Chesil Bank and nestling beneath rolling green hills, Abbotsbury is the embodiment of everyone's idea of a typical English village. The charming thatched village is home to many tea rooms, olde inns, a craft centre and a working pottery.

THE SWANNERY
Tucked away at the reed fringed western end of the Fleet lagoon, the Swannery is home for the only managed colony of Mute Swans in the world and retains a wildness seldom found elsewhere. Visitors can wander freely amongst nesting swans and marvel as parents and cygnets mingle with the public. The reedbed walk takes the visitor past the ancient duck decoy, the oldest of its kind still in operation in Britain. Viewing hides offer a chance to view the birdlife on the Fleet lagoon and the information centre helps the visitor to understand and appreciate the 600 year history of the Swannery.

THE SUB TROPICAL GARDENS
A mecca for plant lovers. Set in a sheltered leafy hollow where cold winds do not penetrate, many rare and delicate plants more usually confined to the greenhouse thrive happily in the open. Silver Award Winner at the Chelsea Flower Show 1994, and Silver Gilt Winner at Hampton Court. Many of the plants found in the gardens can be purchased at the country Gift and Plant Centre.

THE TITHE BARN MUSEUM
The magnificent 15th Century Tithe Barn, one of the largest of its kind in England, is virtually all that remains of the former Abbey of St Peter. The interior of the Barn, spectacular in its own right, now house agricultural bygones. This beautiful collection carefully reconstructs the scenes of a bygone age. The Farmworkers Kitchen, Gamekeeper, Reaper, Animal Doctor and Blacksmith are just a few of the many exhibits that vividly portray the ingenuity and hardships of the days before.

To visit Abbotsbury is to spend a day in a way that will stay in the memory for years.

SPECIAL ATTRACTIONS
Sub-tropical gardens, Swannery and Fleet Nature Reserve, Tithe Barn Museum, Chesil Beach, Iron Age Hill Fort, St Catherine's Chapel, Monastery remains, Abbotsbury village.

SUITABILITY FOR OTHER EVENTS
Music Concerts (in the Tithe Barn), garden parties, filming and television, garden tours for Horticultural Clubs, summer music festivals, conference facilities.

HIGHLIGHTS '95
Giant Easter Egg Hunt at the Gardens Good Friday 14 April to Monday 17 April. Cygnet season, end of May to end of June. Over 100 nests start hatching around your ankles, Cygnets abound.

ADVICE TO GROUP ORGANISERS
Free coach parking. Setting down and picking up points directly opposite attractions. This year we are giving a massive 25% off our single rates to all group bookings of 50 persons or more.

Guided tours of the Swannery for pre-booked coach parties.

FACILITIES FOR THE DISABLED
All paths at Swannery, and most at the Gardens, negotiable by wheelchair. Wheelchair available for loan free of charge. Disabled toilets are available at the Swannery and Gardens.

PARKING FOR COACHES & CARS
Free car parking and coach parking at all attractions.

GUIDED TOURS
Guided tours are available at an extra cost by arrangement.

CATERING
Teas, light lunches etc at Gardens. Many cafés, inns and tea rooms in the village.

CONTACT

Swannery
Tel: (01305) 871684

Gardens
Tel: (01305) 871387

Tithe Barn
Tel: (01305) 871817

or write to:
Tourism Office
West Barn Yard
West Street
Abbotbury
Weymouth
DT3 4JT

Fax: (01305) 871092

LOCATION

Located on B3157 coastal road between Weymouth and Bridport. From Bournemouth and South A35 via Dorchester.

Rail: Weymouth 9 miles.

OPENING TIMES

Summer
March - End October

SWANNERY Open
GARDENS Open
TITHE BARN Open

Winter
GARDENS
7 days a week.

TITHE BARN
Sundays only

ADMISSION

Summer
SWANNERY
Adult £4.00
OAP/Student . . .£3.25
Child £1.25
Family Saver . . .£9.00
GARDENS
Adult £3.80
OAP/Student . . .£3.25
Child £1.00
Family Saver . . .£8.00
TITHE BARN
Adult £2.20
OAP/Student . . .£1.70
Child £0.80
Family Saver . . .£4.50

ATHELHAMPTON HOUSE & GARDENS

OPEN

2 Apr -29 Oct.
Tues, Wed, Thurs,
Suns and Bank Hols.
Also Mons and Fris
July & Aug.
12 Noon - 5.00pm.
Craft Fairs Easter &
Aug Bank Hol.
weekends.
Flower festival
Spring Bank Hol.

Tel: 01305 848363
Fax: 01305 848135

ATHELHAMPTON, DORCHESTER, DORSET DT2 7LG

Owner: *R.P.G. Cooke Esq.*   **Contact:** *R.P.G. Cooke Esq.*

Athelhampton is one of the finest examples of 15th Century domestic architecture in the Kingdom. Enjoy the lived in family house with its Great Hall, Great Chamber, Wine Cellar and Kings Room - all exquisitely furnished. Wander through 20 acres of beautiful grounds including 8 walled gardens with fountains, pavilions and topiary pyramids, all encircled by the River Piddle. Home-made cream teas, gift shop and free car park.

Location: On A35, 5 miles east of Dorchester.
Admission: House & Garden: Adult £4.20, Child £1.70, Family ticket (2 adults & up to 4 children) £10.00. Garden: Adult £2.50, Child Free.

ABBOTSBURY

See page 48 for full page entry.

ABBOTSBURY ABBEY REMAINS

Abbotsbury, Dorset.
Owner: English Heritage   **Contact:** The Administrator
In a delightful village of stone and thatch cottages are the remains of a cloister building of this Benedictine Abbey, founded in 1044.
Location: In Abbotsbury, off B3157, near churchyard.
Opening Times: Any reasonable time.

BROWNSEA ISLAND   **Tel:** 01202 707744

Poole Harbour, Dorset, BH15 1EE.
Owner: The National Trust   **Contact:** The Property Manager
A beautiful wildlife haven in the middle of Poole Harbour, where Lord Baden-Powell held his first Scout camp. Nature reserve (maintained by the Dorset Trust for Nature Conservation) attracting terns and waders in their thousands.
Location: Boats run from Poole Quay and Sandbanks. Visitors may land on the beach with a dinghy.
Opening Times: 1 Apr - 1 Oct: daily, 10.00am - 8.00pm (or dusk if earlier). Check times of last public boat.
Admission: Landing fee: Adult £2.20, Child £1.10. If pre-booked 2 weeks prior to visit: Adult £1.90, Child 90p.

CHETTLE HOUSE   **Tel:** 01258 830209   **Fax:** 01258 830380

Chettle, Blandford Forum, Dorset, DT11 8DB.
Owner: Patrick Bourke Esq   **Contact:** Patrick Bourke Esq
Fine Queen Anne house by Thomas Archer set in 5 acres of garden.
Location: 6m NE of Blandford off A354.
Opening Times: 14 Apr - 8 Oct.
Admission: Standard £2.00, Child free, Groups by arrangement.

CHRISTCHURCH CASTLE & NORMAN HOUSE

Christchurch, Dorset.
Owner: English Heritage   **Contact:** The Administrator
Early 12th century Norman keep and Constable's house, built c.1160.
Location: In Christchurch, near the Priory.
Opening Times: Any reasonable time.

CLOUDS HILL    **Tel:** 01985 843600

Wareham, Dorset, BH20 7NQ.
Owner: The National Trust   **Contact:** The Administrator
T E Lawrence (Lawrence of Arabia) bought this cottage in 1925 as a retreat; it contains his furniture.
Location: 9m E of Dorchester, 1^{1}/2m E of Waddock crossroads B3390.
Opening Times: 22 Apr - 29 Oct: Wed, Thur, Fri, Sun & BH Mon, 2.00pm - 5.00pm or dusk if earlier.
Admission: £2.20, no reduction for children or parties.

COMPTON ACRES GARDENS   **Tel:** 01202 700778   **Fax:** 01202 707537

Canford Cliffs Road, Canford Cliffs , Poole, Dorset, BH13 7ES.
Owner: Compton Acres Ltd   **Contact:** P Willsher Esq
Cliff top series of gardens overlooking Poole Harbour, very colourful planting.
Location: Canford Cliffs Road
Opening Times: 7 days a week, 10.30am - 6.30pm (or dusk if earlier). Last entry 5.45pm.
Admission: Adult £3.90, Child £1, Family £8, Senior citizens/students £2.90, Groups £3.20.

CORFE CASTLE   **Tel:** 01929 481294

Wareham, Dorset, BH20 5EZ.
Owner: The National Trust   **Contact:** The Administrator
One of the most impressive ruins in England, this former Royal castle was besieged and sleighted by Parliamentary forces in 1646.
Location: On A351.
Opening Times: 6 Feb - 25 Mar: daily 10.00am - 4.30pm, 26 Mar - 29 Oct: daily 10.00am - 5.30pm, 30 Oct - 3 Mar: daily 12.00pm - 3.30pm, Closed 25 & 26 December.
Admission: Adult £3.00, Child £1.50, Parties £2.50.

The Swannery, Abbotsbury

EDMONSHAM HOUSE

Tel: 01725 517207

Cranborne, Wimbourne, Dorset, BH21 5RE.

Owner: Mrs Julia E Smith   **Contact:** Mrs Julia E Smith

Charming blend of Tudor and Georgian architecture with interesting contents. Old fashioned walled garden.

Location: Between Cranborne and Verwood, 9m from Ringwood.

Opening Times: Gardens; Sun & Wed, 2.00pm - 5.00pm. House and Gardens; April and Oct, BH Mons, Wed, 2.00pm - 5.00pm.

Admission: House & Gardens; Gardens only; Adult £2.00, Child £1.00, under fives free, Groups by arrangement.

FIDDLEFORD MANOR

Sturminster Newton, Dorset.

Owner: English Heritage   **Contact:** The Administrator

Part of a medieval manor house, with a remarkable interior. The splendid roof structures in the hall and upper living room are the best in Dorset.

Location: 1 m E of Sturminster Newton off A357.

Opening Times: 1 Apr - 30 Sept Daily, 10.00am - 6.00pm. 1 Oct - 31 Mar Daily, 10.00am - 4.00pm. (Closed 24 - 26 Dec, 1 Jan).

HARDY'S COTTAGE

Tel: 01305 262366

Higher Bockhampton, Dorchester, Dorset, DT2 8QJ.

Owner: The National Trust   **Contact:** The National Trust

A small thatched cottage where the novelist and poet Thomas Hardy was born in 1840. It was built by his great grandfather and little altered, furnished by the Trust.

Location: 3m NE of Dorchester, ^{1}/2m S of A35.

Opening Times: 1 Apr - 31 Oct, daily (except Thur) 11.00am - 6.00pm or dusk if earlier Open Good Fri.

Admission: £2.50.

HORN PARK

Tel: 01308 862212   **Fax:** 01308 863778

Beaminster, Dorset, DT8 3HB.

Owner: John Kirkpatrick Esq   **Contact:** John Kirkpatrick Esq

Extensive garden with good views.

Location: Beaminster, Dorset.

Opening Times: 1 Apr - 31 Oct, Tues, Wed, Sun and BH Mon, 2.00pm - 6.00pm.

Admission: Adult £2.50, Child under 14 free , Group £2.50 pp.

ILSINGTON HOUSE

Tel: 01305 848454   **Fax:** 01305 848909

Puddletown, Dorchester, Dorset, DT2 8TQ.

Owner: P J Duff Esq   **Contact:** Mrs P Duff

This family home, set in the picturesque village of Puddletown (Thomas Hardy's Weatherbury). A classical William and Mary mansion built by the 7th Earl of Huntingdon. Home of George III's illegitimate grandson, born to HRH Princess Sophia in 1800, kept a secret until the Royal Scandal of 1829. Ilsington was visited by many members of the Royal Family during George III's reign. Fine furniture and present owner's private collection of pictures and sculpture. A fully guided house tour given. Formal and landscape gardens with probably the longest haha in Dorset. Large collection of beautiful bearded irises and unusual peonies.

Location: Puddletown, Dorchester.

Opening Times: House tours: 1 May - 29 Sept, Wed and Thurs 2.00pm - 6.00pm, last tour 5.00pm. Also Suns and Bank Hol Mons in August.

Admission: £3.00.

John Makepeace, with some of his furniture at Parnham House

KINGSTON LACY

Tel: 01202 883402

Wimborne Minster, Dorset, BH21 4EA.

Owner: The National Trust   **Contact:** The Administrator

17th century house designed by Sir Roger Pratt but with considerable alterations by Sir Charles Barry in the 19th century. Important Italian and English paintings collected by W J Bankes. Collection of Egyptian artifacts. Set in 250 acres of wooded park.

Location: On B3082 - Blandford/Wimborne road, 1.5m W of Wimborne.

Opening Times: 1 Apr - 31 Oct: daily except Thurs & Fri. House: 12.00pm - 5.30pm. Last admission 4.30pm. Park: 11.00am.

Admission: House, Garden & Park: Adult £5.50, Child £2.70. Parties: Adult £4.80, Child £2.50. Garden & Park only: Adult £2.20, Child £1.10.

KINGSTON MAURWOOD COLLEGE

OPEN

Conference Centre Throughout the year

Farm aninmals, Gardens, Lake and Parklands

Good Friday to 15 October 10.00 - 5.00pm.

Tel: 01305 264738
Fax: 01305 250059

KINGSTON MAURWOOD COLLEGE, DORCHESTER, DORSET DT2 8PY

Owner: The Trustees of Kingston Maurwood   *Contact:* Mike Hancock

Located in parkland within an 800 acre estate. The fine Georgian house forms the administrative centre for the college – providing education and training in all aspects of countryside use. Conference facilities include many fine rooms within the house, affording magnificent views of the lake and fine Edwardian and Elizabethan walled gardens. The farm animal park provides an excellent education facility.

Location: 2 miles east of Dorchester (signed from east end of by-pass)

Admission: Adult £3.00, Child £1.50. Special school and party rates.

KNOLL GARDENS

Tel: 01202 873931   **Fax:** 01202 870842

Staplehill Road, Hampreston, Wimbourne, Dorset, BH21 7ND.

Owner: John Flude Esq   **Contact:** John Flude Esq

Rare, unusual and exotic collection of plants from all over the world on compact six acre site.

Location: Off B3073 (Hampreston) Exit A31 Canford Bottom Roundabout (signed 1 ^{1}/2m). Between Wimborne and Ferndown.

Opening Times: Mar - 1 Nov, daily, 10.00am - 5.30pm.

Admission: Adult £3.45, Child aged 4 - 16 £1.70, Family £9 Senior citizens £2.90, Student £2.40, Group; Adult £2.95, Senior citizen £2.60.

LULWORTH CASTLE

Tel: 01929 41352

East Lulworth, Wareham, Dorset.

Owner: English Heritage   **Contact:** The Administrator

Built in the early 16th century as a romantic hunting lodge, Lulworth Castle was changed into a fashionable country house set in beautiful parkland during the 18th century. Gutted by fire in 1929 the exterior of the castle is now being restored by English Heritage.

Location: In East Lulworth off the B3070, 3 m NE of Lulworth Cove.

Opening Times: 30 Mar - 31 Oct Daily, 10am - 6pm, 1 Nov - 22 Dec Daily, 10am - 4pm.

Admission: Adult £1.50, Child £1.20, Conc 75p.

MACPENNYS GARDENS

Tel: 01425 672348

154 Burley Road, Bransgore, Christchurch, Dorset, BH23 8DB.

Owner: T Lowndes Esq   **Contact:** T Lowndes Esq

Location: 5 m NE of Christchurch.

Opening Times: Throughout the year, except Christmas and New Year holidays. Mon - Sat, 9.00am - 5.00pm. Sun 2.00pm - 5.00pm.

Admission: By voluntary donation to charity - National Garden Scheme.

MAPPERTON

OPEN

Gardens.
1 March - 31 Oct.
Daily
2.00 - 6.00pm

House:
Open only to groups
by appointment
(times as above)

Tel: 01308 862645
Fax: 01308 863348

BEAMINSTER, DORSET DT8 3NR

Owner: Mr and Mrs John Montagu   *Contact: Mr and Mrs John Montagu*

Jacobean 1660's manor with Tudor features and classical north front. Italianate upper garden with orangery, topiary and formal borders descending to fish ponds and shrub gardens. All Saints Church forms south wing opening to courtyard and stables. Area of outstanding natural beauty with fine views of Dorset hills and woodlands.

Location: 1 mile off B3163, 2 miles off B3066, 2 miles Beaminster, 5 miles Bridport.
Admission: Gardens: £3.50, House (tour) £3.50. Under 18 £1.50, under 5 free.

MINTERNE GARDENS   **Tel:** 01300 341370 **Fax:** 01300 341747

Minterne Magna, Nr Cerne Abbas, Dorchester, Dorset, DT2 7AU.
Owner: The Lord Digby   **Contact:** The Lord Digby
Large wild woodland garden landscaped in 18th century with over a mile of walks. Many rare rhododendrons and magnolias tower over small lakes, cascades and streams.
Location: Sherborne/Dorchester road A352 2m North of Cerne Abbas.
Opening Times: Daily, Apr - end October.
Admission: £2.00, accompanied children free.

PARNHAM HOUSE

OPEN

2 Apr - 29 Oct
Wed, Suns and
Bank Holidays
10.00am - 5.00pm

Tues & Thurs
groups only.

Tel: 01308 862204
Fax: 01308 863494

BEAMINSTER, DORSET DT8 3NA

Owner: John Makepeace   *Contact: The House Manager - Bruce Hunter-Inglis*
Inspiring 20th century craftmanship. displayed in the home of John and Jennie Makepeace, who have restored and enlivened this fascinating tudor Manor House. Exhibitions of exciting contemporary work in glass, wood, textiles and ceramics. Licensed buttery, shop and furniture workshop, romantic terraces and topiary in 14 acres of fine gardens and woodland walks.
Location: On A3066 5 miles north of Bridport, 1/2 mile south of Beaminster.
Admission: Adult £4.00, Child 10-15 yrs. £2.00, Child under 10 Free.

PORTLAND CASTLE   **Tel:** 01305 820539

Portland, Weymouth, Dorset.
Owner: English Heritage   **Contact:** The Administrator
One of the best preserved of Henry VIII's coastal forts, built of white Portland stone. Now standing quietly overlooking the harbour, it was originally intended to thwart attack by the Spanish and French, and changed hands several times during the Civil War.
Location: Overlooking Portland harbour adjacent to RN helicopter base.
Opening Times: 1 Apr - 30 Sept, daily 10am - 6pm, 1 Oct - 31 Oct, daily 10am - 4pm.
Admission: Adult £2.00, Child £1.00, Conc £1.50.

SANDFORD'S ORCAS MANOR HOUSE   **Tel:** 01963 220206

Sandford Orcas, Sherborne, Dorset, DT9 4SB.
Owner: Sir Mervyn Medlycott Bt.   **Contact:** Sir Mervyn Medlycott Bt.
Tudor Manor House with gatehouse, fine panelling, furniture, pictures. Terraced gardens.
Location: 2 1/2m N of Sherborne, Dorset.
Opening Times: Easter Mon, 10am - 6pm. May - Sept, Sun, 2pm - 6pm. Mon 10am - 6pm.
Admission: Adult £2.00. Child £1.00. Group: Adult £1.60, Child 80p.

SHERBORNE CASTLE

OPEN

Easter Sat - Sept.
Thurs, Sats, Suns and
Bank Hol. Mons.

Castle:
1.30 - 5.00pm

Grounds & Tea
Room
12.30 - 5.00pm

Tel: 01935 813182
Fax: 01935 816727

SHERBORNE, DORSET DT9 3PY

Owner: Mr Simon Wingfield Digby   *Contact: Jane Taylor*

A fully furnished Historic House built by Sir Walter Raleigh in 1594 and home of the Digby family since 1617, reflecting various styles from the Elizabethan Hall to the Victorian Solarium. Splendid collections of art, furniture and porcelain. Well informed guides are happy to answer questions. Set in beautiful parkland with lawns, wooded walks and a 50 acre lake.
Location: 3/4 mile south east of Sherborne town centre. Follow brown signs from A30 or A352
Admission: Grounds & Castle: Adult £3.60, OAP £3.00, Child £1.80
Grounds only £1.50

SHERBORNE OLD CASTLE   **Tel:** 01935 812730

Sherborne, Dorset.
Owner: English Heritage   **Contact:** The Administrator
The ruins of this early 12th century castle are a testament to the 16 days it took Cromwell to capture it during the Civil War, after which it was abandoned.
Location: 1/2 m E of Sherborne off B3145.
Opening Times: 1 Apr - 30 Sept daily, 10.00am - 6.00pm, 10 Oct - 31 Oct daily, 10.00am - 4.00pm, 1 Nov - 31 Mar, Wed - Sun 10.00am - 4.00pm. (Closed 24 - 26 Dec, 1 Jan).
Admission: Adult £1.30, Child £1, Conc 70p.

SMEDMORE HOUSE

OPEN

14 May

17 Sept

Garden only
21 May

2.00 - 5.00pm

Groups by
arrangement

Tel: 01929 480719

SMEDMORE, KIMMERIDGE, WAREHAM, DORSET BH20 5BG

Owner: Dr. Philip Mansel   *Contact: Mr T Gargett*

The home of the Mansel family for nearly 400 years nestles at the foot of the Purbeck hills looking across Kimmeridge Bay to Portland Bill. Originally built in 1620 by the present owner's ancestor William Clavell, the imposing Georgian front was added in the 1760s. Beautiful walled garden which contains many special and interesting plants. Popular for Holiday lets, Weddings, Business and Private functions.
Location: 15 miles south west of Dorchester.
Admission: Full details from the Warden.

ST CATHERINE'S CHAPEL

Abbotsbury, Dorset.

Owner: English Heritage   **Contact:** The Administrator

A small stone chapel, set on a hilltop, with an unusual roof and small turret used as a lighthouse.

Location: ¹/₂ m S of Abbotsbury by pedestrian track.

Opening Times: Any reasonable time.

THE MANOR HOUSE

Tel: 01963 250 400

Purse Caundle, Sherborne, Dorset, DT9 5DY.

Owner: Michael de Pelet Esq   **Contact:** Michael de Pelet Esq

15th & 16th century manor house. Great Hall with minstrels gallery. Family home.

Location: 4m E of Sherborne, just off A30.

Opening Times: Easter Mon and then May - 30 Sept, Thurs, Sun and BHs, 2 - 5.00pm.

Admission: Adult £2.00, Child 50p, Groups by appointment. Tea available.

THE PRIEST'S HOUSE MUSEUM

Tel: 01202 882533   **Fax:** 01202 882533

23-27 High Street, Wimborne Minster, Dorset, BH21 1HR.

Owner: Priest's House Museum Trust   **Contact:** Ms K Osborne

Location: 8m N of Poole/Bournemouth off A31.

Opening Times: 1 Apr - 28 Oct, Mon - Sat, 10.30am - 5.00pm. BH Suns and Suns Jun - Sept, 2 - 5.00pm.

Admission: Adult £1.50, Child 50p, Family £3.50, Conc £1, Groups 10% discount for 30+.

WOLFETON HOUSE

OPEN

May - Sept.
Tues, Thurs and
Bank Holiday
Mondays
2.00 - 6.00pm

At other times
throughout the
year parties by
appointment

Tel: 01305 263500
Fax: 01305 265090

NEAR DORCHESTER, DORSET DT2 9QN

Owner: Capt N.T.L.L. Thimbleby   *Contact:* The Steward

A fine mediaeval and Elizabethan Manor House lying in the water-meadows near the confluence of the rivers Cerne and Frome. It was much embellished around 1580 and has splendid plaster ceilings, fireplaces and panelling of that date. To be seen are the Great Hall, Stairs and Chamber, Parlour, Dining Room, Chapel and Cyder House. The mediaeval Gatehouse has two unmatched and older towers. There are good pictures and furniture.

Location: 1¹/₂ miles from Dorchester on the A37 towards Yeovil. Indicated by Historic House signs.

Admission: Adult £3.00, Child £1.50

SPECIAL EVENTS DIARY

- **14th - 17th April**
  Athelhampton
  Craft Fair.

- **16th April**
  Brownsea Island
  Easter Egg Hunt.

- **13th May**
  Kingston Lacy
  Garden Road Show - no extra charge but donations welcome.

- **21st May**
  Sherborne Castle
  Obedience Dog Show.

- **28th - 31st May**
  Athelhampton
  Flower Festival - Fresh and dried flowers in house, special garden displays.

- **4th June**
  Brownsea Island
  Teddy Bears' Picnic - no extra charge

- **10th June**
  Kingston Maurward
  Open Day - Demos and exhibitions of all land-based subjects.

- **16th June**
  Kingston Lacy
  Centenary Jazz Concert with fireworks - tickets £10.00

- **9th July**
  Athelhampton
  MG Owners Club - One free ticket for anyone arriving in an MG.

- **14th July**
  Kingston Lacy
  Centenary Concert by the Bournemouth Sinfonietta with fireworks - tickets £10.00

- **21st, 24th, 26th, 28th, 31st July**
  Brownsea Island
  Brownsea Open Air Theatre
  Richard III - Tickets £9.00.

- **29th - 30th July**
  Sherborne Castle
  Craft Fair.

- **2nd & 4th August**
  Brownsea Island
  Brownsea Open Air Theatre - Richard III - Tickets £9.00.

- **3rd - 4th August**
  Sherborne Castle
  Open Air Production of "Merry Wives of Windsor".

- **18th - 19th August**
  Brownsea Island
  Fantasy Island - the story of Brownsea Island - tickets £5 and £9

- **26th August**
  Mapperton
  Mapperton Courtyard Fair.

- **26th - 28th August**
  Athelhampton
  Craft Fair.

- **21st October**
  Kingston Maurward
  Apple Day - Planting, pruning, propagation and displays of varieties of apples. Stalls selling all apple products.

- **2nd - 10th December**
  Athelhampton
  Christmas Art Exhibition.

RABY CASTLE
Co. Durham

RABY CASTLE, home of Lord Barnard's family for over 360 years, is set in a 200 acre Deer Park. The Castle was mainly built in the 14th Century, on the site of an earlier Manor House, by the powerful Neville family, who owned it until the Rising of the North in 1569, when Raby was seized by the Crown. It remained Crown property until 1626, when it was bought from Charles I by the eminent statesman and politician Sir Henry Vane, Lord Barnard's ancestor.

Despite its appearance, Raby was intended to be a fortified home rather than a fortress, although it played an important part in the Wars of the Roses and the English Civil War.

In the 18th Century, the Castle was transformed from a rugged stronghold to an elegant country residence, with further alterations in the mid 19th Century. Despite this, much of the original exterior remains, with important medieval rooms, notably the Great Kitchen (used for over 600 years until 1952), with its vast ranges and collection of Victorian copper utensils, and the original Garrison of the Castle now the Servants' Hall.

Today, serene in its tranquil setting, Raby still conveys the sense of its historic past, enhanced by its elegant furnishings and renowned collection of Meissen porcelain. Raby is living history, not a dead museum.

❖

SUITABILITY FOR OTHER EVENTS
By arrangement, though Raby is unsuitable for meetings, conferences or corporate catering.

EXTRA FACILITIES
These include: Picnic tables, 200 acres of parkland and 3½ acres of gardens. Lectures can be provided on the Castle, its contents, gardens and history.

ADVICE TO COURIERS & DRIVERS
No photography or video filming is permitted in the Castle: slides are on sale. No dogs allowed in the Castle (except guide dogs). Dogs must be on leads in the park. Unaccompanied children are not admitted to the Castle or park. Unlimited parking on the grass car park and coaches will find hard standing nearby.

FACILITIES FOR THE DISABLED
Disabled or elderly visitors may alight at the entrance to the Castle. The vehicles should then return to the car park. There are two toilets specially adapted for the disabled, near the Car Park and Tearoom. Doors to Tearoom (1 step) are wide enough for wheelchairs.

CATERING
Stables converted to self-service Tearooms, offering light refreshments, seating 60. For other requirements, please contact Curator.

GUIDED TOURS
Tours with experienced guides available at no extra cost, guides posted in most rooms on general open days, when no guided tours are available. Tours last about 1½ hours. For special interest groups, in-depth tours with the Curator may be arranged, for an additional fee. Garden tours with the Head Gardener can also be organised.

GIFT SHOP
There are two gift shops, one in the Castle, the other in the gardens. Open from 1pm - 5pm. A wide variety of gifts are available. Venison, game and soft fruits available in season.

GUIDE BOOKS
Colour guide book currently reprinting. Full text available.

SCHOOL VISITS/CHILDREN
Raby welcomes school parties of up to 60 children, who must be accompanied in a ratio of 1:20. Experienced guides available for school visits. Raby is suitable for several educational purposes: Social history, architecture, art and natural history. Schools are welcome to use the picnic tables, space for supervised games nearby. Room available for picnics when weather inclement.

CONTACT

Mrs E A Steele
Raby Castle
Staindrop
Darlington
Co Durham
DL2 3AH

Tel: (01833) 660202
or (01833) 660888

LOCATION

From Edinburgh, 170 miles via A1 or A68. From London, 250 miles via M1 and A1.

Rail: Darlington Station, 12 miles.

Air: Teeside Airport, 20 miles.

OPENING TIMES

Summer
Easter and all Bank Holiday Weekends
Saturday - Wednesday

May - June
Weds & Suns only
1.00pm - 5.00pm

July - September
Daily except Sats
1.00pm - 5.00pm

Garden and Park open
11.00am - 5.30pm on days shown above

Parties by arrangement
Easter - end June
Mondays - Fridays
10.00am - 4.30pm

July - end September
Mondays - Fridays
Mornings only.

Winter
October -Easter
Closed

ADMISSION

Summer
HOUSE & GARDEN
Adult £3.50
Child* £1.50
OAP £3.20
Bulmer's Tower . .50p
(when open)
GARDEN ONLY
Adult £1.00
Child (5-15yrs) . .£0.75
OAP £0.75

GROUPS (min 25 people)
By arrangement

AUCKLAND CASTLE

Tel: 01388 601627

Bishop Auckland, Durham, DL14 7NP.

Owner: The Church Commissioners   **Contact:** The Warden

Historic home of the Bishops of Durham with parts dating from the 12th century. Staff rooms. Stunning chapel remodelled from 14th century great hall.

Location: Next to Market Square.

Opening Times: Castle & Chapel: BH Mons, 2.00pm - 5.00pm, 2 May - 17 Sept; Tues 10.00am - 12.00pm. Sun, Wed and Thurs, 2.00pm - 5.00pm. Sats in Aug, 2.00pm - 5.00pm. Park open during daylight hours throughout the year.

Admission: Adult £2.00, Conc £1.00. Contact warden for group bookings at special times throughout the year.

AUCKLAND CASTLE DEER HOUSE

Bishop Auckland, Durham.

Owner: English Heritage   **Contact:** The Administrator

A charming building erected in 1760 in the park of the Bishops of Durham so that the deer could shelter and find food.

Location: In Bishops Auckland Park, just N of town centre on A689.

Opening Times: Park opening times.

BARNARD CASTLE

Tel: 01883 38212

Barnard Castle, Durham.

Owner: English Heritage   **Contact:** The Administrator

The substantial remains of this large Castle stand on a rugged escarpment overlooking the River Tees. You can still see parts of the 14th century Great Hall and the cylindrical 12th century tower, built by the Baliol family.

Location: Barnard Castle.

Opening Times: 1 Apr - 30 Sept, daily 10.00am - 6.00pm, 1 Oct - 31 Oct, daily, 10.00am - 4.00pm. 1 Nov - 31 Mar, Wed - Sun, 10.00am - 4.00pm (Closed 24 - 26 Dec, 1 Jan).

Admission: Adult £1.80, Child 90p, Conc £1.40.

DERWENTCOTE STEEL FURNACE

Tel: 01207 562573

Newcastle, Durham.

Owner: English Heritage   **Contact:** The Administrator

Built in the 18th century it is the earliest and most complete authentic steel making furnace to have survived.

Location: 10 m SW of Newcastle on A694 between Rowland's Gill and Hamsterley.

Opening Times: 1 Apr - 30 Sept , 1.00pm - 5.00pm, 1st & 3rd Sunday of every month.

Admission: Free.

DURHAM CATHEDRAL

Tel: 0191 3864266   **Fax:** 0191 3864267

Durham, DH1 3EH.

Contact: Ms W Nugent

A world heritage site. Norman architecture. Burial place of St Cuthbert and the Venerable Bede. Claustral buildings including Monk's Dormitory and Medieval kitchen.

Location: Durham city centre.

Opening Times: Summer: 7.15am - 8.00pm (29 May - 8 Sept), Winter: 7.15am - 6.00pm (9 Sept - 28 May), Sun services: 8.00am, 10.00am, 11.15am and 3.30pm, Weekday services: 7.30am, 9.00am and 5.15pm.

Admission: Tower: Adult £1.00, Child 50p, Monk's Dormitory: Adult 50p, Child 20p, AV: Adult 40p, Child 20p, Treasury: Adult £1.00, Child 20p.

EGGLESTONE ABBEY

Tel: 01325 468771

Durham.

Owner: English Heritage   **Contact:** The Administrator

Picturesque remains of a 12th century abbey, located in a bend of the River Tees. Substantial parts of the church and abbey buildings remain.

1 m S of Barnard Castle on minor road off B6277.

Location: 1 m S of Barnard Castle on minor road off B6277.

Opening Times: Any reasonable time.

FINCHALE PRIORY

Tel: 01388 814417

Durham.

Owner: English Heritage   **Contact:** The Administrator

These beautiful 13th century priory remains are located beside the curving River Wear.

3 m NE of Durham, on minor road off A167.

Location: 3 m NE of Durham, on minor road off A167.

Opening Times: 1 Apr - 30 Sept Daily, 10.00am - 6.00pm. Lunchtime closure 1.00pm - 2.00pm.

Admission: Adult £1.00, Child 80p, Conc 50p.

RABY CASTLE

See page 53 for full page entry.

THE BOWES MUSEUM

Tel: 01833 690606   **Fax:** 01833 637163

Barnard Castle, Durham, DL12 8NP.

Owner: Durham County Council   **Contact:** Mrs Elizabeth Conron

Imposing building standing above the River Tees, having an important collection of European art and antiques.

Location: 2m N of A66 (Bowes or Greta Bridge).

Opening Times: Mon - Sat, 10.00am - 5.30pm. Sun 2.00pm - 5.00pm. Closes at 5.00pm in Apr and Oct and 4.00pm Nov - Feb. Closed Jan - Mar for repairs.

Admission: Adult £2.50, Child £1.50, Conc £1.50, Students free, Groups 10% discount.

Britain's Festival of Arts and Culture 1995 is a year-long celebration - an invitation to visitors to discover the wealth of heritage and contemporary arts that make Britain one of the finest cultural centres in the world.

All over the country you will find popular and classical events and attractions marking the Year and the many anniversaries and national celebrations taking place in 1995.

There's the National Trust Centenary, British Arts Festivals Year, Swansea is City of Literature, the bicentenary of John Keats's birth, the tercentenary of Henry Purcell's death, and the start of Cinema 100 - to mention just a few.

Look out for the Festival symbol and call at Tourist Information Centres for latest details.

AUDLEY END HOUSE & PARK ⊞
Saffron Walden

James I is said to have remarked that Audley End was too large for a king but not for his Lord Treasurer, Sir Thomas Howard, who built it. The house was so large in fact that early in the 18th century about half of it was demolished as being unmanageable, but this still leaves a very substantial mansion. The interior contains rooms decorated by Robert Adam, a magnificent Jacobean Great Hall, a picturesque "Gothic" chapel and a suite of rooms decorated in the revived Jacobean style of the early 19th century.

❖

SUITABILITY FOR OTHER EVENTS
Suitable for open air concerts and other events.

ADVICE TO COURIERS & DRIVERS
Dogs must be kept on a lead. Coach drivers and tour guides have free entry. One additional place for every 20 extra people.

FACILITIES FOR THE DISABLED
Ground floor suitable for disabled access.

PARKING FOR COACHES & CARS
Car parking is available. Coaches to book in advance, £5.00 per coach.

CATERING
Restaurant facilities available.

GUIDED TOURS
By arrangement for groups. Please telephone for details.

GIFT SHOP
Situated in old kitchens, wide range of souvenirs and gifts.

GUIDE BOOKS
Colour Guide available.

SCHOOL VISITS/CHILDREN
School visits are free if booked in advance. Contact Administrator.

CONTACT

The Administrator
Audley End House
Saffron Walden
Essex
CB11 4JF

Tel: (01799) 522842

Fax: (01799) 521276

LOCATION

1 mile west of Saffron Walden on B1383, M11 exits 8 and 9 northbound , exit 10 southbound.

Rail: Audley End - 1 mile

OPENING TIMES

House

1 April - 30 September

12 Noon - 6.00pm
Wednesday - Sunday and Bank Holidays

Last admission 5.00pm

Park & Gardens

1 April - 30 September

10.00am - 5.00pm
Wednesday - Sunday and Bank Holidays

ADMISSION

House and Grounds
Adult £5.50
Child* £2.80
OAP/Students/
UB40 holders . .£4.10

Grounds only
Adult £3.00
Child* £1.50
Concessions . . .£2.30

*Child 5-15yrs.
Under 5 free.

GROUPS
15% off groups of 11 or more.

HEDINGHAM CASTLE
Essex

Hedingham Castle is one of the finest Norman keeps in England and is in an excellent state of preservation. It was built in 1140 by the famous medieval family the de Veres, Earls of Oxford, and is still owned by their descendants. For 500 years the kings and queens of England looked to this family to fill the highest positions in the land. In 1137 Aubrey de Vere was created Lord Great Chamberlain and this office was held by the de Veres until the death of the 18th Earl of Oxford in 1623. He died aged 32 from wounds received at the Battle of the Hague, a year after his marriage to Diana Cecil, a great beauty, daughter of the the Earl of Exeter. The castle was besieged by King John and visited by King Henry VII, King Henry VIII and Queen Elizabeth I. A dry moat separates the Inner and Outer Baileys and is spanned by a lovely, brick Tudor bridge, built to replace the drawbridge by the 13th Earl in 1496. The four floors include the Garrison, a magnificent Banqueting Hall with fine Minstrels' Gallery, decorative stonework and a splendid Norman arch. On the Outer Bailey can be seen the Queen Anne house built in 1719 by Sir Thomas Ashhurst.

GROUNDS

The five, spring fed, medieval fishponds were made into the formal Canal in the eighteenth century. The Valley Walk shows the huge scale of the original earthworks and the beautiful grounds and woodland contain much of natural interest. There is a peaceful lakeside meadow ideal for family picnics. Allow time to visit the medieval village and superb Norman church.

SUITABILITY FOR OTHER EVENTS
The Castle, 18th century house (closed to the public), and grounds are available for filming and a variety of events by arrangement.

ADVICE TO COURIERS & DRIVERS
Parties are very welcome by prior arrangement if possible. No smoking in the castle please. Dogs on leads only. Free refreshments for coach drivers.

FACILITIES FOR THE DISABLED
The disabled are very welcome and are given free entry. They can enjoy the grounds, but the steep steps up to the Castle make a visit to the interior unsuitable. Cars/coaches carrying disabled may disembark by the Tudor bridge at the top of the drive.

PARKING FOR COACHES AND CARS
Ample free parking in the Castle grounds.

CATERING
Tea, coffee, home-made cakes and light refreshments.

GIFT SHOP
A wide range of gifts, books and historical items are always on sale in the Castle.

GUIDE BOOKS
Colour Guide Books on sale. Basic guide sheets are available in French, German and Dutch, also children's guide/colouring sheets.

SCHOOL VISITS / CHILDREN
School visits welcome all year by appointment and there is no charge for teachers/helpers. Teachers' Information Pack supplied on booking. Preliminary visits free. Children's work sheets available. In wet weather schools can work/have their packed lunches on the top floor of the Castle.

CONTACT

The Manager
Hedingham Castle
Castle Hedingham
Nr. Halstead
Essex
C09 3DJ

Tel: (01787) 460261

LOCATION

On B1058, 1 mile off A604 between Cambridge (30m) and Colchester (16m).

Close to Lavenham and Constable country, within easy reach of London (60m) via the M25, M11, A12.

OPENING TIMES

Summer

CASTLE & GROUNDS
8 Apr - 10 Sept
Daily
11.00am - 5.00pm

10 Sept - 29 Oct
Sats and Suns only
11.00am - 5.00pm

Bank Hol Weekends and Good Friday open 10.00am

HOUSE
Closed

Winter

Open for Schools/Parties by appointment only.

ADMISSION

CASTLE & GROUNDS

Adult £2.75
Child £1.75
OAP/Student . . .£2.50
Family Ticket . .£7.50
Groups (min 20 people)
Per person £2.50

LAYER MARNEY TOWER
Colchester

LAYER MARNEY TOWER, built in the reign of Henry VIII, is the tallest Tudor gatehouse in Great Britain.

Lord Henry Marney clearly intended to rival Wolsey's building at Hampton Court, but he died before his masterpiece was finished. His son John died two years later, in 1525, and building work stopped.

Layer Marney Tower has some of the finest terracotta work in the country, most probably executed by Flemish craftsmen trained by Italian masters. The terracotta is used on the battlements, windows, and most lavishly of all, on the tombs of Henry and John Marney.

Visitors may climb The Tower, passing through the recently restored History Room, and enjoy the marvellous views of the Essex countryside. There are fine outbuildings, including the Long Gallery with its magnificent oak roof and the medieval barn which now houses some of the Home Farm's collection of Rare Breed Farm animals.

❖

CONTACT

Nicholas and Sheila Charrington
Layer Marney Tower
Colchester
Essex
CO5 9US

Tel: (01206) 330784

Fax: (01206) 330784

LOCATION

Layer Marney Tower is 5 miles south west of Colchester. Signposted off B1022 (Colchester - Maldon Road).

Road: From London A12 53 miles

Rail: Kelvedon Station

SUITABILITY FOR OTHER EVENTS
Corporate Events, Film Location, Clay Pigeons, Wedding Receptions, Banquets, Concerts and Opera.

ADVICE TO COURIERS & DRIVERS
Parking and cup of tea free for drivers.

FACILITIES FOR THE DISABLED
Tower excepted, there is reasonable access and a "disabled loo".

PARKING FOR COACHES & CARS
Free parking on hard standing.

CATERING
Teas, coffee and cakes available. Parties of 20 and more may book in advance for morning coffee, lunch, full tea or an evening meal. Tudor banquets are also organised by arrangement.

GUIDED TOURS
By arrangement for parties of 20 and over. The tour lasts about 1$^{1}/_{2}$ hours. Price £4.00 per person.

GIFT SHOP
Small gift shop with a range of attractive items and a Farm Shop specialising in venison and meat from the rare breed animals on the farm.

GUIDE BOOKS
Colour guide £1.65, walkabout guide 50p.

SCHOOL VISITS/CHILDREN
School visits are welcomed throughout the year, with Basic classroom facilities offered, price £1.50 per child, with one adult free with every 10 children.

The Long Gallery

OPENING TIMES

Summer
1 April - 30 September

Daily except Saturdays
2.00 - 6.00pm

Also Sats and Suns in July & Aug
12 - 6.00pm

Bank Holidays
11.00am - 6.00pm

Winter
1 October - 31 March
Closed

Open by arrangement for guided tours and school visits.

ADMISSION

Summer

Adult £3.00
Child £1.50
OAP £3.00
Family* £8.00
* 2 adults & 2 children.

Groups (20 or more)
Adult £2.50
Child £1.50
Guided Tour . . .£4.00

CONFERENCE AND FUNCTION FACILITIES

ROOM	DIMENSIONS	CAPACITY	LAYOUT	POWER POINTS	SUITABLE FOR A/V
Long Gallery	75' x 19'	120	Seated	2	
		200+	Buffet		
		200	Theatre		
Carpenters Shop	46' x 24'	80	Seated	10	✓
		120	Buffet		
		150	Theatre		

MOYNS PARK
Birdbrook

MOYNS PARK is the home of Lord and Lady Ivar Mountbatten: Lord Ivar is the younger son of the late 3rd Marquess of Milford Haven: Set in 250 acres of classical rolling parkland, Moyns is one of the country's finest examples of an Elizabethan manor house.

Situated on the Essex/Suffolk border, within one hour's drive of London, and 30 minutes from Cambridge and Newmarket, the Estate takes its name from the Le Moign family, who owned the lands from the time of the Norman Conquest in 1066. During the reign of Henry VII the manor passed to the Gent family, who retained ownership until 1880, when Moyns was sold to General St Ives, Silver-Stick-in-Waiting to Queen Victoria and grandfather of the late Ivar Bryce, previous owner and uncle to Lord Ivar Mountbatten.

Moyns Park is not only steeped in its own fabulous history, but reflects the fascinating history of the Mountbatten and Milford Haven family and their relationship to every Royal household in Europe.

Ian Fleming based the exploits of James Bond on those of his great friend, the late Ivar Bryce, who was an OSS Agent during the Second World War.

Moyns Park is not open to the public, but available on an exclusive use basis for guests seeking complete privacy in relaxed, elegant and traditional surroundings.

❖

CONTACT

Rosie Coutts
Moyns Park
Birdbrook
Essex
CO9 4BP

Tel: (01440) 730073
Fax: (01440) 730060

LOCATION

London - 1 hour
Cambridge - 30 minutes
Newmarket - 30 minutes

15 minutes from Junct. 9 off the M11, just 2 miles south of Haverhill.

Please ring for details and Colour Brochure.

FACILITIES
The House is available for Conferences, Seminars, Incentive Programmes, Corporate Hospitality Events, Wedding Receptions, Private Parties and Banquets.
A full range of outdoor activities can be organised within the Estate and located close to the House. Multi-Activity Events are particularly well suited.
There is plenty of space for Marquee or Steel Framed Structures including utilisation of the Stables and Courtyards for additional Exhibitions and Product Launches.

CATERING
An exceptionally high standard of in-house catering is guaranteed, matched with professional and friendly service. Clients are treated as guests and leave as friends.

ACCOMMODATION
9 Principal Bedrooms, all with private or en-suite bathrooms, currently available. Further secondary bedrooms available if required. Lord and Lady Ivar Mountbatten believe in maintaining the Moyns Park tradition of style and service rarely offered nowadays, including Maid Service and breakfast in bed for the ladies.

OPENING TIMES

Available throughout the year.

ADMISSION

Day Delegate Rate
from £35 per person

24 hour Delegate Rate
from £125 per person

Private Dinner Party/ Banquet
from £25.00 per head

Venue Hire From
from £500

For full Tariff and Terms of Business, please contact Rosie Coutts.

CONFERENCE AND FUNCTION FACILITIES

ROOM	DIMENSIONS	CAPACITY	LAYOUT	POWER POINTS	SUITABLE FOR A/V
Great Hall	41' x 30'	60	Boardroom	6	✓
		80	Dining		
		130	Theatre		
Drawing Room	22' x 24'	24	Boardroom	6	✓
		18	U-Shaped		
		36	Theatre		
		30	Dining		
Library	22' x 16'	8	Boardroom/Dining	3	✓
Dining Room	22' x 19'	20	Boardroom	5	✓
		16	U-Shaped		
		34	Theatre		
		40	Dining		

AUDLEY END HOUSE & PARK

See page 55 for full page entry.

BOURNE MILL

Tel: 01206 572422

Colchester, Essex.
Owner: The National Trust   **Contact:** The Administrator
Originally a fishing lodge built in 1591. It was later converted into a mill with a 4 acre mill pond. Much of the machinery, including the waterwheel, is intact.
Location: 1 m S of Colchester centre, in Bourne Road, off the Mersea Road B1025.
Opening Times: Only BH Mon & Sun preceding BH Mon; also Sun & Tues in Jul and Aug, 2.00pm - 5.30pm.
Admission: £1.30, children must be accompanied by an adult, no reduction for parties.

CHELMSFORD CATHEDRAL

Tel: 01245 263660

Colchester, Essex.
     Contact: Mrs J Orton
15th century building became a Cathedral in 1914. Extended in 1920s, major refurbishment in 1980s with contemporary works of distinction and a splendid new organ in 1994.
Location: 1 m S of Colchester centre, in Bourne Road, off the Mersea Road B1025.
Opening Times: 8.00am - 5.30pm daily. Sun services: 8.00am, 9.30am, 11.15am and 6.00pm. Weekday services 8.15am and 5.15pm.

COGGESHALL GRANGE BARN

Tel: 01376 562226

Coggeshall, Colchester, Essex, CO6 1RE.
Owner: The National Trust   **Contact:** The Administrator
The oldest surviving timber framed barn in Europe, dating from around 1140, and originally part of the Cistercian Monastery of Coggeshall. It was restored in the 1980s by the Coggeshall Grange Barn Trust, Braintree District Council and Essex County Council. Features a small collection of farm carts and wagons.
Location: Signposted off A120 Coggeshall bypass.
Opening Times: 26 Mar - 29 Oct: Tues, Thurs, Sun and BH Mon, 1.00pm - 5.00pm.
Admission: £1.10, parties 90p, joint ticket with Paycocke's £2.00.

COLCHESTER CASTLE MUSEUM

Tel: 01206 712937

14 Ryegate Road, Colchester, Essex, CO1 1YG.
Owner: Colchester Borough Council   **Contact:** The Resource Centre
The largest Norman Castle Keep in Europe with fine archaeological collections on show. In Colchester town centre, off A12.
Location: In Colchester town centre, off A12.
Opening Times: Mar - Nov, Mon - Sat, 10.00am - 5.00pm. Sun 2.00pm - 5.00pm.
Admission: Adult £2.50, Child £1.50, Family £7, Conc £1.50, Groups of 20 or more booked in advance £1.20.

FLATFORD BRIDGE COTTAGE

Tel: 01206 298260

Flatford, East Bergholt, Colchester, Essex, C07 60L.
Owner: The National Trust   **Contact:** The Administrator
Just upstream from Flatford Mill, the restored thatched cottage houses a display about John Constable, several of whose paintings depict this property. Facilities include a tea garden, shop, boat hire and an Information Centre.
Location: On N bank of Stour, 1m S of East Bergholt B1070.
Opening Times: 25 Mar - end May & Oct: Wed to Sun & BH Mon 11.00am - 5.30pm. Jun - end Sept: daily 10.00am - 5.30pm (closed Good Fri). Nov: Wed to Sun 11.00am - 3.30pm.
Admission: Guided tours £1.50, accompanied children free.

GOSFIELD HALL

Tel: 01787 472914

Gosfield, Halstead, Essex, CO9 1SF.
Owner: Country Houses Association   **Contact:** Mr G Brown
Very fine Tudor gallery.
Location: On the A1017 between Braintree and Sible Hedingham. 2¹/₂ m SW of Halstead.
Opening Times: 1 May - 30 Sept, Wed and Thur, 2.00pm - 5.00pm. Guided tours of the house 2.30pm - 3.15pm.
Admission: Adult £2.50, Child under 12 £1, Group driver and organiser free.

HARWICH REDOUBT

Tel: 01255 503429

The Harbour, Harwich, Essex.
Owner: The Harwich Society   **Contact:** Mr Sheard
180ft diameter circular fort built in 1808 to defend the port against Napoleonic invasion. Being restored by Harwich Society and part is a museum. Eleven guns and battlements.
Location: On the A1017 between Braintree and Sible Hedingham. 2¹/₂ m SW of Halstead.
Opening Times: Every Sun throughout the year.
Admission: Adult £1.00, Accompanied child free.

HEDINGHAM CASTLE

See page 56 for full page entry.

INGATESTONE HALL

OPEN

15 April - 24 Sept.
Fri, Sat, Sun and
Bank Holiday
Mondays
Also
12 July - 31 August
Wed & Thurs.
1 - 6pm.

Tel: 01277 353010
Fax: 01245 248979

HALL LANE, INGATESTONE, ESSEX CM4 9NR
Owner: The Lord Petre   *Contact:* Phillip Paterson
16th century mansion, set in 11 acres of grounds (formal garden and wild walk), built by Sir William Petre, Secretary of State to four tudor monarchs, which has remained in the hands of his family ever since. The 2 Priests' hiding places can be seen, as well as the furniture, portraits and family memorabilia accumulated over the centuries.
Location: Off A12 between Brentwood & Chelmsford. Take Station Lane at the London end of High Street, cross level crossing and continue for ¹/₂ mile.
Admission: Adult £3.50, OAP and Students £3.00, Child £2.00. Under 5's Free. 50p per head discount for parties of 20+. Family Ticket (admits five including up to 3 adults) £10.50.

LAYER MARNEY TOWER

See page 57 for full page entry.

LOWER DAIRY HOUSE GARDEN

Tel: 01206 262220

Water Lane, Nayland, Colchester, Essex, CO6 4JS.
Owner: D J Burnett Esq   **Contact:** D J Burnett Esq
Plantsman's garden, approx 1¹/₂ acres.
Location: 7m N of Colchester off A134.
Opening Times: Apr; 1/2, 8/9, 15/16/17, 29/30. May; 6/7/8, 20/21, 27/28/29. Jun; 3/4, 10/11, 17/18, 24/25. Jul; 1/2, 8/9. 2.00pm - 6.00pm.
Admission: Adult £1.50, Child 50p, Groups welcome by appointment.

MISTLEY TOWERS

Tel: 01206 393884

Colchester, Essex.
Owner: English Heritage   **Contact:** Mrs G Owens
The remains of one of only two churches designed by the great architect Robert Adam. Built in 1776, it is unusual in having towers at both the east and west ends.
Location: On B1352, 11/2 m E of A137 at Lawford, 9m E of Cholchester.
Opening Times: Apr; 1/2, 8/9, 15/16/17, 29/30. May; 6/7/8, 20/21, 27/28/29. Jun; 3/4, 10/11, 17/18, 24/25. Jul; 1/2, 8/9. 2.00pm - 6.00pm.
Admission: Tel: 01206 393884 for times.

MOYNS PARK

See page 58 for full page entry.

PAYCOCKE'S

Tel: 01376 561305

West Street, Coggeshall, Colchester, Essex, C06 1NS.

Owner: The National Trust   **Contact:** The Tenant

A merchant's house, dating from about 1500, with unusually rich panelling and wood carving. A display of lace for which Coggeshall was famous is on show. Delightful garden leading down to small river.

Location: Signposted off A120.

Opening Times: 26 Mar - 29 Oct: Tues, Thurs, Sun & BH Mon, 2.00pm - 5.30pm, last admission 5.00pm.

Admission: £1.40, parties of 6+ by prior arrangement, no reduction for parties. Joint ticket with Coggeshall Grange Barn £2.00.

PRIORS HALL BARN

Tel: 01842 750714

Widdington, Newport, Essex.

Owner: English Heritage   **Contact:** The Administrator

One of the finest surviving medieval barns in south east England and representative of the group of aisled barns centred on north west Essex.

Location: In Widdington, on unclassified road 2m SE of Newport, of B1383.

Opening Times: Apr; 1/2, 8/9, 15/16/17, 29/30. May; 6/7/8, 20/21, 27/28/29. Jun; 3/4, 10/11, 17/18, 24/25. Jul; 1/2, 8/9. 2.00pm - 6.00pm.

Admission: Telephone for details of opening on 01842 750714.

WALTHAM ABBEY GATEHOUSE AND BRIDGE

Waltham Abbey, Essex.

Owner: English Heritage   **Contact:** The Administrator

The late 14th century abbey gatehouse, part of the north range of the cloister and the medieval "Harold's Bridge" of one of the great monastic foundations of the Middle Ages.

Location: 1/2m E of Tilbury off A126.

Opening Times: Any reasonable time.

RHS GARDEN HYDE HALL

OPEN

26 March - 29 Oct

Weds, Thurs,
Sats, Sun and
Bank Holidays

11.00am - 6.00pm

Tel: 01245 400256
Fax: 01245 401363

RETTENDON, NR. CHELMSFORD, ESSEX

Owner: The Royal Horticultural Society

A charming hilltop garden which extends to over eight acres. Highlights include the gold garden, the modern tall and intermediate bearded irises in late May, and the rope walk of climbing roses and large beds ablaze with floribunda and hybrid tea roses in midsummer. There is also a small plant centre and delightful refreshment facilities are available when the garden is open.

Location: Rettendon, six miles South East of Chelmsford. Signed off the A130.

Admission: Adults £2.50, Child (under 6) Free, Child (6 - 16) 50p, Groups of 20+ £2.00

SALING HALL GARDEN

Tel: 01371 850 243   **Fax**: 01371 850 274

Great Saling, Braintree, Essex, CM7 5DT.

Owner: Hugh Johnson Esq   **Contact:** Hugh Johnson Esq

12 acres of walled garden dated 1698. Extensive new collection of unusual plants with emphasis on trees.

Location: 6m NW of Braintree, 2m N of A120.

Opening Times: Jun and Jul, Wed, 2.00pm - 5.00pm. Sun 25 Jun, 2.00pm - 6.00pm.

Admission: Standard £2, Child free.

TILBURY FORT

Tel: 01375 858489

Tilbury, Essex.

Owner: English Heritage   **Contact:** The Administrator

The best and largest example of 17th century military engineering in England, commanding the Thames and showing the development of fortifications over the following 200 years. Exhibitions, the powder magazine and the bunker-like 'casemates' demonstrate how the fort protected London from seaborne attack.

Location: 1/2m E of Tilbury off A126.

Opening Times: 1 Apr - 30 Sept, daily 10.00am - 6.00pm, 1 Oct - 31 Oct, daily, 10.00am - 4.00pm, 1 Nov - 31 Mar, Wed - Sun, 10.00am - 4.00pm, (Closed 24 - 26 Dec, 1 Jan). Lunchtime closure 1.00pm - 2.00pm.

Admission: Adult £1.80, Child £1.40, Conc 90p.

Audley End House, Essex

BERKELEY CASTLE
Berkeley

Not many can boast of having their private house celebrated by Shakespeare nor of having held it in the possession of their family for nearly 850 years, nor having a King of England murdered within its walls, nor of having welcomed at their table the local vicar and Castle Chaplain, John Trevisa (1342-1402), reputed as one of the earliest translators of the Bible, nor of having a breach battered by Oliver Cromwell, which to this day it is forbidden by law to repair even if it was wished to do so. But such is the story of Berkeley.

This beautiful and historic Castle, begun in 1117, still remains the home of the famous family who gave their name to numerous locations all over the word, notably Berkeley Square in London, Berkeley Hundred in Virginia and Berkeley University in California. Scene of the brutal murder of Edward II in 1327 (visitors can see his cell and nearby the dungeon) and besieged by Cromwell's troops in 1645, the Castle is steeped in history but twenty-four generations of Berkeleys have gradually transformed a Norman fortress into the lovely home it is today.

The State Apartments contain magnificent collections of furniture, rare paintings by primarily English and Dutch masters, and tapestries. Part of the world-famous Berkeley silver is on display in the Dining Room. Many other rooms are equally interesting including the Great Hall upon which site the Barons of the West Country met in 1215 before going to Runnymede to force King John to put his seal to the Magna Carta.

The Castle is surrounded by lovely terraced Elizabethan Gardens with a lilypond, Elizabeth I's bowling green, and sweeping lawns.

SUITABILITY FOR OTHER EVENTS
Wedding receptions, fashion shows, corporate entertainment, receptions, filming.

EXTRA FACILITIES
Butterfly farm; hundreds of exotic butterflies in free flight.

ADVICE TO COURIERS & DRIVERS
No photography allowed inside the Castle. No dogs admitted beyond car park. Evening parties by arrangement. GROUP VISITS MUST BE BOOKED.

FACILITIES FOR THE DISABLED
In exceptional circumstances disabled/elderly visitors may alight in the Outer Bailey. No toilet facilities for the disabled.

PARKING FOR COACHES & CARS
Free Car Park: 150 yds from the Castle. Up to 15 coaches can be parked 250 yds from the Castle.

CATERING
Tea Rooms serving light lunches and home-made teas. Separate room for up to 60 people (pre-book groups).

GUIDED TOURS
At no extra charge. Max. size 120. Min. tour time 1 hour.

GIFT SHOP
Open at the same time as the Castle. It is well-stocked with quality gifts for adults and children.

GUIDE BOOKS
Colour guide book by Vita Sackville West £1.50. Special children's guide book.

SCHOOL VISITS/CHILDREN
School groups welcome. The Castle has much of interest for all age groups, in particular general history, social history and architecture. School groups visiting the Castle have free admission to Butterfly Farm.

CONFERENCE AND FUNCTION FACILITIES

ROOM	DIMENSIONS	CAPACITY	LAYOUT	POWER POINTS	SUITABLE FOR A/V
Great Hall		128	Dinner	2	✓
		160	Theatre style		
		200	Reception		
		100	School room style		
Long Drawing Room		100	Reception	2	✓
		40	Dinner		
		40	School room style		

CONTACT

The Custodian
Berkeley Castle
Gloucestershire
GL13 9BQ

Tel: (01453) 810332

LOCATION

Midway between Bristol and Gloucester, just off the A38.

From motorway M5 use exit 14 (5 miles) or exit 13 (9 miles).

Bus: No 308 from Bristol and Gloucester

OPENING TIMES

Summer
Open Bank Holiday Mondays
11.00am - 5.00pm

April
Daily   2.00 - 5.00pm
(except Mons)

May - Sept
Tue - Sat
11.00am - 5.00pm
Sundays   2.00 - 5.00pm

Winter
October
Suns only   2 - 4.30pm

November - March
Closed

NB Groups must book

ADMISSION

Summer
HOUSE & GARDEN
Adult £4.00
Child £2.00
OAP £3.20
Groups (min 25 people)
Adult £3.50
Child(5-16yrs) £1.80
OAP £3.00
BUTTERFLY FARM
Adult £1.00
Child/OAP £0.50

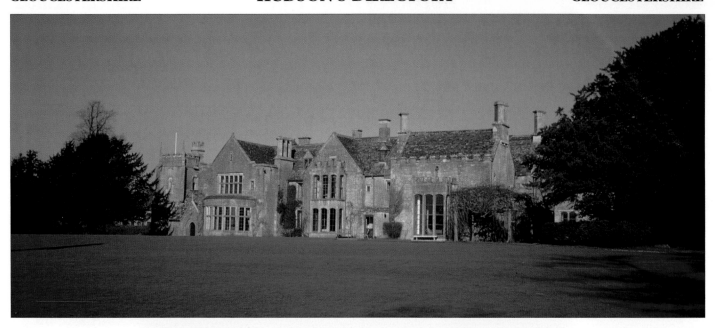

CHAVENAGE
Tetbury

D Lowsley - Williams
Chavenage
Tetbury
Gloucestershire
GL8 8XP

Tel: (01666) 502329
Fax: (01453) 836778

LOCATION

Less than 20 miles from M4 Junctions 16, 17 or 18. Signed from Tetbury ($1^3/4$ miles) on the B4104. Less than 15 miles from M5 junction 13 or 14. Signed from the A46 (Stroud -Bath road)

Rail: Kemble Station, 7 miles.

Taxi: Tetbury Cars, Tetbury 503393

CHAVENAGE is a wonderful Elizabethan house of mellow grey Cotswold stone and tiles which contains much of interest for the discerning visitor.

The approach aspect of Chavenage is virtually as it was left by Edward Stephens in 1576. Only two families have owned Chavenage; the present owners since 1891 and the Stephens family before them. A Colonel Nathaniel Stephens, M.P. for Gloucestershire during the Civil War was cursed for supporting Cromwell giving rise to legends of weird happenings at Chavenage since that time.

Inside Chavenage there are many interesting rooms housing tapestries, fine furniture, pictures and many relics of the Cromwellian period. Of particular note are the Main Hall,

where a contemporary screen forms a minstrel's gallery and two tapestry rooms where it is said Cromwell was lodged.

Recently Chavenage has been used as a location for T.V. and film productions including a Hercule Poirot story 'The Mysterious Affair at Styles Manor', many episodes of the sequel to 'Are you Being Served' now called 'Grace & Favour' a "Gotcha" for 'The Noel Edmunds House Party' and an episode of "The House of Elliot".

Chavenage is especially suitable for those wishing an intimate, personal tour, usually conducted by the owner, or for small groups wanting a change from large establishments. It also provides a charming venue for small conferences and functions.

SUITABILITY FOR OTHER EVENTS
Corporate entertaining. Clay pigeon shooting, archery, cross-bows, pistol shooting, A.T.V. driving, weddings, dinners, lunches, small fashion shows, concerts, plays, seminars, filming, product launching, photography.

ADVICE TO COURIERS & DRIVERS
Coaches only by appointment. Stop at the front gates for instructions as to parking.

PARKING
Up to 100 cars and 2-3 coaches.

FACILITIES FOR THE DISABLED
Ground floor accessible to 'chairs'. There are toilet facilities for the disabled.

CATERING
In-house catering available for Weddings, functions, lunches, teas, dinners and picnics by arrangement.

GUIDED TOURS
Normally the owner gives a guided tour to all visitors. Larger groups are given a talk about the house prior to viewing on their own but with the owner present to answer questions. (No extra charge for the above services). Couriers and group leaders should arrange the format required prior to the visit.

GUIDE BOOKS
New colour guide book available.

SCHOOL VISITS/CHILDREN
School groups are welcome. Chairs can be arranged for lecturing. Tour of working farm, modern dairy and corn facilities can be arranged.

Summer
May - Sept,
Easter Sun & Mon
and Bank Holidays

Mon Bank Hols only
2.00 - 5.00pm

Weds, Thurs, Sats, Suns
2.00 - 5.00pm

NB Open at other times by prior arrangement for groups.

Winter
October - March
By appointment only
for groups.

Summer
Adult £2.50
Child (0 - 16 yrs). . .£1.25
Friend of HHA . .Free

CONCESSIONS
By prior arrangement, concessions may be given to groups of 20+ and also to disabled and to exceptional cases.

Winter
Groups only: Rates by arrangement.

CONFERENCE AND FUNCTION FACILITIES

ROOM	DIMENSIONS	CAPACITY	LAYOUT	POWER POINTS	SUITABLE FOR A/V
Ballroom	70' x 30'	100	Theatre	8	
		120	Schoolroom		
		70	U-shape		
		26	Boardroom		
		100	Dinner/Dance		
		100	Lunch/Buffet		
Oak Room	25 'x 20'	30	Schoolroom	4	
		16	U-shape		
		12	Boardroom		

STANWAY HOUSE
Cheltenham

STANWAY, home of Lord Neidpath, is a jewel of Cotswold Manor houses, very much lived in rather than a museum.

All rooms visited are used daily and there is an atmosphere of stepping back in time. Most of the furniture has been in the house since it was built. The paintings, nearly all family portraits give a vivid impression of Stanway's often colourful owners and their relatives over five centuries - for instance one was a gunpowder plotter, two died in "drinking match", one was sentenced to death for rape and one sat in Parliament for a (record) 72 years.

Visit the Audit Room where Estate tenants still assemble every quarter day to pay their rent in person; the Great Hall with its funeral hatchments and 23ft shuffleboard table; the drawing room with its Chippendale Chinese Day Beds.

The evocative landscape includes a typical village cricket field (with a pavilion built by Sir James (Peter Pan) Barrie - a frequent guest). The mellow Jacobean architecture, the exquisite Gatehouse, the old Brewery, the Medieval Tithe Barn, the Pyramid and formal landscape contribute to the timeless charm of one of the most romantic and beautiful houses in England.

❖

CONTACT

Liz Foley
Stanway House
Stanway
Cheltenham
Gloucestershire
GL54 5PQ

Tel: (01386) 584469

LOCATION

From London M40, A40 to Burford, A424 to Stow, B4077 towards Tewkesbury. Stanway is 9 miles past Stow. London, 2 hours.

Motorway: M5 Exit 9, approx 8 miles. (Take A438 towards Stow).

SUITABILITY FOR OTHER EVENTS
Stanway House is suitable for fashion shows, archery, clay pigeon shooting, equestrian events, garden parties, rallies, shows, filming and wedding receptions.

EXTRA FACILITIES
These include: Piano, parkland, farm, fields, cricket pitch, arboretum and old mill.

ADVICE TO COURIERS & DRIVERS
No unaccompanied children. No dogs or photography. Morning coffee and biscuits or afternoon tea with sandwiches and cakes can be provided for pre-booked groups on days when the house is not open to the public.

FACILITIES FOR THE DISABLED
There are no toilet facilities for the disabled.

PARKING FOR COACHES & CARS
Capacity of the car park: 200 cars and 5 coaches, 20 yds from the House.

CATERING
For special functions/conferences, buffets, lunches and dinners can be arranged. Teas are available during opening hours, at the Old Bakehouse in the village from June - August.

GUIDED TOURS
Tours can be arranged for up to 70 people. During winter cost per tour £4.50 per head. Tea or coffee and tour £5.50 per head. Tours are available in French. If requested, the owner may meet groups visiting the House. Average time taken for tour 1$\frac{1}{4}$ hours.

GUIDE BOOKS
A guide book can be purchased, price £1.00.

SCHOOL VISITS/CHILDREN
Groups of children are welcome. Cost per child £1.00. If requested a guide can be provided. There are nature walks.

CONFERENCE AND FUNCTION FACILITIES

ROOM	DIMENSIONS	CAPACITY	LAYOUT	POWER POINTS	SUITABLE FOR A/V
Great Hall	40' x 25'	100	Buffet	5	✓
		50	Boardroom		
		40	Lunch/Dinner		
Dining Room	25' x 20'	25	Boardroom	3	✓
		20	Lunch/Dinner		
Tithe Barn	90' x 30'	300	Various	4	✓

OPENING TIMES

Summer
June - September
Mon, Wed
By appointment

Tues, Thur
2.00pm - 5.00pm

Fri, Sat, Sun
By appointment

Winter
Open by appointment for guided tours only.

ADMISSION

Summer

Adult £3.00
Child* £1.00
OAP £2.50
Student £2.50

Groups**
Adult £2.50
Child* £1.00
OAP £2.50
Student £2.50

** Min payment £50.00

Winter (Tours only)

HOUSE & GARDEN
Adult £4.50
Child* £3.50
OAP £4.50
Student £4.00

HOUSE & GARDEN
WITH TEA
Adult £5.50
Child* £4.00
OAP £5.50
Student £5.50

* Under 16

SUDELEY CASTLE
Winchcombe

CONTACT

Sudeley Castle
Winchcombe
Nr Cheltenham
Gloucestershire
GL54 5JD

Tel: (01242) 602308
Fax: (01242) 602959

LOCATION

8 Miles Northeast of
Cheltenham on B4632.
From Bristol or
Birmingham M5, Exit 9.
Take A438 towards
Stow-on-the-Wold.

Bus: Castleways to
Winchcombe.

Rail: Cheltenham
Station 8 miles.

Set against the picturesque splendour of rolling Cotswold hills, Sudeley Castle is one of England's great historic houses.

Sudeley has royal connections stretching back 1000 years. Once the property of King Ethelred the Unready, Sudeley was later the magnificent palace of Queen Katherine Parr, who is buried in the Castle Church.

Henry V111, Anne Boleyn, Lady Jane Grey and Elizabeth I stayed at the Castle, Charles I resided here while Prince Rupert established Sudeley as his headquarters during the Civil War.

During the Victorian era, a sympathetic programme of reconstruction enhanced Sudeley's earlier magnificence. Today the Castle is home to Lord and Lady Ashcombe. Among a wealth of history on show is an impressive collection of art treasures including masterpieces by Turner, Van Dyck and Rubens.

SUITABILITY FOR OTHER EVENTS
Wedding receptions, filming, concerts, product launches, exclusive banquets, corporate entertainment, fashion shows.

EXTRA FACILITIES
A wide range corporate events, such as a vintage car treasure trail, clay pigeon shooting and archery can be arranged.

ACCOMMODATION
16 holiday cottages, each accommodating 2 - 7 people.

ADVICE TO COURIERS & DRIVERS
Coach operators: meal vouchers plus rest room with TV. No dogs, photography or video cameras in the Castle. Colour guide book available, £2.50. Parking for 1,000 cars

GARDENS

There are eight delightful gardens where visitors can wander at leisure through avenues of majestic trees, wide stretches of still water, grand yew hedges and fragrant roses.

Centrepiece of the gardens is the famous Queens Garden - reconstructed from the original Tudor parterre which has been planted with old fashioned roses in herb edged beds, flanked by dramatic 15ft high, double yew hedges. The other gardens to visit include those set against the backdrop of the 15th century Tithe Barn ruins featuring Roses, Clematis and Wisteria; the Secret Garden by the Church with Shrubs and Annuals; the White Garden with climbing Roses and Perennials; the Mulberry Garden; the Banqueting Hall Ruins Garden with Rosemary, Lavenders and Box Hedge and the Knot Garden.

Special Events for 1995 include Open Air Theatre, Concerts, Special Plant Fair and Falconry.

❖

and 50 coaches.

CASTLE SHOP
Gift shop and specialist plant centre open 10.30 - 5.30pm.

CATERING
The Stableyard Restaurant can cater for up to 130 people for morning coffee, lunches and afternoon tea. Meals can be booked if required in advance with menus available on request. Receptions, dinner and medieval banquets can be arranged within the Castle apartments .

GUIDED TOURS
By prior arrangement only. Guide Book £2.50

SCHOOL VISITS/CHILDREN
Worksheets available on request. For a small fee a preliminary talk can be given in the Church. A guide can be provided on request. Areas of particular interest include: Adventure playground and wildfowl.

CONFERENCE AND FUNCTION FACILITIES

ROOM	DIMENSIONS	CAPACITY	LAYOUT	POWER POINTS	SUITABLE FOR A/V
Chandos Hall		40	Boardroom	✓	✓
		50	Theatre		
		100	Reception		
		60	Dining		
Medieval Hall		20	Boardroom	✓	✓
		50	Reception		
		24	Dining		
Library		50	Boardroom	✓	✓
		80	Theatre		
		100	Reception		
		50	Dining		
Banqueting Hall		100	Reception	✓	
		80	Dining		

OPENING TIMES

Summer
March
GARDENS, PLANT
CENTRE & SHOP
Daily
11.00am - 4.00pm

1 April - 31 October
GARDENS, CHURCH,
EXHIBITION CENTRE,
SHOP & PLANT CENTRE
Daily 10.30am - 5.30pm

RESTAURANT
Daily 10.30am - 5.00pm

CASTLE APARTMENTS.
Daily 11.00am - 5.00pm

Winter
1 Dec - 21 Dec
SHOP & PLANT CENTRE
Daily 11.00am - 3.30pm.

ADMISSION

Summer
CASTLE & GARDEN
  Adult £4.95
  Child (5-15 yrs.) . . £2.75
  OAP £4.55
  Family £13.00
  (2 Adults & 2 children)
Groups (min 20 people)
  Adult £3.80
  Child (5-15 yrs.) . . . £2.00
  OAP £3.50
GARDENS ONLY
  Adult £3.35
  Child (5-15 yrs.) . . £1.60
  OAP £2.95
SEASON
  Adult £19.00
  Child £9.50
  Family £36.00
  Gardens £12.00
ADVENTURE PLAY-
GROUND ONLY . . .£0.75

ASHELWORTH TITHE BARN
Tel: 01684 850051

Ashelworth, Gloucestershire.
Owner: The National Trust   **Contact:** The Administrator
A 15th century tithe barn with two projecting porch bays and fine roof timbers with queen-posts.
Location: 6m N of Gloucester, 1¼ E of Hartpury A417.
Opening Times: Apr - end Oct: daily 9.00am - 6.00pm or sunset if earlier. Closed Good Fri, other times by prior appointment only.
Admission: 60p.

HAILES ABBEY
Tel: 01242 602398

Winchcombe, Cheltenham, Gloucestershire, GL54 5PB.
Owner: English Heritage   **Contact:** The Administrator
Seventeen cloister arches and extensive excavated remains in lovely surroundings of an abbey founded by Richard, Earl of Cornwall, in 1246. There is a small museum and covered display area.
Location: 2m NE of Winchcombe off B4632.
Opening Times: 1 Apr - end Oct, daily 10.00am - 6.00pm, 1 Nov - 31 Mar, Wed - Sun, 10.00am - 4.00pm, (Closed 24 - 26 Dec, 1 Jan).
Admission: Adult £2.00, Child £1.00, Conc £1.50, Family £5.50.

BARNSLEY HOUSE GARDENS

OPEN

Garden only

Every Mon, Wed, Thur, Sat. all year round.

10.00am - 6.00pm

Nursery open Mon - Sat.

Tel: 01285 740281
Fax: 01285 740628

CIRENCESTER, GLOUCESTERSHIRE GL7 5EE
Owner: Charles Verey   Contact: RosemaryVerey

Mature 4½ acre garden designed by Rosemary Verey with interesting collection of trees and shrubs; spring bulbs and autumn colour, mixed borders, knot garden, herbs, laburnam walk (late May to early June). Decorative vegetable garden. Garden furniture by Charles Verey. Fountain and statues by Simon Verity. 18th century wall and summerhouses. Winner (1988) HHA/Christies award.

Location: In Barnsley village - 4 miles north east of Cirencester on B4425.
Admission: Adult £2.00, OAP £1.00, Child free. No charge in December & January.

HIDCOTE MANOR GARDENS

National Trust / K. Statham

OPEN

April to 31 Oct Daily except Tues & Fri 11.00am - 7.00pm

Last admission 6.00pm or 1 hour before sunset if earlier.

Closed Good Friday.

Tel: 01386 438333

CHIPPING CAMPDEN, GLOUCESTERSHIRE
Owner: The National Trust   Contact: The National Trust

One of the most delightful gardens in England, created this century by the great horticulturist Major Lawrence Johnston; a series of small gardens within the whole separated by walls and hedges of different species; famous for rare shrubs, trees, herbaceous borders, 'old' roses and interesting plant species.

Location: 4 miles north east of Chipping Campden, 1 mile east of B4632 (originally A46) off B4081.
Admission: Adult £5.00, Child £2.50, Family Ticket £13.75.

BATSFORD ARBORETUM
Tel: 01608 650722   **Fax**: 01608 650290

Moreton-in-the-Marsh, Gloucestershire, GL56 9QF.
Owner: The Batsford Foundation   **Contact:** Polly Blick
50 acres containing over 1,000 species of trees and shrubs.
Location: 1½m NW of Moreton-in-Marsh off A44 to Broadway Rd.
Opening Times: Mar - mid-Nov, daily, 10.00am - 5.00pm.
Admission: Adult £2.00, Child £1.50, Child under 14 free, Senior citizens £1.50. Party bookings by prior arrangement at £1.50 pp for 12 plus.

BERKELEY CASTLE
See page 61 for full page entry.

BLACKFRIARS
Tel: 01608 650722   **Fax**: 01608 650290

Southgate Street, Gloucester.
Owner: English Heritage   **Contact:** The Administrator
A small Dominican priory church converted into a rich merchant's house at the Dissolution. Most of the original 13th century church remains, including a rare scissor-braced roof.
Location: In Ladybellegate St, off Southgate St and Blackfriars Walk.
Opening Times: 1 Apr - 30 Sept, weekdays only, 10.00am - 3.30pm. (Closed Bank Holidays and following Tuesdays).

CHAVENAGE
See page 62 for full page entry.

CHEDWORTH ROMAN VILLA
Tel: 01242 890256

Yanworth, Cheltenham, Gloucestershire, GL54 3LJ.
Owner: The National Trust   **Contact:** The Administrator
The remains of a Romano British villa, excavated 1864. Set in beautiful wooded combe. Includes fine 4th century mosaics, two bath houses, spring with temple. A museum houses the smaller finds.
Location: 3m NW of Fossebridge on A429.
Opening Times: Mar - end Oct: Tues to Sun & BH Mon, 10.00am - 5.30pm, last admission 5.00pm. 1 Nov - 3 Dec: Wed to Sun, 11.00am - 4.00pm, also 9 & 10 Dec.
Admission: £2.70, Family £7.40. Pre-booked parties by arrangement, no reduction.

KELMSCOTT MANOR

OPEN

April - Sept Every Wednesday 11.00am - 1.00pm and 2.00 - 5.00pm

Thursdays and Fridays by appointment.

Tel: 01367 252486
Fax: 01367 253754

KELMSCOTT, NR. LECHLADE, GLOUCESTERSHIRE GL7 3HJ
Owner: Society of Antiquaries   Contact: Mrs Helen Webb

Kelmscott Manor was the country home of William Morris, poet, craftsman and socialist - from 1871 until his death in 1896. The house contains an interesting collection of the possessions and works of Morris and his associates including furniture, textiles, carpets and ceramics.

Location: 2 miles south East of Lechlade off the Lechlade/Faringdon Road.
Admission: Adults £5.00, Children up to 16 and full-time students £2.50.

KIFTSGATE COURT GARDENS

OPEN

1 Apr - 30 Sept
Wed, Thur and Suns
2.00 - 6.00pm
also Sats in
June & July
2.00 - 6.00pm
and Bank Hol Mons
2.00 - 6.00pm
Coaches by
appointment only.

Tel: 01386 438777

CHIPPING CAMDEN, GLOUCESTERSHIRE GL55 6LW

Owner: Mr and Mrs J.G Chambers   *Contact:* J.G. Chambers

Magnificently situated garden on the edge of the Cotswold escarpment with views towards the Malvern Hills. Many unusual shrubs and plants including trees peonies, abutilons, specie and old fashioned roses. Tea room with light refreshments from Spring Bank Holiday to August Bank Holiday. Unusual plants for sale on opening days.

Location: 3 miles North East of Chipping Campden.
Admission: Adult £3.00, Child £1.00.

OWLPEN MANOR

OPEN

2 April - 30 Sept
Tues, Thurs, Sun &
Bank Hol. Mons.
2.00 - 5.00pm

Also Wed, in
July and August
2.00 - 5.00pm

Tel: 01453 860261
Fax: 01453 860819

ULEY, NR DURSLEY, GLOUCESTERSHIRE GL11 5BZ

Owner: Mr and Mrs Nicholas Mander   *Contact:* Mrs M Turnbull

Romantic Tudor manor house, 1450-1616, with some Cotswold Arts and Crafts restoration. Remote wooded valley setting, with 16th and 17th century formal terraced gardens and magnificent yews. Contains unique painted cloth wall hangings, family collections. Mill (1726), Court House (1620); licensed restaurant in medieval tithe barn. Fine Victorian estate church. Nine period holiday cottages. Corporate events. "Owlpen - ah, what a dream is there!" - Vita Sackville-West

Location: 3 miles east of Dursley, 1 mile east of Uley, off B4066, by Old Crown pub.
Admission: Adult £3.25, Child £1.50.

LITTLEDEAN HALL

Tel: 01594 824 213

Littledean, Gloucestershire, GL14 3NR.
Owner: D M Macer Wright Esq   **Contact:** D M Macer Wright Esq
An early house with 17th century interiors. Site of Roman temple.
Location: 2m S of Cinderford off A4151.
Opening Times: 1 Apr - 31 Oct, daily, 10.30am - 6.00pm.
Admission: Adult £2.50, Child £1.25, Groups £2 pp (by appointment).

LYDNEY PARK GARDENS

Tel: 01594 842 884

Lydney, Gloucestershire, GL15 6BU.
Owner: The Viscount Bledisloe   **Contact:** Mrs Beryl Butcher
8 acres of extensive valley gardens with trees and lakes. Roman temple site and museum.
Location: 2m S of Cinderford off A4151. On A48 between Lydney and Aylburton.
Opening Times: Easter - 4 Jun, Sun, BHs and Wed, 11 am - 6pm. Garden closed 21 May.
Admission: Adult £2.00 (Wed £1), Child free, Carpark free, Groups of 25 + (min) by appointment.

PAINSWICK ROCOCO GARDENS

THE STABLES, PAINSWICK HOUSE, PAINSWICK, GLOUCESTERSHIRE GL6 6TH

Owner: Painswick Rococo
Garden Trust
Contact: P.R Moir

Tel: 01452 813204

Unique 18th century garden restoration situated in a hidden 6 acre Cotswold combe. Charming contemporary buildings are juxtaposed with winding woodland walks and formal vistas. Famous for its early spring show of snowdrops. Coffee, light lunches and teas.

Location: 1/2 mile outside village of Painswick on B4073

Admission: Adult £2.60, Senior Citizens £2.20, Child £1.30

OPEN

2nd Wed in Jan to 30 Nov.
Wed - Sun and Bank Hols.
11.00am - 5.00pm

MISARDEN PARK GARDENS

OPEN

5 April - 29 Sept
Tuesdays,
Wednesdays,
Thursdays

9.30am - 4.30pm

Tel: 01285 821303
Fax: 01285 821530

STROUD

Owner: Major M T N H Wills   *Contact:* Major M T N H Wills

Noted in the spring for its bulbs and flowering trees and in mid summer for the large double herbaceous borders. Fine topiary throughout and a traditional rose garden. Outstanding position, standing high overlooking the "Golden Valley". Garden nurseries open daily (except Mondays). Garden featured in Country Life 1992.

Location: 6 miles north west Cirencester. Follow signs off A417 from Gloucester or Cirencester or B4070 from Stroud.
Admission: Adult £2.00 children free. 10% reduction for groups (20 or more) who book in advance.

RODMARTON MANOR

Tel: 01285 841253

Cirencester, Gloucestershire, GL7 6PF.
Owner: Simon Biddulph Esq   **Contact:** Simon Biddulph Esq
Rodmarton Manor was one of the last country houses to be built in the old traditional style when everything was done by hand with local stone, wood and metal. Built by Ernest Barnsley, for Claud and Margaret Biddulph between 1909 and 1929 it is the finest example of the Cotswold tradition showing the quality and splendour of Craftsmanship in stone, wood and metal. Here there is beautifully constructed and hand painted furniture, pottery, appliqué work and finely crafted stone and iron work.
Location: Cirencester.
Opening Times: House: open to groups by prior written appointment. Garden: 13 May - 26 Aug, 2.00pm - 5.00pm and at other times by appointment.
Admission: Conducted tour of house with unconducted tour of garden is £4.00 pp (£2 child under 16). Minimum of 7 or minimum charge £28.00.

SEZINCOTE

Tel: 01386 700444

Moreton-in-Marsh, Gloucestershire, GL56 9AW.
Owner: D Peake Esq   **Contact:** D Peake Esq
Exotic oriental water garden by Repton and Daniell. Large semi-circular orangery. House by S P Cockerell in Indian style was the inspiration for Brighton Pavilion.
Location: 1 1/2 m SW of Moreton-in-Marsh. Turn W along A44 to Evesham and left just before Bourton-on-the-Hill..
Opening Times: Garden: Thurs, Fri & Bank Hol Mons, 2.30pm - 6pm. House: May - Jul & Sept, 2 - 6pm.

SNOWSHILL MANOR

OPEN

Daily except Tues.
Apr & Oct
1 to 5.00pm
May to end Sept.
1 to 6.00pm
Grounds and visitor
facilities open from
12 Noon.
Closed Good Fri.
Last admissions to
house and restaurant
1/2hr before closing.
Timed tickets will be
issued for the house.

Tel: 01386 852410

SNOWSHILL, NR. BROADWAY, WORCESTERSHIRE WR12 7JU

Owner: The National Trust   *Contact: The National Trust*

A Tudor house with a c.1700 facade; 21 rooms containing Charles Paget Wade's collection of craftsmanship, including musical instruments, clocks, toys, bicycles, weavers' and spinners' tools, Japanese armour; small formal garden and Charles Wade's cottage.

Location: 3 miles south west of Broadway, turning off the A44. [150:SP096339].
Admission: Adult £5.00, Child £2.50, Family ticket £13.75 (2 adults, 1-4 children). Grounds restaurant and shop only £2.00.

STANWAY HOUSE   **See page 63 for full page entry.**

ST MARY'S CHURCH

Kempley, Ross-on-Wye, Gloucestershire.
Owner: English Heritage   **Contact:** The Administrator
A delightful Norman church with superb wall paintings from the 12th - 14th centuries which were only discovered beneath white-wash in 1871.
Location: 1^1/2 m SW of Moreton-in-Marsh. Turn W along A44 to Evesham. and left just before Bourton-on-the-Hill..
Opening Times: 1m N of Kempley off B4024, 6 m NE of Ross-on-Wye.

SUDELEY CASTLE   **See page 64 for full page entry.**

WESTBURY COURT GARDEN

OPEN

April to end Oct.
Wed. to Sun. and
Bank Hol. Mons
11.00am-6.00pm

Closed Good Friday.

Tel: 01452 760461

WESTBURY-ON-SEVERN, GLOUCESTERSHIRE

Owner: The National Trust   *Contact: The National Trust*

A formal water garden with canals and yew hedges, laid out between 1696 and 1705; the earliest of its kind remaining in England. Restored in 1971 and planted species dating from pre 1700 including apple, pear and plum trees.
Location: 9 miles south west of Gloucester on A48 [162: SO718138]
Admission: Adult £2.30, Child £1.15.

WESTONBIRT ARBORETUM   **Tel:** 01666 880220   **Tel:** 01666 880559

Tetbury, Gloucestershire, GL8 8QS.
Owner: The Forestry Commission   **Contact:** Mr A Russell
600 acres arboretum begun in 1829, now with 15,000 catalogued trees. Excellent visitor centre.
Location: 1^1/2 m SW of Moreton-in-Marsh. Turn W along A44 to Evesham. and left just before Bourton-on-the-Hill.
Opening Times: 365 days a year, 10.00am - 8.00pm (or dusk if earlier).
Admission: Adult £2.50, Child £1.00, Senior citizen £1.50.

WHITTINGTON COURT   **Tel:** 01242 820556

Whittington, Cheltenham, Gloucestershire, GL54 4HF.
Owner: Mrs J C Charleston   **Contact:** Mrs J Stringer
Elizabethan manor house. Family possessions.
Location: 4m E of Cheltenham on A40.
Opening Times: 15 - 30 Apr and 12 - 28 Aug, 2.00pm - 5.00pm daily.
Admission: Adult £2, Child £1, Senior citizen £1.50, Groups by arrangement at £3 per head, minimum charge £75.00.

WOODCHESTER PARK MANSION   **Tel:** 01453 750455

High Street, Stroud, Gloucestershire, GL5 1AP.
Owner: Woodchester Mansion Trust   **Contact:** Mr R Shipton
Gothic style mansion in secret wooded valley, started in 1856 but abandoned before completion.
Location: 5m S of Stroud on B4066.
Opening Times: First w/e each month from Easter - Oct and BH w/es 11.00am - 4.00pm.
Admission: Adult £3.00, Child under 12 £1.00, Student £2,.00 Groups by arrangement.

SPECIAL EVENTS DIARY

- **23rd April: Stanway House**
  Daffodil Show.

- **30th April - 1 May: Stanway House**
  Craft Fair.

- **4th June: Sudeley Castle**
  Falcons Fly at Sudeley.

- **4th - 8th July: Hidcote Manor Garden**
  Open Air Theatre - She Stoops to Conquer performed by the Gloucestershire County Players 7.30pm

- **7th - 8th July: Sudeley Castle**
  An evening of music in the gardens.

- **10th - 15th July: Chavenage**
  Shakespeare play on lawn. Covered seating.

- **14th - 15th July: Barnsley House Garden**
  "A Midsummer Night's Dream" performed in the garden.

- **16th July: Sudeley Castle**
  Court of Queen Elizabeth I.

- **16th July: Westbury Court Garden**
  Band Concert by Pillowell Silver Band - 7pm.

- **23rd July: Sudeley Castle**
  Specialist Plant Fair

- **13th August: Sudeley Castle**
  Falcons Fly at Sudeley.

- **19th - 20th August: Sudeley Castle**
  Open Air Festival Players - "A Winters Tale".

- **7th - 8th October: Stanway House**
  Craft Fair.

BEAULIEU
Beaulieu

BEAULIEU, in the beautiful New Forest between Bournemouth and Southampton, has been Lord Montagu's family home since 1538, when it was purchased by Lord Montagu's ancestor, Thomas Wriothesley, 1st Earl of Southampton. Palace House and gardens have been open to the public since 1952, when the present Lord Montagu inherited.

Beaulieu Abbey was founded in 1204 and, although most of the buildings were destroyed during the Dissolution, much of beauty and interest remains. The Domus, a fine remaining building, houses an exhibition which takes the visitor back to the ages of King John and medieval monastic life.

The inclusive admission to Beaulieu covers entry to the National Motor Museum, Palace House and Gardens, Beaulieu Abbey and Exhibition of Monastic Life.

SUITABILITY FOR OTHER EVENTS
Rallies, product launches, promotions, banquets, filming, outdoor events, exhibitions. Most requests considered.

EXTRA FACILITIES
Helicopter landing point, audio-visual facilities, lectures, private dining room of Palace House available for receptions, dinners, lunches etc., hardstanding exhibition arena adjacent to Motor Museum, veteran and vintage cars and buses available to transport guests.

ADVICE TO COURIERS & DRIVERS
During the season the very busy period is from 11.30am to 1.30pm. It is advisable to allow 2 hours or more for visits. Last admission 40 minutes before closing. On arrival at the Information Centre, where hostesses are on hand to welcome and assist you. Coach drivers should sign in at the Information Desk. Free admission is given to coach drivers and they receive a voucher which can be exchanged for food, drink and souvenirs. No dogs in the buildings.

FACILITIES FOR THE DISABLED
Disabled and elderly visitors may be left at the entrance to the Palace House, before parking in the allocated areas. There are toilets for the disabled. There are some concessions for handicapped parties. Wheelchairs are available at the Information Centre for use within the grounds.

PARKING FOR COACHES & CARS
Parking for 1,500 cars and 30 coaches.

CATERING
The Brabazon seats 300 in a self-service Restaurant and Bar. Open daily. Prices from £4 for tea and £7 for lunch. Groups can book in advance. Further details and menus available from Catering Manager (01590) 612102.

GUIDED TOURS
Attendants on duty in Palace House and National Motor Museum. Guided tours by prior arrangement.

GIFT SHOP
Information Centre Shop, open as property. Palace House Shop, Kitchen Shop, Herb Shop, Abbey Shop open Summer only. Gifts include motoring items, books, comestibles and toiletries.

GUIDE BOOKS
Colour guide books available.

SCHOOL VISITS/CHILDREN
Beaulieu offers an extensive education service to student groups of all ages. Professionally qualified staff are available to assist in planning of visits to all attractions. Services include introductory talks, films, guided tours, role play and extended projects.

In general, educational services incur no additional charges, and publications are sold at cost. Starter sets of material are available free of charge to pre-booked parties. Full information pack available from Education at Beaulieu, John Montagu Building, Beaulieu, Hampshire. SO42 7ZN.

Responsible behaviour is expected at all times.

CONTACT

Lesley Ann Harnett
John Montagu Building
Beaulieu
Hampshire
SO42 7ZN

Tel: (01590) 612345

LOCATION

From London, M3 West, M27, M271, A35 then B3056 from Lyndhurst.

Bus: Bus stops within complex.

Rail: Stations at Brockenhurst and Beaulieu Rd both 7 miles away.

OPENING TIMES

Summer

Easter - October
Daily 10.00am - 6.00pm

Winter

October - Easter
Daily 10.00am - 5.00pm

ADMISSION

All Year

Individual rates upon application.

Groups (min 15 people)

Adult £6.50
Child (4-16yrs) . .£4.20
OAP £5.50
Student £5.00

BEAULIEU CONTINUED...

CATERING/FUNCTIONS

New conference and function brochure available for those requesting it.

The Brabazon and Domus (pictured above) banqueting halls can be hired all year round. For a fee Lord Montagu may meet groups and participate in functions.

Groups can be booked in advance for buffets, lunches, dinners and Royal Feasts. Please contact the Catering Manager for further details and menus. Tel: (01590) 612102.

CONFERENCE AND FUNCTION FACILITIES

ROOM	DIMENSIONS	CAPACITY	LAYOUT	POWER POINTS	SUITABLE FOR A/V
Brabazon (3 sections)	40'x40'(x3)	120(each)	Theatre	3	✓
		70	Schoolroom		
		40	U-shape		
		40	Boardroom		
		100	Buffet		
		300	Dinner/Dance		
		80 (each)	Lunch/Dinner		
Domus	69'x27'	170	Theatre	3	✓
		60	Schoolroom		
		40	U-shape		
		40	Boardroom		
		120	Lunch/Dinner		
Classic Car Theatre		200	Tiered Theatre Style Seating	3	✓

THE NATIONAL MOTOR MUSEUM

When Lord Montagu inherited Beaulieu, he displayed a handful of early vehicles in the Front Hall as a memorial to his father, one of the leading pioneers of motoring in Britain. From this beginning the now famous National Motor Museum grew.

The Museum traces the story of motoring from 1894 to the present day, with many special displays and 250 cars, commercial vehicles and motorcycles. It is especially proud to have four World Land Speed Record Breaking Cars (see left).

'Wheels - The Legend of the Motor Car', is a major feature in the Museum. This spectacular ride-through display is a tribute to man's motoring achievements. 'Wheels' transports visitors in space-age 'pods' through 100 years of motoring, from the early pioneers and their problems, to fantasies of the future, and shows how the motor vehicle has revolutionised our lives.

A monorail transports visitors to the Motor Museum, entering the building at roof level. There are rides on a 1912 open-topped London Bus or in Miniature Veteran Cars; Remote Controlled Model Cars; and a superb Model Railway, one of the largest layouts of its kind in the world.

Entry to the museum is included in the inclusive admission price.

HIGHCLERE CASTLE
Newbury

Designed by Charles Barry in the 1830s at the same time as he was building the Houses of Parliament, this soaring pinnacled mansion provided a perfect setting for the 3rd Earl of Carnarvon one of the great hosts of Queen Victoria's reign. The extravagant interiors range from church Gothic through Moorish flamboyance and rococo revival to the solid masculinity in the long Library. Old master paintings mix with portraits by Van Dyck and 18th Century painters. Napoleon's desk and chair rescued from St. Helena sits with other 18th and 19th Century furniture.

The 5th Earl of Carnarvon, discovered the Tomb of Tutankhamun with Howard Carter. The castle houses a unique exhibition of some of his discoveries which were only rediscovered in the castle in 1988. The current Earl is the Queen's Horseracing Manager. In 1993 to celebrate his 50th year as a leading owner and breeder "The Lord Carnarvon Racing Exhibition" was opened to the public, and offers a fascinating insight into a racing history that dates back three generations.

GARDENS
The magnificent parkland with its massive cedars was designed by Capability Brown. The walled gardens also date from an earlier house at Highclere but the dark yew walks are entirely victorian in character. The glass Orangery and Fernery add an exotic flavour. The Secret Garden has a romance of its own with a beautiful curving lawn surrounded by densely planted herbaceous gardens. A place for poets and romantics.

❖

SUITABILITY FOR OTHER EVENTS
Ideal for conferences, exhibitions, receptions, dinners, activity days, filming, concerts and corporate hospitality.
OUTDOOR EVENTS
Stunning backdrop for concerts, (cap. 8000) Fairs and displays.
ADVICE TO COURIERS & DRIVERS
No dogs are permitted in the house or gardens. No photography in the house. Ample Parking.
FACILITIES FOR THE DISABLED
Disabled and elderly visitors may alight at the entrance to the house. There are toilet facilities for the disabled.
CATERING
Exceptional catering for corporate events. During public openings the tea rooms can accommodate 60. Lunches for parties of 24+ can be booked in advance.
GIFT SHOP
The Gift Shop is open throughout the Castle open season.
GUIDED TOURS
They are available for visits outside normal opening hours. Average time taken to see the house is 2 hours.

GUIDE BOOKS
Colour guide book, £2.50.
SCHOOL VISITS/CHILDREN
Groups welcome by prior arrangement. Areas of interest: The Egyptian collection belonging to the 5th Earl of Carnarvon, discoverer of the Tomb of Tutankhamun, nature walks, beautiful old follies, Secret Garden.

CONTACT

T Howland
HMH Management
Highclere Park
Near Newbury
Berkshire
RG15 9RN

Tel: (01635) 253210
Fax: (01635) 810193

LOCATION

Approx 4¹/₂ miles out of Newbury on A34 towards Winchester. From London: M4 Junct 13; A34, Newbury-Winchester 20 mins. M3 Junct. 5 approx 15 miles.
Air: Heathrow M4 45 mins.
Rail: Paddington-Newbury 45 mins.
Taxi: 4¹/₂ miles (01635) 40829.

OPENING TIMES

Summer
1 July - 30 September

Daily except Mondays and Tuesdays.

CASTLE   1.00 - 6.00pm

GROUNDS, GARDENS AND TEAROOMS
12 Noon - 6.00pm

Winter
October-July
By appointment only.

ADMISSION

Adult £5.00
Child £3.00
OAP £4.00
Gardens only . . £3.00
Family(2 + 2) . . £13.00
Groups (Min. 30 people)
Adult £4.50
Child £2.50
OAP £3.50

CONFERENCE AND FUNCTION FACILITIES

ROOM	DIMENSIONS	CAPACITY	LAYOUT	POWER POINTS	SUITABLE FOR A/V
Library	43' x 21'	120	Theatre	✓	✓
Saloon		150	Reception	✓	✓
Dining Room		70	Lunch/Dinner Seated	✓	
Library, Saloon, Drawing Room Music Room, Smoking Room		400	Reception	✓	

SOMERLEY
Ringwood

To visit Somerley, even briefly, is to taste the elegant lifestyle. The architectural grandeur, the elegance of its interiors and its magnificent setting on the edge of the New Forest combine to make it one of Britain's finest houses. The house was designed by Samuel Wyatt in the mid 1700s and has been the residence of the Normanton family for almost 200 years. The sixth Earl and Countess live here today with their three children.

The house is not open to the public; the magnificently proportioned rooms with high gilded ceilings house a treasure trove of fine antique furniture, porcelain, paintings and objets d'art, and can be enjoyed by guests who visit to conduct business meetings, conferences, concerts, receptions, product launches and top level corporate hospitality. The house is 1¹/₂ miles from the nearest road and although easily accessible, provides privacy for meetings demanding security and complete confidentiality. The 7,000 acres of parkland can be used for incentive fun days, promotions and Golf events.The high standard of service and cuisine (much of the food comes from the Estate and gardens) and the warm friendly atmosphere are very rarely found in a house of this size. The peace and tranquillity of the grounds are a sheer delight.

❖

SUITABILITY FOR OTHER EVENTS
Specialising in game and clay pigeon shooting, filming, archery, and golf. Large scale events, fashion shows, air displays, equestrian events, gardenparties, shows, rallies, wedding receptions.

EXTRA FACILITIES
Also available for use: Grand Piano, organ, billiard room, parkland, formal gardens, croquet, tennis and golf driving range and 4-hole practice course, outdoor pool, salmon fishing, clay shoot. Picture Gallery includes work by Reynolds, Canaletto, Gainsborough, Murillo and Etty. Furniture mainly Louis XIV and XVI.

ACCOMMODATION
Somerley offers 1 single and 8 twin/doubles with bathrooms. All rooms to be taken by house party. Smaller numbers negotiable.

ADVICE TO COURIERS & DRIVERS
Liaise with Pamela Benton or the Earl of Normanton: 01425 480819. No individual visits. All uses of Somerley are on an exclusive basis, by application only.

FACILITIES FOR THE DISABLED
Disabled and elderly visitors may alight to the Front Entrance of the House.

PARKING FOR COACHES & CARS
There is parking for up to 200 cars and 20+ coaches adjacent to the house.

CATERING
The Dining Room is available for private parties (capacity 50 people). Parties must book in advance and menus are available on request. Meals from £23.00 per head. Outside caterers may be used in the Grounds if requested.

BROCHURES
A colour brochure is complimentary, given to conference/ function enquirers.

CONFERENCE AND FUNCTION FACILITIES

ROOM	DIMENSIONS	CAPACITY	LAYOUT	POWER POINTS	SUITABLE FOR A/V
Picture Gallery	80' x 30'	150	Reception	8	
Drawing Room	38' x 30'	50	Various	6	
Dining Room	39' x 19'	50	Various	4	
East Library	26' x 21'	20	Boardroom	4	
		20	Lunch/Dinner		
		30	Reception		

STRATFIELD SAYE HOUSE
Reading

AFTER Waterloo the first Duke of Wellington, or the Great Duke as he was universally known was regarded as the saviour of his country and of Europe. A grateful nation voted a large sum of money to buy him a house and an estate worthy of a national hero, and in 1817, after carefully considering many other far grander houses, he chose Stratfield Saye.

The south stable block houses the Wellington Exhibition which portrays the Great Duke's life both as a soldier and a politician. A major feature of this exhibition is the 18 ton Funeral Hearse which was constructed, from the metal of French cannons captured at Waterloo, for the Great Duke's funeral in 1852.

GARDENS

The gardens have been completely restored since 1975 after being virtually abandoned for several decades.

They include a rose garden and the American garden, so named because of the vogue for American shrubs in the early 19th Century, created in the first Duke's time, and a walled garden dating from the 18th Century.

In the Ice House paddock stands a spreading Turkey Oak planted in 1843. The tree and a headstone mark the place where Copenhagen, the Great Duke's favourite charger was buried with full military honours in 1836 at the age of 28.

SUITABILITY FOR OTHER EVENTS
The House and grounds are available for events and corporate hospitality functions. Functions in the House can range from dinner for 20 to cocktail parties for 200 whilst, in the grounds, garden parties of any size are a possibility. Game Fairs, Country Fairs and Craft Fairs with numbers ranging from 20,000 to 200,000 visitors have all been held here.

Filming within the House and Grounds will be considered on request.

ADVICE TO COURIERS & DRIVERS
If possible, please book in advance; if not, telephone with arrival times and numbers.

FACILITIES FOR THE DISABLED
Disabled and elderly visitors may alight at the entrance before parking in the allocated area. There are toilet facilities for the disabled.

PARKING FOR COACHES & CARS
Free parking for up to 250 cars and 20 coaches 500 yards from the house.

CATERING
There is a restaurant (capacity 80 people). Parties can booked in advance for tea and other meals, special rates given to groups. Menus available on request. Prices from £1.50 - £10.00. Special functions can be catered for.

GUIDED TOURS
There are no guided tours, but there are stewards in all rooms. Tours can be arranged for groups on payment of an extra charge.

GIFT SHOP
Open at the same time as the house and contains many items which can only be purchased at Stratfield Saye.

GUIDE BOOKS
Colour Guide book, French and Spanish translations.

SCHOOL VISITS/CHILDREN
Groups are welcome at £2.25 per child. A spotter pack can be provided at an additional cost of 20p. Areas of interest include: state coach, 18 ton funeral hearse, ice house, Copenhagen's grave.

THE VYNE
Basingstoke

Built in the early 16th century by William Sandys, Lord Chamberlain to Henry VIII and one of the few nobles to survive the vagaries of this king's reign the Vyne was extensively remodelled in the mid 17th century. Visitors to the house today will discover a remarkable amalgamation of Tudor and neo-classical architecture within a romantic lakeside setting. The Vyne's furnishings reflect the different tastes of successive generations of occupants and the result is a country house atmosphere rich in history and warmth. The panelled long gallery and the chapel with renaissance glass are some of the finest examples in Britain and the collections of textiles and ceramics are much-admired.

THE GROUNDS
The house is divided from rich meadowland and woods by a stream-fed lake and rolling lawns. The traditionally planted herbaceous borders are a delight in all seasons.

❖

EXTRA FACILITIES
Woodlands walks. Programme of events through the summer.

ADVICE TO COURIERS & DRIVERS
Picnics and dogs allowed in car park areas only.

FACILITIES FOR THE DISABLED
Access to grounds and ground floor only. Shop accessible. Disabled visitors may be driven to the door by prior arrangement. WC. Braille guide.

PARKING FOR COACHES & CARS
Available 100 yards from the house.

CATERING
Light refreshments and home-made teas in Old Brew House

(licensed) open same days as grounds. 12.30 - 2.00 and 2.30 - 5.30.

GUIDED TOURS
Available by prior arrangement with Administrator (extra charge).

GIFT SHOP
Open as grounds and for Christmas shopping. Tel (01256) 880039 for dates.

GUIDE BOOKS
Available at house and gift shop. Children's Quiz and Children's Guide.

CHILDREN
Changing facilities. No backpacks or pushchairs in house.

CONTACT

The Administrator
The Vyne
Sherborne St John
Basingstoke
Hampshire
RG26 5DX

Tel: (01256) 881337

LOCATION

4 miles north of Basingstoke between Bramley and Sherborne St John. From Basingstoke ring road, follow signs for Basingstoke District Hospital until property signs are picked up.

Bus/Rail: Hampshire Bus 45 from Basingstoke, passing BR Basingstoke Tel: (01256) 464501.

OPENING TIMES

Summer

25 Mar - 30 Sept

Daily except Mon & Fri. (open Good Fri. and Bank Hol Mons. but closed Tues. following).

HOUSE
1.30 - 5.30pm

GROUNDS
12.30 - 5.30pm

Last admission 30 minutes before closing.

Winter

October

Grounds only - daily except Mon and Fri.

12.30 - 5.30pm

ADMISSION

HOUSE & GROUNDS
Adult £4.00
Child . . . . .Half Price
Fam. ticket . . .£10.00
Groups (pre-booked min 15)
Tues, Weds, Thurs only
Adult £3.00

GROUNDS ONLY
Adult £2.00

AVINGTON PARK

OPEN

May - Sept.
Suns & Bank Hols

2.30 - 5.30pm

Tea Bar open at
these times.

Pre-booked coaches
welcome.

Other times by
appointment only.

Tel: 01962 779260
Fax: 01962 779715

WINCHESTER, HAMPSHIRE SO21 1DD

Owner: Lt. Col and Mrs J B Hickson   *Contact:* Mrs S L Bullen

Avington Park, where Charles II and George IV both stayed at various times is an old house enlarged in 1670 by the addition of two wings and a classical Portico surmounted by three statues. The State rooms are magnificently painted and lead onto the unique pair of conservatories flanking the South Lawn. The Georgian St. Mary's Church, is in the grounds. Avington Park is available for Conferences, Filming and Receptions.

Location: 4 miles North East of Winchester off the B3047 in Itchen Abbas.
Admission: Adults £2.50, half price for children under 14.

BASING HOUSE

Tel: 01256 467294

Redbridge Lane, Basing, Basingstoke, Hampshire, RG24 7HB.
Owner: Hampshire County Council   **Contact:** Alan Turton
Ruins, covering 10 acres, of huge Tudor palace. Recent recreation of Tudor formal garden.
Location: 2m from Basingstoke town centre.
Opening Times: 1 Apr -30 Sept, Wed - Sun, 2.00pm - 6.00pm.
Admission: Adult £1.50, Child 70p.

BEAULIEU

See page 68 and 69 for full page entry.

BISHOP'S WALTHAM PALACE

Tel: 01489 892460

Winchester, Hampshire.
Owner: English Heritage   **Contact:** The Administrator
This medieval seat of the Bishops of Winchester once stood in an enormous park. There are still wooded grounds and the remains of Great Hall can still be seen and the three storey tower.
Location: In Bishop's Waltham.
Opening Times: 1 Apr -30 Sept daily 10.00am - 6.00pm. Only open as a keykeeper site in Winter. Tel: 01705 527667 for details.
Admission: Adult £2.00, Child £1.50, Conc £1.00.

BOHUNT MANOR

Tel: 01428 7222080

Liphook, Hampshire, GU30 7DL.
Owner: Worldwide Fund for Nature   **Contact:** Lady Holman
Woodland gardens with lakeside walk, collection of ornamental waterfowl, herbaceous borders and unusual trees and shrubs.
Location: In Liphook village.
Opening Times: All year round, daily, 10.00am - 6.00pm.
Admission: Adult £1.50, Child under 14 free, Conc £1.00, Group 10% off.

BRAMDEAN HOUSE

Tel: 01962 771 214   **Fax:** 01962 771 095

Bramdean, Alresford, Hampshire, SO24 0JU.
Owner: Mrs H Wakefield   **Contact:** Mrs H Wakefield
Walled garden with famous herbaceous borders.
Location: In Bramdean village on A272 midway between Winchester and Petersfield.
Opening Times: Garden only 19 Mar, 16/17 Apr, 21 May, 18 Jun, 16 Jul, 2.00pm - 5.00pm. Also by prior appointment.

BREAMORE HOUSE

Tel: 01725 512233

Breamore, Fordingbridge, Hampshire, SP6 2DF.
Owner: Sir Westrow Hulse Bt   **Contact:** Edward Hulse Esq
Elizabethan Manor with fine collections of pictures and furniture. Countryside Museum takes visitors back to when a village was self sufficient. The Carriage Museum is in the Queen Anne stables.
Location: Off the A338, between Salisbury and Ringwood.
Opening Times: Countryside Museum: 1.00pm - 5.30pm. House: 2.00pm - 5.30pm April: Tues, Wed, Sun and Easter Holiday. May, Jun, Jul, Sept: Tues, Wed, Thur, Sat, Sun and all holidays. Aug: Daily.
Admission: Combined ticket for house and garden: Adult £4.50, Child £3.00.

CALSHOT CASTLE

Tel: 01703 892023

Fawley, Hampshire.
Owner: English Heritage   **Contact:** The Administrator
Henry VIII built this coastal fort in an excellent position, commanding the sea passage to Southampton. The fort houses an exhibition and recreated pre-World War I barrack room.
Location: On spit 2m SE of Fawley off B3053.
Opening Times: 1 Apr - 30 Sept, daily 10.00am - 6.00pm, 1 Oct - 31 Oct, daily 10.00am - 4.00pm. 1 Nov - 31 Mar, daily 10.00am - 4.00pm, (Closed 24 - 26 Dec, 1 Jan).
Admission: Adult £1.60, Child 80p, Conc £1.20.

ELING TIDE MILL

Tel: 01703 869575

The Toll Bridge, Eling, Totton, Hampshire, SO40 9HF.
Owner: Martin Mears Esq.   **Contact:** Martin Mears
Location: 4m W of Southampton.
Opening Times: Wed - Sun, 10.00am - 4.00pm.
Admission: Adult £1.15, Child 65p, Family £3.50, Conc 85p, Groups 85p.

EXBURY GARDENS

Tel: 01703 891203

Exbury, Southampton, Hampshire, SO4 1AZ.
Owner: Edmund de Rothschild Esq   **Contact:** Charles Orr-Ewing
Celebrated landscaped woodland garden overlooking Beaulieu River.
Location: 5m SW of Southampton, 3m from Beaulieu.
Opening Times: Open daily, mid-Feb - late Oct, 10.00am - 5.00pm.

FORT BROCKHURST

Tel: 01705 581059

Hampshire.
Owner: English Heritage   **Contact:** The Administrator
This was a new type of fort, built in the 19th century to protect Portsmouth with formidable fire-power. Largely unaltered, the parade ground, gun ramps and moated keep can all be viewed. An exhibition illustrates the history of Portsmouth's defences.
Location: Off A32, in Gunner's Way, Elson, on N side of Gosport.
Opening Times: 1 Apr - 30 Sept, daily 10.00am - 6.00pm, 1 Oct - 31 Oct, daily 10.00am - 4.00pm, 1 Nov - 31 Mar, Wed - Sun, 10.00am - 4.00pm (Closed 24 - 26 Dec, 1 Jan).
Admission: Adult £2.00, Child £1.00, Conc £1.50.

FURZEY GARDENS

Tel: 01703 812464

Minstead, Lyndhurst, Hampshire, SO43 7GL.
Owner: Furzey Garden Charitable Trust   **Contact:** M A Selwood
8 acres of informal garden surrounding a 16th century cottage with gallery of local arts and crafts.
Location: Signposted in Minstead. Off A31 or A337.
Opening Times: Throughout the year, except 25/26 Dec. 10am - 5pm (earlier in winter).
Admission: Nov - Feb: Adult £1.50, Child 75p, Conc £1.00. Mar - Oct: Adult £3.00, Child £1.50, Groups 10% discount .

GREATHAM MILL

Tel: 01420 538 245   **Fax:** 01420 538 219

Greatham, Liss, Hampshire, GU33 6HH.
Owner: Mrs E N Pumphrey   **Contact:** Mr E Groves
Interesting garden with large variety of plants surrounding a mill house.
Location: 2m from Liss; 7m from Alton.
Opening Times: April - Sept, Sat, Sun, and Bank Hol Mon.
Admission: Adult £1, Child free, Groups £2 per head.

GUILDHALL GALLERY

Tel: 01962 848296   **Fax**: 01962 841365

Winchester, Hampshire, SO23 7DW.
Owner: Winchester City Council   **Contact:** Mr C Hardman Bradbury
19th century Guild Hall. Changing contemporary exhibitions.
Location: 2m from Liss; 7m from Alton.
Opening Times: Tue - Sat: 10.00am - 5.00pm, Sun & Mon: 2.00pm - 5.00pm. Closed Mondays Oct - Mar.

HIGHCLERE CASTLE

See page 70 for full page entry.

HILLIER GARDENS

Tel: 01794 368787

Jermyns Lane, Ampfield, Romsey, Hampshire, SO51 OQA.
Owner: Hampshire County Council   **Contact:** Mrs S Wilson
Gardens and arboretum extending over 160 acres with wide diversity of plants. Started by Sir Harold Hillier in the 1950s.
Location: 3m NE of Romsey, off A31.
Opening Times: Telephone for details.

HINTON AMPNER

Tel: 01962 771305

Bramdean, Alresford, Hampshire, SO24 0LA.
Owner: The National Trust   **Contact:** The Administrator
The house was remodelled by the late Ralph Dutton in 1936, but was gutted by a fire in 1960, destroying much of his collection. He rebuilt and refurnished the house with fine Regency furniture, 17th century Italian pictures and porcelain. Set in superb countryside, the garden combines formal design and informal planting, producing delightful walks with many unexpected vistas.
Location: On A272, 1m W of Bramdean village, 8m E of Winchester.
Opening Times: 1 Apr - end Sept: Garden: Sat, Sun, Tues, Wed (closed Good Fri & Easter Mon, but open BH Mon thereafter), 1.30pm - 5.30pm. House: Tues & Wed only, also Sat & Sun in Aug, 1.30pm - 5.30pm, last admission 5.00pm.
Admission: House & Garden: £3.70, Garden only: £2.40, Pre-booked parties £3.20.

HOUGHTON LODGE

OPEN

Garden

March - Sept.
Sats. & Suns.
10.00am - 5.00pm

Mon, Tues, Fri
2 - 5.00pm

Other times by appointment,

House by appointment only.

Tel: 01264 810177
or 01264 810502

STOCKBRIDGE, HAMPSHIRE

Owner: Captain M W Busk   *Contact: Captain M W Busk*

Perhaps among the most 'picturesque' of 18th century gothic "cottages ornees" with its architectural fantasy and perfect garden setting overlooking the tranquil beauty of the Test valley. The kitchen garden surrounded by rare chalkcob walls contains The Hydroponicum, a living exhibition of horticulture without soil, demonstrating its application worldwide and in space.
Location: 1¹/₂ mls south of Stockbridge (A30) on minor road to Houghton village.
Admission: £2.50. Discounts for parties. House prices on application.

HURST CASTLE

Tel: 01590 642344

Keyhaven, Lymington, Hampshire.
Owner: English Heritage   **Contact:** The Administrator
This was one of the most sophisticated fortresses built by Henry VIII, and later strengthened in the 19th and 20th centuries, to command the narrow entrance to the Solent. There is an exhibition in the Castle, and two huge 38 ton guns from the fort's armaments.
Location: On Pebble Spit S of Keyhaven.
Opening Times: 1 Apr - 22 Jul, daily 10.00am - 5.30pm, 22 Jul - 31 Aug, daily 10.00 - 6.00pm, 1.00pm - 30 Sept, daily 10.00am - 5.30pm.
Admission: Adult £2.00, Child £1.00, Conc £1.50.

JANE AUSTEN'S HOUSE

Tel: 01420 83262   **Fax**: 01420 83262

Chawton, Alton, Hampshire, GU34 1SD.
Owner: Jane Austen Memorial Trust   **Contact:** Jean Bowden
17th century house where Jane Austen lived from 1809 - 1817.
Location: Off roundabout of A31 and A32 junction.
Opening Times: Apr - Dec, daily. Nov, Dec & Mar, Wed - Sun. Jan & Feb, Sat & Sun 11.00am - 4.30pm.
Admission: Adult £2.00, Child (8-18) 50p, Groups of 15 plus £1.50.

JENKYN PLACE

Tel: 01420 23118

Bentley, Hampshire, GU10 5LU.
Owner: Mrs G Coke   **Contact:** Mrs G Coke
Well designed plantsman's garden with interesting shrubs and perenials.
Location: 400 metres N of A31 (Farnham to Alton).
Opening Times: Apr - Sep, Thur - Sun, 2.00pm - 6.00pm.
Admission: Adult £2.00, Child 75p.

MEDIEVAL MERCHANTS HOUSE

Tel: 01703 221503

58 French Street, Southampton, Hampshire.
Owner: English Heritage   **Contact:** The Administrator
The life of the prosperous merchant in the Middle Ages is vividly evoked in this recreated, faithfully restored 13th century town house.
Location: 58 French Street. ¹/₄m S of city centre just off Castle Way (between High Street and Bugle Street).
Opening Times: 1 Apr - 30 Sept daily 10.00am - 6.00pm. 1 Oct - 31 Oct, 10.00am - 4.00pm. Lunchtime closure 1.00pm - 2.00pm. Open as a keykeeper site in winter, Tel: 01705 527667 for details.
Admission: Adult £2.00, Child £1.50, Conc £1.00.

MOTTISFONT ABBEY GARDEN

Tel: 01794 341220

Mottisfont, Romsey, Hampshire, SO1 OLP.
Owner: The National Trust   **Contact:** The Administrator
A tributary of the River Test flows through the garden forming a superb and tranquil setting for a 12th century Augustinian priory, which, after the Dissolution, became a house. It contains the spring or "font" from which the place name is derived. The magnificent trees, walled gardens and the national collection of old fashioned roses combine to provide interest throughout the seasons.
Location: 4¹/₂m NW of Romsey, ³/₄m W of 3057.
Opening Times: Garden: 19 & 26 Mar, 1 Apr - end Oct: Sat - Wed 12.00pm - 6.00pm or dusk if earlier. Jun: Sat - Thur 12.00pm - 8.30pm. Last admissions 1 hr before closing. Note: Due to an extensive restoration project, the whole house will be closed while work is underway and the Abbey will be scaffolded.
Admission: Garden: £2.50, £3.50 during June (rose season). No reduction for parties, coaches please book in advance.

NETLEY ABBEY

Netley, Southampton, Hampshire.
Owner: English Heritage   **Contact:** The Administrator
There is a peaceful and beautiful setting for the extensive ruins of this 13th century Cistercian abbey converted in Tudor times for use as a house.
Location: In Netley, 4m SE of Southampton, facing Southampton Water.
Opening Times: Any reasonable time.

OLD BISHOP'S PALACE

Tel: 01962 854766

College Street, Wolvesey, Southampton, Hampshire.
Owner: English Heritage   **Contact:** The Administrator
The fortified palace of Wolvesey was the chief residence of the Bishops of Winchester and one of the greatest of all medieval buildings in England. Its extensive ruins still reflect the importance and immense wealth of the Bishops of Winchester, occupants of the richest seat in medieval England. Wolvesey was frequently visited by medieval and Tudor monarchs and was the scene of the wedding feast of Philip of Spain and Mary Tudor in 1554.
Location: ¹/₄ m SE of Winchester Cathedral, next to the Bishop's Palace; access from College Street.
Opening Times: 1st Apr - 30 Sept Daily, 10.0am - 6.00pm. 1 Oct - 31 Oct, 10.00am - 4.00pm daily. Lunchtime closure 1.00pm - 2.00pm.
Admission: Adult £1.50, Child £1.10, Conc 80p.

PORTCHESTER CASTLE 🏰
Tel: 01705 378291

Portchester, Southampton, Hampshire.
Owner: English Heritage　　　　　　　　**Contact:** The Administrator
A residence for Kings and a rallying point for troops, the history of this grand castle stretches back for nearly 2,000 years. There are Roman walls, the most complete in Europe, substantial remains of the Royal castle and an exhibition which tells the story of Portchester.
Location: On S side of Portchester off A27.
Opening Times: 1 Apr - 30 Sept, daily 10.00am - 6.00pm, 1 Oct - 31 Mar, daily 10.00am - 4.00pm. (Closed 24 - 26 Dec, 1 Jan).
Admission: Adult £2.50, Child £1.90, Conc £1.30.

PORTSMOUTH CATHEDRAL
Tel: 01705 823300　**Fax:** 01705 823300

Portsmouth, Hampshire, PO1 2HH.
　　　　　　　　Contact: Rosemary Fairfax
Maritime Cathedral founded in 12th century and finally completed in 1991. A member of the ships crew of Henry VIII flagship Mary Rose is buried in Navy Aisle.
Location: 1¹/₂m from end of M275. Follow signs to Historic Ship and Old Portsmouth.
Opening Times: 7.45am - 6.00pm all year. Sun: 8.00am, 9.30am, 11.00am, 6.30p. Weekday: 7.20am, 7.45am, 6.00pm (Choral on Tue and Fri in term time).
Admission: Donation appreciated.

SANDHAM MEMORIAL CHAPEL 🌳
Tel: 01635 278292

Burghclere, Newbury, Hampshire, RG15 9JT.
Owner: The National Trust　　　　　　　**Contact:** Rosemary Fairfax
A First World War memorial built in the 1920s, and notable for the paintings by Stanley Spencer of war scenes in Salonica, which cover the chapel walls. *"The outstanding English monument to painting of the pioneering years of the 20th century"* (Pevsner).
Location: 4m S of Newbury, ¹/₂m E of A34.
Opening Times: 25 Mar - 31 Oct, Wed - Sun and BH Mons (closed Wed after BHM), 11.30am - 6.00pm. Nov 1995 and Mar 1996: Sat & Sun only 11.30am - 4.00pm. Dec - Feb: by appointment only.
Admission: Adult £1.50, Child 75p, no reductions for pre-booked parties.

SOMERLEY 🏛
See page 71 for full page entry.

STANSTED PARK 🏛
Tel: 01705 412265　**Fax:** 01705 413 773

Rowlands Castle, Hampshire, PO9 6DX.
Owner: Trustees of Stansted Park Foundation　　　**Contact:** John Gowan
Built in 1903 on the site of its 17th century predecessor. Spectacular avenues through ancient Forest of Bere. 30 acres of grounds includes an arboretum.
Location: Follow brown heritage signs from A3 (Rowlands Castle) and A27 (Havant).
Opening Times: BH Suns & Mons, and 2 Jul - 29 Sept , Sun - Tues, 2.00pm - 5.30pm.
Admission: House & Grounds: Adult £3.50, Child £1.50, Groups £3. Grounds Only: Adults £1.00, Child 50p.

STRATFIELD SAYE HOUSE 🏛
See page 72 for full page entry.

THE GILBERT WHITE MUSEUM

OPEN

End of Mar to
End of Oct
Daily
11.00am - 5.00pm

Weekends only
during winter

Day and Evening
for groups by
appointment

Tel: 01420 511275

THE WAKES, SELBORNE, ALTON HAMPSHIRE GU34 3JH
Owner: *Oates Memorial Trust*　　**Contact:** *Mrs. Anna Jackson*

Historic 18th century House and glorious garden, home of Rev. Gilbert White, author of 'The Natural History of Selborne': Also museum devoted to the Captain Oates of Antarctic fame. Unusual plants fair, 24/25 June, 'Jazz in June' 24 June, Mulled Wine Day Sunday, 26 Nov.
Location: On B3006 in village of Selborne close to A3.
Admission: Adult £2.50, OAP £2.00, Child £1.00. First child free.

THE GRANGE 🏰
Tel: 01705 412265　**Fax:** 01705 413 773

Northington, Basingstoke, Hampshire.
Owner: English Heritage　　　　　　　　**Contact:** The Administrator
This magnificent neoclassical country house, built at the beginning of the 18th century could easily be mistaken for a Greek temple, with portico front and grand steps.
Location: 4m N of New Alresford off B3046.
Opening Times: Any reasonable time (exterior viewing only).

THE GREAT HALL
Tel: 01962 846476

Winchester Castle, Winchester, Hampshire, SO23 8ZB.
Owner: Hampshire County Council　　　　　**Contact:** Mrs K Mann
Remaining part of William the Conquerors Castle built in 1235. Small medieval garden, Queen Elizabeth's garden, off main hall.
Location: 4m N of New Alresford off B3046.
Opening Times: Open all year, 10.00am - 4.00pm. (Except Good Fri, 25 & 26 Dec).
Admission: Donations.

THE MANOR HOUSE
Tel: 01256 862827

Upton Grey, Basingstoke, Hampshire, RG25 2RD.
Owner: Mrs J Wallinger　　　　　　　**Contact:** Mrs J Wallinger
4 acre garden designed by Gertrude Jekyll in 1908, meticulously restored to original plans.
Location: 6m SE of Basingstoke.
Opening Times: By appointment for groups May - Jul.
Admission: Standard £3.00, Groups £2.00.

THE VYNE 🌳
See page 73 for full page entry.

TITCHFIELD ABBEY 🏰

Titchfield, Southampton, Hampshire.
Owner: English Heritage　　　　　　　　**Contact:** The Administrator
Remains of a 13th century abbey overshadowed by the grand Tudor gatehouse. Reputedly some of Shakespeare's plays were performed here for the first time.
Location: ¹/₂ mile N of Titchfield off A27.
Opening Times: Telephone regional office 01732 778000 for details of times.

TUDOR HOUSE MUSEUM
Tel: 01703 635904　**Fax:** 01703 339601

Bugle Street, Southampton, Hampshire.
Owner: Southampton City Council　　　　**Contact:** Sian Jones
Late 15th century half timbered house. Unique Tudor knot garden.
Location: Follow signs to Old Town and waterfront from M27/M3.
Opening Times: Tues - Fri, 10am - 12 Noon, 1 - 5pm. Sat 10am - 12 Noon, 1- 4.00pm. Sun 2 - 5.00pm. Closed Mons.
Admission: Adult £1.50, Child 75p, Family £3.00, Senior citizens 75p, Group discount for advanced bookings.

WINCHESTER CATHEDRAL
Tel: 01962 853137　**Fax:** 01962 841519

Winchester, Hampshire, SO23 9LS.
　　　　　　　　Contact: K Bamber
The Cathedral was founded in 1079 on a site where Christian worship had already been offered for over 400 years. Among its treasures are the 12th century illuminated Winchester Bible, the font, medieval wall paintings, six chantry chapels and much more. Winchester town centre.
Location: Winchester town centre.
Opening Times: 7.15am - 6.30pm. East End closes 5.00pm. Access may be restricted during services. Weekday services: 7.40am, 8.00am, 5.00pm. Sun services: 8.00am, 10.30am, 11.30am, 3.30pm.
Admission: Recommended donations: Adult £2.00, Child 50p, Conc £1.50, Family party £4.00, charges apply for Triforium gallery and Library - £1.50. Group tours £2.50 should be booked through the Education centre. (Tel: 01962 866854 between 9.00am - 1.00pm).

WINCHESTER COLLEGE
Tel: 01962 868778　**Fax:** 01962 84020

77 Kings Gate Street, Winchester, Hampshire, SO23 9PE.
Owner: Winchester College　　　　　　**Contact:** Mr McClure
One of the oldest public schools, founded by Bishop William of Wykeham in 1382.
Location: 77 Kings Gate Street.
Opening Times: 7 Apr - Sept, Mon - Sat, 10.00am - 1.00pm and 2.00am - 5.00pm. Oct - Mar, Mon - Sat, 10.00am - 1.00pm and 2.00pm - 4.00pm. Closed Sun mornings.
Admission: Adult £2.50, Child £2.00, Conc £2.00, Guided tours may be booked for parties over 10.

Somerley, Hampshire

SPECIAL EVENTS DIARY

- **9th April: Beaulieu**
  Boat Jumble

- **Easter 14th - 17th April: Highclere Castle**
  Highclere Flower Show

- **13th - 14th May: Breamore House & Museums**
  Breamore Rally - Countryside Museum working day; a mini rally

- **13th - 14th May: Beaulieu**
  Spring Classic Autojumble

- **21st May: Beaulieu**
  Jaguar Drivers Club Rally

- **27th - 29th May: Breamore House & Museums**
  Breamore Craft Show

- **27th - 29th May: Stratfield Saye House**
  Craft Fair

- **3rd - 4th June: Breamore House & Museums**
  Living History - Breamore House returns to 1863 with full staff.

- **4th June: Beaulieu**
  Gardening & Country Show

- **10th June: Beaulieu**
  Day for people with Disabilities

- **24th June: Gilbert White's House & Garden**
  Jazz in June - Bring a picnic and listen to Basil Moss & His Chicago Jazz Ensemble !

- **24th June: Highclere Castle**
  Firework & Laser Symphony Concert

- **24th - 25th June: Gilbert White's House & Garden**
  Unusual Plants Fair Rare & Unusual plants from specialist nurseries.

- **24th - 25th June: Beaulieu**
  Morgan Rally

- **1st July: Beaulieu**
  Palace House Prom

- **9th July: Beaulieu**
  Bike Bonanza

- **21st - 22nd July: The Vyne**
  Fireworks Concerts 8pm

- **23rd July: Highclere Castle**
  Classic Car Show

- **23rd July: Beaulieu**
  Buckler's Hard Village Festival (at Buckler's Hard)

- **5th - 6th August: Breamore House & Museums**
  Living Steam Model Show. Around 100 models - many in steam.

- **5th - 6th August: Highclere Castle**
  Craft Fair

- **6th August: Beaulieu**
  MG Car Club Rally

- **12th - 13th August: Breamore House & Museums**
  V E Day Celebration. Military vehicles and historic display

- **13th August: Beaulieu**
  Graham Walker Run

- **26th August: Stratfield Saye House**
  Wellington Prom - Open Air Concert

- **27th August: Highclere Castle**
  Last Night of the Proms & Fireworks

- **27th August: Beaulieu**
  Rover SDI Rally

- **9th - 10th September: Beaulieu**
  International Autojumble & Automart

- **23rd-24th: Beaulieu**
  Holiday & Park Homes Exhibition

- **4th November: Beaulieu**
  Fireworks Fair

- **26th November: Gilbert White's House & Garden**
  Mulled Wine Day - Sip a glass of mulled wine and enjoy Christmas Shopping in our exciting gift shop.

EASTNOR CASTLE
Ledbury

Encircled by the Malvern Hills and surrounded by a famous arboretum and lake this fairytale castle is as dramatic inside as it is outside.

The atmosphere Everyone is struck by it. The vitality of a young family brings the past to life and the sense of warmth and optimism is tangible. Eastnor, however grand, is a home.

"Sleeping" for the past fifty years, the Castle has recently undergone a triumphant renaissance - 'looking better than it probably ever has' Country Life 1993.

Hidden away in attics and cellars since the war, many of the castle's treasures are now revealed for the first time – early Italian Fine Art, 17th century Venetian furniture and Flemish tapestries, Mediaeval armour and paintings by Van Dyck, Reynolds, Romney and Watts, photographs by Julia Margaret Cameron. Drawing Room by Pugin.

'The princely and imposing pile' as it was described in 1812 when it was being built to pitch the owner into the aristocracy remains the home of his descendants. The Castle contains letters diaries, clothes and furnishing belonging to friends and relations who include: Horace Walpole, Elizabeth Barret Browning, Tennyson, Watts, Julia Margaret Cameron and Virginia Woolf.

Encircled by the Malvern Hills, the mediaeval beauty of the estate remains unchanging.

GARDENS
Castellated terraces descend to a 21 acre lake with a newly opened lakeside walk. An arboretum holds a famous collection of mature specimen trees. There are spectacular views of the Malvern hills across a 900 acre deer park, once part of a mediaeval chase and now designated a Site of Special Scientific Interest.

CONTACT

Simon Foster
Eastnor Castle
Portcullis Office
Nr. Ledbury
Herefordshire
HR8 1RN
Tel: (01531) 633160
or (01531) 632302
Fax: (01531) 631776/
or (01531) 631030

LOCATION

2^1/$_2$ miles east of Ledbury on the A438 Tewksbury road. Alternatively M50 junct. 2 and from Ledbury take the A449/A438.

Tewksbury 20 mins, Malvern 20 mins, Gloucester 25 mins Hereford 25 mins, Worcester 30 mins, Cheltenham 35 mins Birmingham 1 hour, London 2^1/$_2$ hours

Taxi: Meredith Taxis
(01531) 632852
Redline Taxis
(01432) 890313

Summer/Winter
12.00 - 5.00pm
Bank Holiday Mondays
Sundays from Easter to
End September
July & August: Sun to Fri

Other times and dates throughout the year by appointment.

NB Parties must pre-book. Groups by appointment at any time, including evenings, when the Castle is closed to casual visitors.

ADMISSION

Summer
HOUSE & GROUNDS
  Adult £3.50
  Child (5-14yrs) . . .£1.75
  Group* £3.00
GROUNDS ONLY
  Adult £1.75
  Child (5-14yrs) . . .£1.00
* Min. payment £60 for 20 people.

Winter
Closed except by appointment.

SUITABILITY FOR OTHER EVENTS
The Castle is at the centre of an unspoilt 5,000 acre estate, used with great success for off-road driving, clay pigeon shooting, quad bikes, archery and falconry. The varied terrain ideal for team building activity days and survival training for which accommodation is available. The impressive interior of the castle makes an original setting for product launches, corporate hospitality, fashion shows, concerts, weddings, charity events, craft fairs, television & feature films.

EXTRA FACILITIES
Exclusive off-road driving on the "Land Rover" test track with qualified instructors. Luxury Accommodation within the castle for small exclusive groups. Meeting Room/Dormitory for Survival/Team Building days with showers and kitchen. Chapel for small Weddings/Christenings.

ADVICE TO COURIERS & DRIVERS
Please telephone in advance to arrange parking space near the Castle and any catering requirements. Free meal for drivers. No smoking in the house

FACILITIES FOR THE DISABLED
Disabled and elderly visitors may alight at the Castle entrance. Priority for nearby parking.

PARKING FOR COACHES & CARS
70 cars and a few coaches. 10-100 yds from the Castle.

GIFT SHOP
Eastnor souvenirs, books, gifts and toys. All excellent value

GUIDE BOOKS
Guide Book, £2.00. Additional room notes in every room.

CATERING
Excellent country house cooking within the Castle for booked events. Home-made light lunches, teas and ice-cream in the Tea Room. Menus on request. Groups please book in advance..

GUIDED TOURS
Throughout the year by appointment

SCHOOL VISITS/CHILDREN
School parties welcome £1.50 per child. Guides available if required. Day out combining Castle with new Countryside study Centre.

CONFERENCE AND FUNCTION FACILITIES

ROOM	DIMENSIONS	CAPACITY	LAYOUT	POWER POINTS	SUITABLE FOR A/V
Library		120	Various	✓	✓
Great Hall		160	Various	✓	✓
Dining Room		120	Various	✓	✓
Gothic Room		50	Various	✓	✓
Octagon Room		50	Various	✓	✓

ABBEYDORE COURT GARDENS
Tel: 01981 240419   **Fax:** 01981 240279

Abbey Dore, Hereford, Herefordshire, HR2 0AD.
Owner: Mrs C L Ward   **Contact:** Mrs C L Ward
5 acre rambling garden, intersected by the river Dore. Shrubs and herbaceous perennials, rock garden and ponds. Small nursery. Country gift gallery and Teddy Bear loft. Licensed restaurant, home made food.
Location: 3 m W of A465 midway Hereford - Abergavenny.
Opening Times: 4 Mar to 22 Oct 11.00am - 6.00pm. Closed Wed. Christmas opening 1 Nov to 1 Jan daily from 10.00am for gift gallery.
Admission: Adult £1.75, Child 50p.

BERRINGTON HALL

OPEN

April to end Sept.
Wed to Sun
1.30 - 5.30pm
(closed Good Fri)
October
Wed to Sun
1.30 - 4.30pm
Grounds open
12.30 - 6.30 (Oct 5.30)
Park walk only:
Jul, Aug, Sept, Oct
time/days as house.

Last admission to
house 1/2hr
before closing

Tel: 01568 615721

NR. LEOMINSTER, HEREFORDSHIRE HR6 0DW
Owner: The National Trust   *Contact:* The Administrator

An elegant late 18th century house designed by Henry Holland and set in Capability Brown Park. The formal exterior belies the delicate interior with beautifully decorated ceilings and fine furniture and restored bedroom suite, nursery, Victorian laundry and pretty tiled Georgian dairy. Attractive garden with interesting plants and historic apple orchard in walled garden.
Location: 3 miles N of Leominster, 7 miles south of Ludlow on west side of A49.
Admission: Adult £3.60, Child £1.80, Family £9.90. Grounds only: £1.65

BROBURY HOUSE GARDENS
Tel: 01981 500229

Brobury, Hereford, Herefordshire, HR3 6BS.
Owner: E Okarma Esq   **Contact:** Mrs L Weaver
A Victorian Gentleman's Country House set in 8 acres of magnificent gardens with stunning views over the Wye Valley. Overnight accommodation available, art gallery with antique maps and prints on site.
Location: Off the A438 Hereford/Brecon Road at Brewardine Bridge.
Opening Times: All year, except Christmas and New Year. Mon to Sat, 10am - 4.30pm.

CROFT CASTLE

OPEN

April and October
1.30 - 4.30pm

Closed Good Friday

Easter: Sat, Sun & Mon
1.30 - 4.30pm

May to end of Sept
Wed to Sun and
Bank Hol Mon
1.30 - 5.30pm

Last admission to
house 1/2hr before
closing

Tel: 01568 780246

LEOMINSTER, HEREFORDSHIRE HR6 9PW
Owner: The National Trust   *Contact:* The Administrator

Home of the Croft family since Domesday (with a break of 170 years from 1750). Walls and corner towers date from 14th and 15th centuries, interior mainly 18th century when fine Georgian-Gothic staircase and plasterwork ceilings were added; splendid avenue of 350 year old spanish chestnuts. Iron age Fort (Croft Ambrey) may be reached by footpath. The walk is uphill (approx. 40 minutes).
Location: 5 miles north-west of Leominster, 9 miles south-west of Ludlow; approach from B4362.
Admission: Adult £3.10, Child £1.55, Family £8.50.

CWMMAU FARMHOUSE
Tel: 01497 831251

Brilley, Whitney on Wye, Herefordshire, HR3 6JP.
Owner: The National Trust   **Contact:** Mr D Joyce
Early 17th century timber-framed and stone-tiled farmhouse.
Location: 4m SW of Kington between A4111 & A438, approach by a narrow lane leading S from Kington - Brilley road at Brilley Mountain.
Opening Times: Easter, May Spring & Summer BH weekends only, Sat, Sun & Mon, 2.00pm - 6.00pm. Also 2, 9, 16, 20, 23 & 30 Aug, 2.00pm - 6.00pm.
Admission: £2.00.

DINMORE MANOR
Tel: 01432 830503   **Fax:** 01432 830322

Hereford, Herefordshire, HR4 8EE.
Owner: Mr R G Murray   **Contact:** Mr P Smollett
A range of impressive architecture from 14th - 20th century, Chapel, Cloisters and Great Hall, stained glass from 1930s. Outstanding views.
Location: 6 1/2m N of Hereford on A49.
Opening Times: 10.00am - 5.30pm throughout year.
Admission: Standard £2.50, Child accompanied by adult free.

EASTNOR CASTLE
See page 78 for full page entry.

GOODRICH CASTLE
Tel: 01608 890538

Ross-on-Wye, Herefordshire.
Owner: English Heritage   **Contact:** The Administrator
This magnificent red sandstone castle is remarkably complete, with a 12th century keep and extensive remains from the 13th and 14th centuries. From the battlements there are fine views of the Wye valley.
Location: 5m S of Ross-on-Wye off A40.
Opening Times: 1 Apr - 30 Sept, daily 10.00am - 6.00pm, 1 Oct - 31 Mar, daily 10.00am - 4.00pm. (Closed 24 - 26 Dec, 1 Jan).
Admission: Adult £2.00, Child £1.00, Conc £1.50.

HELLEN'S
Tel: 01531 660 668

Much Marcle, Ledbury, Herefordshire, HR8 2LY.
Owner: Pennington Mellor-Munthe Charity Trust   **Contact:** Mrs J C Pennington Mellor
Built in 1292 as a fortress and lived in since by descendants of the original builder, Mortimer, Earl of March.
Location: Ledbury - Ross on Wye A449, turn left at crossroads and follow sign in Much Marcle.
Opening Times: Good Fri - 2 Oct on Wed, Sat, Sun and BHs, 2.00pm - 6.00pm. Guided tours on the hour, last tour 5.00pm.
Admission: Adult £3.00, Child £1.00.

Eastnor Castle, Herefordshire

HEREFORD CATHEDRAL

Tel: 01432 359880

Hereford, Herefordshire, HR1 2NG.

Contact: Mr D Harding

Location: Hereford city centre on A49.
Opening Times: 7.30am - 6.00pm. Sun services: 8.00am, 10.00am, 11.30am and 3.30pm. Weekday services: 8.00am and 5.30pm.
Admission: Admission charge only for Mappa Mundi and Chained Library.

HERGEST CROFT GARDENS

OPEN

14 April - 29 Oct

1.30 - 6.30pm

Winter
By appointment

Tel: 01544 230160
Fax: As phone

Photo: Jerry Harper

KINGTON, HEREFORDSHIRE HR5 3EG

Owner: W L Banks and R A Banks　　*Contact:* Elizabeth Banks

From spring bulbs to autumn colour this is a garden for all seasons. One of the finest collections of trees and shrubs developed over 130 years by four generations of the Banks family. An old fashioned kitchen garden has spring and summer borders. Park Wood is a hidden valley with Rhododendrons up to 30 ft tall.
Location: Situated on the west side of Kington. $^1/_2$ mile off A44 turn left at the Rhayader end of bypass. Turn right and gardens are $^1/_4$ mile on left. Signposted from bypass.
Admission: Adult/OAP £2.50, Child up to 15 Free.
　　　　　　 Groups: Adult/OAP £1.80, Child Free.

HOW CAPLE COURT GARDENS

Tel: 01989 740626　**Fax:** 01989 740611

How Caple, Herefordshire, HR1 4SX.
Owner: P Lee Esq　　**Contact:** P Lee Esq
Exciting 11 acre garden overlooking river Wye. Combining terraced Edwardian gardens with water features and sunken Floretine garden. Mature trees and shrubs. Nursery selling interesting roses, herbaceous plants. Norman church.
Location: In How Caple, nr Ross-on-Wye.
Opening Times: Daily 9.30am - 5.00pm, Mon - Sat, 10.00am - 5.00pm, Sun April - Oct.
Admission: Adult £2.50, Child £1.25.

LONGTOWN CASTLE

Abbey Dore, Herefordshire.
Owner: English Heritage　　**Contact:** The Administrator
An unusual cylindrical keep built c.1200 with walls 15ft thick. There are excellent views of the nearby Black Mountains.
Location: 4m WSW of Abbey Dore.
Opening Times: Any reasonable time.

ROTHERWAS CHAPEL

Hereford, Herefordshire.
Owner: English Heritage　　**Contact:** The Administrator
This chapel, dating from the 14th and 16th centuries is testament to the past grandeur of the Bodenham family and features an interesting mid-Victorian side chapel.
Location: $1^1/_2$ m SE of Hereford on B4399.
Opening Times: Any reasonable time. Keykeeper at nearby filling station.

THE WEIR

Tel: 01684 850051

Swainshill, Hereford, Herefordshire.
Owner: The National Trust　　**Contact:** The Administrator
Delightful riverside garden particularly spectacular in early spring, with fine view over the River Wye and Black Mountains.
Location: 5m W of Hereford on A438.
Opening Times: 15 Feb - end Oct, Wed to Sun (inc Good Fri) & BH Mon, 11am - 6.pm.
Admission: £1.50.

SPECIAL EVENTS DIARY

- **7th - 8th May: Eastnor Castle**
  Giant Craft Fair.

- **8th May: Hergest Croft Gardens**
  NCCPG Plant Sale - 11am-6.30pm.

- **14th May: Eastnor Castle**
  Steam Fair.

- **16th May: How Caple Court Gardens**
  Concert in Gardens.

- **17th May: How Caple Court Gardens**
  "Magic Flute" performed in full dress with orchestra by Opera Box.

- **July - August : Eastnor Castle**
  Pugin Exhibition in our own Gothic Drawing Room designed by Pugin. Exhibition of Film and TV productions at Eastnor Castle.

- **4th July: Berrington Hall**
  Ludlow Festival Concert.

- **11th July: Berrington Hall**
  Tapestry of Music - music workshop for children followed by evening concert.

- **18th July: Berrington Hall**
  Classical Concert.

- **25th July: Berrington Hall**
  Classical Concert.

- **7th - 8th August: Eastnor Castle**
  Giant Craft Fair.

 THE NATIONAL TRUST　　 ENGLISH HERITAGE　　 HISTORIC HOUSES ASSOCIATION

HATFIELD HOUSE
Hatfield

This celebrated Jacobean house, which stands in its own great park, was built between 1607 and 1611 by Robert Cecil, 1st Earl of Salisbury and Chief Minister to King James I. It has been the family home of the Cecils ever since.

The main designer was Robert Lyminge helped, it is thought, by the young Inigo Jones. The interior decoration was the work of English, Flemish and French craftsmen, notably Maximilian Colt. The State Rooms are rich in world-famous paintings including The Rainbow Portrait of Queen Elizabeth I, and The Ermine Portrait by Nicholas Hilliard. Other paintings include works by Hoefnagel, Mytens, John de Critz the Elder and Sir Joshua Reynolds. Fine furniture from the 16th, 17th and 18th Centuries, rare tapestries and historic armour can be found in the State Rooms.

Within the delightful gardens stands the surviving wing of The Royal Palace of Hatfield (1497) where Elizabeth I spent much of her girlhood and held her first Council of State in November 1558. Some of her possessions can be seen in the House.

GARDENS
The West Gardens contain a formal garden, a scented garden with a herb garden at its centre, and a knot garden, planted with plants and bulbs which would have grown there in the 15th, 16th and 17th Centuries.

❖

SUITABILITY FOR OTHER EVENTS
Archery, equestrian events, shows, filming, wedding receptions, lunches and dinners up to 250 people.

EXTRA FACILITIES
The National Collection of Model Soldiers, 3,000 models in panoramic display. William IV Kitchen Exhibition. Nature Trails with supporting handbook or leaflet. Small children's Venture Play Area. Indoor and outdoor picnic areas.

ADVICE TO COURIERS & DRIVERS
Hardstanding for coaches. No dogs in House or gardens, and only in Park on leads. No photography is allowed in the House.

FACILITIES FOR THE DISABLED
Disabled and elderly visitors may alight at the entrance to the House, before parking. Toilet and lift facilities for the disabled.

PARKING FOR COACHES & CARS
Unlimited free parking for cars and coaches.

CATERING
The Old Palace Yard Restaurant/Coffee Shop seats up to 120. Prices from £2.00 to £6.00. Pre-booked lunch and tea available for parties of 10 or more: (01707) 262030. Special rates offered for groups. Catering facilities for special functions can be arranged Elizabethan Banquets held in the Old Palace throughout the year: (01707) 262055.

GUIDED TOURS
Groups of 40 or more are split into two, no extra charge for tour. Available in French, German, Italian or Spanish, by prior arrangement. Garden tours may be booked in advance: price £10.00 per tour. House Tours can be tailored to special interests.

GIFT AND GARDEN SHOPS
Open one hour before the House, selling items such as pot pourri made at Hatfield. Open six weekends prior to Christmas

GUIDE BOOKS
House Guide Book £1.20, Garden Guide Book £1.70. Leaflets available in French, German, Spanish, Italian and Japanese

SCHOOL VISITS/CHILDREN
Groups are welcome. 1 teacher free per 15 children. A guide is provided. Areas of interest include: kitchen exhibition, model soldier collection, adventure playground and picnic trails.

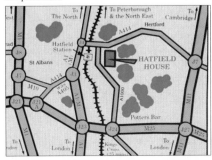

CONTACT

Col D McCord
Hatfield House
Hatfield
Hertfordshire
AL9 5NQ

Tel: (01707) 262823
Fax: (01707) 275719

LOCATION

21 miles North of London, A1(M), 8 miles North of M25 on A1000.

Bus: Local bus services from St Albans, Hertford, Hitchen and Barnet.

Rail: From Kings Cross and Moorgate every 30 mins. Hatfield BR Station is immediately opposite entrance to Park.

OPENING TIMES

Summer
25 March - 8 October

PARK
Daily 10.30am - 8.00pm

GARDENS
Daily 11.00am - 6.00pm

Last entry 5.00pm

HOUSE
Closed Mondays
Tues, Wed, Thurs, Fri
& Sat   Noon - 5.00pm
Last admission 4.00pm
Sun   1.30 - 5.00pm

NB Open Easter, May Day, Spring and August Bank Hol Mondays. 11.00am - 5.00pm Closed Good Friday

Winter
9 October - 24 March
Closed.

ADMISSION

HOUSE, GARDENS & EXHIBITIONS
Adult £5.00
Child* £3.20
OAP £4.10
Groups (Min 20m people)
Adult £4.10
Child* £2.70

PARK, GARDENS & EXHIBITIONS
Adult £2.80
Child* £2.10
OAP £2.50

Groups (Min 20 people)
Adult £2.50
Child* £1.90

* Aged 5-15

CONFERENCE AND FUNCTION FACILITIES

ROOM	DIMENSIONS	CAPACITY	LAYOUT	POWER POINTS	SUITABLE FOR A/V
The Old Palace	112' x 33'	300	Theatre	3	✓
		240	Schoolroom		
		100	U-shape		
		250	Buffet		
		250	Dinner/Dance		
		250	Lunch/Dinner		

KNEBWORTH HOUSE
Knebworth

Knebworth House has been the home of the Lytton family for over 500 years. Originally a Tudor Manor House, it was transformed 150 years ago with spectacular High Gothic decoration by Victorian romantic novelist Edward Bulwer-Lytton. There are many beautiful rooms, important portraits and furniture. The magnificent Jacobean Hall, where Charles Dickens acted in private theatricals and Winston Churchill painted at his easel, recently underwent restoration work which revealed an unknown early 17th Century hand-painted archway under the original panelling, now on permanent display to the public. Knebworth was the home of Constance Lytton, the suffragette, and Robert Lytton, Viceroy of India. Lord Lytton's Viceroyalty and the Great Delhi Durbar of 1877 are commemorated in a fascinating exhibition and audio-visual display.

GARDENS
The elaborate formal gardens of the Victorian era were simplified by Sir Edwin Lutyens. The unique quincunx pattern Herb Garden was designed for Knebworth in 1907 by Gertrude Jekyll and contains a delightful mixture of many herbs. A new feature for 1995 is the reinstated Maze. The House stands in 250 acres of parkland, with herds of Red and Sika Deer, Fort Knebworth, (a large Adventure Play-ground) Miniature Railway and is the setting for many Special Events.

❖

SUITABILITY FOR OTHER EVENTS
Fashion shows, air displays, archery, clay pigeon shooting, equestrian events, garden parties, shows, rallies and filming. Marquees and semi-permanent structures can be erected for a variety of requirements.

EXTRA FACILITIES
Evening House tours available by prior arrangement. Parkland, cricket pitch, helicopter landing facilities and Knebworth Barns (capacity 450) are all available for use. Speciality evenings, incorporating full use of all Knebworth facilities, can be arranged to suit your requirements. These include Indian Raj Evenings and Elizabethan Banquets with jousting.

ADVICE TO COURIERS & DRIVERS
All group visits must be booked in advance with Estate Office. In the House no dogs, pushchairs, photography, smoking or drinking are allowed. Dogs on leads are allowed in the Park.

FACILITIES FOR THE DISABLED
Disabled and elderly visitors may be driven to the entrance to the House, before parking in the allocated areas. The ground floor of the House is accessible to wheelchairs. Guide dogs are welcome in the House.

PARKING FOR CARS & COACHES
Parking for coaches and cars is unlimited.

CATERING BY LYTTON CATERING
Restaurant in 400 year old tithe barn. Special rates are available for groups who can book in advance. Menus available on request. Lytton Catering offers a full catering service in the Park as well as an extensive high quality outside catering service.

GUIDED TOURS
Guided tours operate Tuesdays - Fridays, at approx 30 minute intervals, or at specifically booked times up to 4.30pm. Tours at other times, including evenings, are available by prior arrangement. Average tour time 1 hour. Shorter tours by arrangement. Room Wardens on duty at weekends. A special 'Gothick Visions' tour is also available.

GIFT SHOPS
Open when the House is open to the public. Colour Guide Book £2.50 (1994 price).

SCHOOL VISITS/CHILDREN
National Curriculum based worksheets and children's guide available, covering a variety of topics ranging from the Tudors to the Victorians.

CONTACT

John Hoy
The Estate Office
Knebworth House
Knebworth
Hertfordshire
SG3 6PY

Tel: (01438) 812661
Fax: (01438) 811908

LOCATION

Public entrance direct from A1(M) at Junct. 7, 30 miles North of Central London and 12 miles North of M25.
Rail: Stevenage Station 2 miles (from Kings Cross).
Air: Luton Airport 8mls.
Taxi: (01438) 811122.

Landing facilities

OPENING TIMES

Summer
PARK AND
FORT KNEBWORTH
April 1 - 2 & 8 - 23 incl.

27 May - 4 Sept.
Daily: 11am - 5.30pm
(Closed June 30 - 3 July incl.)

Plus: Weekends & Bank Hols from 29 Apr -21 May; and weekends only from 9 Sept - 1 Oct.
11.00 am - 5.30pm

HOUSE AND GARDENS
As above but closed Mondays, except Bank Holiday Mondays.
Noon - 5.00pm.

Pre-booked Parties
1 April - 1 October
(Subject to special events)

Winter
Closed, except to pre-booked parties.

ADMISSION

All Year
HOUSE, GARDEN, PARK & PLAYGROUND
Adult £4.50
Child*/OAP £4.00
Groups (min. 20 people)
Adult £3.60
Child*/OAP £3.20
GARDENS, PARK & PLAYGROUND
All persons £3.50
Fam. Ticket (4 persons)
. . . .£12.00
Groups (min. 20 people)
All persons £2.80
SUPPLEMENT TICKETS TO HOUSE (individuals)
Adult £1.00
Child*/OAP 50p

Season Tickets available on Site.
* Age 3 - 16

CONFERENCE AND FUNCTION FACILITIES

ROOM	DIMENSIONS	CAPACITY	LAYOUT	POWER POINTS	SUITABLE FOR A/V
Banqueting Hall	26 'x 41'	45 - 80	Various	2	
Dining Parlour	21' x 38'	25 - 50	Various	3	
Library	32' x 21'	20 - 40	Various	2	
In Knebworth Barns Conference & Banqueting Centre, adjacent to Knebworth House:					
Manor Barn	70' x 25'	50 - 300	Various	8	✓
Lodge Barn	75' x 30'	30 - 250	Various	6	

ROSSWAY PARK
Berkhamsted

ROSSWAY PARK is probably the finest example of a privately-owned family estate within the green belt. It lies just south of Berkhamsted and has good access from the north and London.

The house itself is an excellent example of a mid-19th Century residence, retaining many of its original architectural and domestic features. It has been meticulously restored and the use of authenticated colours, fabrics and materials have re-created its high Victorian splendour.

Guests are assured of complete privacy and exclusive use of the house's facilities whilst at Rossway. Apart from the usual conference and catering requirements, a full range of outdoor activities can be organised in the extensive parkland.

The Hadden-Patons work very hard to create an atmosphere that is at once business-like and professional, yet warm and friendly. Clients are very much treated as guests, with personalised service and attention to detail being their hallmark.

SUITABILITY FOR OTHER EVENTS
Wedding Receptions, Dances, Lunch and Dinner parties. Large-scale Corporate events with full Event Management available. Film and still photography location work.

EXTRA FACILITIES
Outdoor heated swimming-pool. Trout fishing. Tennis Court. Six mile Riding Course with jumps. Croquet Lawn.

ADVICE TO COURIERS & DRIVERS
Note that the A41 By-Pass from M25 (Exit 20) is now open. Use A416 Chesham exit.

Guests to use main entrance, sub-contractors use Farm entrance.

FACILITIES FOR THE DISABLED
The toilets are not specially built but are able to accommodate disabled guests.

CATERING
In-house catering of the highest quality is available. Three outside caterers are used on a regular basis.

ACCOMMODATION
May sometimes be available in connection with events. Please enquire for further details.

CONTACT

Nigel Hadden-Paton
Rossway Park
Berkhamsted
Hertfordshire
HP4 3TZ

Tel: (01442) 865160
Fax: (01442) 863697

LOCATION

Road: Just south of Berkhamsted (A41 By-Pass) with good access from M1 (exit 12 from North, exit 8 from London), M25 (exit 20) and M40 (exit 2)

Rail: Berkhamsted Station (Euston).

Taxi: Gates Taxi (01442) 870223.

OPENING TIMES

All Year for Corporate Events, Conferences, Functions, etc.

ADMISSION

CONFERENCES
From £47.50 per person inclusive of venue hire and full catering.

ACTIVITY DAYS
from £52.50 per person inclusive of venue hire and full catering.

CONFERENCE AND FUNCTION FACILITIES

ROOM	DIMENSIONS	CAPACITY	LAYOUT	POWER POINTS	SUITABLE FOR A/V
Drawing Room	30' x 18'	36	Schoolroom	8	✓
		18	U-Shape		
		22	Boardroom		
		40	Theatre		
Library	15' x 15'	8	Boardroom	4	✓
Dining Room	26' x 18'	60	Buffet		
		40	Lunch/Dinner		

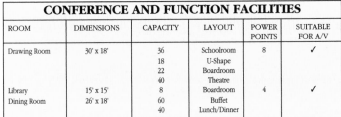

ASHRIDGE

Tel: 01442 851227

Ringshall, Berkhamsted, Hertfordshire, HP4 1NS.

Owner: The National Trust   **Contact:** Mr T Harvey

The Ashridge Estate comprises over 4,000 acres of woodlands, commons and downland. At the northerly end of the Estate the Ivinghoe Hills are an outstanding area of chalk downland which supports a rich variety of plants and insects. The Ivinghoe Beacon itself offers splendid views from some 700ft above sea level. This area may be reached from a car park at Steps Hill. The rest of Ashridge is an almost level plateau with many fine walks through woods and open commons.

Location: Between Northchurch & Ringshall, just off B4506.

Opening Times: Estate: open all year. Monument, Shop & Info Centre: Apr - end Oct: Mon to Thur & Good Fri, 2.00pm - 5.00pm. Sat, Sun & BH Mon 2.00pm - 5.30pm, last admission $1/2$ hour before closing.

Admission: Monument: £1.00.

BENINGTON LORDSHIP GARDENS

OPEN

Gardens only

April - August
Weds & Bank
Hol Mons.
Thurdays in Jul &
Aug only
12 noon - 5.00pm

Suns 2. - 5.00pm

Sept : Weds only
Parties anytime by
arrangement.

Tel: 01438 869668
Fax: 01438 869622

STEVENAGE, HERTFORDSHIRE

Owner: C H A Bott   *Contact:* Mrs C H A Bott

Terraced garden on the spectacular site of Norman castle ruins, fine folly, renowned double herbaceous borders, roses, rockery, kitchen garden with vegetables grown in raised beds and a small nursery surround Queen Ann manor with Edwardian verandah overlooking lakes and parkland.

Location: In village of Benington next to the church.

Admission: Adult £2.40, Accompanied Child under 18 Free. Wheelchairs Free.

BERKHAMPSTED CASTLE

Tel: 01536 402840

Berkhampsted, St Albans, Hertfordshire.

Owner: English Heritage   **Contact:** The Administrator

The extensive remains of a large 11th century motte and bailey castle which held a strategic position on the road to London.

Location: Adjacent to Berkhampsted station.

Opening Times: Any reasonable time.

CATHEDRAL & ABBEY CHURCH OF ST ALBANS

Tel: 01727 860780   **Fax:** 01727 850944

St Albans, Hertfordshire, AL1 1BY.

Contact: Nicholas Bates

Abbey church of Benedictine Monastery founded 793. Britain's first martyr. Rebuilt 1077 became Cathedral in 1877. Many 13th century wall paintings, ecumenical shrine of St Alban (1308).

Location: Centre of St Albans.

Opening Times: Summer 9am - 6.45pm. Winter 9am - 5.45pm. Telephone for details of services, concerts and special events Mon - Sat 11.00am - 4.00pm.

Admission: Free of charge.

CROMER WINDMILL

Tel: 01438 861662

Ardeley, Stevenage, Hertfordshire, SG2 7QA.

Owner: Hertfordshire Building Preservation Trust   **Contact:** Simon Bennett

17th century Post Windmill under restoration to working order.

Location: 4m NE of Stevenage on B1037.

Opening Times: Sun 14th May - Sun 10th Sept, and Bank Hols. 2nd & 4th Weds 17th May - 6th Sept, 2.30pm - 5.00pm.

Admission: Adults £1.00, Child 25p, Coach parties £10.00.

GORHAMBURY HOUSE

Tel: 01727 855000   **Fax:** 01727 843675

St Albans, Hertfordshire, AL3 6AH.

Owner: The Earl Of Verulam   **Contact:** The Earl Of Verulam

Late 18th century house by Sir Robert Taylor. Extensive collection of 17th century portraits.

Location: In St Albans.

Opening Times: Thurs, May - Sept, 2.00pm - 5.00pm.

Admission: Adult £3.50, Child £2.50, Conc £2.00, Groups of 12 plus.

Hatfield House, Hertfordshire

HATFIELD HOUSE

See page 81 for full page entry.

KNEBWORTH HOUSE

See page 82 for full page entry.

OLD GORHAMBURY HOUSE

Tel: 01727 54051

St Albans, Hertfordshire.
Owner: English Heritage   **Contact:** The Administrator
The remains of the Elizabethan mansion, particularly the porch of the Great Hall, illustrate the impact of the Renaissance of English architecture.
Location: $^1/_4$ m W of Gorhambury House and accessible only through private drive from A4147 at St Albans (2m).
Opening Times: May - Sept, Thur only 2.00pm - 5.00pm, or other times by appointment.

ROSSWAY PARK

See page 83 for full page entry.

SCOTT'S GROTTO

Tel: 01920 464131

Ware, Hertfordshire.
Owner: East Hertfordshire District Council   **Contact:** Mr J Watson
One of the finest grottos in England built in the 1760s by Quaker Poet John Scott.
Location: Off A119 Hertford Road.
Opening Times: 1 Apr - 30 Sept, Sat and BH Mon, 2.00pm - 4.30pm. Also by appointment.
Admission: Suggested donation of £1.00 for adults and children free.

SHAW'S CORNER

Tel: 01438 820307

Ayot St. Lawrence, Welwyn, Hertfordshire, AL6 9BX.
Owner: The National Trust   **Contact:** The Administrator
An early 20th century house, and the home of George Bernard Shaw from 1906 until his death in 1950. Many literary and personal relics are shown in the downstairs rooms, which remain as in his lifetime. Shaw's bedroom and bathroom are also on view, and there is a display room upstairs.
Location: At SW end of village, 2m NE of Wheathampstead, approx. 2m from B653.
Opening Times: 1 Apr - end Oct, Wed to Sun & BH Mon, 2.00pm - 6.00pm, closed Good Fri. Parties by written appointment only, Mar to end Nov. Last admission 5.30pm.
Admission: £3.00, family £7.50, no reduction for parties.

THE GARDEN OF THE ROSE

Tel: 01727 850461   **Fax:** 01727 850360

Chiswell Green, St Albans, Hertfordshire, AC2 3NR.
Owner: Royal National Rose Society   **Contact:** Lt Col Grapes
Showgrounds of the Royal National Rose Society with over 30,000 plants in 1,650 varieties.
Location: 2m S of St Albans.
Opening Times: Mon - Sat, 9.00am - 5.00pm. Sun and Aug BH 10.00am - 6.00pm.
Admission: Adult £4.00, Senior citizens £3.50, Conc £3.50, Groups of 20 plus £3.50. Accompanied child under 16 free.

Benington Lordship Gardens, Hertfordshire

SPECIAL EVENTS DIARY

- **16th - 17th April: Knebworth House**
  American Civil War Battle Re-Enactments - The Southern Skirmish Association.

- **30th April: Knebworth House**
  10th Knebworth/Windsor Archery Tournament (Provisional).

- **7th - 8th May: Knebworth House**
  Knebworth Country Show - falconry, archery, gun dogs, sheep dogs clay shooting etc.

- **11th - 14th May: Hatfield House**
  Living Crafts. The Largest Craft Fair in Europe over 300 craftsmen selling or demonstrating their skills.

- **13th - 14th May: Knebworth House**
  Hertfordshire Garden Show

- **8th May: Hergest Croft Gardens**
  NCCPG Plant Sale - 11am-6.30pm.

- **11th June: Knebworth House**
  MG Owners Club National Rally (Provisional).

- **18th June: Knebworth House**
  Morris Minor Owners Club National Rally

- **24th - 25th June: Hatfield House**
  The Festival of Gardening at Midsummer – A unique mixture of Flower Show and Garden Party.

- **16th July: Knebworth House**
  Pre-50 American Auto Club "Rally of the Giants" - Large display of classic american cars.

- **23rd July: Knebworth House**
  The Corvette Nationals '95 ((Provisional).

- **30th: Knebworth House**
  Fireworks and Laser Symphony Concert - Ticket Hotline: 01625 573477.

- **5th - 6th August: Knebworth House**
  NSRA Hot Rod Supernationals - Rally of Street Rods with Custom and Classic American cars of the 50's and 60's.

- **6th August: Hatfield House**
  Transport Spectacular Victorian, Vintage and classic cars.

- **11th - 13th August: Hatfield House**
  Great British Pottery and Ceramics Festival.

- **19th - 20th August: Knebworth House**
  Hertfordshire Craft Fair.

- **27th-28th: Knebworth House**
  Classic Car Roadshow.

- **3rd September: Knebworth House**
  Classic American Auto Club Rally - some of the finest pre-1943 vehicles on display.

- **10th September: Knebworth House**
  Sport Age Mountain Bike Event (Provisional).

- **23rd-24th: Knebworth House**
  NAFAS Festival of Flowers "The Story of Knebworth House".

OSBORNE HOUSE
East Cowes

Built by Queen Victoria in 1845 as a refuge from the affairs of state, and designed by Thomas Cubitt, Osborne House has been preserved almost unchanged since the Queen's death in 1901. The house itself is an Italinate villa with two tall towers and the apartments and rooms contain many mementoes of royal travels abroad. Included in the cost of admission is a ride in a Victorian horse-drawn carriage through the extensive grounds to the Swiss Cottage with its charming gardens and museum

❖

SUITABILITY FOR OTHER EVENTS
Filming , Concerts, Drama.

ADVICE TO COURIERS & DRIVERS
No photography in the House. Coach drivers and tour leaders have free entry. One extra place for every additional 20 people.

FACILITIES FOR THE DISABLED
Wheelchairs available. Access to house via ramp. Ground floor access only. Adapted toilet in reception centre.

PARKING FOR COACHES & CARS
Plenty of car and coach spaces available.

CATERING
Teas. coffees and light snacks.

GUIDED TOURS
Personal stereos available.

GIFT SHOP
A wide selection of souvenirs available.

GUIDE BOOK
Souvenir Guides available for purchase.

SCHOOL VISITS/CHILDREN
School visits are free, please book in advance. An education room is available.

CONTACT

The House Administrator
Osborne House
Royal Apartments
East Cowes
Isle of Wight
PO32 6JY

Tel: (01983) 200022

LOCATION

1 mile south east
of East Cowes.

Isle of Wight ferry terminal: East Cowes.

OPENING TIMES

Summer

House
1 April - 30 September
Daily
10.00am - 5.00pm

Last admission 4.30pm

Grounds
1 April - 30 September
Daily
10.00am - 6.00pm

Winter
House & Grounds

1 October - 31 October
Daily
10.00am - 5.00pm
Last admission 4.00pm

ADMISSION

Adult £5.80
Child* £2.90
OAP/Students/ . . . . . .
UB40 Holders . . £4.40

Grounds only
Adult £3.00
Child* £1.50
OAP/Students/ . . . . . .
UB40 Holders . . £2.30

* 5 - 15 yrs. Under 5's free.

GROUPS
15% off groups of 11 or more.

CARISBROOKE CASTLE

**NEWPORT,
ISLE OF WIGHT PO32 1XY**
Owner: English Heritage
Contact: The Head Custodian
Tel: 01983 522107

Dating from Norman times and famous as the prison for Charles I in 1647-8. There are seven acres of castle and earthworks to explore with sweeping views in every direction from the battlements. In the centre of the castle are the great hall and chamber containing the Isle of Wight Museum. Perhaps the most charming sight is the well-house where donkeys work a 16th century wheel to pull water from the castle's well.

Location: 1¹/₂ miles south of Newport, south of the village of Carisbrooke.

Admission: Adults £3.50, OAP/Student/UB40 £2.60, Child £1.80.
15% discount for parties of 11+.

OPEN
1 April - 30 Sept: Daily   10.00am - 6.00pm
1 Oct - 31 March: Daily   10.00am - 4.00pm

APPULDURCOMBE HOUSE

Tel: 01983 852484

Wroxhall, Shanklin, Isle Of Wight.
Owner: English Heritage   **Contact:** The Administrator
The bleached shell of a fine 18th century baroque style house standing in grounds landscaped by Capability Brown.
Location: ¹/₂ m W of Wroxall off B3327.
Opening Times: 1 Apr - 30 Sept daily, 10.00am - 6.00pm.
Admission: Adult £1.30, Child 70p, Conc £1.00.

BARTON MANOR GARDENS

Tel: 01983 292835   **Fax:** 01983 293923

East Cowes, Isle Of Wight, PO32 6LB.
Owner: Mrs Julia Richards   **Contact:** Mrs Julia Richards
Location: A3201, on the East Cowes Rd
Opening Times: 1 Apr - 9 Oct, daily, 10.30am - 5.30pm.
Admission: Adult £3.75, OAP/party/conc £3.20, 1 Child under 15 per adult is free.

BEMBRIDGE WINDMILL

Tel: 01983 873945

Bembridge, Isle of Wight, PO35 5NT.
Owner: The National Trust   **Contact:** The Custodian
Dating from around 1700. The only windmill to survive on the island. Much of the wooden machinery can still be seen.
Location: ¹/₂m S of Bembridge on A3395.
Opening Times: 2 Sept - 31 Oct: daily except Sat (but open Easter Sat & daily in Jul & Aug), 10.00am - 5.00pm.
Admission: £1.20, no reduction for parties.

HASELEY MANOR

Tel: 01983 865420   **Fax:** 01983 867547

Arreton, Isle Of Wight, PO30 3AN.

Contact: Mr R J Young
The oldest and largest manor open to the public on the Island, recently restored with over 20 rooms on view.
Location: Main Sandown to Newport Road.
Opening Times: Easter - 31 Oct, daily, 10.00am - 5.30pm.
Admission: Adult £3.65, Child £2.75, Conc £3.10, Groups £3.10.

MORTON MANOR

Tel: 01983 406186

Brading, Isle Of Wight.
Owner: Mr J B Trzebski   **Contact:** Mr J B Trzebski
Morton was a hamlet on the edge of Brading Harbour, built in 1249 on the existing site for the de Aula family, of Norman descent. Since then it was structurally altered with the addition of a Tudor Longhouse, followed by major rebuilding in 1680. Refurbished in the Georgian period. Magnificent gardens.
Location: Off A3055 in Brading.
Opening Times: 2 Apr - 31 Oct, daily except Sat, 10.00am - 5.30pm.
Admission: Adult £3.00, Conc £2.50, Group £2.

NUNWELL HOUSE & GARDENS

Tel: 01983 407240

Brading, Isle Of Wight, PO36 OJQ.
Owner: Mrs J A Aylmer   **Contact:** Mrs J A Aylmer
A lived in family home with fine furniture, attractive gardens and historic connections with Charles I.
Location: 3 m S of Ryde signed off A3055.
Opening Times: 2 Jul - 27 Sept (groups at other dates by arrangement). Sun 1.00pm - 5.00pm. Mon, Tues, Wed, 10.00am - 5.00pm. Thurs, Fri and Sat, closed.

OSBORNE HOUSE

See page 86 for full page entry.

OLD TOWN HALL

Tel: 01983 741052

Newtown, Isle Of Wight.
Owner: The National Trust   **Contact:** The Custodian
The small, now tranquil, village of Newtown once sent two members to Parliament, and the Town Hall was the setting for these often turbulent elections.
Location: Between Newport & Yarmouth, 1m N of A3054.
Opening Times: 27 Mar - 30 Oct: Mon, Wed & Sun (but open Good Fri, Easter Sat and Tues & Thur in Jul & Aug), 2.00pm - 5.00pm, last admission 4.45pm.
Admission: £1.10, no reduction for parties.

THE NEEDLES OLD BATTERY

Tel: 01983 754772

Alum Bay, Isle of Wight.
Owner: The National Trust   **Contact:** The Administrator
A Victorian coastal fort built in 1862, 250ft above sea level. A 200ft tunnel leads to spectacular views of Needles Rocks, lighthouse and Hampshire and Dorset coastline. Two original Rifled Muzzle Loader gun barrels are mounted on carriages in the parade ground, and the Laboratory. Searchlight Position and Position Finding Cells have been restored.
Location: At Needles Headland, W of Freshwater Bay and Alum Bay (B3322).
Opening Times: 30 Mar - 2 Nov: Sun to Thur (but open Easter weekend and daily in Jul & Aug), 10.30am - 5.00pm, last admission 4.30pm.
Admission: £2.40, Family ticket £6.00, no reduction for parties.

YARMOUTH CASTLE

Tel: 01983 760678

Yarmouth, Isle of Wight.
Owner: English Heritage   **Contact:** The Administrator
This last addition to Henry VIII's coastal defences was completed in 1547 and is, unusually for its kind, square with a fine example of an angle bastion. It was garrisoned well into the 19th century. It houses exhibitions of paintings of the Isle of Wight and photographs of old Yarmouth.
Location: In Yarmouth adjacent to car ferry terminal.
Opening Times: 1st Apr - 30 Sept daily, 10am - 6pm. 1 Oct - 31 Oct daily, 10 am - 4pm.
Admission: Adult £2.00, Child £1.50, Conc £1.00.

Osborne House, Isle of Wight

BOUGHTON MONCHELSEA PLACE
Maidstone

A Battlemented manor house of Kentish Ragstone, situated above its own landscaped deer park. The house was built in 1576 by Robert Rudston. The home of the late Michael Winch, the house has been in the Winch family since 1903. Standing in a prominent position 310 feet above sea level with the 'reputed' finest view of the Weald of Kent.

The interior is still that of an inhabited home, and contains fine examples of period furniture and works of art to which successive generations have added. Nursery, schoolroom displays of dresses and agricultural bygones.

GARDENS AND GROUNDS
The 60 acre Deer Park has a herd of fallow deer - records of which go back as far as 1669. Two walled gardens: the lower contains a fine mixture of unusual herbaceous plants and shrubs, the top older varieties of fruit trees and unusual shrubs.

❖

CONTACT
C W Gooch
Boughton Monchelsea
Place
Boughton Monchelsea
Maidstone
Kent
ME17 4BU

Tel: (01622) 743120

LOCATION
Junction 8 off M20, take B2163 through Leeds to A274. Cross A274 on to B2163. Boughton Monchelsea Place is 3 miles on left.

4¹/₂ miles south of Maidstone. A229 from Maidstone at Linton on B2163.

London 1 hour, 10 mins.

Rail: Maidstone Station

SUITABILITY FOR OTHER EVENTS
Wedding Receptions, fashion shows, product launches, conferences, seminars, clay pigeon shoots, archery, quad biking, fly fishing casting, garden parties, fetes, filming. Exquisite site for marquees.

EXTRA FACILITIES
Deer Park.

ADVICE TO COURIERS & DRIVERS
Free refreshments for coach drivers and couriers. No photography or dogs in the House.

FACILITIES FOR THE DISABLED
Disabled toilets available. Disabled and elderly visitors may alight at the rear entrance to the House. Access for disabled into Tea Room and lower floor of the House.

PARKING FOR COACHES & CARS
Unlimited parking for cars and coaches 300 yards from House.

CATERING
Afternoon Teas in Tudor Tea Room, or Inner Courtyard (weather permitting). Lunches, Suppers, Dinners available, menus on request.

PRIVATE DINING
Luncheons, Suppers and Dinners in House (Max. formal seating 45 in either Red Dining Room, Drawing Room or Courtyard Room; informal (buffets) 140 in House, 55 in Courtyard Room.

GIFT SHOP
The Gift Shop is open whenever house is open.

GUIDED TOURS
Visitors are always guided. Average time taken to see the House 55 minutes.

GUIDE BOOKS
Colour guide book available.

SCHOOL VISITS/CHILDREN
Educational Booklet available. Discounted admission. Any day during open season, by prior arrangement. Groups of 20 or more.

GROUP VISITS
By prior arrangement. On days of the week morning or afternoon, during open season. Discounted admission. Groups of 20 or more.

OPENING TIMES

Summer

Easter - 15 October
Sundays   2 - 6.00pm

June, July & August
Wednesdays   2 - 6.00pm

Bank Holiday Sundays and Mons.   2 - 6.00 pm

Last Tour 5.15pm

Groups by appointment at any time.

Winter
October - Easter
Closed

ADMISSION

HOUSE & GROUNDS
Adult £3.75
Child* £2.50
OAP/Disabled . . .£3.50

Groups (min 20 people)
Adult £3.25
Child* £2.25
OAP/Disabled . . .£3.25

GROUNDS ONLY
Adult £2.25
Child* £1.50
OAP/Disabled . . .£2.50

Groups (min 20 people)
Adult £2.25
Child* £1.75
OAP/Disabled . . .£2.25

* Aged 0 - 14.

CONFERENCE AND FUNCTION FACILITIES

ROOM	DIMENSIONS	CAPACITY	LAYOUT	POWER POINTS	SUITABLE FOR A/V
Red Dining Room	31' 3" x 19' 6"	25 - 60	Various	3	✓
Drawing Room	31' 3" x 19' 6"	25 - 60	Various	5	✓
Courtyard Room	36' 9" x 13' 5"	25 - 75	Various	8	✓
Entrance Hall	26' x 19'	50 - 60	Buffet	2	✓

COBHAM HALL
Cobham

"One of the largest, finest and most important houses in Kent" Cobham Hall is an outstandingly beautiful, red brick mansion in Elizabethan, Jacobean, Carolean and 18th Century styles.

It yields much of interest to the student of art, architecture and history. The Elizabethan wings were begun in 1584 whilst the central section contains the Gilt Hall, wonderfully decorated by John Webb, Inigo Jones' most celebrated pupil, 1654. Further rooms were decorated by James Wyatt in the 18th century.

Cobham Hall, now a girls' school, has been visited by several of the English monarchs from Elizabeth I to Edward VIII, later Duke of Windsor. Charles Dickens used to walk through the grounds from his house in Higham to the Leather Bottle Pub in Cobham Village. In 1883, the Hon Ivo Bligh, later the 8th Earl of Darnley, led the victorious English cricket team against Australia bringing home the "Ashes" to Cobham.

GARDENS

The gardens, landscaped for the 4th Earl by Humphry Repton, are gradually being restored by the Cobham Hall Heritage Trust. Extensive tree planting and clearing have taken place since the hurricanes of the 1980s. The Gothic Dairy and some of the classical garden buildings are being renovated. The gardens are particularly delightful in Spring, when they are resplendent with daffodils and a myriad of rare bulbs.

❖

SUITABILITY FOR OTHER EVENTS
Cobham Hall is a unique venue for any function, business or social. Providing for residential (250 beds) or non-residential courses. A wide choice of period or modern rooms, including the magnificent 1,200 sq.m .Gilt Hall, to suit every occasion. 150 acres of parkland ideal for sports events and open air concerts.

EXTRA FACILITIES
New multi-purpose sports centre and indoor 25m swimming pool. Use of Art Studios, Music Wing, Tennis Courts. Helicopter landing area, field study area, nature conservation. Lectures on the property, gardens and history can be arranged in the Gilt Hall for up to 180 people.

ADVICE TO COURIERS & DRIVERS
Pre-booked coach parties are welcome outside advertised opening times. Coffee, teas, lunch (cap. 200). Special events days. No smoking. Large free parking area.

FACILITIES FOR THE DISABLED
Disabled and elderly visitors should be aware that the house tour involves two staircases. Limited access for wheelchairs, ground floor only.

CATERING
Excellent in-house catering team for private and corporate events (cap. 200). Afternoon Teas served when open to public. Other meals by arrangement.

GUIDED TOURS
All tours guided: Historical guided tours of house for up to 25 people; time taken 1¹/₂ hours. Tours of garden by arrangement.

GIFT SHOP
Open as House. Guide books of house and garden, £1 each.

SCHOOL VISITS/ CHILDREN
Guide provided, £2.00 per child: special guide book and worksheets for 1995.

CONTACT

Mrs Sue Anderson
Cobham Hall
Cobham
Kent
DA12 3BL

Tel: (01474) 824319
or (01474) 823371
Fax: (01474) 822995

LOCATION

Situated adjacent to the A2/M2, 8 miles east of Junc. 2 on M25, between Gravesend and Rochester.
London - 25 miles
Rochester - 5 miles
Canterbury - 30 miles

Rail: Meopham 3 miles.
Gravesend 5 miles.
Taxis at both stations.

Air: Gatwick 45 mins.
Heathrow 60 mins,
Stansted 50 mins.

OPENING TIMES

Summer
April: 5, 6, 9, 14, 15, 16, 17, 19, 20.
June: 1, 2.
July: 5, 6, 9, 12, 13, 19, 20, 23.
August: 2, 3, 6, 9, 10, 13, 16, 20, 23, , 27, 28.
2.00 - 5.00pm
(Last tour 4.45pm).
The historical guided tour lasts approx 1¹/₂ hrs. Special tours arranged outside standard opening times.

Winter
By arrangement

ADMISSION

Adults £2.50
Child (4 - 14yrs.) . . £2.00
OAP £2.00

GARDENS & PARKLAND

• Self-guided tour and booklet £1.00
• Historical/Conservation tour of Grounds (by arrangement) Per person £2.50

CONFERENCE AND FUNCTION FACILITIES

ROOM	DIMENSIONS	CAPACITY	LAYOUT	POWER POINTS	SUITABLE FOR A/V
Gilt Hall	41' x 34'	180	Theatre	4	✓
		90	Banquet		
Wyatt Dining Room	49' x 23'	135	Theatre	6	✓
		85	Banquet		
Clifton Dining Room	24' x 23'	75	Theatre	3	✓
		50	Banquet		
Activities Centre	119' x 106'	300	Theatre	10	✓
		250	Banquet		

FINCHCOCKS
GOUDHURST

In 1970 Finchcocks was acquired by Richard Burnett, leading exponent of the early piano, and it now contains his magnificent collection of some eighty historical keyboard instruments: chamber organs, harpsichords, virginals, spinets and early pianos. About half of these are restored to full concert conditions and are played whenever the house is open to the public. The house, with its high ceilings and oak panelling provides the perfect setting for music performed on period instruments, and Finchcocks is now a music centre of international repute. Many musical events take place there.

There is also a fascinating collection of pictures and prints, mainly on musical themes, and there is a special exhibition on display on the theme of the eighteenth century Pleasure Gardens, such as Vauxhall and Ranelalgh, which includes costumers and tableaux.

Finchcocks is a fine Georgian baroque manor noted for its outstanding brickwork, with a dramatic front elevation attributed to Thomas Archer. Named after the family who lived on the site in the 13th century, the present house was built in 1725 for barrister Edward Bathurst, kinsman to Earl Bathurst. Despite having changed hands many times, it has suffered remarkably little alteration and retains most of its original features. It stands in a beautiful garden, now fully restored, and offers extensive views over the Kentish landscape of parklands, farmland and hopgardens.

CONTACT

Mrs Katrina Burnett
Finchcocks
Goudhurst
Kent
TN17 1HH

Tel: 01580 211702

Fax: 01580 211007

LOCATION

Off A262, 2 miles west of village of Goudhurst. 5 miles from Cranbrook, 10 miles from Tunbridge Wells, 45 miles from London (1 ¹/₂ hours)

Rail: Marden 6 miles (no taxi), Paddock Wood 8 miles (taxi), Tunbridge Wells 10 miles (taxi).

Air: Gatwick, 1 hour.

SUITABILITY FOR OTHER EVENTS
Ideal for musical events : chamber music concerts, demonstration recitals on instruments of the collection, as well as lectures, workshops and courses. Speciality: musical evenings with dinners. Also very suitable for wedding receptions, corporate entertaining, conferences, seminars and promotions. The gardens lend themselves to garden parties and events like archery and ballooning.

EXTRA FACILITIES
There is a brick terrace to the side of the house made for a marquee. Ideal for functions which would be too large for the house itself, such as larger weddings, opera, masked balls and fairs. Marquees can also be set up on the back lawn and the recently restored walled garden.

ADVICE TO COURIERS & DRIVERS
Groups welcome most days from start of April to the end of October. In some circumstances groups can be taken up to Christmas. Most private group visits include a personal tour of the house and collection by Richard and Katrina Burnett, and a demonstration by Richard Burnett (see Guided Tours) Min. no. usually 25, max. 100. All groups must pre-book. No videos in the house, and photography by permission only. No dogs in the garden but allowed in the parkland to the front of the house. Free meals for couriers and drivers.

FACILITIES FOR THE DISABLED
Limited. Good parking close to the house. Toilets on the level, but main indoor toilets involve stairs. Very suitable for visually handicapped visitors.

PARKING FOR COACHES & CARS
2 to 3 coaches and 100 cars on gravel forecourt in front of house. Additional parking available for special events.

CATERING
The vaulted cellar restaurant can accommodate up to 100. Full catering available by arrangement from formal waitress served dinners, buffets, teas and light refreshments. Wide range of prices from £2.90 to £25.00. Fully licensed. Picnics permitted in the grounds.

GUIDED TOURS
Demonstrations/recitals on instruments of the collection whenever required. These are usually given by Richard Burnett himself, and are extremely lively and entertaining, and suitable for those who have no interest in classical music as well as musical audiences. Average length of visit 2 ¹/₂ - 4 hours, to allow time for looking round house, instruments, exhibition and garden, the demonstration/ recital and a meal or refreshments.

GIFT SHOP
Well stocked shop with wide range of goods, and many musical items, including second-hand sheet music. Many compact discs and cassettes, over 50 of which were recorded at Finchcocks.

GUIDE BOOKS
A general guide book with coloured photographs at £2.50; catalogues of the collection also £2.50.

SCHOOL AND STUDENT VISITS/ CHILDREN
Opportunity to play instruments. Can be linked to special projects and National Curriculum syllabus. Also special visits for children: 'A Window on the Eighteenth Century' with costumes and talk.

OPENING TIMES

Summer
Easter Sun – end of Sept
Suns & Bank Hol Mons
Daily in August except
Mondays and Tuesdays
2.00 - 6.00pm

Pre-booked groups welcome most days: April to October and in some circumstances up to Christmas.

Winter
Closed Jan - March
Mainly closed in
Nov - Dec.
(Min. No. for special opening 50 people)

ADMISSION

OPEN DAYS
House Garden & Music
  Adults/OAP £4.80
  Child £3.20
  Student £3.80

PRIVATE DAYS
  Day from £5.00
  Evening £5.50 - £6.80
  dependent on programme

GARDEN ONLY:
  Adult £1.50
  Child 50p

*Groups: Open Days and Non-Open Days minimum of 20 persons.

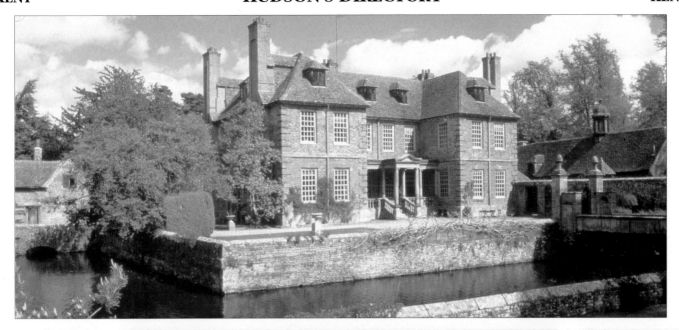

GROOMBRIDGE PLACE GARDENS 🏛
Tunbridge Wells

Surrounded by 164 acres of breathtaking parkland this mystical site has an intriguing history stretching back to medieval times. The gardens at Groombridge Place have been described as a most remarkable and a very special survival. Laid out in the 17th century by Philip Packer, a friend of Sir Christopher Wren, and admired by the famous diarist and horticulturist John Evelyn these are gardens to delight the senses.

- The stunning period setting for Peter Greenaway's acclaimed film "The Draughtman's Contract"
- Medieval moat with water lily collection.
- 17th century formal gardens with ancient topiary and fountain displays.

- Canal boat rides to Enchanted Forest with its mystical spring fed pools and dramatic views over the Weald below.
- One of Englands largest Birds of Prey Sanctuaries.
- Award winning children's garden.

"Extreme and almost sylvan beauty" W Oustram Tristram. Moated Houses - 1910.

"The beautiful moat, as still and luminous as quicksilver." Sir Arthur Conan Doyle.

"So satisfying", "A charm that enticed". Vita Sackville-West. The Heir - 1922

"Enjoy a gem from the Restoration period" The Times - 1994

"A myterious beauty that feeds the imagination". Homes & Gardens - 1994

❖

CONTACT

The Estate Office
Groombridge Place
Groombridge
Tunbridge Wells
Kent
TN3 9QG

Tel: (01892) 863999

OPENING TIMES

Summer
1 April - 31 October

Daily 10.00am - 6.00pm

Winter
1 November to 31 March.
Closed to the general public.

ADMISSION

Adult	£3.50
Child (under 17)	£2.25
OAP	£3.00
Groups Per person	£3.00
Guided Tour Per person	£4.00

LOCATION

Groombridge Place is located on the B2110 just off the A264. South-West of Royal Tunbridge Wells and 9 miles east of Grinstead.

Rail: London Charing Cross to Tunbridge Wells 55minutes.

SUITABILITY FOR OTHER EVENTS
Suitable for a wide variety of events.

EXTRA FACILITIES
164 acres of parkland, helicopter landing area and marqueé sites.

ADVICE TO COURIERS & DRIVERS
Free refreshments for drivers. No dogs allowed.

FACILITIES FOR THE DISABLED
Toilets for the disabled.

PARKING FOR COACHES AND CARS
50 yards from the the gardens.

CATERING
Refreshment facilities for afternoon tea. Groups should book in advance.

GUIDED TOURS
Tours last approximately 1¼hrs. £4.00 per head for groups of 20.

GIFT SHOP
The Country Store.

CONFERENCE AND FUNCTION FACILITIES

ROOM	DIMENSIONS	CAPACITY	LAYOUT	POWER POINTS	SUITABLE FOR A/V
Baron's Hall	42' 6" x 17' 6"	100		3	✓
Wren Room	24' x 3" x 17' 9"	40		2	✓

HEVER CASTLE
Edenbridge

LOCATION

M25 Junct. 5 and 6

M23 Junct. 10,

A21 North Tonbridge
exit, follow signs.

Rail: Hever Station
1 mile (no taxis),
Edenbridge Town
3 miles (taxis).

Taxi: Relyon Car
Services,
Tel: (01732) 863800,
Beeline Taxis
Sevenoaks 456214

HEVER CASTLE dates back to 1270, when the gatehouse, outer walls and the inner moat were first built. 200 years later the Bullen (or Boleyn) family added the comfortable Tudor Manor house constructed within the walls. This was the childhood home of Anne Boleyn, Henry VIII's second wife and mother of Elizabeth I. A costume exhibition in the Long Gallery includes all of the familiar characters from this royal romance. The Castle was later given to Henry VIII's fourth wife, Anne of Cleves.

In 1903, the estate was bought by the American millionaire William Waldorf Astor, who became a British subject and the First Lord Astor of Hever. He invested an immense amount of time, money and imagination in restoring the castle and grounds. Master craftsmen were employed and the castle was filled with a magnificent collection of furniture, tapestries and other works of art.

The Miniature Model Houses exhibition, depicting life in English Country Houses through the ages, has been extended this year to include rooms from the Victorian period.

GARDENS

Between 1904-8 over 30 acres of formal gardens were laid out and planted, these have now matured into one of the most beautiful gardens in England. The unique Italian garden is a four acre walled garden containing a superb collection of statuary and sculpture exhibited amongst the flowers and shrubs. Other areas include the rose garden, Anne Boleyn's Tudor style garden, a traditional yew maze and some unusual topiary. The grounds contain many water features, along with a 35 acre lake there are fountains, cascades, grottoes and an inner and outer moat, fountains cascades and pools - and some fine topiary. The yew-hedge maze is open to the public.

SUITABILITY FOR OTHER EVENTS
Filming, product launches and wedding receptions. Dinner dances in Pavilion Restaurant.

EXTRA FACILITIES
Lectures on the property, its contents, gardens and history for up to 70 people in summer and 250 in winter. Prices on application. Projectors, and screen can be provided. Additional facilities for clients using the Tudor Village include outdoor heated pool, tennis court, billiard room, gardens/grounds.

ADVICE TO COURIERS & DRIVERS
Free coach parking. Free admission for driver and tour leader. Voucher for driver. Advisable to book in advance. Group rates for 15+. Allow 2 hours for visit.

FACILITIES FOR THE DISABLED
There are toilets for the disabled. Gardens mostly accessible, but ground floor only of Castle. No ramps into castle so can be difficult. Access to restaurants, gift shop and book shop. Some additional wheelchairs available.

PARKING FOR COACHES & CARS
Capacity of car park - approx 1000 cars, 100 yards from the Castle and 30 coaches, 200 yards from the Castle.

CATERING
Two self-service restaurants offer visitors lunch, tea and refreshments. Supper is provided during Open Air Theatre season. Special rates are offered to groups and menus/prices on request. Catering facilities for special functions/conferences include buffets, lunches and dinners.

SCHOOL VISITS/CHILDREN
School groups are welcome at a cost of £2.70 per child.

A guide can be provided for groups of 20 at £4.20 per person. Areas of particular interest: Kent and Sharpshooters Museum, torture instruments, exhibition on Anne Boleyn, adventure playground and maze. 1 teacher/adult free per 10/12 children. Free preparatory visits for teachers within normal opening hours.

GUIDED TOURS
Pre-booked guided tours can be arranged outside normal opening hours. 25 people per guide. Basic £8.10 per head, £10.20 with guide book, £13.10 Connoisseurs including coffee, sherry and guide book. Tours in French, German, Dutch, Italian, Spanish and Japanese for a small additional premium.

GIFT SHOP/GUIDE BOOKS
The Gift, Book and Garden shops are open at the same times as the Gardens, Castle Guide £2.10 Garden Guide £1.80.

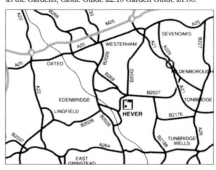

HAVER CASTLE CONTINUED...

The Tudor Village was built for William Waldorf Astor in the style of the Tudor period, but with every modern comfort and luxury.

All twenty, individually decorated, rooms have private bathrooms, colour televisions, direct dial telephones, tea/coffee making facilities and hair dryers. Guests can enjoy a Billiard Room, outdoor heated swimming pool, tennis court and croquet lawn.

The village is available year round for groups requiring high standards of accommodation and service, delicious foods and wines and top-level conference facilities. There are three interconnecting reception rooms which can be used for conferences, dining or meetings. There are also a number of smaller syndicate rooms.

The Hever Castle Estate includes Stables House, an imposing five bedroomed property overlooking the River Eden. This is an ideal venue for smaller groups, which can also make use of the Tudor Village amenities.

In addition the magnificent Dining Hall (see picture to the right) in the Castle is available for a truly memorable dinner. Guests can enjoy a private guided tour of the Castle and a Tudor Banquet with minstrels.

Laser Clay Pigeon Shooting, Archery, Fishing, Riding, Golf and other pursuits can be arranged on or near the estate.

In all, the Tudor Village provides a unique and unusual venue for private meetings, receptions, product launches or corporate hospitality.

Hever Castle/Tudor village offers the following accommodation (see picture below):
- 4 singles with bath
- 10 twins with bath
- 6 doubles with bath
- 4 twins and 1 double (in the Stables House)

CONFERENCE AND FUNCTION FACILITIES

The Dining Hall, Breakfast Room and Sitting Room (which together form the Tudor Suite) are available throughout the year. Smaller seminar rooms are also available. The Pavilion can be hired between November and March. Overhead projector, carousel projector and screen can be provided and audio-visual equipment hired.

Catering facilities for special functions and conferences include buffets, lunches and dinners.

ROOM	DIMENSIONS	CAPACITY	LAYOUT	POWER POINTS	SUITABLE FOR A/V
Dining Hall	35' x 20'	70	Theatre	5	✓
		32	Schoolroom		
		25	U-shape		
		32	Boardroom		
		70	Lunch/Dinner		
Breakfast Room	22' x 15'	20	Theatre	3	✓
		16	Schoolroom		
		16	Boardroom		
		16	Lunch/Dinner		
Sitting Room	24' x 20'	12	Boardroom	4	✓
		12	Lunch/Dinner		
Pavilion	96' x 40'	250	Theatre	24	✓
		200	Schoolroom		
		250	Buffet		
		250	Dinner/Dance		
Moat Restaurant	25 'x 60'	75	Dinner/Dance	6	

LEEDS CASTLE
Maidstone

Surrounded by 500 acres of magnificent parkland and gardens, and built on two small islands in the middle of a natural lake, Lord Conway christened Leeds "the loveliest Castle in the world."

The site of a manor of the Saxon royal family in the 9th Century, it was then re-built in stone by the Normans and later converted into a Royal Palace by Henry VIII.

For some 300 years, the Castle was home to the Kings and Queens of medieval England. Now lovingly restored and beautifully furnished, it contains a magnificent collection of medieval furnishings, tapestries and paintings.

The Castle was purchased in 1926 by the late the Hon Olive, Lady Baillie, whose American Whitney inheritance helped restore the Castle and cement strong Anglo-American links. The Leeds Castle Foundation now preserves the Castle for the Nation, hosts important medical conferences and supports the Arts.

A unique collection of Dog Collars can be viewed in the Castle Gate House.

Popular attractions within the Castle grounds include the colourful Culpeper Garden, Wood Garden, Duckery, Castle greenhouses and vineyard. An aviary houses rare and endangered species from around the world, beyond which can be found a traditional maze and underground grotto. A challenging nine hole golf course surrounds the Castle, whose moat occasionally comes into play!

❖

SUITABILITY FOR OTHER EVENTS
Residential conferences and corporate hospitality (including large scale marquee events); exhibitions, wedding receptions, sporting days with clay shooting, falconry, field archery, hot air ballooning, war games and golf.

EXTRA FACILITIES
Parkland, golf course, croquet lawn, swimming pool and heli-pad. Talks given by specialist staff can be arranged for horticultural, viticultural, historical and cultural groups.

ADVICE TO COURIERS & DRIVERS
Pre-booking advisable but not essential. Couriers/guides and coach drivers admitted free. Voucher for refreshments. Shuttle transport for elderly / disabled. No dogs, or radios.

FACILITIES FOR THE DISABLED
Accessible mini-bus, wheelchairs on loan, wheelchair lift in Castle, purpose-built toilets. Special rates - leaflet available.

PARKING FOR COACHES & CARS
5,000 cars and 20 coaches, 800 yds from the Castle. For special functions/tours parking nearer the Castle can be arranged.

CATERING
17th Century tithe barn, self-service restaurant plus the new Terrace Restaurant (waitress service) offer a full range of hot meals, salads & cream teas. Group lunch menus available. For special functions/conferences, buffets and dinners can arranged.

GUIDED TOURS
Guides in every room except winter mid-week when there are regular guided tours. French, Spanish, Dutch and German, Italian & Russian guides. Average tour time 1 hr.

GIFT SHOPS
Castle Shop, Book Shop, Park Shop and Special Christmas Shop (Nov - Dec).

GUIDE BOOKS
Illustrated Guide available in English, French, German Dutch, Spanish, Italian and Japanese, £3.00. Aviary Guide and Children's Activity Book 95p.

SCHOOL VISITS/CHILDREN
Educational groups welcome, outside normal opening hours private tours can be arranged. Teachers Resource Pack including Fact Sheets and Discovery Sheets on six different topics.

CONTACT

Nick Day
Leeds Castle
Maidstone
Kent
ME17 1PL

Tel: (01622) 765400
Fax: (01622) 735616

LOCATION

From London, A20/M20, Exit 8, 40 miles, 1 hour .
Rail: BR combined train and admission, London Charing Cross and Victoria - Bearsted.
Coach: Nat Express/ Invictaway coach & admission from Victoria.
Air: Gatwick 45 miles, Heathrow 65 miles.
Channel Tunnel: 25 miles. Dover: 38 miles.

OPENING TIMES

Summer
1 March - 31 October
Daily   10am - 6.00pm
NB. Last Entry 5.00pm

Winter
Nov - End Feb
Daily   10am - 4.00pm
(except Christmas Day)
NB. Last Entry 3.00pm

Also special private tours for pre-booked groups at any other time by appointment

ADMISSION

Proposed 1995 rates from 1 March

CASTLE & PARK
  Adult £7.30
  Child (5 -15yrs) . .£4.80
  OAP/Student . . .£6.20
  Family (2+2) . . .£20.00
Disabled Visitors
  Adult £4.00
  Child (5 -15yrs) . .£2.80
Groups (Min 20 people)
  Adult £5.70
  Child (5 -15yrs) . .£4.00
  OAP/Student . . .£4.50
Disabled Visitors
  Adult £4.00
  Child (5 -15yrs) . .£2.80

PARK & GARDENS
  Adult £5.50
  Child (5 -15yrs) . .£3.30
  OAP/Student . . .£4.50
  Family (2+2) . . .£15.00
Disabled Visitors
  Adult £3.00
  Child (5 -15yrs) . .£1.80
Groups (Min 20 people)
  Adult £4.50
  Child (5 -15yrs) . .£3.00
  OAP/Student . . .£3.50
Disabled Visitors
  Adult £3.00
  Child (5 -15yrs) . .£1.80
Leeds Castle Privilege Card - season pass.

CONFERENCE AND FUNCTION FACILITIES

ROOM	DIMENSIONS	CAPACITY	LAYOUT	POWER POINTS	SUITABLE FOR A/V
Fairfax Hall	64' 6" x 36'	50 - 250	Various	✓	✓
Gate Tower	34' x 20'	16 - 120	Various	✓	✓
Culpeper	20' 8" x 25'	8 - 30	Various	✓	✓

PENSHURST PLACE
Nr. Tonbridge

PENSHURST PLACE is one of England's greatest family-owned stately homes with a history going back six and a half centuries.

In some ways time has stood still at Penshurst; the great House is still very much a mediaeval building with improvements and additions made over the centuries but without any substantial rebuilding. Its highlight is undoubtedly the mediaeval Baron's Hall, built in 1341, with its impressive 60ft-high chestnut beamed roof.

A marvellous blend of paintings, tapestries and furniture from the 15th, 16th and 17th Centuries can be seen throughout the House, including the helm carried in the state funeral procession to St Paul's Cathedral for the Elizabethan courtier and poet, Sir Philip Sidney, in 1587. This is now the family crest.

GARDENS
The Gardens, first laid out in the 14th Century, have been developed over successive years by the Sidney family who first came to Penshurst in 1552. A twenty-year restoration and re-planting programme undertaken by the late Viscount De L'Isle has ensured that they retain their historic splendour. He is commemorated with a new Arboretum, planted in 1991. The Gardens are divided by a mile of yew hedges into "rooms", each planted to give a succession of colour as the seasons change. There is also a Venture Playground, Nature Trail and Toy Museum for children.

———————————— ❖ ————————————

SUITABILITY FOR OTHER EVENTS
Private Banqueting, product launches, wedding receptions, garden parties, photography, filming, fashion shows.

EXTRA FACILITIES
Archery, clay pigeon shooting, falconry. Parkland available for hire for public events, fairs, product launches. Lectures on the property, its contents and history can be arranged for up to 60. Specialist garden tours can be arranged.

ADVICE TO COURIERS & DRIVERS
No access to bus park by double decker buses; these to be parked in village. Entrance arrangements for morning booked parties notified in advance to organisers. No dogs. No photography in the House. Parking for unlimited cars and 10 coaches 250 yds from the house.

GUIDED TOURS
Tours available (mornings only) by arrangement. Adult £4.95, child £2.50. Lunch/Dinner can be arranged in Private Dining Room Out of season, tours by appointment: adult £4.95, minimum charge £150.00. Guided tours of the gardens also available at £5.95.

CATERING
Self-service Restaurant for light refreshments, lunches and teas. Restaurant and waitress service can be booked by groups of 20+.

FACILITIES FOR THE DISABLED

Wheelchair-bound visitors' access limited due to age/architecture of buildings. Disabled and elderly visitors may be left at entrance while vehicles are parked in allocated area.

GIFT SHOP
Open seven days a week, hours as House.

GUIDE BOOKS
Colour Guide Book, £2.80. Room Guides available in French, German, Dutch and Japanese.

SCHOOL VISITS/CHILDREN
Visits all year by appointment. Discount rates. Education room and packs available.

CONTACT

Stephanie Ward
Penshurst Place
Penshurst
Nr Tonbridge
Kent
TN11 8DG

Tel: (01892) 870307

Fax: (01892) 870866

LOCATION

From London M25 Junct. 5 then A21 to Tonbridge North, B2027 via Leigh; from Tunbridge Wells A26, B2176.

Bus: Maidstone & District 231, 232, 233 from Tunbridge Wells.

Rail: Charing Cross/ Waterloo- Hildenborough, Tonbridge or Tunbridge Wells; then taxi

OPENING TIMES

Summer
1 April - 1 October

HOUSE
Daily   Noon - 5.30pm
Last Entry 5.00pm

GROUNDS
Daily   11.00am - 6.00pm

Winter
2 October - 31 March

Open to Groups by appointment only (see Guided Tours).

House and Grounds only open weekends in March and October 1995.

ADMISSION

Summer
HOUSE & GARDEN
  Adult £4.95
  Child* £2.75
  Concessions** . .£4.50
  Fam. Ticket . . .£13.00

Groups***
  Adult £4.50

GARDEN ONLY
  Adult £3.50
  Child* £2.25
  Concessions** . .£3.00
  Fam. Ticket £9.80

Wheelchairs Welcome

* Aged 5-16; under 5s FREE.

** Concessions: OAP/Students/UB40

*** Min 20 people, afternoons only. Special rates for morning Guided Tours

CONFERENCE AND FUNCTION FACILITIES

ROOM	DIMENSIONS	CAPACITY	LAYOUT	POWER POINTS	SUITABLE FOR A/V
Sunderland Room	45' x 18'	100	Various	6	✓
Baron's Hall	64' x 39'	250	Theatre	4	✓
Buttery	20' x 23'	50	Various	4	✓

PHOTOGRAPH: JEREMY WHITAKER

SQUERRYES COURT
Westerham

SQUERRYES COURT has been the home of the Wardes since 1731 and is still lived in by the family today . Although it was built in Charles II's reign in 1681 it is a typical William and Mary Manor House. Squerryes is 22 miles from London and easily accessible from the M25. Surrounded by parkland, there are fine views over the lake to an ancient lime avenue and the hills beyond.

The house has an important collection of Italian, 18th Century English and 17th Century Dutch paintings acquired and commissioned by the family in the 18th Century. John Warde who inherited in 1746 purchased 93 paintings in the space of 25 years. He did not go on the Grand Tour but bought from auction houses, dealers and private sales in England. This gives an insight into the taste of a man of his time and also what was available on the art market in England in the mid eighteenth century.

The furniture and porcelain have been in the house since the 18th Century and the Tapestry Room contains a fine set of Soho tapestries made c.1720. General Wolfe of Quebec was a friend of the family and there are items connected with him in the Wolfe Room.

GARDENS

These were laid out in the formal style but were re-landscaped in the mid 18th Century. Some of the original features in the 1719 Kip print survive. The family have restored the formal garden using this print as a guide. The garden is lovely all year round with bulbs, wild flowers and woodland walks, azaleas, summer flowering herbaceous borders and roses.

SUITABILITY FOR OTHER EVENTS
Fashion shows, archery, clay pigeon shooting, garden parties, promotions, shows, wedding receptions (marquee in garden).

EXTRA FACILITIES
Grand Piano, Parkland, Lake for fly fishing.

ADVICE TO COURIERS & DRIVERS
Groups welcome any day. Please book in advance. No photography in the House. Dogs on leads in grounds. Free teas for drivers and couriers.

FACILITIES FOR THE DISABLED
Disabled and elderly visitors may alight at the entrance to the property. Toilets for the disabled.

PARKING FOR COACHES & CARS
Parking for up to 60 cars and 2 coaches on the gravel forecourt.

CATERING
Teas are served in the Old Library (capacity 53 people). Parties must book in advance for lunch/tea/supper. Menus are available upon request. Teas from £2.20. Lunch/Supper prices on request. Facilities for buffets, lunches and dinners.

GUIDED TOURS
Available for groups of up to 55 people, small additional charge payable. The owner will meet groups visiting the house, by prior arrangement. Average time to see the house ³/₄ hour.

GIFT SHOP
The small Gift Shop is open at the same time as the House.

GUIDE BOOKS
Colour guide book, £1.00.

SCHOOL VISITS/CHILDREN
Groups are welcome, cost £1.50 per child. A guide is provided. Areas of interest include: Nature Walk, ducks and geese.

CONTACT

Curator or Mrs Warde
Squerryes Court
Westerham
Kent
TN16 1SJ

Tel: (01959) 562345
(01959) 563118

Fax: (01959) 565949

LOCATION

Off the M25, Junct. 6, 6 miles, ¹/₂ mile west of Westerham.

London 1-1¹/₂ hours.

Rail: Oxted Station 4 miles.
Sevenoaks 6 miles.

Air: Gatwick, 30 minutes.

OPENING TIMES

Summer
March: Sundays only

1 April - 30 September
Mon Bank Hols only
2pm - 6pm

Tues, Thur, Fri. Closed

Wed, Sat, Sun
2pm - 6pm

NB Pre-booked groups welcome any day.

Winter
October - end February
Closed

ADMISSION

HOUSE & GARDEN
  Adult £3.50
  Child* £1.60
  OAP/Student . . .£3.20
Groups**
  Adult £3.00
  Child* £1.50
  OAP £3.00

HOUSE ONLY
  Adult £3.50
  Child* £1.60
  OAP £3.20
Groups**
  Adult £3.00
  Child* £1.50
  OAP £3.00

GARDEN ONLY
  Adult £2.00
  Child* £1.00
  OAP £1.80
Groups**
  Adult £1.80
  Child* £0.90
  OAP £1.80

* Aged 0-14
** Min 20 people.

CONFERENCE AND FUNCTION FACILITIES

ROOM	DIMENSIONS	CAPACITY	LAYOUT	POWER POINTS	SUITABLE FOR A/V
Hall	32' x 32'	80	Buffet U-shape Boardroom Lunch/Dinner	4	✓
Old Library	20' x 25' 6"	40	Buffet Boardroom	5	✓

WALMER CASTLE & GDNS.
Deal

Since its completion as part of Henry VIII's chain of coastal defences in 1540, Walmer Castle has been transformed over the centuries into an elegant stately home. As the official residence of the Lords Warden of the Cinque Ports, it was much used by the Duke of Wellington and is still used today by HM the Queen Mother. Rooms used by Her Majesty are open to the public as are those once used by Wellington. The delightful castle gardens should not be missed.

❖

CONTACT

The Head Custodian
Walmer Castle
Kingsdown Road
Deal
Kent
CT14 7LJ

Tel: (01304) 364288

LOCATION

On the coast at Walmer, 2 miles south of Deal off the Dover-Deal road.

Rail: Walmer
(1 $\frac{1}{2}$ miles).

OPENING TIMES

Summer

1 April - 30 September
Daily
10.00am - 6.00pm

Winter

1 October - 31 October
Daily
10.00am - 4.00pm

1 November - 31 March
Wednesday - Sunday
10.00am - 4 00pm

Closed Jan & Feb and when Lord Warden in residence.

ADMISSION

Adult £3.50
Child* £1.80
OAP/Student/UB40
holder £2.60

15% discount on groups of 11 or more.

* 5 - 15 years.
Under 5's free

ADVICE TO COURIERS & DRIVERS
Photography in grounds only. Coach drivers and tour leaders have free entry. 1 extra free place for every additional 20 people.

FACILITIES FOR THE DISABLED
Gatehouse and 3 ground floor rooms accessible to wheelchair users. Special tape tours for visually impaired and hearing impaired.

PARKING FOR COACHES & CARS
Near approach to castle park before entrance. No coach parking.

GUIDED TOURS
A free personal stereo tour is available.

GIFT SHOP
A selection of souvenirs are available.

GUIDE BOOKS
These are available.

SCHOOL VISIT/CHILDREN
School visits are free if booked in advance.

BEDGEBURY NATIONAL PINETUM

Tel: 01580 211044

Goudhurst, Cranbrook, Kent, TN17 2SL.
Owner: Forestry Commission   **Contact:** Mr C Morgan
Comprehensive collection of conifers on a dramatic site.
Location: 7m E of Tunbridge Wells on A21, turn N on to B2079 for 1m.
Opening Times: All year.

BELMONT

OPEN

16 Apr - 30 Sept
Sat, Sun and
Bank Hols.
2.00 - 5.00pm
Last adm: 4.30pm
Groups of 10+ on
other days by
appointment.

Tel: 01795 890202

BELMONT PARK, THROWLEY, FAVERSHAM ME13 0HH

Owner: Harris (Belmont) Charity   *Contact:* Lt. Col F.E. Grant

Charming late 18th century country mansion by Samuel Wyatt set in fine parkland. Seat of the Harris family since 1801 when it was acquired by general George Harris, the victor of Seringaptam. The mansion remains in its original state and contains interesting mementos of the family's connections with India and the colonies, plus the fifth Lord Harris' fine clock collection.
Location: 4¹/₂ miles south south-west of Faversham, off A251.
Admission: House & Garden: Adult £4.00, Child £2.50.
        Garden only: Adult £2.00, Child 75p.

BOUGHTON MONCHELSEA PLACE

See page 88 for full page entry.

CANTERBURY CATHEDRAL

Tel: 01227 762862 **Fax:** 01227 762897

Canterbury, Kent, CT1 2EH.
Contact: Mr D Earlam
Founded in 597, Mother Church of the Anglican Communion, Norman Crypt, , 14 - 15th century Nave. Site of Becket's martyrdom. Notable stained glass.
Location: Canterbury city centre.
Opening Times: Easter - 30 Sept 8.45am - 7.00pm, 1 Oct - Easter 8.45am - 5pm Mon - Sat.
Admission: Donation.

CHARTWELL

OPEN

House, Garden
& Studio
1 Apr - 31 Oct
Daily except
Fri & Mon
11.00am - 5.30pm
Last adm: 4.30pm

House only:
Mar - Nov
Sats, Suns & Weds
11.00am - 4.30pm
Last adm: 4.00pm

Tel: 01732 866368

WESTERHAM, KENT TN16 1PS

Owner: The National Trust   *Contact:* The Administrator

Home of Sir Winston Churchill from 1924 until the end of his life. The rooms, left as they were in his lifetime evoke his career and interests, with pictures, maps and mementos. Exhibition giving an insight into Churchill's life during his years at Chartwell. Terraced gardens, lake, garden studio containing many of his paintings. Shop and restaurant.
Location: 2 miles south of Westerham, fork left off B2026 after 1¹/₂ miles.
Admission: House & Garden: Adult £4.50, Child £2.25.
        Garden only: Adult £2.00, Child £1.00.
        House only (Mar + Nov) Adult £2.50, Child £1.25.

CHIDDINGSTONE CASTLE

Tel: 01892 870347

Edenbridge, Kent, TN8 7AD.
Owner: Trustees of Denys Eyre Bower Bequest   **Contact:** The Custodian
17th century house remodelled into fantasy castle c1800. Contains Stuart and Jacobite paintings, Japanese lacquer and swords, and Egyptian antiquities.
Location: Off B2027 (Edenbridge - Tonbridge Road). Turn at Bough Beech.
Opening Times: Apr - Oct: Apr, May, Oct; Easter hol, Wed, Sun and Public Holidays. Jun - Sept; Tues - Sun. Weekdays 2.00pm - 5.30pm. Sun and Public Holidays, 11.30am - 5.30pm. Booked parties of at least 20 can be arranged at other times and out of season.
Admission: Adult £3.50; Parties of 20 plus £3.00, Child 5 - 15 years £1.50, Child under 5 free but must be accompanied by an adult. Group of 20 plus booked in advance £3.00 (deposit needed for out of hours visit).

COBHAM HALL

See page 89 for full page entry.

DEAL CASTLE

Tel: 01304 372762

Victoria Road, Deal, Kent.
Owner: English Heritage   **Contact:** The Administrator
Crouching low and menacing, the huge, rounded bastions of this austere fort, built by Henry III, once carried 119 guns. It is a fascinating castle to explore, with long, dark passages, battlements, and a huge basement with an exhibition on England's coastal defences.
Location: SW of Deal town centre.
Opening Times: 1 Apr - 30 Sept, daily 10.00am - 6.00pm, 1 Oct - 31 Oct, daily 10.00am - 4.00pm, 1 Nov - 31 Mar, Wed - Sun, 10.00 - 4.00pm (Closed 24 - 26 Dec, 1 Jan).
Admission: Adult £2.50, Child £1.90, Conc £1.30.

DODDINGTON PLACE GARDENS

Tel: 01795 886101

Doddington, Sittingbourne, Kent, ME9 OBB.
Owner: The Hon Mrs R Oldfield   **Contact:** The Hon Mrs R Oldfield
10 acres of landscaped gardens overlooking wooded area of outstanding natural beauty. Woodland garden (spectacular May/Jun); Edwardian rock garden; formal terraces with mixed borders; impressive clipped yew hedges, fine trees and lawns..
Location: 4m S from A20 at Lenham or N from A2 at Ospringe. Signposted.
Opening Times: Easter Mon to end Sept , Wed and Bank Hol Mons. Suns in May only 11.00am - 6.00pm. Other times by appointment for groups.
Admission: Adult £2.00, Child 25p.

DOVER CASTLE

OPEN

1 Apr - 30 Sept
Daily
10.00am - 6.00pm

1 Oct - 31 March
10.00am - 4.00pm

Evenings by
appointment.

Tel: 01304 201628

DOVER, KENT CT16 1HH

Owner: English Heritage   *Contact:* The General Manager

Dramatically sited above the famous White Cliffs, Dover Castle has the longest recorded history of any major fortress in England, beginning in the Iron Age and continuing beyond World War II. There is much to see, including the great keep, towering up to 95 feet, the Roman lighthouse, the restored Saxon church of St Mary Castro and ancient tunnels dating back to 1216. Special attractions include Hellfire Corner, the underground complex of tunnels from which the Dunkirk evacuation was masterminded.
Location: To the East of Dover. From London via M2/A2.
Admission: Adult £5.50, OAP/Student/UB40 £4.10, Child £2.80.
        15% discount on groups of 11 or more.

DYMCHURCH MARTELLO TOWER

Tel: 01424 63792

Dymchurch, Kent.
Owner: English Heritage   **Contact:** The Administrator
One of many artillery towers which formed part of a chain of strongholds intended to resist an invasion by Napoleon. It is fully restored with an original 24 pounder gun on the roof.
Location: Access from High Street, not from seafront.
Opening Times: Good Fri, Sat, Easter Sun & Mon, 12.00pm - 4.00pm. 23 Apr - 16 July, Sat & Sun only, 12.00pm - 4.00pm. 22 Jul - 2 Sept Daily 12.00pm - 4.00pm.
Admission: Adult £1.00, Child 80p, Conc 50p.

EMMETS GARDEN

Tel: 01732 750367

Ide Hill, Sevenoaks, Kent, TN14 6AY.

Owner: The National Trust   **Contact:** The Administrator

This charming garden boasts the highest treetop in Kent and is noted for its rare trees and shrubs, bluebells, rose and rock gardens. Wonderful views across the Weald and Bough Beech Reservoir. 18 acres of grounds open to public.

Location: 1 1/2m S of A25 on Sundridge to Ide Hill Road, 11/2m N of Ide Hill off B2042.

Opening Times: Mar: Sat & Sun only, 2.00pm - 5.00pm. Apr - end Oct: Wed to Sun & BH Mon, 1.00pm - 6.00pm. Last admission 5.00pm.

Admission: Adult £2.50, Child £1.30, pre-booked parties £2.00.

FINCHCOCKS

See page 90 for full page entry.

GODINTON HOUSE

Tel: 01233 620773

Godinton Park, Ashford, Kent, TN23 3BW.

Owner: A Wyndham Green Esq   **Contact:** A Wyndham Green Esq

Location: 1 1/2m from Ashford at Potter Corner on A20.

Opening Times: The house is open to visitors by permission of Mr Alan Wyndham Green on; Easter Sat, Sun and Mon and on Suns and Bank Hols; or by appointment from 1 Jun to 30 Sept from 2.00pm - 5.00pm.

Admission: Standard £2.00, Child under 16 70p, Parties over 20 £1.50.

GREAT COMP GARDEN

OPEN

1 March - 31 Oct
Open Daily

11.00am - 6.00pm

Tel: 01732 886154

COMP LANE, PLATT, BOROUGH GREEN, KENT TN15 8QS

Owner: R Cameron Esq.   *Contact: Mr W Dyson*

One of the finest gardens in the country, comprising ruins, terraces, tranquil woodland walks and sweeping lawns with a breathtaking collection of trees, shrubs, heathers and perennials, many rarely seen elsewhere. The truly unique atmosphere of Great Comp is further complemented by its Festival of Chamber Music held in July/September. Unusual plants for sale. Teas on Sundays, Bank Holidays and by prior arrangement.

Location: 2 miles east of Borough Green, B2016 off A20. First right at Comp crossroads. 1/2 mile on left.

Admission: Adult £2.50, Child £1.00. Parties of 20+ Adults £2.00. Annual ticket £7.50. OAP £5.00.

GROOMBRIDGE PLACE

See page 91 for full page entry.

HEVER CASTLE

See page 92 - 93 for full page entry.

HISTORIC DOCKYARD

Tel: 01634 812251

Chatham, Kent, ME4 4TE.

Contact: Ms F Leinster-Evans

Most complete Georgian/Early Victorian dockyard in the world. 80 acre working museum.

Location: Access from High Street, not from seafront.

Opening Times: Easter - 30 Oct, Daily.

KNOLE

SEVENOAKS, KENT TN15 0RP

Owner: The National Trust
Contact: The Administrator

Tel: 01732 450608

The largest private house in England sitting in 1,000 acre deer park open by courtesy of Lord Sackville. Dating from 1456 the house has been in the Sackville family since the 16th century. Thirteen state rooms are open and contain important collections of paintings, silver, tapestries and furniture. A must for the connoisseur. Shop and restaurant.

Location: At south end of Sevenoaks town; just east of A225.

Admission: Adult £4.00, Child £2.00. Parking 2.50

OPEN
House: Apr - end of Oct
Wed, Fri, Sat, Sun & Bank Hol Mon 11 am - 5.00pm
Thur: 2.00 - 5.00pm   Last adm: 4.00pm
Park open daily to pedestrians.
Garden open by courtesy of Lord Sackville
May - Sept: first Wed in each month

LADHAM HOUSE

Tel: 01580 211203

Ladham Lane, Goudhurst, Kent, TM17 1DB.

Owner: Lady Jessel   **Contact:** Lady Jessel

10 acre gardens with spectacular twin mixed borders and fine specimen and newly planted arboretum.

Location: NE of Goudhurst off A262.

Opening Times: 16 Apr, 7 and 28 May, 9 Jul, Sun, 11.00am - 5.30pm. Other times by appointment.

Admission: Open days: Adult £2.00, Child under 12 50p, Group £2.00 pp. Private days: Adults £2.50, Child 50p, Group £2.50.

LEEDS CASTLE

See page 94 for full page entry.

LULLINGSTONE GARDENS

Tel: 01322 862114

Eynsford, Kent, DA4 0JA.

Owner: Guy Hart-Dyke Esq   **Contact:** Guy Hart-Dyke Esq

Fine state rooms, family portraits and armour in beautiful grounds. The 15th century gatehouse was one of the first ever to be made of bricks.

Location: 1m S Eynsford on A225.

Opening Times: Apr - Sept, Wed, Fri, Sat, Sun, BHs, 2.00pm - 6.00pm.

Admission: Adult £3.50, Child £1.50, Conc £3.00, Groups over 25 midweek 25% discount.

LULLINGSTONE ROMAN VILLA

Tel: 01322 863467

Eynsford, Kent.

Owner: English Heritage   **Contact:** The Administrator

Some splendid mosaic tiled floors can be seen among the remains of this large country villa which has been extensively excavated in recent years. Four distinct periods of building have been identified as well as one of the earliest private Christian chapels.

Location: 1/2m SW of Eynsford off A225.

Opening Times: 1 Apr - 30 Sept, daily 10.00am - 6.00pm, 1 Oct - 31 Mar, daily 10.00am - 4.00pm. (Closed 24 - 26 Dec, 1 Jan).

Admission: Adult £2.00, Child £1.00, Conc £1.50.

LYMPNE CASTLE

Tel: 01303 267571

Hythe, Kent, CT21 4LQ.

Owner: H H Margary Esq   **Contact:** H H Margary Esq

Ancient Castle, rebuilt 1360 and restored in 1905, situated on high ground with magnificent views.

Location: 4 m from Hythe. 9 miles from Folkstone.

Opening Times: Easter - 30 Sept, 10.30am - 6.00pm. Closed occasionally Sat.

Admission: Adult £2.00, Child 50p.

 THE NATIONAL TRUST    ENGLISH HERITAGE   HISTORIC HOUSES ASSOCIATION

MAISON DIEU

Ospringe, Faversham, Kent.
Owner: English Heritage   **Contact:** The Administrator
This forerunner of today's hospitals remains largely as it was in the 16th century with exposed beams and an overhanging upper storey. It contains an exhibition about Ospringe in Roman times.
Location: In Ospringe on A2 1/2 m W of Faversham.
Opening Times: Easter - 31 Oct, w/ends only, 12.00pm - 6.00pm.

MARLE PLACE GARDENS

OPEN
1 Apr - 31 Oct
Daily
Gardens only
9.00am - 5.30pm

Evenings by appointment.

Tel: 01892 722304
Fax: 01892 724099

BRENCHLEY, NR. TONBRIDGE, KENT TN12 7HS

Owner: Mr G.B. M. Williams   *Contact:* Mrs Lindel Williams

Marle Place is a romantic, privately owned Wealden Garden, 10 acres close to Sissinghurst and Scotney Castles. A plantsmans garden with many interesting trees and shrubs, featuring a Victorian Gazebo and Edwardian rockery (now a herb garden) walled fragrant garden and ornamental ponds. Yew hedges and herbaceous borders. Plant nursery. The 17th century house is not open, but is of considerable architectural note.
Location: On the outskirts of Brenchley 8 miles south-east of Tonbridge. Map reference OS 188TQ681397.
Admission: Admission £2.00, Child £1.50. Coaches by appointment.

MILTON CHANTRY

New Tavern Fort Gardens, Gravesend, Kent.
Owner: English Heritage   **Contact:** The Administrator
A small 14th century building which housed the chapel of the leper hospital and the chantry of the de Valence and Montechais families and later became a tavern and in 1780 part of a fort.
Location: In New Tavern Fort Gardens E of central Gravesend off A226.
Opening Times: Easter - 30 Sept, 10.30am - 6.00pm. Closed occasionally Sat.
Admission: Telephone the keykeeper 01643 842852 for details.

MOUNT EPHRAIM   **Tel:** 01227 751496   **Fax:** 01227 750940

Hernhill, Faversham, Kent, ME13 9TX..
Owner: Mrs M N Dawes   **Contact:** Mrs M N Dawes
Gardens with topiary, herbaceous borders, rose terraces leading to small lake. Japanese rock garden.
Location: 1 m from end of M2. Follow tourist signs from A2 and A299
Opening Times: Mid Apr - 30 Sept.
Admission: Adult £2.00, Child 50p, Groups £1.50.

NORTHBOURNE COURT GARDENS   **Tel:** 01304 611281 **Fax:** 01304 614512

Northbourne, Deal, Kent, CT14 ONT.
Owner: The Hon Charles James Esq   **Contact:** The Hon Charles James Esq
Originally the site of a Saxon palace, given to St Augustines Abbey and later to Sir Edwyn Sandys. A fine and beautifully preserved example of Tudor terraced gardens.
Location: Village of Northbourne, signposted from A256/A258.
Opening Times: Every Sun only in Jun, Jul and Aug 2.00pm - 5.00pm. Groups anytime by appointment.
Admission: Adult £2.50, Child/OAP £1.50.

OLD SOAR MANOR   **Tel:** 01892 890651

Plaxtol, Borough Green, Kent, TN15 0QX.
Owner: The National Trust   **Contact:** The Administrator
The solar block of a late 13th century knight's dwelling.
Location: 1 m E of Plaxtol.
Opening Times: Apr - end Sept, daily, 10.00am - 6.00pm.

PENSHURST PLACE   See page 95 for full page entry.

PORT LYMPNE

OPEN

Summer
1 Apr - 30 Sept
Daily
10.00 - 5.00pm

Winter
1 Oct - 31 Mar
Daily
10.00 - 4.00pm

Not open Christmas day.

Tel: 01303 264646
Fax: 01303 264944

LYMPNE, HYTHE, KENT CT21 4PD

Owner: John Aspinall   *Contact:* Robert Boutwood

Described as the "Last Historic House built this century" Port Lympne encompasses the essence of Roman villas and the English country house. Built by Sir Herbert Baker for Sir Philip Sassoon, the house features a moorish patio, marble columns, an intriguing hall floor plus the exquisitely painted tent room by Rex Whistler. There are 15 acres of terraced gardens and a wild animal park.
Location: From London M20 towards Folkstone, exit 11, follow signs to Lympne and then wild animal park signs.
Admission: House, Garden & Zoo: Adult £6.99, OAP/Child(4-14) £3.00 Family (2+2) £14.00. Groups: Adult £4.50, OAP/Child(4-14) £2.50

QUEBEC HOUSE   **Tel:** 01959 562206

Westerham, Kent, TN16 1TD.
Owner: The National Trust   **Contact:** The Custodian
General Wolfe spent his early years in this gabled, red-brick 17th century house. Four rooms containing portraits, prints and memorabilia relating to Wolfe's family and career are on view. In the Tudor stable block is an exhibition about the Battle of Quebec (1759) and the parts played by Wolfe and his adversary, the Marquis de Montcalm.
Location: At E end of village, on N side of A25, facing junction with B2026, Edenbridge Road.
Opening Times: 2 Apr - end Oct: daily, 2.00pm - 6.00pm but closed Thur & Sat. Last admission 5.30pm. Parties during weekday opening times only and by prior arrangement.
Admission: £2.00, pre-booked parties £1.50, Child 80p.

RECULVER TOWERS AND ROMAN FORT   **Tel:** 01227 366444

Reculver, Herne Bay, Kent.
Owner: English Heritage   **Contact:** The Administrator
This 12th century landmark of twin towers has guided sailors into the Thames estuary for seven centuries, but you can also see the walls of a Roman fort, which were erected nearly 2,000 years ago.
Location: At Reculver 3 m E of Herne Bay.
Opening Times: Any reasonable time.

RICHBOROUGH CASTLE   **Tel:** 01304 612013

Richborough, Sandwich, Kent.
Owner: English Heritage   **Contact:** The Administrator
This fort and township date back to the Roman landing in AD43. The fortified walls and the massive foundations of a triumphal arch which stood 80 feet high still survive.
Location: 1 1/2m N of Sandwich off A257.
Opening Times: 1 Apr - 30 Sept, daily 10.00am - 6.00pm, 1 Oct - 31 Oct, daily 10.00 - 4.00pm.
Admission: Adult £2.00, Child £1.00, Conc £1.30.

RIVERHILL HOUSE   **Tel:** 01732 458802

Sevenoaks, Kent, TN15 ORR.
Owner: Mrs J Rogers   **Contact:** Mrs J Rogers
Small early 18th century stone house (open by appointment only). Historic hillside garden with specimen trees, roses and choice shrubs. Extensive views.
Location: 2m S of Sevenoaks on A225.
Opening Times: Apr - Jun, every Sun & BH w/e 12.00pm - 6.00pm.
Admission: Adult £2.00, Child 50p.

ROCHESTER CASTLE

Tel: 01634 402276

Rochester, Medway, Kent.

Owner: English Heritage   **Contact:** The Administrator

Built in the 11th century to guard the point where the Roman road of Watling Street crossed the River Medway, the size and position of this grand Norman Bishop's castle, founded on the Roman city wall, eventually made it an important royal stronghold for several hundred years. The keep is truly magnificent - over 100 feet high and with walls 12 feet thick. At the top you will be able to enjoy fine views over the river and surrounding city of Rochester.

Location: By Rochester Bridge (A2).

Opening Times: 1 Apr - 30 Sept, daily 10.00am - 6.00pm, 1 Oct - 31 Mar, daily 10.00am - 4.00pm. (Closed 24 - 26 Dec, 1 Jan).

Admission: Adult £2.50, Child £1.30, Conc £1.90.

ROCHESTER CATHEDRAL

Tel: 01634 401301   **Fax:** 01634 401410

Rochester, Kent, ME1 1JY.

Contact: Ms M Hawes

Founded in 604, Rochester Cathedral has been a place of Christian worship for nearly 1,400 years. The present building is a blend of Norman and Gothic architecture. In the cloister are the remains of the 12th century Chapter House and priory. A focal point is the Doubleday statue of Christ and the Blessed Virgin.

Location: Signposted from Junction 6 on the M20 and Junction 3 on the A2/M2.

Opening Times: 8.30am - 5.00pm. Visiting may be restricted during services.

Admission: Donation.

ROMAN PAINTED HOUSE

Tel: 01304 225922   **Fax:** 01304 203279

New Street, Dover, Kent, CT17 9AJ.

Owner: Dover Roman Painted House Trust   **Contact:** Mr B Philip

Discovered in 1970. Built around AD200 as a hotel for official travellers. Well preserved impressive wall paintings, central-heating systems and the Roman fort wall built through the house.

Location: Dover town centre.

Opening Times: 10.00am - 5.00pm except Mons.

Admission: Adult £1.50, Child 50p, Senior citizens 50p, Conc 50p.

SCOTNEY CASTLE GARDEN

Tel: 01892 890651

Lamberhurst, Tunbridge wells, Kent, TN3 8JN.

Owner: The National Trust   **Contact:** The Administrator

One of England's most romantic gardens, surrounding the ruins of a 14th century moated castle. Rhododendrons, azaleas, water lilies and wisteria flower in profusion.

Location: 1m S of Lamberhurst on A21.

Opening Times: Garden: Apr - end Oct (Old Castle: May - 11 Sept) Wed to Fri 11.00am - 6.00pm: Sat & Sun 2.00pm - 6.00pm, or sunset if earlier: BH Sun & Mon 12.00pm - 6.00pm (closed Good Fri). Last admission 1 hour before closing.

Admission: £3.20, pre-booked parties £2.00 (no reduction on Sat, Sun or BH Mon).

SISSINGHURST CASTLE GARDEN

Tel: 01580 712850

Sissinghurst, Cranbrook, Kent, TN17 2AB.

Owner: The National Trust   **Contact:** The Administrator

The 5½ acre famous connoisseurs' garden created by Vita Sackville-West and her husband, Sir Harold Nicolson, between the surviving parts of an Elizabethan mansion. A series of small, enclosed gardens, intimate in scale and romantic in atmosphere with much to see in all seasons. Also, the study where Vita Sackville-West worked, and the Long Library.

Location: 2m NE of Cranbrook, 1m E of Sissinghurst village A262.

Opening Times: 1 Apr - 15 Oct, Tues to Fri, 1.00pm - 6.30pm; Sat, Sun & Good Fri, 10.00 - 5.30pm. Closed all Mon, inc BH. Last admission 1/2 hour before closing.

Admission: £5.00, coaches and parties by appointment only: no reduction.

SMALLHYTHE PLACE

Tel: 01580 762334

Smallhythe, Tenterden, Kent, TN30 7NG.

Owner: The National Trust   **Contact:** The Administrator

An early 16th century half-timbered house, home of the Victorian actress Ellen Terry from 1899 to 1928. The house contains many personal and theatrical mementoes. The Barn Theatre also open most days by courtesy of the Barn Theatre Society. Charming cottage garden including Ellen Terry's rose garden.

Location: 2m S of Tenterden on E side of the Rye road B2082.

Opening Times: Apr - end Oct: Sat to Wed & Good Fri, 2.00pm - 6.00pm or dusk if earlier. Last admission 1/2 hour before closing.

Admission: Adult £2.50, Child £1.30. Pre-booked parties Tues am only, no reduction.

SPRIVERS GARDEN

Tel: 01892 723553

Horsmonden, Kent, TN12 8DR.

Owner: The National Trust   **Contact:** The Administrator

This garden includes flowering and foliage shrubs, herbaceous borders, old walls and spring and summer bedding.

Location: 2m N of Lamberhurst on B2162.

Opening Times: May - 30 Sept: Wed, 2.00pm - 5.30pm. Last admission 5.00pm.

Admission: £1.00, no reduction for children or parties.

SQUERRYES COURT

See page 96 for full page entry.

ST AUGUSTINES ABBEY

Tel: 01227 767345

Longport, Canterbury, Kent.

Owner: English Heritage   **Contact:** The Administrator

Founded in 598, this was one of the earliest monastic sites in southern England. Here you will find remarkable remains of the foundations of the original 6th century churches, the Norman church and medieval monastery.

Location: In Longport 1/4 m E of Cathedral Close.

Opening Times: 1 Apr - 30 Sept Daily, 10.00am - 6.00pm. 1 Oct - 31st Mar Daily 10.00am - 4.00pm. (Closed 24 - 26 Dec, 1 Jan).

Admission: Adults £1.50, Child £1.10, Conc 80p.

ST JOHN'S COMMANDERY

Tel: 01634 842852

Densole, Swingfield, Kent.

Owner: English Heritage   **Contact:** The Administrator

A medieval chapel built by the Knights Hospitallers, ancestors of the St John Ambulance Brigade. It has a moulded plaster ceiling and a remarkable timber roof.

Location: 2 m NE of Densole off A260.

Opening Times: By appointment only.

STONEACRE

Tel: 01622 862871

Otham, Maidstone, Kent, ME15 8RS.

Owner: The National Trust   **Contact:** The Administrator

A half-timbered mainly late 15th century yeoman's house, with great hall and crownpost, and newly restored cottage style garden.

Location: At N end of Otham village, 3m SE of Maidstone, 1m S of A20.

Opening Times: Apr - end Oct: Wed & Sat, 2.00pm - 6.00pm. Last admission 5.00pm.

Admission: £2.00, no reduction for parties.

TEMPLE MANOR

Tel: 0634 842852

Strood, Rochester, Kent.

Owner: English Heritage   **Contact:** The Administrator

The 13th century manor house of the Knights Templar which mainly provided accommodation for members of the order travelling between London and the Continent.

Location: In Strood (Rochester) off A228.

Opening Times: Telephone keykeeper on 01634 842852 for details.

THE ARCHBISHOP'S PALACE

Tel: 01622 663006   **Fax:** 01622 682451

Mill Street, Maidstone, Kent, ME15 6YE.

Owner: Maidstone Borough Council   **Contact:** The Heritage Services Manager

Recently refurbished 14th century Palace used as a resting place for Archbishops travelling from London to Canterbury. Also houses Maidstone's heritage centre.

Location: On the banks of the River Medway in the centre of Maidstone.

Opening Times: 1 Nov - 28/29 Feb, 12.00pm - 4.00pm. 1 Mar - 31 Oct, 10.00am - 4.30pm. Open 7 days a week.

Admission: To 1st floor rooms entrance is free. Heritage Centre (including Carriage Museum) Adults £2.95, Child £1.95.

THE FRIARS

Tel: 01622 717272   **Fax:** 01622 715575

Aylesford Priory, Aylesford, Kent, ME20 7BX.

Owner: The Order of The Carmelites   **Contact:** Mrs M Dunk

Location: Aylesford village.

Opening Times: Summer; daily, 10.00am - 5.00pm. Winter; daily, 10.00am - 4.00pm.

Admission: Free.

TONBRIDGE CASTLE

Tel: 01811 732 770929   **Fax:** 0181 732 770449

Castle Street, Tonbridge, Kent, TN9 1BG.
Owner: Tonbridge& Melling Borough Council   **Contact:** Ms S Kostryka
Remains of Norman motte and bailey castle with 13th century gatehouse set in gardens overlooking River Medway.
Location: Off Tonbridge High Street.
Opening Times: Mon - Fri, 8.30am - 5.00pm. Sat 9.00am - 5.00pm. Sun/BH 10.30am - 5.00pm. Oct - Mar, 4.00pm closure Sat/Sun.
Admission: Adult £2.50, Child £1.20, Family £6.50, Conc £1.20, Groups of 10 or more entitled to 10% discount.

TUDOR YEOMAN'S HOUSE

Tel: 01832 890651

Sole Street, Cobham, Kent, DA12 3AX.
Owner: The National Trust   **Contact:** The Administrator
A 15th century yeoman's house of timber construction.
Location: 1m SW of Cobham on W side of B2009, just N of Sole Street Station.
Opening Times: Main Hall only, by written application.
Admission: 50p, no reduction for children or parties.

UPNOR CASTLE

Tel: 01634 718742

Upnor, Kent.
Owner: English Heritage   **Contact:** The Administrator
This well preserved 16th century gun fort was built to protect Queen Elizabeth I's warships. However in 1667 it failed to prevent the Dutch navy which stormed up the Medway destroying half the English fleet.
Location: At Upnor, on unclassified road off A228.
Opening Times: 1 Apr - 30 Sept, daily 10.00am - 6.00pm.
Admission: Adult £2.50, Child £1.30, Conc £.190.

WALMER CASTLE & GARDENS

See page 97 for full page entry.

WILLESBOROUGH WINDMILL

Tel: 01634 718742

Nill Lane, Willesborough, Ashford, Kent.

Location: Off A292 close to J10/M20.
Opening Times: April - Oct; Sat, Sun and BHs, 2.00pm - 5.00pm.
Admission: Adult £1.00, Child 50p, Conc 50p.Groups 10% reduction by arrangement only.

WOOL HOUSE

Tel: 01892 890651

Wells Street, Loose, Maidstone, Kent, ME15 OEH.
Owner: The National Trust   **Contact:** The Tenant
A 15th century half-timbered house, thought to have been used for the cleaning of wool.
Location: 3m SE of Maidstone, 1/4m W of the Cranbrook road A229.
Opening Times: Apr - end Sept by written application.
Admission: 50p, no reduction for children or parties.

YALDING GARDENS

Tel: 01203 303517   **Fax:** 01203 639229

Benover Road, Yalding, Maidstone, Kent, ME18 6EX.
Owner: Henry Doubleday Research Association   **Contact:** J Gear or P Clark
Exciting new gardens illustrating a "Green History of Gardening" from medieval times, through the Victorian era to the present day. Come to Yalding for an enjoyable and fascinating day out.
Location: 6m Southwest of Maidstone, 1/2m South of Yalding on B2162.
Opening Times: 10.00am - 5.00pm May to Sept, Wed to Sun and Bank Hol Mons. Oct: Sat and Sun only.
Admission: Adult £2.00, Child (5-16) £1.00, OAP £1.50, family £5.00.

SPECIAL EVENTS DIARY

- **11th - 12th March: Boughton Monchelsea Place**
  Craft Show & Craft Demonstrations, falconry displays, ferret racing 10am-6pm.

- **31st March - 2nd April: Cobham Hall**
  Antiques Fair.

- **14th - 17th April: Cobham Hall**
  Medway Craft Fair (10am-6pm).

- **16th - 17th April: Boughton Monchelsea Place**
  Country Show - Longbow archery, fly casting, gun dog displays, clay shoot, country crafts, trade stands.

- **6th - 8th May: Penshurst Place & Gardens**
  Craft Fair.

- **7th - 8th May: Hever Castle**
  Musical Memories to commemorate VE Day local bands will play war times tunes in the grounds.

- **27th - 28th May: Hever Castle**
  Merrie England - Medieval crafts, dancing, falconry and archery.

- **28th May: Penshurst Place & Gardens**
  Penshurst Choral Society in the Barons Hall.
  Classic Car Rally (28th - 29th).

- **28th - 29th May: Boughton Monchelsea Place**
  Kent Festival of Transport.

- **29th May: Penshurst Place & Gardens**
  Penshurst Wool Race and Live Craft & Demonstrations.

- **All Sundays in June and August: Hever Castle**
  Local Band concerts in the grounds.

- **1st - 2nd June: Cobham Hall**
  Dickens Festival - House and Garden Open (2pm-5pm).

- **10th June: Chartwell**
  Music, Memories and Moonlight.

- **23rd - 25th June: Hever Castle**
  "In Praise of Herbs" Castle will be decorated with herbs to celebrate the opening of the new Tudor Herb Garden.

- **Weekends of July 1st - 2nd, 8th - 9th, 15th-16, 22nd - 23rd and 29th - 30th: Penshurst Place & Gardens**
  Weekend of Revelry - period music, dance, theatre, poetry reading, sword fighting etc.

- **2nd, 9th, 16th and 23rd July, : Hever Castle**
  South Coast Falconry, static and flying displays in the grounds.

- **8th July: Cobham Hall**
  Red Cross Open Air Concert.

- **28th - 30th July: Cobham Hall**
  Antiques Fair.

- **28th - 29th July: Penshurst Place & Gardens**
  Stately Homes Music Festival.

- **29th July: Hever Castle**
  The Knights of Royal England; Traditional jousting tournament.

- **30th July: Hever Castle**
  The Kent Bowman will demonstrate the use of the Longbow.

- **5th, 12th, 19th, 26th August: Hever Castle**
  The Knights of Royal England; Traditional jousting tournament.

- **6th, 13th, 20th August: Hever Castle**
  The Kent Bowman will demonstrate the use of the Longbow.

- **27th - 28th August: Hever Castle**
  South Coast Falconry, static and flying displays in the grounds.

- **2nd September: Hever Castle**
  The Knights of Royal England; Traditional jousting tournament.

- **3rd September: Hever Castle**
  South Coast Falconry, static and flying displays in the grounds.

- **8th - 10th September: Penshurst Place & Gardens**
  Craft Fair.

- **15th - 17th September: Hever Castle**
  Patchwork and Quilting Exhibition.

- **21st - 22nd September: Cobham Hall**
  Medway Craft Fair (10am-6pm).

HOGHTON TOWER
Nr. Preston

HOGHTON TOWER, home of the 14th Baronet Sir Bernard de Hoghton, is one of the most dramatic looking houses in Lancashire. The symmetrical fortified front castellated gatehouse and flanking towers is reached by steep straight avenue over half a mile long.

The present House was built almost entirely by Thomas Hoghton in 1562 - 1565, though stylistically it could date from 100 years earlier. In 1617, King James I visited the house and knighted the Loin of Beef hence 'Sirloin'. During the Civil War, Sir Richard's son Gilbert held Lancashire for the Crown and the keep of Hoghton was blown up and never replaced.

In the late 17th Century the 4th Baronet repaired and modernised the House.

Sir Henry Hoghton Bt, in 1862 started restoration of the House. This was completed in 1901 under a London architect R D Oliver, who designed the Ballroom and grand chimney pieces. The King's Ante-chamber, the King's Bed-Chamber and the Buckingham Room all retain their 17th Century interiors.

GARDENS
The grounds are sited on the hill commanding extensive views to the sea, the Lakes, and North Wales. Walled gardens

CONTACT

The Administrator
Hoghton Tower
Hoghton
Lancashire
PR5 OSH

Tel: (01254) 852986
Fax: (01254) 852109

LOCATION

M6 Junct. 28 (10 mins)
$3^1/2$ hrs to London
M61 (10 mins)
30 mins Manchester
Rail: Preston Station 15 mins: 3 hrs. London
Bus: Ribble Bus Co. buses to the bottom of drive.
Taxi: Preston Railway Station and locals.

SUITABILITY FOR OTHER EVENTS
Hoghton Tower provides a suitable setting for fashion shows, archery, clay pigeon shooting, equestrian events, garden parties, shows, rallies and filming, wedding receptions, corporate functions.

EXTRA FACILITIES
Lectures can be arranged, or a video can be shown, in the Conference Room for up to 100 people. Facilities such as projectors and screens can be provided. When the weather is wet indoor facilities can be offered for picnicking (Gt Barn). Hire and/or use of a grand piano, parkland, cricket pitch, golf course and airstrip can be arranged; cost negotiable.

ADVICE TO COURIERS & DRIVERS
Please telephone in advance to seek advice as to where to park prior to releasing the party or parties. Please ask visitors to treat the grassland with respect and advise the ground staff of any damage created. No interior photography, no dogs, no fires in the woods and no unaccompanied children.

PARKING FOR COACHES & CARS
Parking available for 300 cars or 200 cars and 20 coaches. Further parking by arrangement.

FACILITIES FOR THE DISABLED
Although disabled visitors are welcome to enjoy the extensive views from outside the House, there are no special facilities (toilets etc.) provided for them.

CATERING
A Tea Room is available for up to 80 people at any one time. Banqueting Hall available for max 120 persons. Groups can book in advance and menus are available upon request. Special rates for groups are negotiable.

GUIDE BOOKS
Colour guide book is available giving a detailed history of the family and the estate. Translations are available in French, German, Italian, Spanish and Swedish.

GUIDED TOURS
Tours are available and in some cases the owner may meet the group. Duration of the tour is approx $1^1/2$ hours. Minimum 25 persons.

OPENING TIMES

Summer
Easter Sat - End October

Mondays Closed
(Open some bank hol Mons)

Tues, Wed, Thurs
July and Aug only
11.00am - 4.00pm

Fris and Sats Closed
Sundays 1.00 - 5.00 pm
NB Group visits may be arranged all year round. Contact the Administrator.

Winter
31 Oct - Good Friday
Open for private events and functions.

ADMISSION

Summer
GARDENS, SHOP & TEAROOM
Adult £1.00
Child . . . . .FREE

HOUSE TOURS
Adult £2.50
Child (under 5) FREE
Child (5-15) £1.25
OAP/Student . . .£2.00
Family (4) £6.00

PRIVATE TOURS
Adult £3.50
Child £1.75

Winter
Negotiable

CONFERENCE AND FUNCTION FACILITIES

ROOM	DIMENSIONS	CAPACITY	LAYOUT	POWER POINTS	SUITABLE FOR A/V
Banqueting Hall	45' x 26'	150	Various	✓	✓
Smoking Room	41' x 20'	70	Various	✓	✓
Billiards	48' x 20' 6"	70	Various	✓	✓

The Banqueting Hall, Ballroom, Smoking Room and Billiards Room are all available throughout the year subject to availability. If requested the owner may meet the group visiting the House and when invited may participate in these functions. Slide and overhead projectors, screens and audio-visual equipment can be hired if required.
PLEASE TELEPHONE FOR FURTHER DETAILS AND RATES

LEIGHTON HALL
Carnforth

LEIGHTON HALL is one of the most beautifully sited houses in the British Isles, situated in a bowl of parkland, with the whole panorama of the Lakeland Fells rising behind. The Hall's neo-Gothic facade was superimposed on an 18th century house, which, in turn, had been built on the ruins of the original mediaeval house. The present owner is descended from Adam d'Avranches who built the first house in 1246.

The whole house is lived in by the Reynolds family and emphasis is put on making visitors feel welcome in a family home.

Connoisseurs of furniture will be particularly interested in the 18th Century pieces by Gillow of Lancaster. Mr Reynolds is directly descended from the founder of Gillow and Company, hence the strong Gillow connection with the house. Also on show are some fine pictures, clocks, silver and objets d'art.

GARDENS
The main garden has a continuous herbaceous border and rose covered walls, while the Walled Garden contains flowering shrubs, a herb garden, an ornamental vegetable garden and a maze. Beyond is the Woodland Walk, where wild flowers abound from early Spring.

A varied collection of Birds of Prey is on display in the Bird Garden, and flown each afternoon that the Hall is open - weather permitting.

❖

SUITABILITY FOR OTHER EVENTS
Product launches, small seminars, filming, garden parties, wedding receptions, rallies, overland driving, archery and clay pigeon shoots.

EXTRA FACILITIES
Lectures on the property, its contents, gardens and history can be arranged . Grand piano.

ADVICE TO COURIERS & DRIVERS
Photography is not allowed in the House. Please leave sufficient time (2hrs) for both tour of House and flying display. No dogs in the gardens. By appointment, parties of 25 and over may visit the Hall in the evening and out of season.

FACILITIES FOR THE DISABLED
Disabled and elderly visitors may alight at the entrance to the property, before parking in the allocated areas.

PARKING FOR COACHES & CARS
100 cars and 6 coaches, 150 yards from the Hall

CATERING
The Restaurant/Tea Room can cater for 55 people. Prices range form £2.95 for afternoon tea to £6.00 for other meals. Groups must book in advance and menus are available on request. For special functions/conferences buffets, lunches and dinners can be arranged.

GIFT SHOP
Open at the same time as the Hall. Items include small souvenirs. Colour guide book, £1.00.

GUIDED TOURS
Parties are taken round in groups. There is no additional cost for the facility. By prior arrangement the owner may meet the groups. Average time taken for a tour 45 minutes/1 hour.

SCHOOL VISITS/CHILDREN
Groups of children are welcome. School Programme from 10am-2pm daily May-Sept. except Mondays and Saturdays. Birds of prey flown for schools at midday. Cost per child £1.80. The Schools Visit Programme won the Sandford Award for Heritage Education in 1983 and again in 1989.

During the afternoon when the house and grounds are open to the general public a large collection of birds of prey are on display, some of which fly at 3.30pm - weather permitting.

CONTACT

Mrs C. S. Reynolds
Leighton Hall
Carnforth
Lancashire
LA5 9ST

Tel: (01524) 734474
Fax: (01524) 720357

LOCATION

9 miles North of Lancaster,
10 miles South of Kendal,
3 miles from M6/A6, Junct. 35, signed from Junct. 35A.
Rail: Lancaster Station 9 miles.

Air: Manchester Airport, 65 miles.

Taxi: Carnforth Radio Taxis Carnforth 732763.

OPENING TIMES

Summer
1 May - 30 September

Daily except Mons and Sats   2.00 - 5.00pm

Open Bank Holidays Mondays.

August only 11.30-5.00pm

NB Pre-booked parties of 25 or more at any time by appointment

Winter
1 October-30 April
Open to parties of 25 or more which must be pre-booked.

ADMISSION
Summer

HOUSE, GARDEN AND BIRDS
Adult £3.30
Child* £2.10
OAP £2.80

Groups**
Adult £2.80
Child* £1.80
OAP £2.80
Family Ticket .£10.00
(2 adults & up to 3 children)

*Age 0-16
**Minimum payment £65.00.

Winter
As above but groups by appointment only.

Where eagles fly

CONFERENCE AND FUNCTION FACILITIES

ROOM	DIMENSIONS	CAPACITY	LAYOUT	POWER POINTS	SUITABLE FOR A/V
Music Room	24' x 21' 6"	80	Theatre	6	✓
		50	Dinner		
		60	Buffet		

BLACKBURN CATHEDRAL

Tel: 01254 51491   **Fax**: 01254 667309

Blackburn, Lancashire, BB1 5AA.

Contact: The Very Rev D Frayne

On a historic Saxon site in town centre. Built as the Parish Church in 1826, subsequent extensions give a uniqueness to both interior and exterior. Features including the lantern tower, central altar with corona above, fine Walker organ, stained glass from medieval period onwards. Recent restoration work gives a new magnificence.

Location: 9m E of exit 31 on M6, via A59 and A677.

Opening Times: Mon - Fri: 9.00am - 5.30pm, Sat: 9.30am - 4.00pm, Sun: 8.00am - 5.00pm.

Admission: Donation. Guided tours by prior arrangement.

BROWSHOLME HALL

Tel: 01254 826719

Clitheroe, Lancashire, BB7 3DG.

Owner: R R Parker Esq   **Contact:** R R Parker Esq

Tudor house with Elizabethan front, home of the Parker family since 1507.

Location: Clitheroe.

Opening Times: Easter W/e Fri - Mon; Spring Bank Hol; Every Sat And Sun In Aug: From 2.00am - 5.00pm. Parties May Be Arranged For Any Other Time.

Admission: Grounds only: £2.00: conc - Historic House Association Members free; reduced rates for parties. Guided tour of house: Adults £3, Child £1.50.

GAWTHORPE HALL

Tel: 01282 778511

Padiham, Burnley, Lancashire, BB12 8UA.

Owner: The National Trust   **Contact:** The Administrator

The house was built in 1600-05, and restored by Sir Charles Barry in the 1850s. Barry's designs have been re-created in the principal rooms. Gawthorpe was the home of the Shuttleworth family, and the Rachel Kay-Shuttleworth textile collections are on display in the house, private study by arrangement. A recently restored 17th century estate building houses a broad programme of art, craft and management courses.

Location: On E outskirts of Padiham, 3/4m drive to house on N of A671.

Opening Times: Hall: 1 Apr - 29 Oct: daily except Mon & Fri, but open Good Fri & BH Mon, 1.00pm - 5.00pm. Last admission 4.15pm. Garden: All year, daily, 10.00am - 6.00pm.

Admission: Hall: Adult £2.30, Child £1.00, Family £6.00. Garden: free. Parties by prior arrangement.

HOGHTON TOWER

See page 103 for full page entry.

LEIGHTON HALL

See page 104 for full page entry.

MARTHOLME

Great Harwood, Blackburn, Lancashire, BB6 7UJ.

Owner: Thomas H Codling Esq   **Contact:** Thomas H Codling Esq

Part of medieval manor house with 17th century additions and Elizabethan gatehouse.

Location: 2m NE of Great Harwood off A680 to Whalley.

Opening Times: Daytime by appointment.

Admission: Exterior £1.00, Interior £2.00.

SPECIAL EVENTS DIARY

- **4th - 5th March: Hoghton Tower**
  Book Fair - Rare and Antiquarian

- **9th April: Hoghton Tower**
  Motor Cycle Sprint

- **11th May: Hoghton Tower**
  Music/Firework Display

- **12th - 14th May: Hoghton Tower**
  Flower Festival

- **18th - 20th May: Hoghton Tower**
  Antique Fair

- **17th June: Hoghton Tower**
  Ballet

- **30th September -1st Oct: Hoghton Tower**
  Craft Fair

ROSSENDALE MUSEUM

Tel: 01706 217777 / 226509

Whitaker Park, Rawtenstall, Rossendale, Lancashire, BB4 6RE.

Owner: Rossendale Borough Council   **Contact:** Mrs S Cruise

19th century mansion, former home of textile manufacturing family, with displays of decorative arts and furniture.

Location: Off A681 Haslingden Road.

Opening Times: Mon - Fri, 1.00pm - 5.00pm. Sat 10.00am - 5.00pm (Apr - Oct), 12.00pm - 4.00pm (Nov - Mar). BHs 1.00pm - 5.00pm.

Admission: Free.

RUFFORD OLD HALL

OPEN

1 April - 1 November

House:
1.00 - 5.00pm

Garden:
12 Noon - 5.30pm

(Except Thurs & Fris)

Tel: 01704 821254

NR. ORMSKIRK, LANCASHIRE L40 1SG

Owner: The National Trust   *Contact: Mrs Maureen Dodsworth*

One of the finest 16th century buildings in Lancashire with a magnificent great hall, particularly noted for its immense moveable screen. There is a fine collection of 17th century oak furniture, 16th century arms, armour and tapestries. Relics of 18th century and 19th century domestic life. Tea room and gift shop.

Location: Close to Rufford, 7 miles north of Ormskirk, on east side of A59.

Admission: Adult £3.00, Child £1.50. Family ticket £8.00.
Garden only: £1.60. School holidays children free.

SAMLESBURY HALL

OPEN

15 Jan - 15 Dec

Summer
Noon - 5.00pm

Winter
Noon - 4.00pm.

Open daily except Mondays

Coach parties by prior arrangement.

Tel: 01254 812229

Fax: 01254 812174

PRESTON NEW ROAD, SAMLESBURY, PRESTON, LANCS PR5 0UP

Owner: Samlesbury Hall Trust   *Contact: Mr. D.E. Hornby*

A magnificent medieval manor house preserved by a trust, featuring black and white oak timbered exterior decorated with distinctive quartrefoils. The great hall dates from 1325. Other features include the chapel, long gallery, minstrels gallery, bow window and extensive gardens. Displays include antiques for sale, exhibitions and 'at work' displays throughout the year.

Location: A677, 5 miles from Preston, 4 miles from Blackburn (junc. 31 - M6)

Admission: Adult £2.00, Child 80p. 25% reduction for pre-arranged groups.
Coach parties welcome, only by prior arrangement.

WARTON OLD RECTORY

Warton, Carnforth, Lancashire.

Owner: English Heritage   **Contact:** The Administrator

A rare medieval stone house with remains of the hall, chambers and domestic offices.

Location: At Warton, 1 m N of Carnforth on minor road off A6.

Opening Times: 1 Apr - 31 Oct daily, 10.00am - 6.00pm. 1 Nov - 31 Mar daily, 10.00am - 4.00pm. Closed 24 - 26 Dec, 1 Jan.

NOSELEY HALL
Billesdon

NOSELEY HALL, is one of the most friendly and successful locations in the East Midlands for all types of function. The house is not open to the public, but is available for private and corporate hire. It is especially suitable for outdoor activities and country pursuits.

The tranquillity of the setting, and the marvellous views, just 15 minutes from Leicester, make Noseley one of the nicest and most central locations for film and photographic work, board meetings, business seminars, conferences, product launches and private parties. Noseley's extensive parkland is ideal for outside events such as Multi-Activity Days. The five acres of lawn, immediately in front of the house, provide the

perfect fully-serviced marquee site. All functions are personally overseen by the owner and his wife.

The present house, which dates from 1728, enjoys panoramic views over unspoilt parkland and has a very beautiful 13th Century chapel on the lawn. The well preserved interior includes an exceptionally fine two storey Hall, in which guests are greeted on arrival, a panelled Dining Room and an elegant Drawing Room. The house has been the seat of the Hazlerigg family since 1419. The most famous Hazlerigg was one of the five members of parliament who led the rebellion against King Charles I in 1642. He was later Cromwell's general in the North East.

❖

CONTACT

The Hon Arthur or Mrs Hazlerigg
Noseley Hall
Billesdon
Leicestershire
LE7 9EH
Tel: (01162) 596606
(01162) 596322
Fax: (01162) 596774

LOCATION

From London M1 Junct. 15, A508 through N'hamton to Market Harborough, A6, B6047. 12 mls east of Leicester. A1 via A14 (A1-M1 link)
Rail: Mkt. Harborough or Leicester.
Air: Leicester (private). Helicopters: may land on lawn.

EXTRA FACILITIES
All activities can be arranged. The chapel has excellent acoustics for concerts. Challenging 4 wheel drive course. Lawn for marquees. Noseley regularly holds multi-activity and other corporate days.

ACCOMMODATION
Can occasionally be arranged within the House in connection with functions held therein.

FACILITIES FOR THE DISABLED.
Disabled and elderly visitors may alight at the entrance to the property, before parking in the allocated areas. There are no special toilets for the disabled.

PARKING FOR COACHES & CARS
100 cars within 50 yards. 10 more acres can be made available.

CATERING
The House is available for Corporate Entertainment functions only. Delicious Cordon Bleu menus.

RATES
Noseley Hall is not open to the public. As a guide to rates for conferences and corporate entertainment, the following

are given, but please contact the owners for full details and a quotation.

Conferences: Daily delegate rate to include morning coffee, lunch, afternoon tea: From £37.50 + VAT.

Activity Days: Average £60 + VAT per head fully catered.

Lunches & Dinners: please apply for prices.

Facility Fee: Exclusive use of grounds and facilities will be based on £800 + VAT per day but each event will be quoted for individually.

Not open to the public. Available for corporate events, conferences, filming, etc. throughout the year.

ACTIVITIES

Clay Pigeon Shooting
Archery
Pistols
Fly Casting
Quad Bikes
Pilot Buggies
Trials Cars
Argocat
Hovercraft
Land Rovers
Reverse Steer Car
Blind Driving
4 x 4 Troop Transporter
Grass Karts
Radio Controlled
Minitrux
Autotest Driving Game
Tractor Driving Test
Laser Clay Shooting
Video Activities
Falconry
Scalextric
Golf Swing Analyser
Croquet
Virtual Reality
Management Training

CONFERENCE AND FUNCTION FACILITIES

ROOM	DIMENSIONS	CAPACITY	LAYOUT	POWER POINTS	SUITABLE FOR A/V
Stone Hall	28' x 21'	60	Buffet	5	
Drawing Room	42' x 22'	70	Theatre	4	✓
		40	Schoolroom		
		30	U-shape/Boardroom		
Dining Room	45' x 22'	70	Theatre	4	✓
		70	Schoolroom		
		100	Buffet		
		40 - 80	Lunch/Dinner		
Library	34' x 18'	50	Theatre	8	✓
		30	Schoolroom/Boardroom		
		25	U-shape		
Marquee on Lawn			Dinner/Dance		

STANFORD HALL
Nr Rugby

Summer

Easter - 24 September

Mon Bank Hols & Tues
following 2.30 - 6.00pm

Closed Wed, Thur, Fri.

Sat & Sun 2.30 - 6.00pm

Last admission 5.30pm

NB On Bank Holidays and
Events Days, open at 12 noon
(House at 2.30pm). Open any
day or evening for pre-booked
parties.

Winter

October - Easter
Closed to public.
Open during October
for Corporate Events.

STANFORD has been the home of the Cave family, ancestors of the present owner, Lady Braye, since 1430. In the 1690s, Sir Roger Cave commissioned the Smiths of Warwick to pull down the old Manor House and build the present Hall, which is an excellent example of their work and of the William and Mary period.

As well as over 5000 books, the handsome Library contains many interesting manuscripts, the oldest dating from 1150. The splendid pink and gold Ballroom has a fine coved ceiling with four trompe l'oeil shell corners. Throughout the house are portraits of the family and examples of furniture and objects which they collected over the centuries. There is also a collection of Royal Stuart portraits, previously belonging to the Cardinal Duke of York, the last of the male Royal Stuarts. An unusual collection of family costumes is displayed in the Old Dining Room, which also houses some early Tudor portraits and a fine Empire chandelier.

The Hall and Stables are set in an attractive Park on the banks of Shakespeare's Avon. There is a walled Rose Garden behind the Stables. An early ha-ha separates the North Lawn from the mile-long North Avenue.

CONTACT

Lt Col E H L Aubrey-
Fletcher
Stanford Hall
Lutterworth
Leicestershire LE17 6DH
Tel: (01788) 860250
Fax: (01788) 860870

LOCATION

M1 Junct. 18 , 6 miles,
M1 Junct. 19 (from/to
the North only) 2 miles
M6 Exit/access at A14
/M1(N) junct. 2 miles,
A14, 2 miles.
Follow Historic House signs.
Rail: Rugby Station
7¹⁄₂ miles.
Air: Birmingham
Airport 27 miles.
Taxi: Fone-A-Car.
(01788) 543333

SUITABILITY FOR EVENTS
Clay pigeon shoots, corporate incentive days, lunches, dinners, wedding receptions, filming and photography, fashion shows, car launches. Motor Car and Motorcycle Club Rallies held in the Park most Sundays from early May to end September. Further details on application.

EXTRA FACILITIES
These include parkland, Bluthner piano, helicopter landing area, river for fishing, raft races, canoe parties. Lecture Room available for up to 60 people. Cost for hire of the room £70.

ADVICE TO COURIERS & DRIVERS
Free meals for coach drivers. Coach parking on gravel in front of house. Dogs on leads in the park. No dogs or photography inside the house. Parking for 1,000 cars, 100 yds from the house and 6 to 8 coaches 25yds from the house.

CATERING
Groups of up to 70 can book in advance for homemade afternoon tea, lunches, high teas and suppers. Outside Catering facilities are available for special functions/ conferences.

FACILITIES FOR THE DISABLED
Disabled and elderly visitors may alight at the entrance to the house. There is a toilet for the disabled.

GUIDED TOURS
Tours last approx ³⁄₄ hr. in groups of about 25 people.

GIFT SHOP
Souvenir Shop opens 2.30pm (12 noon on Bank Holidays and Event Days). Craft Centre (most Sundays) from 11.00am.

SCHOOL VISITS/CHILDREN
Groups are welcome, price per child £1.30. By prior arrangement a guide can be provided. There is a nature trail with special guide book and map. The Motorcycle Museum is of particular interest.

ADMISSION

HOUSE & GROUNDS
Adult £3.20
Child* £1.50
Groups**
Adult £2.90
Child* £1.30
OAP £2.70

GROUNDS ONLY
Adult £1.80
Child* £0.70

MOTORCYCLE
MUSEUM
Adult £1.00
Child* £0.30
School Group
Adult . . . . FREE
Child* £0.20

* Aged 4 - 15
** Min payment £58.00.

CONFERENCE AND FUNCTION FACILITIES

ROOM	DIMENSIONS	CAPACITY	LAYOUT	POWER POINTS	SUITABLE FOR A/V
Ballroom	39' x 26'	70	Theatre	4	✓
		60	Schoolroom		
		40	U-shape		
		100	Buffet		
		64 - 80	Lunch/Dinner		
Old Dining Room	30' x 20'	50	Theatre	4	✓
		30	Schoolroom		
		25	U-shape/Boardroom		
		70	Buffet		
		30	Lunch/Dinner		
Crocodile Room	39' x 20'	60	Theatre	1	✓

ASHBY DE LA ZOUCH CASTLE

Tel: 0116 2413343

Ashby de la Zouch, Leicestershire.
Owner: English Heritage   **Contact:** The Administrator
The impressive ruins of this late medieval castle are dominated by a magnificent tower, over 80 feet high, which was split in two during the Civil War, when the castle defended the Royalist cause.
Location: In Ashby de la Zouch, 12 m S of Derby on A50.
Opening Times: 1 Apr - 30 Sept, daily 10am - 6pm, 1 Oct - 31 Oct, daily 10am - 4pm. 1 Nov - 31 Mar, Wed - Sun, 10am - 4pm, (Closed 24 - 26 Dec, 1 Jan).
Admission: Adult £1.30, Child 70p, Conc £1.00.

BELGRAVE HALL

Tel: 0116 2666590

Church Road, Thurcaston Road, Leicester, LE4 5PE.
Owner: Leicestershire Museums, Arts & Records Service   **Contact:** The Administrator
Queen Anne House. Period room settings from late 17- 19thCentury. Interesting gardens.
Location: Church Road, Leicester.
Opening Times: Mon - Sat; 10.00am - 5.30pm Sun: 2.00pm - 5.30pm every day throughout the year except Christmas Day/Boxing Day And Bank Hols.
Admission: Free.

KIRBY MUXLOE CASTLE

Tel: 0116 2386886

Kirby Muxloe, Leicestershire.
Owner: English Heritage   **Contact:** The Administrator
Picturesque, moated, brick built castle begun in 1480 by William Lord Hastings. It was left unfinished after Hastings was executed in 1483.
Location: 4 m W of Leicester off B5380.
Opening Times: Telephone keykeeper 01604 730320 for opening details.

LYDDINGTON BEDE HOUSE

Tel: 0157282 2438

Lyddington, Corby, Leicestershire.
Owner: English Heritage   **Contact:** The Administrator
The Bede House was originally a medieval palace of the Bishops of Lincoln. It was later converted to an alms house.
Location: In Lyddington, 6m N of Corby, 1 m E of A6003.
Opening Times: 1 Apr - 30 Sept daily, 10am - 6pm. Lunchtime closure 1 - 2pm.
Admission: Adult £1.30, Child £1.00, Conc 70p.

NOSELEY HALL

See page 106 for full page entry.

PRESTWOLD HALL

OPEN

Corporate Entertainment Venue, Management Training and Conference Centre by arrangement only.

Tel: 01509 880236
Fax: 01509 881464
or 01636 812187

LOUGHBOROUGH, LEICESTERSHIRE LE12 5SQ

Owner: S.J. Packe-Drury-Lowe   *Contact:* Mrs. Weldon

A magnificent private house, largely remodelled in 1843 by William Burn. For the past 350 years it has been the home of the Packe family and contains fine Italian plaster work, 18th Century English and European furniture and a collection of family portraits. The house is not open to the general public but offers excellent facilities as a conference and corporate entertainment venue. Up to 170 guests can be seated and the 20 acres of gardens provide a perfect setting for larger meetings using marquees. Also available are excellent chefs providing a varied menu, a fully stocked wine cellar as well as clay pigeon shooting, motor sports and archery. Activity days on request.
Location: At the heart of the Midlands, 3 miles east of Loughborough on B675.

STANFORD HALL

See page 107 for full page entry.

WHATTON HOUSE GARDEN

Tel: 01509 842268   **Fax:** 01509 842268

Long Whatton, Loughborough, Leicestershire, LE12 5BG.
15 acres of garden with unique Chinese/Japanese garden.
Location: On A6 4m N of Loughborough, 2m S of Kegworth. 3m from exit 24/M1.
Opening Times: Every Sun & BH Mon Easter - 31 Aug. Also 18 Apr, 9 May, 30 May. Also by appointment.
Admission: Adult £2.00, Child £1.00, Conc £1.00, Groups by arrangement.

SPECIAL EVENTS DIARY

- **16th-17th April: Stanford Hall**
  Crafts at Stanford Hall.

- **7th May: Stanford Hall**
  Volkswagen Owners Club Rally (Warks. & Leics.Branch).

- **14th May: Stanford Hall**
  South Leics MG Owners Club Rally .
  Volvo Owners Club - 164 Register Rally .

- **20th May: Stanford Hall**
  Wartburg/IFA Owners Club (UK) Rally.
  Unloved, Soviet & Socialist Register Rally.
  Tatra Owners Club Rally.

- **21st May: Stanford Hall**
  Leicestershire Ford RS Owners Club Rally (Provisional).

- **27th - 29th May: Stanford Hall**
  National Hovercraft Racing Championships.

- **4th June: Stanford Hall**
  Lea-Francis Owners Club Rally .

- **11th June: Stanford Hall**
  Alfa-Romeo Owners Club National Rally.

- **18th June: Stanford Hall**
  Ford AVO Owners Club National Rally. The Capri Collection Rally.

- **24th - 25th June: Stanford Hall**
  Fiat Motor Club Rally.

- **25th June: Stanford Hall**
  The Rugby Charity Raft Races on the River Avon.

- **1st week July: Noseley Hall**
  International Hazelrigg reunion to mark 350th anniversary of The Civil Wars "Decisive Campaign" in Leicestershire.

- **2nd July: Stanford Hall**
  Velocette Motorcycle Owners Club Rally.

- **15th - 16th July: Stanford Hall**
  BP Schools Hovercraft Competition.

- **16th July: Stanford Hall**
  Sporting Escort Owners Club Rally.

- **23rd July: Stanford Hall**
  Vintage Motorcycle Club Founders Day Rally.

- **30th: Stanford Hall**
  Honda Owners Club (GB) Honda 400/4 Classic Gathering.

- **6th August: Stanford Hall**
  Triumph Sports 6 Owners Club Rally.

- **26th - 28th August: Stanford Hall**
  National Hovercraft Racing Championships.

- **3rd August: Stanford Hall**
  Midlands Austin 7 Car Club Rally.
  Scott Motorcycle Owners Club Rally

- **Stanford Hall**
  Salmons Tickford Enthusiasts Club Meeting

- **10th August: Stanford Hall**
  Mini Owners Club National Rally.

- **17th August: Stanford Hall**
  L E Velo Motorcycle Owners Club Rally

- **30th September - 1st October: Stanford Hall**
  Lady Fayre (Crafts).

BELVOIR CASTLE
Grantham

CONTACT

Richard Fenn
Castle Estate Office
Belvoir Castle
Grantham
Lincolnshire
NG32 1PD

Tel: (01476) 870262
Fax: (01476) 870443

LOCATION

A1 from London
(110mls), York (100mls)
& Grantham (7mls).
A607 Grantham-Melton
Mowbray.
Air: East Midlands Int'l.
Rail: Grantham Stn 7mls
Bus: Melton Mowbray -
Vale of Belvoir via
Castle Car Park.
Taxi: Grantham Taxis
63944/63988.

BELVOIR CASTLE, home of the Duke and Duchess of Rutland, commands a magnificent view over the Vale of Belvoir. The name, Belvoir, meaning beautiful view, dates back to Norman times, when Robert de Todeni, Standard Bearer to William the Conqueror, built the first Castle on this superb site. Destruction caused by two Civil Wars and by a catastrophic fire in 1816 have breached the continuity of Belvoir's history. The present building owes much to the inspiration and taste of Elizabeth, 5th Duchess of Rutland and was built after the fire.

Inside the Castle are notable art treasures including works by Poussin, Holbein, Rubens, and Reynolds, Gobelin and Mortlake tapestries, Chinese silks, furniture, fine porcelain and sculpture.

The Queens Royal Lancers Museum at Belvoir has a fascinating exhibition of the history of the Regiment, as well as a fine collection of weapons, uniforms and medals.

GARDENS

The Statue Gardens are built into the hillside below the Castle and take their name from the collection of 17th Century sculptures on view. The garden is planted so that there is nearly always something in flower.

The Duchess' private Spring Gardens are available for viewing throughout the year by pre-booked groups of 10 persons or more. Details from the Estate Office.

SUITABILITY FOR OTHER EVENTS
Ideal location for banquets, exhibitions, product launches and conferences. Filming welcomed.

EXTRA FACILITIES
Any activity or event is a possibility and we would be delighted to discuss requirements, regardless of size.

ADVICE TO COURIERS & DRIVERS
Coaches should report to the Main Car Park and Ticket Office on arrival. Photography welcomed (permit £1.00).

FACILITIES FOR THE DISABLED
Ground floor of Castle is easily accessible for disabled people, including the Restaurant and Toilet Facilities. Further access to Castle is restricted for wheelchairs. Please telephone for advice.

GUIDED TOURS (BY APPOINTMENT)
Guided tours available by prior arrangement. £7.50 per group (up to 20 persons). Duration approx 1¼ hours.

PARKING FOR COACHES & CARS
150 cars, next to the Castle and a further 500 spaces, 500 yds from the Castle. Up to 40 coaches can be parked. Coaches can take passengers to entrance by arrangement..

CATERING
Extensive choice of hot and cold home-made food available throughout the day in the 100-seat Licensed Restaurant. Groups and parties catered for, from afternoon tea to a set three-course meal. Private room available.

GIFT SHOP
Open when Castle is open to the public, offering many quality gifts and souvenirs. There is also an unusual plant stall open at the Castle on Sundays in Season.

GUIDE BOOKS
Pictorial guide with details of the Castle and contents. Translations in French, German, Italian and Spanish. Braille guide book available.

SCHOOL VISITS/ CHILDREN
Guided tours available to all schools parties, along with a private room for education or packed lunch purposes, subject to availability. Picnic area and Adventure Playground.

OPENING TIMES

Summer
1 April - 1 October

Mon Bank Hols only
11.00am - 6.00pm

Tues, Wed, Thur, Sat
11.00am - 5.00pm

Fridays Closed
Open Good Friday
11.00am - 6.00pm

Sundays
11.00am - 6.00pm

Winter
Groups welcome by appointment.

ADMISSION

Adult £4.25
Child £2.65
OAP £3.00
Groups*
Adult £3.25
Child** £2.20

* 20 or more adults.
** School or Youth groups.

CONFERENCE AND FUNCTION FACILITIES

ROOM	DIMENSIONS	CAPACITY	LAYOUT	POWER POINTS	SUITABLE FOR A/V
State Dining Room	52' x 31'	100	Schoolroom	8	✓
		60	U-shape		
		80	Boardroom		
		150	Buffet		
		130	Theatre		
		100	Lunch/Dinner		
Regents Gallery	131' x 16' 6"	300	Reception		✓
Old Kitchen	45' x 22' 6"	120	Buffet	4	✓
		80	Lunch/Dinner		

BURGHLEY HOUSE
Stamford

BURGHLEY HOUSE, home of the Cecil family for over 400 years, was built as a country seat during the latter part of the 16th Century by Sir William Cecil, later Lord Burghley, principal adviser and Lord Treasurer to Queen Elizabeth.

The House was completed in 1587 and there have been few alterations to the architecture since that date thus making Burghley one of the finest examples of late Elizabethan design in England.

The interior was remodelled in the late 17th Century by John, 5th Earl of Exeter who was a collector of fine art on a huge scale, establishing the immense collection of art treasures at Burghley.

Burghley is truly a 'Treasure House', containing one of the largest private collections of Italian art, unique examples of Chinese and Japanese porcelain and superb items of 18th Century furniture. The remodelling work of the 17th Century mean that examples of the work of the principal artists and craftsmen of the period are to be found here at Burghley: Antonio Verrio, Grinling Gibbons and Louis Laguerre all made major contributions to the beautiful interiors.

GARDENS

The House is set in a 300 acre Deer Park landscaped by Capability Brown under the direction of the 9th Earl. As was usual with Brown's designs a lake was created and delightful avenues of mature trees feature largely. The park is home to a herd of Fallow Deer and is open to the public at all times of the year. The gardens surrounding the House are only open on certain weekends, usually Bank Holidays. Please telephone for details.

SUITABILITY FOR OTHER EVENTS
Burghley is suitable for a wide variety of events.

EXTRA FACILITIES
Large park, golf course, helicopter landing area, cricket pitch.

ADVICE TO COURIERS & DRIVERS
Parking and refreshments free for drivers. No dogs within the House. Please advise clients that there is no photography inside.

FACILITIES FOR THE DISABLED
Disabled and elderly visitors may alight at the entrance, before parking in the allocated areas. Toilets for the disabled. Chair lift to the Orangery Coffee Shop. Disabled visitors should be aware that the house tour involves two staircases.

PARKING FOR COACHES & CARS
Capacity of the Car Park, 500 cars, 100 yards from the House, and 20 coaches, 120 yards from the House.

GUIDE BOOKS
Colour guide book, £2.50.

CATERING
Restaurant/Tea Room seating up to 100/120 people. Groups can book in advance for afternoon tea and lunch. Prices from £2.80 for afternoon tea to £8.00 for lunch (three course).

GUIDED TOURS
Tours lasting approximately $1^1/_2$ hours start at 15 minute intervals. Maximum size of each party taken round is 25.

SCHOOL VISITS/CHILDREN
School visits are welcome, a guide will be provided. Cost per child, £2.50. A children's guide book can be obtained.

CONTACT

J Culverhouse
Burghley House
Stamford
Lincolnshire
PE9 3JY

Tel: (01780) 52451

Fax: (01780) 480125

LOCATION

Burghley House is 1 mile north of Stamford. From London A1, 2hours.

Rail: Stamford Station $1^1/_2$ miles.

Taxi: Merritt (01780) 66155.

OPENING TIMES

Summer
1 April - 8 October

Daily 11.00am - 5.00pm
NB Closed 2 September

Winter
8 October - 1 April
Closed to the general public.

ADMISSION

Adult* £5.10
Child** £2.50
OAP £4.80
Groups (min 20 people)
Adult £3.95
Child* £2.50

* One child (under 14) admitted FREE per paying adult.
** Aged up to 14

CONFERENCE AND FUNCTION FACILITIES

ROOM	DIMENSIONS	CAPACITY	LAYOUT	POWER POINTS	SUITABLE FOR A/V
Great Hall	70' x 30'	180	Theatre	2	
		90	Schoolroom		
		60	U-shape		
		42	Boardroom		
		100	Dinner		
Orangery	100' x 20'	120	Buffet	6	✓

AUBOURN HALL
Tel: 01522 788270   **Fax:** 01522 788199

Lincoln, Lincolnshire, LN5 9DZ.
Owner: Sir Henry Nevile   **Contact:** Sir Henry Nevile
Late 16th century house with important staircase and panelled rooms.
Location: 6m SW of Lincoln.
Opening Times: Weds in Jul and Aug, 2.00pm - 6.00pm. Sun 21 May. Sun 4 Jun.
Admission: Adult £2.50, Senior citizen £2.00.

BELTON HOUSE PARK AND GARDENS
Tel: 01476 66116

Grantham, Lincolnshire, BG32 2LS.
Owner: The National Trust   **Contact:** The Administrator
The crowning achievement of Restoration country house architecture, built 1685 - 88 for Sir John Brownlow, and altered by James Wyatt in the 1770s. Plasterwork ceilings by Edward Goudge and fine wood carvings of the Grinling Gibbons school. The rooms contain portraits, furniture, tapestries, oriental porcelain, family silver gilt and Speaker Cust's silver. Formal gardens, an orangery and a magnificent landscaped park with a lakeside walk and the Bellmount Tower. Fine church with family monuments.
Location: 3m NE of Grantham on A607.
Opening Times: House: 1 Apr - end Oct. Wed to Sun & BH Mon (closed Good Fri), 1.00pm - 5.30pm. Garden & Park: 11.00am - 5.30pm, last admission to house, garden and park 5.00pm.
Admission: House & Garden: Adult £4.30, Child £2.10, Family £10.70. Discount for parties.

BELVOIR CASTLE
See page 109 for full page entry.

BISHOP'S PALACE
Tel: 01522 527468

Lincoln, Lincolnshire.
Owner: English Heritage   **Contact:** The Administrator
In the shadow of Lincoln Cathedral are the remains of this medieval palace of the Bishop of Lincoln.
Location: S side of Lincoln Cathedral.
Opening Times: 1 Apr - 30 Sept daily, 10.00am - 6.00pm.
Admission: Adult £1.00, Child 50p, Conc 80p.

DODDINGTON HALL

OPEN

2.00 - 6.00pm Spring Garden Sun 12 March - 30 April (except Easter Sun but including Easter Mon)

May – September Weds, Suns and Bank Hol Mons. Licensed Restaurant opens at 12 Noon.

Tel: 01522 694308
Fax: 01522 682584

LINCOLN LN6 4RU

Owner: Mr and Mrs A. Jarvis   *Contact:* Mr and Mrs A. Jarvis

Magnificent Smythson mansion completed in 1600 and standing complete with contemporary walled gardens and Gatehouse. The Hall has an elegant Georgian interior with fine collections of porcelain, furniture, paintings and textiles representing 400 years of unbroken family occupation. Wild garden, nature trail and gift shop. Fully licensed restaurant open from 12.00 noon. Sandford award winning schools project.
Location: 5 miles west of Lincoln on the B1190, clearly signposted off the A46 Lincoln Bypass.
Admission: Adult £3.60, Child £1.80. Gardens half price. Family Ticket £10.25

BURGHLEY HOUSE
See page 110 for full page entry.

FULBECK HALL
Tel: 01400 272205   **Fax:** 01400 272205

Grantham, Lincolnshire, NG32 3JW.
Owner: Mrs M Fry   **Contact:** Mrs M Fry
18th century house, home of the Fry family since 1632.
Location: On A607 11m N of Grantham, 1m S of crossing with A17.
Opening Times: Easter, May and Aug BH Mons and every day from 2.00pm. 30 Jul, 2.00pm - 5.00pm.
Admission: Adult £3.00, Child £1.00, Senior citizens £2.50, Group of 20 plus £3.00 pp.

GAINSBOROUGH OLD HALL
Tel: 01427 810318   **Fax:** 01427 810318

Parnell Street, Gainsborough, Lincolnshire, DN21 2NB.
Owner: English Heritage   **Contact:** Ms Heather Cummins
A large medieval house with a magnificent Great Hall and suites of rooms. A collection of historic furniture and a re-created medieval kitchen are on display.
Location: In centre of Gainsborough.
Opening Times: Mon - Sat, 10.00am - 5.00pm. Sun 2.00pm - 5.30pm. Closed Suns Nov - Easter.
Admission: Adult £1.75, Child 95p, Senior citizens 95p.

GRIMSTHORPE CASTLE, PARK & GDNS

OPEN

16 April - 30 Sept Suns, Thurs and Bank Hols from Easter Sun. Also daily except Fris & Sats in Aug.

Park & Gardens: 11.00am - 6.00pm

Castle: 2.00 - 6.00pm Last Adm: 5.00pm

Tel: 01778 591205
Fax: 01778 591259

GRIMSTHORPE, BOURNE, LINCOLNSHIRE PE10 ONB

Owner: Grimsthorpe and Drummond Castle Trust Ltd.   *Contact:* Michael Tebbutt

Grimsthorpe Castle, with its extensive parklands and gardens, is a Tudor Mansion full of fine furniture and paintings. Coach House Tea Room, Woodland Adventure Playground, Red Deer Herd, Nature Trails, Events Programme - a family paradise close to the the A1.
Location: 4 miles north west of Bourne.
Admission: Park: Adult £2.00, Concessions £1.00. Additional separate charge for Castle - Adult £3.00, Concessions £1.50. Combined ticket and Party Rate (20 or more) - Adult £4.00, Concessions £2.00.

GUNBY HALL
Tel: 01909 486411

Gunby, Spilsby, Lincolnshire, PE23 5SS.
Owner: The National Trust   **Contact:** J D Wrisdale
A red brick house with stone dressings, built in 1700 and extended in 1870s. Within the house, there is good early 18th century wainscoting and a fine oak staircase, also English furniture and portraits by Reynolds. Also of interest is the contemporary stable block, a walled kitchen and flower garden, sweeping lawns and borders. Gunby was reputedly Tennyson's "haunt of ancient peace".
Location: 2m W of Burgh Le Marsh, 8m W of Skegness. Approached by Gunby Lane off A158.
Opening Times: Ground floor of house & garden: 1 Apr - end Sept, Wed 2.00pm - 6.00pm. Last admissions 5.30pm. Closed public holidays. Garden also open Thur 2.00pm - 6.00pm. House and garden also open Tues, Thurs and Fri by written appointment only with J D Wrisdale at above address.
Admission: House and garden £3.00. Garden only £1.80. No reduction for parties. Access roads unsuitable for coaches which must park in layby at gates 1/2m from Hall.

HARLAXTON MANOR
Tel: 01476 64541   **Fax:** 01476 70730

Harlaxton, Grantham, Lincolnshire, NG32 1AG.
Owner: University of Evansville   **Contact:** Mrs F Watkins
Neo-Elizabethan house. Grandiose and imposing exterior by Anthony Salvin. Internally an architectural tour de force with a mixture of various styles and an unparalleled Cedar Staircase.
Location: 3 m W of Grantham (10 mins along A1) A607.
Opening Times: 7/8 May 1.00pm - 5.00pm; 11 Jun 1.00pm - 5.00pm. 9 Jul 1.00pm - 5.00pm. House open at other times for group tours only by appointment.

LINCOLN CATHEDRAL
Tel: 01522 544544

Lincoln, Lincolnshire, LN2 1PZ.
    Contact: Communications Office
Medieval Gothic Cathedral of outstanding historical and architectural merit. Shop, Coffee shop, Disabled facilities, Toilets, Schools centre. Parking nearby.
Location: At the centre of Uphill, Lincoln..
Opening Times: All year: May - Aug, 7.15am - 8.00pm, Sun 7.15am - 6.00pm. Sept - May, 7.15am - 6.00pm, Sun 7.15am - 5.00pm. Tours daily: Oct, Nov, Dec, April 11.00am and 2.00pm. May - Sept: 11.00am, 1.00pm, 3.00pm. Jan, Feb & Mar: Sats only at 11.00am & 2.00pm. Roof and Tower Tours also available. Booked tours throughout the year.
Admission: Suggested donation of Adult £2.50, Child £1.00, Conc £1.00, Annual passes £10.00.

SIBSEY TRADER WINDMILL

Sibsey, Boston, Lincolnshire.
Owner: English Heritage   **Contact:** The Administrator
An impressive old mill built in 1877, with its machinery and six sails still intact. It can still be seen in action on occasions.
Location: $1/2$ m W of village of Sibsey, off A16 5 m N of Boston.
Opening Times: 11.00am - 5.00pm on the following dates, 16 - 30 Apr, 28 May, 11 - 25 Jun, 9 & 23 Jul, 13 & 27 Aug, 10 Sept.
Admission: Adults £1.30, Child 70p, Conc £1.00.

TATTERSHALL CASTLE

Tel: 01526 342543

Tattershall, Lincoln, Lincolnshire, LN4 4LR.
Owner: The National Trust   **Contact:** The Administrator
A vast fortified tower built c.1440 for Ralph Bromwell, Lord Treasurer of England. The Castle is an important example of an early brick building, with a tower containing state apartments, rescued from dereliction and restored by Lord Curzon 1911-14. Four great chambers, with ancillary rooms, contain late Gothic fireplaces and brick vaulting. There are tapestries and information displays in turret rooms.
Location: On S side of A153, 15m NE of Sleaford; 10m SW of Horncastle.
Opening Times: 1 Apr - end Oct: Sat to Wed & BH Mon (closed Good Fri), 10.30am - 5.30pm. Nov - 17 Dec: Sat & Sun only 10.30am - 4.00pm. Last admission $1/2$ hour before closing.
Admission: Adult £2.20, Child £1.10, Family £5.50. Discount for parties.

WOOLSTHORPE MANOR

Tel: 01476 860338

23 Newton Way, Woolsthorpe-by-Colsterworth, Grantham, NG33 5NR.
Owner: The National Trust   **Contact:** The Custodian
This small 17th century farmhouse was the birthplace and family home of Sir Isaac Newton. Some of his major work was formulated here, during the Plague years (1665 - 66); an early edition of his Principia Mathematica, pub. 1687, is on display. The orchard includes a descendant of the famous apple tree.
Location: 7m S of Grantham, $1/2$m NW of Colsterworth, 1m W of A1.
Opening Times: 1 Apr - end Oct: Wed to Sun & BH Mon (closed Good Fri), 1.00pm - 5.30pm. Last admission 5.00pm.
Admission: Adult £2.30, Child £1.10, Family £5.70, no reduction for parties which must book in advance.

SPECIAL EVENTS DIARY

- **4th - 5th March: Hoghton Tower**
  Book Fair - Rare and Antiquarian

- **9th April: Hoghton Tower**
  Motor Cycle Sprint

- **11th May: Hoghton Tower**
  Music/Firework Display

- **12th - 14th: Hoghton Tower**
  Flower Festival

- **18th - 20th: Hoghton Tower**
  Antique Fair

- **17th June: Hoghton Tower**
  Ballet

- **30th September - 1st Oct: Hoghton Tower**
  Craft Fair

- **1st October: Hoghton Tower**
  Craft Fair

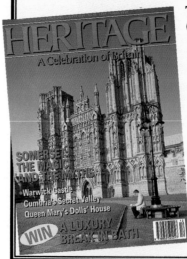

CHISWICK HOUSE
Chiswick

One of the first English Palladian villas, built, c.1725 for Lord Burlington and internationally renowned. The interior decoration is by William Kent, as are the beautiful Italianate gardens, with classical statues and neoclassical temples. Both house and gardens are undergoing extensive restoration. There is an exhibition on the ground floor with a film telling the story of the house and gardens, and of Lord Burlington himself born 300 years ago last year.

CONTACT

The Head Custodian
Chiswick House
Burlington Lane
Chiswick
London
W4 2RP

Tel: (0181) 995 0508

LOCATION

Burlington Lane,
London W4

Rail: 1/4 mile north east of Chiswick Station.

Bus: LT190,290
(Hammersmith to Richmond)

OPENING TIMES

Summer

1 April - 30 September
Daily
10.00am - 6.00pm

1 October - 31 October
Daily
10.00am - 4.00pm

Winter

1 November - 31 March
Wed - Sun
10.00am - 4.00pm

ADMISSION

Adults £2.50
Child* £1.30
OAP/Student/UB40
 holder £1.90

15% discount on groups of 11 or more

* 5 - 15 years.
Under 5's free

SUITABILITY FOR OTHER EVENTS
Filming, plays, photographic shoots.

ADVICE TO COURIERS & DRIVERS
Tour leader and coach driver have free entry. 1 extra place for every 20 additional people.

FACILITIES FOR THE DISABLED
Wheelchair access to the ground floor.

CATERING
Homemade refreshments available in the summer season.

GUIDED TOURS
Guided tours for pre-booked parties take approximately 1 hour. Free audio tours in English, French and German.

GIFT SHOP
Situated at the entrance to the house.

GUIDE BOOKS
Colour guide book £2.25.

SCHOOL VISIT/CHILDREN
Free if booked in advance. Tel: 0181 348 1268/7

KENWOOD HOUSE
Hampstead

Standing in splendid grounds on the edge of Hampstead Heath, Kenwood contains the most important private collection of paintings ever given to the nation, including works by Rembrandt, Turner, Reynolds and Gainsborough. The outstanding neoclassical house was remodelled in the 1760's by Robert Adam who created the magnificent Library. The park was designed by Humphry Repton and features wide sweeps of lawn leading down to ornamental lakes which provide a perfect setting for the open-air concerts held there in the summer.

OPENING TIMES

1 April - 30 September
Daily
10.00am - 6.00pm

1 October - 31 March
Daily
10.00am - 4.00pm

ADMISSION

Free

CONTACT

The Administrator
The Iveagh Bequest
Kenwood
Hampstead Lane
London
NW3 7JR

Tel: (0181) 348 1286

LOCATION

London Transport 210

Rail: Finsbury Park,
Golders Green

Underground:
Highgate station 1 mile

SUITABILITY FOR OTHER EVENTS
Concerts, exhibitions, filming.

EXTRA FACILITIES
The Old Kitchen is available for corporate entertainment and weddings.

ADVICE TO COURIERS & DRIVERS
No photography in the house.

FACILITIES FOR THE DISABLED
Ground floor access for wheelchairs, disabled parking in West Lodge car park.

PARKING FOR COACHES & CARS
West Lodge car park on Hampstead Lane.

CATERING
Refreshment facilities available.

GUIDED TOURS
Tours including some foreign languages available by prior arrangment. Personal stereo tours available.

GIFT SHOP
A wide selection of souvenirs are available.

GUIDE BOOKS
Souvenir guide book £3.50. Foreign language leaflets available.

SCHOOL VISIT/CHILDREN
Free when booked in advance on (0181) 348 1286/7.

THE QUEEN'S HOUSE
Greenwich

At the centre of a group of splendid historical buildings lies The Queen's House, a royal palace designed by Inigo Jones. The house has been sumptuously restored to show the vibrant colours of the decoration when occupied by the dowager queen Henrietta Maria, wife of Charles I. Built in the classical style of Palladio, the house in 1635 marked a major change for English architecture, and demonstrated new rules of proportion. The Great Hall is a 40' cube, and its ceiling is a reproduction of the original by the Gentileschis.

The vaults now house a Treasury of trophies, swords and plate marking great occasions in history. The elegant Tulip Staircase leads to rooms used for audiences which are now decorated with beautifully woven silk damask and brocatelle. A quiet loggia overlooks the royal park with a view of Wren's Observatory building with it's unusual red time ball that marks Greenwich time at 1 o'clock daily.

The 3 site ticket includes admission to The Old Royal Observatory and the adjacent National Maritime Museum which is filled with stories of Britain's great naval heroes and explorers, impressive oil paintings and lots of fascinating exhibits. A new exhibition celebrates the life of Nelson from August 1995.

A visit to all three buildings will occupy a full day or a visit can be combined with a river cruise on the Thames. The park, the oldest of the Royal Parks, is ideal for picnics and has an outstanding herbaceous border.

CONTACT

Bookings Unit
National Maritime
Museum
Romney Road
Greenwich
London
SE10 9NF

Tel: (0181) 858 4422
Fax: (0181) 312 6632

LOCATION

On the South Bank of the Thames at Greenwich. A2/A206 from London, elsewhere M25, Junct. 2 then A2.
Rail: From Charing Cross, Waterloo East or London Bridge to Maze Hill or Greenwich.
River: Cruises from Central London to Greenwich.
Air: London City Airport 4 miles.

SUITABILITY FOR OTHER EVENTS
Corporate hospitality, prestigious functions, fashion photography, filming, small balls.

EXTRA FACILITIES
Parkland and grounds. Lecture room in adjacent museum.

ADVICE TO COURIERS & DRIVERS
Set down only at property. Free coach parking on Blackheath. Pay and display at the Cutty Sark. Guides and drivers admitted free. Childrens groups must be pre-booked for admission to the Queen's House.

FACILITIES FOR THE DISABLED
Queens House accessible for wheelchairs upper floor by "Stairmate". Signed and Touch tours for groups by prior arrangement. Advisory leaflet available. Disabled groups welcome.

PARKING FOR COACHES & CARS
There is car parking for 115 cars within 100 yards and for 25 coaches within 600 yards. Coaches can set down nearby prior to parking.

CATERING
Restaurant seating 150 in adjoining museum. Function catering from approved and recommended caterers.

GIFT SHOP
Open as the House. Located in an adjoining building.

GUIDED TOURS
Pre-book, Tel. 0181-312-6608. Cost approx £33 per group.

GUIDE BOOK
Colour guide book, £1.95. Handouts are also available in French, German, Italian, Spanish and Japanese.

SCHOOL VISITS/CHILDREN
Special educational services linked to National Curriculum available with gallery talks from experienced teaching staff. Education enquiries 0181-312-6608.

Summer
April - September

Mon to Sat
10.00am -5.00pm

Sundays
Noon - 5.00pm

Winter
October - March

Mon to Sat
10.00am -5.00pm

Sundays
Noon - 5.00pm

Closed 24th, 25th, 26th December.

ADMISSION

3 SITE TICKET
Adult £4.95
Concessions* . . .£3.95
Child (5 - 16yrs) . .£2.95

GROUPS
A discount of 20% for groups of 10 or more.

* Concessions for OAPs, Students, UB40, Disabled.

CONFERENCE AND FUNCTION FACILITIES

ROOM	DIMENSIONS	CAPACITY	LAYOUT	POWER POINTS	SUITABLE FOR A/V
Great Hall	40' x 40'	200*	Buffet	3	
		150*	Dinner		
Orangery		150*	Buffet	3	✓
		125*	Dinner		
* Incl. ante-rooms.					

THE RANGERS HOUSE ⊞
Blackheath

A handsome red brick villa built c.1700, on the edge of Greenwich Park, with a splendid bow-windowed gallery. The recently opened Architectural Study Centre in the Coach House, displays an interesting collection of domestic architectural features from London dwellings of the 17th-19th centuries.

CONTACT

The Administrator
The Rangers House
Chesterfield House
Blackheath
London
SE10 8QX

Tel: (0181) 853 0035

LOCATION

Rail: Maze Hill ¹/₂ mile.

Bus: LT53 Oxford Circus - Plumstead

OPENING TIMES

Summer

1 April - 30 September
Daily
10.00am - 6.00pm

1 October - 31 October
Daily
10.00am - 4.00pm

Winter

1 November - 31 March
Wednesday - Sunday
10.00am - 4.00pm

ADMISSION

Adults £2.00
Child* £1.00
OAP/Student/UB40
  holder £1.50

15% discount on groups of 11 or more

* 5 - 15 years.
Under 5's free

SUITABILITY FOR OTHER EVENTS
Plays, concerts, opera, corporate dinners, filming, photographic shoots.

EXTRA FACILITIES
Education room available.

ADVICE TO COURIERS & DRIVERS
No photography in house. Tour leader and coach driver have free entry. 1 extra place for every 20 additional people.

FACILITIES FOR THE DISABLED
Disabled WC, chair lift, hearing loop audio tours..

PARKING FOR COACHES & CARS
Parking is available for cars outside the house.

GUIDED TOURS
Arranged by the custodian on request. Personal stereo tours available.

GIFT SHOP
Located in the Servants Hall.

GUIDE BOOKS
Colour guide book £2.25.

SCHOOL VISIT/CHILDREN
School visits are free if booked in advance on (0181) 348 1286/7.

ROYAL SOCIETY OF ARTS
John Adam Street

The House of the RSA (Royal Society for the encouragement of Arts, Manufacturers and Commerce) was designed specially for the Society by Robert Adam in the early 1770's. Today the RSA's terrace of five 18th Century houses is the finest and historically most interesting remaining section for the Adam brothers' development known as the Adelphi. A complex £4,500,000 building and refurbishment programme has brought the RSA's magnificent vaults into full use for receptions and private dining.

The Great Room. The jewel in the RSA's crown is the Great Room, one of the most spectacular and delightful Lecture Halls in the country. Its walls are decorated by the celebrated sequence of allegorical paintings - The Progress of Human Knowledge - by James Barry, together with portraits by Gainsborough and Reynolds.

A perfect setting for any gathering from Annual General Meeting to concert recital, the Great Room's unique atmosphere allows an audience from 50 to 200 to feel at ease and involved.

Benjamin Franklin Room: The classic Benjamin Franklin Room is a specious assembly room with its chandelier and Adam Fireplaces yet with a controlled ventilation system, ideal for meetings, receptions and banquets for 30-150 persons.

The Vaults: Beneath the Society's house lies the largest remaining part of the Adelphi arches. Originally built for storage and more recently used as wine cellars, the vaults have now been restored and converted to provide a unique venue for all forms of event. They feature the original 18th Century brickwork, and can be dressed to enhance product launches, parties, themed events and private exhibitions.

CONTACT

Ms Christine Bond
Conference Manager
Royal Society of Arts
8 John Adam Street
London
WC2N 6EZ

Tel: (0171) 930 5115
Fax: (0171) 321 0271

LOCATION

Near to two mainline stations.
Rail: Charing Cross, Waterloo.

Nearest tube: Embankment, Charing Cross, Covent Garden

OPENING TIMES

Summer
Closed during the last 2 weeks of August.

9.00am - 8.00pm

Winter
Closed 24th December - 2nd January 1995

9.00am - 8.00pm

ADMISSION

For Room Hire Prices, please contact the RSA Conference Office direct for a brochure.

SUITABILITY FOR OTHER EVENTS
Product launches, themed parties, corporate announcements, film previews, dinner dances, private concerts, exhibitions.

EXTRA FACILITIES
Lectures can be arranged on the history of the house in the Great Room. There is a Steinway Baby Grand piano, which is available for private recitals in the Great Room.

ADVICE TO COURIERS AND DRIVERS
All visits are by prior arrangement. Coaches may only set down and pick up on John Adam Street or the Strand.

FACILITIES FOR THE DISABLED
There is wheel chair access to all the main rooms of the house via a lift. A disabled cloakroom is located on the 1st floor. Unfortunately Westminster Council does not permit disabled parking in restricted parking zones.

PARKING FOR COACHES AND CARS
The closest Coach parking area is at Vauxhall. Meters in John Adam Street. Car parks in Savoy Place and St Martin's Lane.

CATERING
Catering can be arranged for groups in a private room Rooms may be hired for lunches, dinners, receptions. We regret we do not have facilities for individuals.

GUIDED TOURS
Tours of the house for groups of up to 25 people may be arranged in advance. All visitors to the house must pre-book.

CONFERENCE AND FUNCTION FACILITIES

ROOM	DIMENSIONS	CAPACITY	LAYOUT	POWER POINTS	SUITABLE FOR A/V
Great Room	42' x 36'	200	Theatre	✓	✓
Durham St Auditorium	36' x30'	60	Theatre	✓	✓
B. Franklin Room	42' x 36'	150	Reception	✓	✓
Tavern Room	40' x 17'	70	Reception	✓	✓
Folkestone Room	20' x 20'	30	Reception	✓	✓
Gallery	40' x 20'		Reception	✓	✓
THE VAULTS					
Vault 1	55' x 28'	100	Reception	✓	✓
Vault 2	36' x 18'	50	Reception	✓	✓
Vault 3	20' x 18'	30	Reception	✓	✓
Vault4	37' x 11'	75	Reception	✓	✓

SPENCER HOUSE
St. James's Place

SPENCER HOUSE, built 1756-66 for the 1st Earl Spencer, an ancestor of Her Royal Highness The Princess of Wales, is London's finest surviving eighteenth-century town house. The magnificent private palace has regained the full splendour of its late eighteenth century appearance, after a painstaking seven-year restoration programme.

Designed by John Vardy and James 'Athenian' Stuart, the nine state rooms are amongst the first neo-classical interiors in Europe. Vardy's Palm Room, with its spectacular screen of gilded palm trees and arched fronds, is a unique Palladian setpiece, while the elegant mural decorations of Stuart's Painted Room reflect the eighteenth-century passion for classical Greece and Rome. Stuart's superb gilded furniture has been returned to its original location in the Painted Room by courtesy of the V&A and English Heritage. Visitors can also see a fine collection of eighteenth century paintings and furniture, specially assembled for the house, including five major Benjamin West paintings, graciously lent by Her Majesty The Queen.

The state rooms are open to the public for viewing on Sundays. They are also available on a limited number of occasions each year for private and corporate entertaining during the rest of the week.

❖

CONTACT

Stephen Jones
Director
Spencer House
27 St James's Place
London
SW1A 1NR

Tel: 0171 409 0526

Fax: 0171 493 5765

LOCATION

Central London:
off St James's Street,
overlooking Green Park.

Nearest tube:
Green Park.

PARKING FOR COACHES & CARS
No parking facilities. Coaches can drop off at door.

CATERING
Excellent in-house catering team for private and corporate events. However, no catering for Sunday visitors.

GUIDE BOOKS
Comprehensive colour guide book £2.95.

GUIDED TOURS
All visits are by guided tour.

SUITABILITY FOR OTHER EVENTS
Cocktail receptions, lunches, dinners, board meetings, theatre style meetings, contract signings, wedding receptions, private parties.

ADVICE TO COURIERS & DRIVERS
No children under 10. No dogs admitted. No photography inside House.

FACILITIES FOR THE DISABLED
Ramps, lifts and accessible toilets available.

OPENING TIMES

All Year
Except Jan and Aug
Sundays
11.30am - 5.30pm.

Last tour 4.45pm.

Tours begin approx every 15 minutes and last 1 hour. Maximum number on each tour is 15.

Advance reservations:
0171-499-8620
Tues - Fri
10am - 1pm only.

Open for corporate hospitality except during January and August.

ADMISSION

To end March 1995

Adults £6.00
Concessions* . . .£5.00

* Students, Friends of V&A, Tate Gallery and Royal Academy (all with cards), children under 16 (no under 10's admitted).

Prices include guided tour.

CONFERENCE AND FUNCTION FACILITIES

Cocktail receptions for up to 400 (500 if using the Terrace). Lunches and dinners (from 2 - 140). Board meetings (max 40), theatre style meetings (max 100).

BLEWCOAT SCHOOL

Tel: 0171 222 2877

23 Caxton Street, Westminster, London, SW1H 0PY.

Owner: The National Trust   **Contact:** The Administrator

Built in 1709 at the expense of William Green, a local brewer, to provide an education for poor children. The building was in use as a school until 1926.

Location: Near the junction with Buckingham Gate.

Opening Times: All year: Mon to Fri, 10.00am - 5.30pm; late-night shopping Thurs until 7.00pm; also Sat 2, 9 and 16 Dec 11.00am - 4.30pm. Closed BH Mon, Good Fri, 25 Dec - 3 Jan.

BUCKINGHAM PALACE

Tel: 0171 930 4832

Buckingham Palace Road, London, SW1A 1AA.

Owner: H M The Queen

Official London residence of H M The Queen. Bought for George III in 1762 and extensively remodelled by John Nash in the 1820s for George IV. The east wing that one sees today from The Mall was built to the designs of Edward Blore in 1846. The whole facade of the east wing was refaced by Sir Aston Webb in 1912. The state apartments shown are used mainly for official events

Location: Central London

Opening Times: 7 Aug - 28 Sept, daily, 9.30am - 5.30pm. Ticket office opens at 9.00am, last admission 4.30pm.

Admission: State Apartments: Adult £8.50, Age 60+ £6.00, Child under 17 £4.50.

CARLYLE'S HOUSE

Tel: 0171 352 7087

24 Cheyne Row, Chelsea, London, SW3 5HL.

Owner: The National Trust   **Contact:** The Custodian

This 18th century town house was the home of Thomas and Jane Carlyle from 1834 until their deaths. It contains furniture, books, personal relics and portraits.

Location: Off Cheyne Walk, between Battersea and Albert Bridges on Chelsea Embankment, or off Oakley Street.

Opening Times: 1 Apr - end Oct: Wed to Sun & BH Mon, 11.00am - 5.00pm. Closed Good Fri. Last admission 4.30pm.

Admission: £2.90, no reduction for students or parties, which must book in advance.

COLLEGE OF ARMS

Tel: 0171 248 2762

Queen Victoria Street, London, EC4V 4BT.

Owner: Dr Conrad Swan   **Contact:** Dr Conrad Swan

Mansion built in 1670s to house the English Officers of Arms and their records, and the panelled Earl Marshal's Court. Shop - books, souvenirs.

Location: On N side of Queen Victoria Street, S of St Paul's Cathedral.

Opening Times: Earl Marshal's Court only; open all the year (except Public holidays & on State & special occasions) Mon - Fri 10.00am - 4.00pm. Group visits (up to 10) by arrangement only. Record Room: open for tours (groups of up to 20) by special arrangement in advance with the Office in Waiting.

Admission: Free (parties by negotiation). No coaches, parking, indoor photography or dogs.

CHISWICK HOUSE

See page 113 for full page entry.

DR JOHNSON'S HOUSE

Tel: 0171 353 3745   **Fax:** 01308 868995

17 Gough Square, London, EC4A 3DE.

Owner: The Trustees   **Contact:** Mrs B Gathergood

Fine 18th century house, once home to Dr Samuel Johnson, the celebrated literary figure, famous for his English dictionary.

Location: Gough Square, London.

Opening Times: Oct - Apr Mon - Sat, 11.00am - 5.00pm. May - Sept, Mon - Sat, 11.00am - 5.30pm.

Admission: Adult £3.00, Child over 10 £1.00, Child under 10 free, Conc £2.00.

ELTHAM PALACE

Tel: 0181 348 1286

London.

Owner: English Heritage   **Contact:** The Administrator

The most delightful feature of this 13th century Royal Palace is the Great Hall with its splendid roof.

Location: ³/₄ m N off A20 off Court Yard, SE9.

Opening Times: Telephone for details.

FENTON HOUSE

OPEN

March
Sat & Sun only
2.00 - 5.00pm

1 Apr - end Oct
Sat, Sun &
Bank Holiday
11.00am - 5.30pm

Last admissions
half an hour
before closing.

Tel: 0171 4353471

WINDMILL HILL, HAMPSTEAD, LONDON NW3 6RT

Owner: The National Trust   *Contact: The Custodian*

A late 17th century house with an outstanding collection of porcelain and early keyboard instruments. The large walled garden is sometimes used for open air plays.

Location: Visitors' entrance on west side of Hampstead Grove. Hampstead Underground station 300 yds.

Admission: Adult £3.50, Child £1.75, Family Ticket £9.00.

FREUD MUSEUM

Tel: 0171 435 2002   **Fax:** 0171 431 5452

20 Maresfield Gardens, London, NW3 5SX.

Contact: Ms E Davies

Location: Maresfield Gardens, London.

Opening Times: Wed - Sun (inc) 12.00pm - 5.00pm.

Admission: Adults £2.50, Under 12 free, Conc £1.50, Coach parties by appointment.

GEORGE INN

Tel: 0171 407 2056

77 Borough High Street, Southwark, London, SE1.

Owner: The National Trust

The only remaining galleried inn in London, famous as a coaching inn in the 18th and 19th centuries, and mentioned by Dickens in Little Dorrit. The George Inn is leased to and run by Whitbread Plc as a public house.

Location: On E side of Borough High Street, near London Bridge station.

Opening Times: During licensing hours.

GUNNERSBURY PARK MUSEUM

Tel: 0181 5707728   **Fax:** 0181 5724819

London, W3 8LQ.

Owner: London Borough of Ealing & Hounslow   **Contact:** Ms S Levitt

Built in 1802 and refurbished by Sydney Smirke for the Rothschild family. Their attractive park, splendid interiors and original kitchens survive. Now a social history museum with regularly changing displays.

Location: Acton town tube station. Junction of A4, M4 North Circular.

Opening Times: Daily 1.00pm -5.00pm Apr - Oct 1.00pm - 4.00pm Nov - Mar 6.00pm weekends and Bank Hols. Victorian Kitchens summer weekends only. Park: open dawn - dusk.

Admission: Free, but small charge for guided tours and some types of school group visits.

🌿 THE NATIONAL TRUST   ▣ ENGLISH HERITAGE   🏛 HISTORIC HOUSES ASSOCIATION

HOGARTH'S HOUSE

**HOGARTH LANE,
GREAT WEST ROAD,
CHISWICK, LONDON W4 2QN**

Owner: London Borough of Hounslow

Contact: Allan Downend

Tel: 0181 994 6757

This late 17th century house was the country home of William Hogarth, the famous painter, engraver, satirist and social reformer between 1749 and his death in 1764. It contains a collection of his engravings and prints and the house is surrounded by an extensive garden which is in the process of restoration. The gallery of prints shows the development of Hogarth's genius.

Location: 200 yds. west of Hogarth roundabout on the Great West Road - junction of Burlington Lane. Car park in named spaces in Axis Business Centre behind house.

Admission: Free.

OPEN
April - September Mon - Sat 2 - 6.00pm
Sundays 11.00am - 6.00pm
October - March Mon - Sat 2 - 4.00pm
Sundays 11.00am - 4.00pm
Closed Tuesdays

JEWEL TOWER

Tel: 0171 222 2219

Westminster, London.

Owner: English Heritage   **Contact:** The Administrator

Built c. 1365 to house the personal treasure of Edward III and formerly part of the Palace of Westminster. It was used to house valuables which formed part of the King's 'wardrobe', and subsequently used as a storehouse and government office. There is a new exhibition, 'Parliament Past and Present'.

Location: Opposite S end of Houses of Parliament (Victoria Tower).

Opening Times: 1 Apr - 30 Sept, daily 10.00am - 6.00pm,1 Oct - 31 Mar, daily, 10.00am - 4.00pm. Closed 24 - 26 Dec, 1 Jan.

Admission: Adult £1.50, Child 80p, Conc £1.10.

KEATS HOUSE

Tel: 0171 4352062   **Fax:** 0171 4319293

Keats Grove, Hampstead, London, NW3 2RR.

Owner: London Borough of Camden   **Contact:** Mrs C M Gee

Regency home of the poet John Keats, restored in 1974 - 75.

Location: Hampstead, NW3 2RR.

Opening Times: Apr - Oct; Mon - Fri, 10.00am - 1.00pm/2.00pm - 6.00pm. Sat, 10.00am - 1.00pm/2.00pm - 5.00pm. Sun, 2.00pm - 5.00pm. Easter, Spring and late Summer Bank Hols, 2.00pm - 5.00pm. Nov - Mar; Mon - Fri, 1.00pm - 5.00pm. Sat, 10.00am - 1.00pm/2.00pm - 5.00pm. Sun, 2.00pm - 5.00pm. Closed Christmas Eve, Christmas Day, Boxing Day, New Year's Day, Good Fri, Easter Eve and May Day. 1.00pm - 5.00pm Sat.

Admission: Free.

KENWOOD HOUSE

See page 114 for full page entry.

LEIGHTON HOUSE MUSEUM

Tel: 0171 6023316   **Fax:** 0171 3712467

12 Holland Park Road, Kensington, London, W14 8LZ.

Owner: Royal Borough of Kensington and Chelsea   **Contact:** Miss J Findlater

Opulent and exotic example of High Victorian taste, built for Frederick, Lord Leighton, President of the Royal Academy. Astounding Arab Hall with Islamic tiles. Paintings by Leighton and other Victorian artists.

Location: Hampstead, NW3 2RR.

Opening Times: Apr - Oct; Mon - Fri, 10.00am - 1.00pm/2.00pm - 6.00pm. Sat, 10.00am - 1.00pm/2.00pm - 5.00pm. Sun, 2.00pm - 5.00pm. Easter, Spring and late Summer Bank Hols, 2.00pm - 5.00pm. Nov - Mar; Mon - Fri, 1.00pm - 5.00pm. Sat, 10.00am - 1.00pm/2.00pm - 5.00pm. Sun, 2.00pm - 5.00pm. Closed Christmas Eve, Christmas Day, Boxing Day, New Year's Day, Good Fri, Easter Eve and May Day. 1.00pm - 5.00pm Sat.

Admission: Free.

LINDSEY HOUSE

99 -100 Cheyne Walk, London, SW10.

Owner: The National Trust   **Contact:** Mrs A Morgan

Part of Lindsey House was built in 1674 on the site of Sir Thomas More's garden, overlooking the River Thames. It has one of the finest 17th century exteriors in London.

Location: On Cheyne Walk, W of Battersea Bridge near junction with Milman's Street on Chelsea Embankment.

Opening Times: By written appointment.

MUSEUM OF GARDEN HISTORY

Tel: 0171 2611891   **Fax:** 0171 4018869

Lambeth Palace Road, Lambeth, London, SE1 7LB.

Owner: The Tradescant Trust   **Contact:** Mrs R Nicholson

Replica 17th century garden. Exhibits on all aspects of gardening history.

Location: Next to Lambeth Palace.

Opening Times: Mon - Fri, 10.30am - 4.00pm. Sat closed. Sun 10.30am - 5.00pm.

Admission: Free. Groups by appointment.

PITSHANGER MANOR MUSEUM

Tel: 0181 567227   **Fax:** 0181 5670595

Mattock Lane, Ealing, London, W5 5EQ.

Owner: London Borough of Ealing   **Contact:** Ms N Sohal

Built by the architect Sir John Soane as his family home.

Location: Mattock Lane, London.

Opening Times: Tues - Sat 10.00am - 5.00pm. Times may vary, please ring for details. Closed Christmas, New Year and Easter.

Admission: Free. Groups by arrangement only.

ROYAL SOCIETY OF THE ARTS

See page 117 for full page entry.

SIR JOHN SOANES MUSEUM

Tel: 0171 4052107   **Fax:** 0171 8313957

13 Lincoln's Inn Fields, London, WC2A 3BP.

Owner: Trustees of Sir John Soane's Museum   **Contact:** Ms C Scull

The celebrated architect Sir John Soane built this in 1812 as his own house. It now contains his collection of antiquities, sculpture and paintings. included among which are the Rakes Progress paintings by William Hogarth.

Location: Central London.

Opening Times: Tues - Sat, 10.00am - 5.00pm. 6.00pm - 9.00pm on first Tues of the month. Closed BHs And Christmas Eve.

Admission: Free. Groups must book.

SOUTHSIDE HOUSE

Tel: 0181 9472491

Wimbledon Common, London, SW19 4RJ.

Owner: The Pennington-Mellor-Munthe Charity Trust   **Contact:** John Sibun

One of the few houses open only during the winter. Late 17th and 18th century house with intriguing contents and collections.

Location: Opposite 'Crooked Billet' Inn on Wimbledon Common.

Opening Times: 2 Oct - 31 May (closed Christmas), BH Mons, Tues, Thurs, Sat. 2.00pm - 6.00pm. Guided tours every hour - last tour 5.00pm.

Admission: Adult £5.00, Child (11 - 18 years) £3.00.

SOUTHWARK CATHEDRAL

Tel: 0171 4073708   **Fax:** 0171 3577389

Southwark, London, SE1 9DA.

Contact: Ms K Johnson

Location: South side of London Bridge.

Opening Times: Daily 8.30am - 6.00pm. Sunday services: 9.00am, 11.00am and 3.00pm. Weekday services: 9.00am, 12.30pm, 12.45pm and 5.30pm.

Admission: Donation.

SPENCER HOUSE

See page 118 for full page entry.

ST GEORGES'S CATHEDRAL

Tel: 0171 9285256

London, SE1 7HY.

Contact: Rev J P Pannett

Neo-Gothic rebuilt Pugin Cathedral bombed during the last war and rebuilt by Romily Craze in 1958.

Location: Opposite Imperial War Museum.

Opening Times: 8.00am - 8.00pm every day, except Bank Hols.

ST PAUL'S CATHEDRAL

Tel: 0171 2364128   **Fax:** 0171 2483104

St Paul's Chapter House, St Paul's Churchyard, London, EC4M 8AD.

Contact: The Registrar

This is Christopher Wren's masterpiece, begun in 1675 completed in 1710. Attractions include the Crypt where Wren & Nelson are buried and the galleries.

Location: City of London.

Opening Times: Open for Matins 7.30am, Holy Communion 8.00am. Thereafter 8.30am onwards. Open until 4.00pm. Eucharist 5.00pm. Open on Suns 9.00am - 5.00pm. No touring during services.

Admission: Mon - Sat Adults £3.00, Child £2.00, Conc £2.50, Family (2+2) £7.00, Groups (10+)£2.50. Galleries extra.

SUTTON HOUSE ❧

Tel: 0181 9862264

2 - 4 Homerton High Street, Hackney, London, E9 6JQ.

Owner: The National Trust　　　　　　　　**Contact:** The Administrator

In London's East End; a rare example of a Tudor red-brick house, built in 1535 by Sir Rafe Sadleir, Principal Secretary of State for Henry VIII, with 18th century alterations and later additions. The recent restoration has revealed many 16th century details which are displayed even in rooms of later periods. Notable features include original linenfold panelling and 17th century wall paintings.

Location: At the corner of Isabella Road and Homerton High Street.

Opening Times: 1 Feb - 26 Nov & 4 Feb: Wed, Sun & BH Mon 11.30am - 5.30pm (closed Good Fri). Last admission 5.00pm. Also open Wed and Fri evenings during Jul 7.00am - 9.30pm.

Admission: £1.60. Group visits by prior arrangement.

THE BANQUETING HALL

Tel: 0171 9308268　　**Fax:** 0171 9308268

Whitehall, London, SW1A 2ER.

Owner: Historic Royal Palaces　　　　　　**Contact:** Ms L Kennedy

Once part of the Great Palace of Whitehall, designed by Inigo Jones for James I.

Location: Whitehall.

Opening Times: Mon - Sat, 10.00am - 5.00pm. Closed on public hols.

Admission: Adult £2.90, Child £1.90, Conc £2.20, Groups 10% discount.

THE CHELSEA PHYSIC GARDEN

Tel: 0171 3525646　　**Fax:** 0171 3763910

66 Royal Hospital Road, London, SW3 4HS.

Contact: Mrs S Minter

The second oldest botanic gardens in Britain, founded in 1673. For many years this 4 acres of peace and quiet with many rare and unusual plants was known only to a few.

Central London. Off embankment between Chelsea and Albert Bridges.

Location: Central London. Off embankment between Chelsea and Albert Bridges.

Opening Times: 2 Apr - 29 Oct; Wed 2.00pm - 5.00pm. Sun 2.00pm - 6.00pm. 22 - 26 May (Chelsea Flower Show) and 5 to 9 Jun (Chelsea Festival Weeks), 12.00pm - 5.00pm.

Admission: Adult £3.50, Child under 16 £1.80, Conc £1.80.

THE DICKENS HOUSE MUSEUM

48 Doughty Street, London, SW1W 9TR.

Contact: Price Haslan & Associates Ltd

Charles Dickens lived here as a young man, and his drawing room has been reconstructed. Numerous personal mementoes are on view.

Location: Doughty Street, London.

Opening Times: Sat, 10.00am - 5.00pm (last admission 4.30pm). Closed Sun and BH.

Admission: Adult £3.00, Student £2.00, Senior citizen £1.00, Child £1.00, Families £6.00.

THE GEFFRYE MUSEUM

OPEN

Tues - Saturday
10.00am - 5.00pm
Sundays and Bank
Holiday Mondays
2 - 5.00pm

Closed Mondays
(except Bank Hols)
Good Friday,
Christmas Eve,
Christmas Day
Boxing Day,
New Years Day.

Tel: 0171 739 9893
Fax: 0171 729 5647

KINGSLAND ROAD, LONDON E2 8EA

Owner: Geffrye Museum Trust　　　*Contact:* Christine Lalumia

The Geffrye is one of London's most friendly and enjoyable museums, set in elegant grade I listed 18th century almshouses with delightful gardens, just north of the city. It presents the changing, style of the the English domestic interior from 1600 to 1950 through a series of period rooms. Walled herb garden open April to October. Innovative programme of lectures and activities. Shop and coffee bar.

Location: Buses: 22A, 22B, 149, 243, 67. Underground: Liverpool St. or Old St. Parking: available in neighbouring streets.

Admission: Free.

THE MUSEUM OF THE ORDER OF ST. JOHN

ST. JOHN'S GATE, LONDON
Owner: The Order of St. John
Contact: Pamela Willis

Tel: 0171 253 6644
Fax: 0171 4908835

Headquarters of the Order of St John in England, the 16th century Gatehouse contains the most comprehensive collection of items relating to the Knights Hospitaller. Together with the nearby Priory Church and 12th century Crypt it now forms the headquarters of the modern Order whose charitable foundations include St John Ambulance and the Ophthalmic Hospital in Jerusalem. The collection includes Maltese silver, furniture, paintings and pharmacy jars.

Location: St. John's Lane, Clerkenwell, London EC1M 4DA. Nearest tube; Farringdon, Barbican

Admission: Free but donations are welcome.

OPEN
Mon - Fri   10.00am - 5.00pm
Saturdays   10.00am - 4.00pm
Closed Bank Holidays
Tours: Tues, Fri & Sats at 11am, 2.30pm
Ref. Library: Open by appointment.

THE QUEEN'S HOUSE

See page 115 for full page entry.

THE RANGERS HOUSE ⌗

See page 116 for full page entry.

THE WALLACE COLLECTION

Tel: 0171 9350687　　**Fax:** 0171 2242155

Hertford House, Manchester Square, London, W1M 6BN.

Owner: National Museum　　　　　　　**Contact:** Ms B King

Permanent collection of European paintings, miniatures and sculpture. French 18th century furniture and paintings. Home of Fanz Hals, "Laughing Cavalier" - in elegant 18th century town house.

Location: Behind Selfridges, Oxford Street.

Opening Times: Mon - Sat, 10.00am - 5.00pm. Sun 2.00pm - 5.00pm. Closed 24 - 26 Dec, New Years Day, Good Friday, May Day.

Admission: Free.

TOWER BRIDGE

Tel: 0171 4033761　　**Fax:** 0171 3577935

London, SE1 2UP.

Contact: Mr M Waters

Location: In centre of London, close to London Bridge and Tower Hill Tube Station.

Opening Times: Nov - Mar; 10.00am - 5.15pm. Apr - Oct; 10.00am - 6.30pm. Last entry 1¼ hours before closing.

Admission: Adult £5.00, Child £3.50, Family £14.00, Senior citizens/students £3.50, Groups of 20 plus 20% discount except in Jul/Aug when discount is 10%.

WESTMINSTER ABBEY

Tel: 0171 2225152　　**Fax:** 0171 2332072

London, SW1P 3PA.

Contact: Miss E St John Smith

Location: Westminster.

Opening Times: Royal Chapels: Mon - Fri, 9.00am - 4.45pm (last admission 4.00pm), Sat, 9.00am - 2.45pm (last admission 2.00pm) and 3.45pm - 5.45pm.

Admission: Royal Chapels: Adult £4.00, Child (under 16) £1.00, Student & OAP £2.00.

WESTMINSTER ABBEY
(CHAPTER HOUSE, PYX CHAMBER AND ABBEY MUSEUM)

Tel: 0171 222 5152   **Fax:** 0171 233 2072

London, SW1P 3PA.

Contact: Miss E St John Smith

The Chapter House, built by the royal masons in 1250 and faithfully restored in the 19th century, contains some of the finest examples of medieval English sculpture to be seen. The building is octagonal, with a central column, and still has its original floor of glazed tiles. Its uses have varied, but in the 14th century it was used as a meeting place for the Benedictine monks of the abbey, and also for members of Parliament. The 11th century Pyx Chamber now houses the Abbey treasures, reflecting its use as the strongroom of the exchequer from the 14th to 19th centuries. The Abbey museum contains medieval Royal effigies.

Location: Approach either through the Abbey or through Dean's Yard and the cloister.
Opening Times: Royal Chapels: Mon - Fri, 9.00am - 4.45pm (last admission 4.00pm), Sat, 9.00am - 2.45pm (last admission 2.00pm) and 3.45pm - 5.45pm. Chapter House: 16 Mar - 15 Oct, 9.30am - 6.00pm (last admission 5.30pm), 16 Oct - 15 Mar, 9.30am - 4.00pm (last admission 3.30pm).
Admission: Royal Chapels: Adult £4.00, Child (under 16) £1.00, Student & OAP £2.00. Chapter House: Adult £2.50, Child £1.90, Student & OAP £1.30.

WESTMINSTER CATHEDRAL

Tel: 0171 7989055   **Fax:** 0171 8344257

Victoria, London, SW1P 1QW.

Contact: Monsignor G Stack

The Roman Catholic Cathedral of the Archbishop of Westminster. Spectacular building in the Byzantine style, designed by J F Bentley, opened in 1903, famous for its mosaics, marble and music. Westminster Cathedral celebrates the centenary of its foundation in 1995. There will be a major festival of music, a flower festival, an exhibition of its architecture and treasures, plus centenary lectures by leading public figures as well as church services to celebrate this anniversary.

Location: On Victoria Street, between Victoria Station and Westminster Abbey.
Opening Times: Summer: 7.00am - 8.00pm. Winter: 7.00am - 7.00pm, Sunday Mass: 7.00am, 8.00am, 9.00am, 10.30am, 12.00pm, 5.00pm and 7.00pm. Vespers 3.30pm. Weekday Mass: 7.00am, 8.00am, 8.30am, 9.00am, 10.30am, 12.30pm, 1.00pm and 5.30pm. Confession: weekday, 11.00am - 6.00pm, weekends 9.00am - 7.00pm.

WILLIAM MORRIS GALLERY

Tel: 0181 527 3782

Forest Road, Walthamstow, London, E17 4PP.

Owner: Ms Nora Gillow   **Contact:** Ms Nora Gillow
Location: 15 mins walk from Walthamstow tube (Victoria line). 5 - 10 mins from M11/A406.
Opening Times: Tues - Sat and first Sun each month, 10am - 1pm and 2 - 5pm.
Admission: Admission is free for all visitors but a charge is made for guided tours which must be booked in advance.

SPECIAL EVENTS DIARY

- **14th February - 19th March: Geffrye Museum**
  Hackney Contemporaries - Design and Craft from Hackney, furniture, ceramics, stained glass and textiles.

- **4th April - 4th June: Geffrye Museum**
  Rooms within Rooms - Views of the Geffrye by Sally Meyor.

- **Weekends in May: Gunnersbury Park Museum**
  To celebrate VE Day - hands on exhibition of war-time memorabilia.

- **Throughout June & July: Gunnersbury Park Museum**
  "Invaders and Settlers" exhibition of archaeology in Hounslow and Ealing.

- **4th June: Fenton House**
  Children's Day.

- **16th July: Gunnersbury Park Museum**
  Gunnersbury Gala - An afternoon out for all the family on the theme of 1945 victory celebrations. Stalls and musical entertainment for adults and children.

- **Throughout August and September: Gunnersbury Park Museum**
  "Invaders and Settlers" exhibition of archaeology in Hounslow and Ealing.

- **28th November - 6th December: Geffrye Museum**
  JanuaryChristmas Past - Seasonal Traditions in English Homes. 400 years of Christmas decorations as the Geffrye decorates the period rooms in authentic historic style.

Buckingham Palace from St James Park.

Picture: Jeremy Whitaker (01428) 712292

MEOLS HALL

Churchtown, Southport, Merseyside, PR9 7LZ.
Owner: Robert Hesketh Esq   **Contact:** Robert Hesketh Esq
17th century house with subsequent additions. Interesting collection of pictures and furniture.
Location: 3m N of Southport town centre.
Opening Times: All of Aug, 2.00pm - 5.00pm.
Admission: Adult £3.00, Child £1.00.

LIVERPOOL CATHEDRAL CHURCH OF CHRIST THE KING

Tel: 0151 7099222   **Fax:** 0151 7087274

Liverpool, Merseyside, L3 5TQ.
Owner: Roman Catholic Archdiocese of Liverpool   **Contact:** Rt Rev P Cookson
Modern circular cathedral with spectacular glass by John Piper and numerous modern works of art. Extensive earlier crypt by Lutyens. Grade II listed.
Location: Central Liverpool, 1/4m E of Lime Street Station.
Opening Times: 8.00am - 6.00pm (closes 5.00pm Sun in Winter). Sun services: 8.30am, 10.00am, 11.00am, 3.00pm and 7.00pm Weekday services: 8.00am, 12.15pm, 5.15pm and 5.45pm.
Admission: Donation.

PORT SUNLIGHT HERITAGE CENTRE

Tel: 0151 6446466   **Fax:** 0151 6458973

95 Greendale Road, Port Sunlight, Merseyside, L62 4XE.
Contact: Information Officer
Port Sunlight is a picturesque 19th century garden village on the Wirral, built by William Hesketh Lever for the Workers in his soap factory. Includes the Lady Lever Art Gallery with famous pre-Raphaelite paintings.
Location: Follow signs from junction 4 or 5/M53 or follow signs on A51.
Opening Times: 1 Apr - 30 Oct, daily, 10.00am - 4.00pm. Nov - Dec, Mon - Fri, 10.00am - 4.00pm.
Admission: Adult 40p, Child 20p, Conc 40p, Groups under 13 40p per person, Groups over 12 £5. Guided tours available for coach party bookings by prior arrangement.

SPEKE HALL

OPEN

1 Apr - 29 Oct
Daily except Mons
(open Bank
Hol Mons)
1.00 - 5.30pm
Closed Good Friday

4 Nov - 17 Dec
Sats & Suns only
12 Noon - 4.30pm

Last admission 30
mins before closing.

Tel: 0151 427 7231
Fax: 0151 427 9860

THE WALK, LIVERPOOL L24 1XD

Owner: *The National Trust*   **Contact:** *The Property Manager*

An intricately decorated half-timbered house dating back to Tudor times. Victorian interiors, William Morris wallpapers, and life above and below the stairs reveal the rich diversity of this wonderful house.
Location: North bank of the Mersey, 6 miles east of city centre. Follow signs for Liverpool airport.
Admission: House & Garden: £3.60. Garden only: £1.00, half price for children. Family ticket (2 adults/2 children) £9.00.

SPECIAL EVENTS DIARY

- **13th May:** Speke Hall
  Open Day

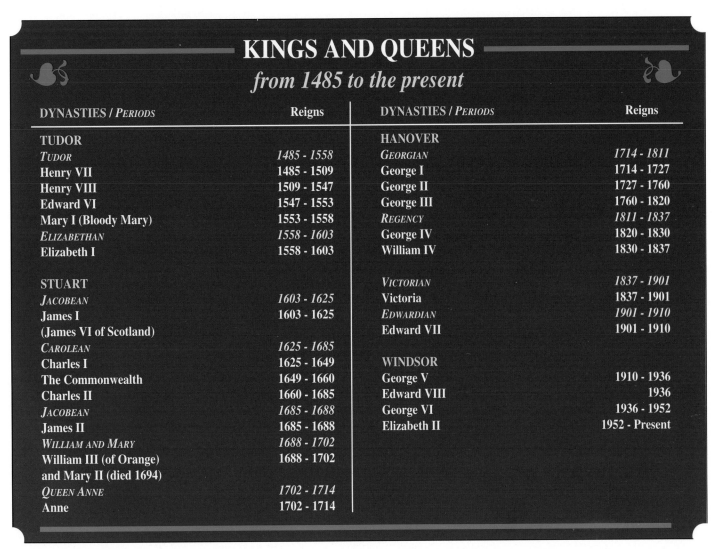

KINGS AND QUEENS
from 1485 to the present

DYNASTIES / *PERIODS*	Reigns	DYNASTIES / *PERIODS*	Reigns
TUDOR		HANOVER	
TUDOR	*1485 - 1558*	*GEORGIAN*	*1714 - 1811*
Henry VII	1485 - 1509	George I	1714 - 1727
Henry VIII	1509 - 1547	George II	1727 - 1760
Edward VI	1547 - 1553	George III	1760 - 1820
Mary I (Bloody Mary)	1553 - 1558	*REGENCY*	*1811 - 1837*
ELIZABETHAN	*1558 - 1603*	George IV	1820 - 1830
Elizabeth I	1558 - 1603	William IV	1830 - 1837
STUART		*VICTORIAN*	*1837 - 1901*
JACOBEAN	*1603 - 1625*	Victoria	1837 - 1901
James I	1603 - 1625	*EDWARDIAN*	*1901 - 1910*
(James VI of Scotland)		Edward VII	1901 - 1910
CAROLEAN	*1625 - 1685*		
Charles I	1625 - 1649	WINDSOR	
The Commonwealth	1649 - 1660	George V	1910 - 1936
Charles II	1660 - 1685	Edward VIII	1936
JACOBEAN	*1685 - 1688*	George VI	1936 - 1952
James II	1685 - 1688	Elizabeth II	1952 - Present
WILLIAM AND MARY	*1688 - 1702*		
William III (of Orange)	1688 - 1702		
and Mary II (died 1694)			
QUEEN ANNE	*1702 - 1714*		
Anne	1702 - 1714		

MARBLE HILL HOUSE ⊞
Twickenham

A magnificent Thames-side Palladian villa built 1724-29 and set in 66 acres of parkland. The Great Room, recently restored, has lavish gilded decoration and architectural paintings by Panini. The house also contains an important collection of early Georgian furniture.

CONTACT

The Administrator
Marble Hill House
Richmond Road
Twickenham
Middlesex
TW1 2NL

Tel: (0181) 892 5115

LOCATION

Richmond Road,
Twickenham

Rail: St Margarets $1/2$ mile; Twickenham 1 mile

OPENING TIMES

Summer
1 April - 30 September
Daily
10.00am - 6.00pm

Winter
1 October - 31 October
Daily
10.00am - 4.00pm

1 November - 31 March
Wed - Sun
10.00am - 4.00pm

ADMISSION

Adult £2.00
Child* £1.00
OAP/Student/UB40
holders £1.50

15% discount on groups of 11 or more

* 5 - 15 years.
Under 5's free

SUITABILITY FOR OTHER EVENTS
Outdoor concerts, plays, photographic shoots, filming.

EXTRA FACILITIES
Sports facilities in the grounds.

ADVICE TO COURIERS & DRIVERS
No photography in the house. Tour leader and Coach driver have free entry. 1 extra place for every 20 additional people.

FACILITIES FOR THE DISABLED
Wheelchair access on ground floor.

PARKING FOR COACHES & CARS
Cars can park in Marble Hill car park. Coaches outside the grounds in Richmond Road.

CATERING
Home made refreshments available.

GUIDED TOURS
Personal stereo tours available, guided tours available by the custodian on request.

GIFT SHOP
Situated inside the house.

GUIDE BOOKS
Colour guide book £2.25.

SCHOOL VISIT/CHILDREN
School visits are free if booked in advance. Please telephone (0181) 348 1286/7.

SYON PARK
Brentford

CONTACT

P.F. Sapte
Syon Park Ltd
Brentford
Middlesex
TW8 8JF

Tel: (0181) 560 0881
Fax: (0181) 568 0936

LOCATION

In London, off A310
and A315.

Rail: Southern Region:
Waterloo to Kew
Bridge, then bus.
Nearest Station
Syon Lane.
Underground: District
or North London Line to
Gunnersbury Station,
then bus.
Bus: Gunnersbury or
Kew Bridge to Brent Lea
Gate, 237 or 267.

SYON takes it's name from a monastery founded in 1415 by Henry V. After the dissolution it was given to the Protector Somerset who re-built it much as it is seen today. On his death Syon reverted to the crown until granted by James I to the Percy family, now Dukes of Northumberland, who own and live in it to this day. In 1762 the First Duke of Northumberland retained Robert Adam to remodel the house, resulting in a set of state rooms, probably his finest work. From the classic Great Hall, the unique scagliola floor, Cipriani ceiling and spectacular Long Gallery, the visitor sees a collection of great paintings and 17th Century furniture, some of which was designed by Adam for the House. Syon Park is available for hire for exclusive events.

GARDENS

The Gardens were transformed in the 1760s by Capability Brown. Syon is thought to be the first garden where trees were used purely for ornament and there is a fine and rare collection. In the gardens stands The Great Conservatory, a beautiful glass and steel structure, designed in 1820 by Charles Fowler. The Great Conservatory is available for hire and is ideal for weddings and parties between May and October.

The gardens contain the steam hauled Syon Park Miniature Railway.

The newly replanted Rose Garden reopens on the 1st April 1995 and will be open at the same times as Syon House.

❖

SUITABILITY FOR OTHER EVENTS
Fashion shows, archery, garden parties, shows, rallies, filming, photography functions and and weddings.

CONFERENCE FACILITIES
The Conference and Banqueting Centre offers 5 individual suites capable of seating between 10 and 200 people. Each Suite has its own patio area which overlooks the Gardens of Syon House. Syon Park is ideal for wedding receptions, dinner dances, conferences and exhibitions. Further information can be obtained by phoning (0181) 568 0778.

ADVICE TO COURIERS & DRIVERS
No dogs in Syon House or Park and no photography permitted in the House.

FACILITIES FOR THE DISABLED
There are toilet facilities for the disabled. Induction loop for the hard of hearing in House.

CATERING
PATIO RESTAURANT A self-service restaurant with ample seating is situated adjacent to the Gardens. A selection of hot food, sandwiches, cakes and pastries are offered daily. Coach parties are welcome and may book in advance. Phone (0181) 568 0778 for further information..

GUIDED TOURS
Tours are given at no additional cost. Average time taken 1¼ hours (not Suns). Free Sound Alive tours for all visitors.

NATIONAL TRUST GIFT SHOP
Open all year.

GUIDE BOOKS
Colour guide books available. House: £1.50 Garden:£1.50

SCHOOL VISITS/CHILDREN
Groups are welcome. Areas to visit include: the butterfly house. Cost per child for guided tour varies according to venue. The formal Gardens provide a safe and enjoyable environment for school picnics.

OPENING TIMES

Summer
1 April - 30 September
HOUSE (& ROSE GARDEN)
Sat, Suns, Bank Holidays
11.00am - 5.00pm

Other days by prior arrangement.

Winter
HOUSE (& ROSE GARDEN)
October
Sun 11.00am - 5.00pm

Rest of year special openings arranged by prior appointment only.

GARDENS & GREAT CONSERVATORY
10.00am - 6.00pm/dusk
Every day except the 25th, 26 Dec.
Season Ticket available.

STEAM RAILWAY
April - October
Weekends & Bank Holidays. Other times by prior arrangement. Runs during Garden opening hours.

ADMISSION

HOUSE & GARDEN
   Adult £5.50
   Concession £4.00
GARDEN ONLY
   Adult £2.50
   Concession £2.00
MINIATURE RAILWAY
(additonal to Garden Admission)
   Adult £1.00
   Concession £0.50
SCHOOL PARTIES
House & Gdns . . .£2.00
Gardens only . . .£1.00

CONFERENCE AND FUNCTION FACILITIES

ROOM	DIMENSIONS	CAPACITY	LAYOUT	POWER POINTS	SUITABLE FOR A/V
Garden	14.95 x 11.47m	200	Various	4	
Lakeside	18.50 x 10.75m	150	Various	6	
Gunters	10.74 x 12.34m	110	Various	4	
Terrace	11.94 x 9.40m	80	Various	4	
Conservatory	12.34 x 6.1m	40	Various	2	

BOSTON MANOR HOUSE

OPEN

28 May - 24 Sept

Sundays only

2.30 - 5.00pm

Park open daily

Tel: 0181 5700622
Fax: 0181 8627602

BOSTON MANOR ROAD, BRENTFORD, MIDDLESEX TW8 9JX

Owner: London Borough of Hounslow   *Contact:* Allan Downend

A fine Jacobean House built in 1623. The rooms that can be viewed include the State Drawing Room with a magnificent ceiling and fireplace designed in 1623. The ceiling is divided into panels representing the senses and the elements. A rare example of a Jacobean House in the London area.

Location: 10 minutes walk south of Boston Manor Station (Piccadilly Line) and 250 yds north of Boston Manor Road junction with A4 - Great West Road. Brentford.

Admission: Free.

CAPEL MANOR GARDENS

OPEN

Daily
10.00am - 5.00pm

Last ticket at 4.30pm or dusk in winter months

Check for winter holiday opening times

Tel: 0181 366 4442
Fax: 01992 717544

BULLSMOOR LANE, ENFIELD, MIDDLESEX EN1 4RQ

Owner: Capel Manor Charitable Organisation   *Contact:* Miss Julie Ryan

These extensive, richly planted gardens are delightful throughout the year offering inspiration, information and relaxation. The gardens include various themes - historical, modern, walled, rock, water, sensory and disabled and an Italianate Maze, Japanese Garden and "Gardening Which?" demonstration and model gardens. Capel Manor is a college of Horticulture and runs a training scheme for heritage gardeners in conjunction with the Historic Houses Association. New visitors Centre and Garden Gift Shop.

Location: Minutes from exit 25 of the M25. Tourist Board sign posted (yellow signs in summer)

Admission: Adult £3.00, Concessions £2.00, Child £1.50, Family Ticket £7.50. Charges alter for special show weekends and winter months.

CARSHALTON HOUSE

Tel: 0181 7704781   **Fax:** 0181 7704777

St Philomena's School, Pound Street, Carshalton, Middlesex, SM1 1EA.

Owner: St Philomena's School   **Contact:** Ms Murphy

Early 18th century house around core of older house, with grounds first laid out by Charles Bridgeman. Main rooms with 18th century decoration. Guided tours.

Location: Off A232 by junction with B278.

Opening Times: Easter BH Mon and Aug BH Mon, 10.00am - 5.00pm.

Admission: Adult £2.50, Child £1.50, Groups by prior arrangement for visits outside normal opening times. Admission charge includes optional guided tour and lecture.

MARBLE HILL HOUSE

See page 124 for full page entry.

OSTERLEY PARK

(photograph of Osterley Park)

OPEN

1 Apr - to end Oct
Wed - Sat
1.00 - 5.00pm
Sun & Bank Hol Mon
11.00 - 5.00.
Closed Good Fri.
Last Adm. 4.30pm

Park & Pleasure Grounds
All year:
9.00 - 7.30pm

Tel: 0181 560 3918

ISLEWORTH, MIDDLESEX EN1 4RQ

Owner: The National Trust   *Contact:* The Administrator

Set in 140 acres of landscaped park with ornamental lakes, Osterley is one of the last great houses with an intact estate in Greater London.

Location: Access via Thornbury Road on north side of A4 between Gillette Corner and Osterley Underground Station.

Admission: Adult £3.60, Child £1.80, Family Ticket £9.00.

SYON PARK

See page 125 for full page entry.

THE OCTAGON, ORLEANS HOUSE GALLERY

Tel: 0181 8920221   **Fax:** 0181 7440501

Riverside, Twickenham, Middlesex, TW1 3DJ.

Owner: London Borough of Richmond upon Thames   **Contact:** Miss Gemma Hunter

Outstanding example of baroque architecture built by James Gibbs c.1720. Adjacent wing now converted to art gallery.

Location: 1/4m S of A305 (Richmond Rd/Richmond Bridge).

Opening Times: Tues - Sat, 1.00pm - 5.30pm (Oct - Mar, 1.00pm - 4.30pm). Suns & BHs, 2.00pm - 5.30pm (Oct - Mar 2.00pm - 4.30pm). Garden open every day 9.00am - sunset.

Admission: Free. Donations to Octagon appeal gratefully received.

SPECIAL EVENTS DIARY

The following events will take place at Syon House (Syon Park)

- **22nd January:** *Antique Fair and Book Fair.*
- **19th February:** *Antique Fair.*
- **5th March:** *Book Fair.*
- **19th March:** *Antique Fair.*
- **23rd April:** *Antique Fair.*
- **30th April:** *Book Fair.*
- **21st May:** *Antique Fair.*
- **10th - 11th June:** *Syon Summer Festival.*
- **11th June:** *Start of London-Brighton Classic Car Rally.*
- **18th June:** *Antique Fair.*
- **24th - 25th June:** *Motor Show.*
- **25th June:** *Book Fair*
- **16th July:** *Antique Fair.*
- **30th July:** *Book Fair.*
- **3rd - 6th August:** *Craft Fair.*
- **20th August:** *Antique Fair*
- **17th September:** *Antique Fair*
- **24th September:** *Book Fair.*
- **15th October:** *Antique Fair*
- **12th November:** *Book Fair.*
- **19th November:** *Antique Fair*

- **5th August: Osterley Park**
  Glen Miller Orchestra Band Concert with Fireworks

HOLKHAM HALL
Wells-next-the-Sea

HOLKHAM HALL has been the home of the Coke family and the Earls of Leicester for almost 250 years. Built by William Kent between 1734 and 1762 it is a fine example of 18th Century Palladian style. Constructed mainly of local yellow brick with a magnificent Entrance Hall of English Alabaster, the House reflects Thomas Coke's natural appreciation of Classical Art developed during the Grand Tour.

The State Rooms occupy the first floor and contain antique statuary, paintings by Rubens, Van Dyck, Claude, Poussin and Gainsborough and original furniture.

The visitors on leaving the House pass the Pottery started by Elizabeth, Countess of Leicester in 1951 and today supervised by Viscountess Coke. A highly skilled team produce a fine range of pottery.

Beyond are the 19th Century stables and the Holkham Bygones Collection. Some 4,000 items range from working steam engines, vintage cars and tractors to craft tools and kitchen ware.

The House is set in a 3,000 acre Park with 600 head of fallow deer. On the lake, 1 mile long, can be seen many species of wildfowl. Two walks encircle either the Lake or Agricultural buildings.

The Holkham Garden Centre occupies the 18th Century walled Kitchen Garden and a large range of stock is on sale to the public.

SUITABILITY FOR OTHER EVENTS
Fashion shows, air displays, archery, clay pigeon shooting, equestrian events, shows, rallies and filming.

ADVICE TO COURIERS & DRIVERS
No smoking, dogs or flash photography in the Hall.

FACILITIES FOR THE DISABLED
Disabled and elderly visitors may be left at the entrance to the property, before parking in the allocated areas. There are toilets for the disabled.

PARKING FOR COACHES & CARS
Capacity of the car park: over 1,000 cars and 20 coaches, 75 yards from the Hall.

CATERING
The Tea Room can cater for up to 100 people. Menus are available on request.

GUIDED TOURS
When the Hall is open to the public, guides are posted in each room. At other times guided tours can be arranged. Average time taken for a tour 1 hour.

GIFT SHOP
Open 10.00am-5.30pm Mon-Fri, 12.00-5.30pm Sundays. Items include books and pamphlets on the local area and wildlife, gifts and souvenirs for children.

GUIDE BOOKS
Colour guide book, £1.75

SCHOOL VISITS/CHILDREN
Groups of children are welcome. Price per child £1.50. Areas of interest: 2 nature walks, deer park, lake and wild fowl. Bygones collection, including dolls house and toy collection.

CONTACT

The Administrator
Holkham Hall
Estate Office
Wells-next-the-Sea
Norfolk
NR23 1AB

Tel: (01328) 710227

Fax: (01328) 711707

LOCATION

From London 120mls, Norwich 35mls, Kings Lynn 30mls.

Rail: Norwich Stn 35mls, Kings Lynn Stn 30mls.

Air: Norwich Airport 32mls.

Taxi: Lavender Taxi Services, Fakenham. (01328) 862906.

OPENING TIMES

Summer
28 May - 28 September

Daily except Fris and Sats   1.30 - 5.00pm

Last admission 4.40pm

Open Sun/Mon on Easter, May, Spring & Summer Bank Hols:
11.30am - 5.00pm

Winter
October - May
Open by appointment.

ADMISSION

Summer

HALL
Adult £3.00
Child* £1.50

BYGONES
Adult £3.00
Child* £1.50

ALL INCLUSIVE
Adult £5.00
Child* £2.50

* Ages 5-15

Discounts on Parties of 20+

Winter
By arrangement

SANDRINGHAM
King's Lynn

The private country retreat of Her Majesty The Queen, Sandringham House is at the heart of the beautiful estate which has been owned by four generations of Monarchs. King George V described his home in the picturesque West Norfolk countryside as "dear old Sandringham, the place I love better than anywhere else in the world".

The neo-Jacobean house was built in 1870 for Albert Edward, Prince of Wales and his wife, Princess Alexandra, later King Edward VII and Queen Alexandra. A grand and imposing building, where all the main rooms used by The Royal Family when in residence are open to the public, Sandringham House has the warmth and charm of a well-loved family home. Visitors see portraits of The Royal Family, collections of porcelain, jade, quartz, enamelled Russian silver, gold and bronze set amongst fine furniture.

GARDENS
Sixty acres of glorious grounds surround the House and offer beauty and colour throughout the seasons with a rich variety of flowers, shrubs and magnificent trees, informally planted round lawns and lakes to provide a multitude of tranquil views.

Sandringham Museum, situated within the grounds, contains fascinating displays of Royal memorabilia ranging from family photographs to vintage Daimlers, and an exhibition of the Sandringham Fire Brigade

New for 1995 - Transport to the house by Land Train.

❖

SUITABILITY FOR OTHER EVENTS
Grounds for open-air concerts/theatre. 140 acre private park for rallies, fairs etc.

EXTRA FACILITIES
600 acre Country Park with Tractor and Trailer tour.

ADVICE TO COURIERS & DRIVERS
Parking, admission and refreshments free to drivers. No dogs inside grounds. No photography inside House.

FACILITIES FOR THE DISABLED
Wheelchair access throughout. Parking and lavatories for disabled persons.

PARKING FOR COACHES & CARS
Parking area for 600 cars/150 coaches close to Visitor Centre, 300 yards from Grounds entrance.

CATERING
A major re-development of the Sandringham Visitor Centre opened at Easter 1994 with air-conditioned restaurant seating up to 200 visitors. Traditional waitress-service tea room seating 60 also available and may be booked by groups. Open Easter to end of October.

GUIDED TOURS
Guided tours may be arranged for groups of up to 25 people at certain times of the season.

GIFT SHOP
Large gift shop at Visitor Centre stocking a large range of quality gifts, books, foods and souvenirs open Easter to end of October.

GUIDE BOOKS
A guide book with colour photographs is available.

SCHOOL VISITS/CHILDREN
School visits are welcome. Educational sheets/questionnaires available for House and Museum.

CONTACT

Mrs Gill Pattinson
The Estate Office
Sandringham
King's Lynn
Norfolk
PE35 6EN

Tel: (01553) 772675

Fax: (01485) 541571

LOCATION

8 miles north east of Kings Lynn off A148.
3 hours from London
1$^{1}/_{2}$ hours from Stansted Airport via M11 and A10.

Rail: King's Lynn 8 miles.

OPENING TIMES

Summer
13 April - 1 October
HOUSE Closed
18 Jul - 3 Aug
GROUNDS & MUSEUM
Closed 23 July -2 Aug

GROUNDS open
10.30am - 5.00pm.

HOUSE open
11.00am - 4.45pm.

MUSEUM open
11.00am - 5.00pm

Winter
2 October - Spring 1995
Closed

ADMISSION

HOUSE, GROUNDS & MUSEUM
Adult £4.00
Child* £2.00
Student £3.00
Sen. Citizen £3.00
Family £10.00

GROUNDS & MUSEUM
Adult £3.00
Child* £1.50
Student £2.50
Sen. Citizen £2.50
Family Ticket . .£7.50

Groups
Discount of 10% for pre-booked, pre-paid parties of 20 or more.
* Aged 5-15.

CONFERENCE AND FUNCTION FACILITIES

ROOM	DIMENSIONS	CAPACITY	LAYOUT	POWER POINTS	SUITABLE FOR A/V
Restaurant	35' x 50'	300 Buffet 150 200 50	Reception/ Dinner Theatre Boardroom	8	✓

BERNEY ARMS WINDMILL ⊞

Tel: 01493 700605

Reedham, Great Yarmouth, Norfolk.
Owner: English Heritage   **Contact:** The Administrator
A wonderfully situated marsh mill, one of the best and largest remaining in Norfolk, with seven floors, making it a landmark for miles around. It was in use until 1951.
Location: 3$\frac{1}{2}$m NE of Reedham on N bank of River Yare.
Opening Times: 1 Apr - 30 Sept, daily 10.00am - 6.00pm.
Admission: Adult £1.00, Child 50p, Conc 80p.

BINHAM PRIORY ⊞

Binham-on-Wells, Norfolk.
Owner: English Heritage   **Contact:** The Administrator
$\frac{1}{4}$ m NW of village of Binham-on-Wells road off B1388.
Location: 3$\frac{1}{2}$m NE of Reedham on N bank of River Yare.
Opening Times: Any reasonable time.

BIRCHAM WINDMILL

Tel: 01485 578393

Snettisham Road, Great Bircham, Norfolk, PE31 6SJ.
Owner: Mr & Mrs G Wagg   **Contact:** Mr & Mrs G Wagg
One of the last remaining complete windmills.
Location: $\frac{1}{2}$m W of Snettisham.
Opening Times: Sun 9 Apr - 31 Sept 10.00am - 6.00pm
Admission: Adult £2.20, Child £1.20, Conc £1.00.

BLICKLING HALL

OPEN

25 March - 5 Nov
Tues, Wed, Fri,
Sat, Sun & Bank
Holiday Mondays.

(Closed Good Friday)

Garden open same as Hall, but daily in July and August.

Tel: 01263 733084
Fax: 01263 734924

NORWICH, NORFOLK NR11 6NF

Owner: The National Trust   *Contact:* The Administrator

A spectacular 17th century red brick house, with extensive colourful garden. Furniture and collections assembled in 18th and 19th century, the Ellis library contains 12,000 books. Garden contains extensive parterre, temple, orangery and secret garden. Parkland offers miles of footpaths. Free parking.
Location: 1 mile west of Aylsham on B1354 off A140 Cromer, Norwich road.
Admission: House & Garden: £4.90 (£5.50 Sunday & Bank Holiday Monday)
        Garden: £2.50 (£2.75). Children half price.
        Coaches welcome. Group discount available.

BRESSINGHAM GARDENS

OPEN

1 April - 29 Oct

10.00am - 5.30pm

7 days a week

Dell Garden open. Adrian Bloom's adjacent "Foggy Bottom Garden" also open every Mon. & Thurs. during the above period.

Tel: 01379 687382

BRESSINGHAM GARDEN, DISS, NORFOLK

Owner: Mr Alan Bloom   *Contact: Mr Alan Bloom*

Enjoy Alan Bloom's world famous "Dell" Garden. Some 47 island beds devoted mainly to perennials and alpine plants, and with over 5,000 species and varieties it is one of the widest collections of hardy perennials in the world. Mature trees, lovely walks and adjacent Plant Centre and Steam Museum make a visit to Bressingham totally enjoyable.
Location: On A1066 2$\frac{1}{2}$ miles west of Diss.
Admission: Rates upon application.

BURGH CASTLE ⊞

Breydon Water, Great Yarmouth, Norfolk.
Owner: English Heritage   **Contact:** The Administrators
Impressive walls, with projecting bastions, of a Roman fort built in the late 3rd century as one of a chain to defend the coast against Saxon raiders.
Location: At far W end of Breydon Water, on unclassified road 3m W of Great Yarmouth.
Opening Times: Any reasonable time.

CASTLE ACRE PRIORY ⊞

Tel: 01760 755394

Castle Acre, Swaffham, Norfolk.
Owner: English Heritage   **Contact:** The Administrator
The great west front of the 12th century church of this Cluniac priory still rises to its full height and is elaborately decorated. Other substantial remains include the splendid prior's lodgings and chapel and the delightful walled herb garden should not be missed.
Location: $\frac{1}{4}$m W of village of Castle Acre, 5m N of Swaffham.
Opening Times: 1 Apr - 30 Sept, daily 10.00am - 6.00pm,1 Oct - 31 Oct, daily 10.00am - 4.00pm, 1 Nov - 31 Mar, Wed - Sun, 10.00am - 4.00pm (Closed 24 - 26 Dec, 1 Jan).
Admission: Adult £2.20, Child £1.10, Conc £1.70.

CASTLE RISING CASTLE ⊞

Tel: 01533 631330

Kings Lynn, Norfolk.
Owner: English Heritage   **Contact:** The Administrator
A fine mid 12th century domestic keep, set in the centre of massive defensive earthworks. The keep walls stand to their original height and many of the fortifications are still intact.
Location: 4m NE of King's Lynn off A149.
Opening Times: 1 Apr - 30 Sept, daily 10.00am - 6.00pm, 1 Oct - 31 Oct, daily 10.00am - 4.00pm, 1 Nov - 31 Mar, Wed - Sun, 10.00am - 4.00pm (Closed 24 - 26 Dec, 1 Jan).
Admission: Adult £1.30, Child 70p, Conc £1.00.

DRAGON HALL

Tel: 01603 663922

115 - 123 King Street, Norwich, Norfolk, NR1 1QE.
Owner: Norfolk & Norwich Heritage Trust Ltd   **Contact:** Ms S Knights
Magnificent medieval merchant's hall described as "one of the most exciting 15th century buildings in England". Timber framed great hall, outstanding crown-post roof, intricately carved dragon and vaulted undercroft.
Location: 115 - 123 King Street.
Opening Times: April - Oct, Mon - Sat, 10.00am - 4.00pm. Nov - Mar, 10.00am - 4.00pm.
Admission: Adult £1.00, Child 25p, Conc 50p.

FAIRHAVEN GARDEN TRUST

Tel: 01603 270449

2 The Woodlands, Wymers Lane, Pilson Green, South Walsham, Norfolk, NR13 6EA.
Owner: Fairhaven Garden Trust   **Contact:** Mr G E Debbage
Woodland and water gardens with private broad. Spectacular displays of candelabra primulas in May.
Location: 9m NE of Norwich off B1140.
Opening Times: 14 Apr - 1 Oct 11.00am - 5.30pm (Sat 2.00pm - 5.30pm). Closed Mons except Bank holidays.
Admission: Adult £3.00, Child £1.00, Conc £2.00, Groups less 25p pp.

FELBRIGG HALL ❀

Tel: 01263 8374449

Felbrigg, Norwich, Norfolk, NR11 8PR.
Owner: The National Trust   **Contact:** The Administrator
One of the finest 17th century houses in Norfolk, with its original 18th century furniture and pictures, an outstanding library and recently opened domestic wing. The Walled Garden has been restored, complete with dovecote, greenhouses and the traditional layout of herbaceous plants and fruit trees, including the national collection of colchicums. There are extensive walks in the Park, woods and around the lake.
Location: Nr Felbrigg village, 2m SW of Cromer; entrance off B1436, signposted from A148 and A140.
Opening Times: House: 25 Mar - 5 Nov: Mon, Wed, Thur, Sat & Sun 1pm - 5pm; BH Mon & Sun preceding BH Mon 11am - 5pm. Garden: same days 11am - 5pm. Woodland, lakeside walks and parkland all year (except Christmas Day): daily, dawn to dusk.
Admission: House & Garden: £4.60. Garden: £1.80. Parties: £3.40 except Tues, Fri & Suns.

GRIME'S GRAVES ⊞

Tel: 01842 810656

Thetford, Great Yarmouth, Norfolk.
Owner: English Heritage   **Contact:** The Administrator
These remarkable Neolithic flint mines, unique in England, comprise over 300 pits and shafts. The visitor can descend some 30 feet by ladder into one excavated shaft, and look along the radiating galleries from where the flint used to make axes and knives was extracted.
Location: 7m NW of Thetford off A134.
Opening Times: 1 Apr - 30 Sept, daily 10.00am - 6.00pm, 1 Oct - 31 Mar, daily 10.00am - 4.00pm, 1 Nov - 31 Mar, Wed - Sun, 10.00am - 4.00pm (Closed 24 - 26 Dec, 1 Jan).
Admission: Adult £1.30, Child 70p, Conc £1.00.

HOLKHAM HALL

See page 127 for full page entry.

HOUGHTON HALL

Kings Lynn, Norfolk, PE31 6UE.
Owner: Marquess of Cholmondeley   **Contact:** Marquess of Cholmondeley
Houghton Hall will not be open during 1995.

HOVETON HALL GARDENS

Tel: 01603 782798   **Fax:** 01603 784564

Wroxham, Norfolk, NR12 8RJ.
Owner: Andrew Buxton Esq   **Contact:** Andrew Buxton Esq
Hoveton Hall was built 1809 - 1812 in gault brick with slate roofs. Design of grounds attributed to Humphrey Repton.
Location: On A1151 8m N of Norwich.
Opening Times: Easter - mid September, Wed, Fri, Sun and BH Mon, 11.00am - 5.30pm.
Admission: Adult £2.00, Child 50p, Groups £1.75 (if booked in advance).

MANNINGTON GARDENS & COUNTRYSIDE

Tel: 01263 584175   **Fax:** 01263 761214

Mannington Hall, Norwich, Norfolk, NR11 7BB.
Owner: Lady Walpole   **Contact:** Lady Walpole
Gardens with lake, moat and woodland. Good rose collection.
Location: Signposted from Saxthorpe crossroads on the Norwich - Holt road B1149.
Opening Times: Gardens; Easter - Oct, Suns, 12.00pm - 5.00pm. Jun - Aug, Wed, Thurs & Fri, 11.00am - 5.00pm. Walks, daily, from 9.00am.
Admission: Adult £2.50, Child under 16 free, Conc £2.00, Groups by application.

NORWICH CASTLE MUSEUM

Tel: 01603 765651   **Fax:** 01603 223624

Norwich, Norfolk, NR1 3JU.
Owner: Norwich City Council   **Contact:** Miss B Yates
Norman Castle keep, having museum with displays particularly of Norwich school of painters, and British ceramic teapots.
Location: Centre of Norwich.
Opening Times: Mon - Sat, 10.00am - 5.00pm. Sun 2.00pm - 5.00pm. Closed Good Fri, Christmas Day, Boxing Day.
Admission: Adult £2.20, Child £1.00, Family £5.50, Conc £1.50, Groups of 10 plus £1.50. Call to verify.

OLD MERCHANT'S HOUSEROW 11 GREYFRIARS CLOISTERS

Tel: 01493 857900

South Quay, Great Yarmouth, Norfolk.
Owner: English Heritage   **Contact:** The Administrator
Two 17th century Row Houses, a type of building unique to Great Yarmouth. Nearby are the remains of a Franciscan friary.
Location: Great Yarmouth on South Quay, $\frac{1}{2}$ m inland from beach. Follow signs to dock and south quay.
Opening Times: 1 Apr - 30 Sept daily, 10.00am - 6.00pm. Entry by tour only. Lunchtime closure from 1.00pm - 2.00pm.
Admission: Adult £1.30, Child 70p, Conc £1.00.

OXBURGH HALL

Tel: 01366 328258

Oxborough, Kings Lynn, Norfolk, PE33 9PS.
Owner: The National Trust   **Contact:** The Administrator
This moated house was built in 1482 by the Bedingfeld family, who still live here. The rooms show the development from medieval austerity to Victorian comfort, with embroidery worked by Mary Queen of Scots, during her captivity, on display. The magnificent Tudor gatehouse rises 80 feet above the moat, and the garden includes lawns, fine trees, colourful borders and a French Parterre. There are also delightful woodland walks, including a new two mile walk through Home Covert.
Location: At Oxborough, 7m SW of Swaffham on S side of Stoke Ferry road.
Opening Times: House: 25 Mar - 5 Nov: Sat to Wed 1.00pm - 5.00pm; BH Mon 11.00am - 5.00pm. Garden: Same days as house, 12.00pm - 5.30pm.
Admission: House, Garden & Estate: £3.80, pre-arranged parties £3.00. Garden & Estate only: £2.00.

RAVENINGHAM HALL GARDENS

Tel: 01508 548206   **Fax:** 01508 548958

Raveningham, Norwich, Norfolk, NR14 6NS.
Owner: Sir Nicholas Bacon Bt   **Contact:** Mrs J Woodard
Gardens laid out approximately 100 years ago around a red brick Georgian house (not open).
Location: Between Beccles and Loddon off B1136/B1140.
Opening Times: Mid Mar - mid Sept, Wed, 1 - 4pm and Sun and Bank Hol Mon 2 - 5pm.
Admission: Adult £2.00, Child free, Groups by prior arrangement.

SANDRINGHAM

See page 128 for full page entry.

ST GEORGE'S GUILDHALL

Tel: 01553 774725

27 Kings Street, Kings Lynn, Norfolk, PE30 1HA.
Owner: The National Trust   **Contact:** The Administrator
The largest surviving English medieval guildhall, with adjoining medieval warehouse, now in use as an Arts Centre.
Location: On W side of King Street close to the Tuesday Market Place.
Opening Times: All year Mon to Fri (closed Good Fri & Aug BH Mon) 10.00am - 5.00pm; Sat 10.00am - 12.30pm & 2.00pm - 3.30pm (10 Jun - 8 Jul, 10.00am - 12.30pm): Sun 2.00pm - 4.00pm (28 May - 24 Sept but closed 16, 23, 30 Jul). Closed 25, 26 Dec & 1 Jan.
Admission: Adult 50p, Child 25p.

STRANGER'S HALL

Tel: 01603 667229   **Fax:** 01603 765651

Norwich, Norfolk, NR1 3JU.
Owner: Norwich City Council   **Contact:** Fiona Strodder / Kathy Terry
Once a medieval merchant's house, now contains a series of rooms furnished in period styles from early Tudor to late Victorian.
Location: Charing Cross, Norwich.
Opening Times: All year, Mon - Sat, 10.00am - 5.00pm. Closed Good Fri, Christmas Day, Boxing Day.
Admission: Adult £1.40, Child 70p, Conc £1.20. Admission price includes entry to Bridewell Museum and the Regimental Museum. Contact administrator to verify.

WALSINGHAM ABBEY GROUNDS

Tel: 01328 820259   **Fax:** 01328 820098

Little Walsingham, Norfolk, NR22 6BP.
Owner: J S Downing   **Contact:** Walsingham Estate Company
Priory ruins in peaceful surroundings, woodland walks.
Location: B1105 from Fakenham - 5 miles.
Opening Times: Apr, May, Jun, Jul and Sept: Wed, Sat and Sun, 2.00pm - 5.00pm. Aug: Mon, Wed, Fri, Sat, Sun and all Bank Hols from Easter - Sept.
Admission: Adult £1.00, Child 50p, Senior citizens 50p. School parties and parties over 100 by arrangement.

WOLERTON PARK

Tel: 01263 584175   **Fax:** 01263 761214

Norwich, Norfolk, NR11 7BB.
Owner: The Lord and Lady Walpole   **Contact:** The Lady Walpole
Historic park with lake. Hawk and Owl Trust display.
Location: Situated near Erpingham village; signposted from Norwich - Cromer Rd A140.
Opening Times: Park: open daily from 9.00am.
Admission: £2.00 car park fee only. Groups by application.

SPECIAL EVENTS DIARY

- **15th - 17th April: Blickling Hall**
  Country Skills and Working Craft Fair.

- **24th May: Blickling Hall**
  Open Air Concert - Viennese Evening with the Norfolk Symphony Orchestra.

- **14th July: Blickling Hall**
  Concert - Pananini Ensemble.

- **22nd - 23rd July: Holkham Hall**
  Country Fair.

- **3rd August: Blickling Hall**
  Family Garden Party.

- **19th August: Blickling Hall**
  Open Air Concert.

ALTHORP HOUSE
Althorp

ALTHORP, home of the Earl and Countess Spencer and their young family, was built in its original, red brick form by Sir John Spencer in 1508. Remodelled in 1660 by Anthony Ellis, the house's present appearance dates from 1790 when Henry Holland 'improved' both the interior and exterior, entirely facing the main house with fashionable grey brick tiles.

Inside, the main rooms show the complexity of the building's history: the Entrance Hall - a marvellous Palladian room by Morris, the Grand Staircase dating from 1650, and the breathtaking Picture Gallery - 115 feet of panelling, covered with masterpieces, culminating in Van Dyck's celebrated double portrait , 'War and Peace'.

Althorp House is available for dinners, luncheon parties, wedding, conferences and cocktail parties. The 450 acres of undulating parkland are used for product launches, open air concerts, craft fairs, car rallies, horse trials, country fairs and filming. A cricket pitch is also available for hire.

Althorp houses one of the finest art collections in England, begun in the 17th Century by Robert, 2nd Earl of Sunderland, and enlarged by nearly every successive Spencer generation. Rubens, Reynolds, Gainsborough and Lely are all well represented. The collection's quality is almost matched by that of the 18th Century furniture, and the porcelain is also outstanding, with pieces from Sevres and Meissen.

The Althorp Carriages are currently on show, with a major conservation programme in place.

GARDENS
When Holland was improving the House, he had the gardens improved by Samuel Lapidge, Capability Brown's chief assistant. The gardens seen today, however, date from 1860 and were designed by the architect W. M. Teulon. The stable block, a grand rectangle of dark, glowing ironstone built in 1732, contrasts sharply with the main house and dominates the approach to Althorp. The gardens are currently being developed with new rose beds already in place.

EXHIBITION
Featuring military and other historical items connected with the Spencer family up to the present day.

❖

EXTRA FACILITIES
Helicopters can land in front of the house.

ADVICE TO COURIERS & DRIVERS
Please book in advance. No dogs, photography (in House) or unaccompanied children.

FACILITIES FOR THE DISABLED
The ground floor is suitable for the disabled and they are welcome in the grounds and tea room. Toilet for the disabled.

PARKING FOR COACHES & CARS
Parking for 40 cars and 5 coaches, 100yds from House. 120 more vehicles, 200yds from the House; limitless parking beyond this.

CATERING
There is a tea room (capacity 100 people). Parties can be booked in advance for lunch and tea. Menus available on request. Catering facilities can be arranged for dinner in the House by prior arrangement. Exclusive luncheons and dinners are also available in the State Dining Room, which holds 20-120 people. Other rooms are ideal for conferences and presentations.

GUIDED TOURS
A free flow system may operate. Tours in French and German by appointment. Average time to see the house is 1 hour.

GIFT SHOP/GUIDE BOOKS
Open when the House is open. Many Althorp souvenirs available. A guide book with colour photographs is available. There are also guide books in Japanese

CONTACT

Lisa Hanlon
Althorp House
Althorp
Northampton
NN7 4HG

Tel: (01604) 770107
or (01604) 770006
Fax: (01604) 770107

LOCATION

From the M1:
Exit 15A, 6 miles
Exit 16 - 7 miles
Exit 18, 10 miles
Situated on A428
Northampton-Rugby.
London on average 85
minutes away.

OPENING TIMES

April 1 - 2 April (Craft Fair in Park additional charge).
April: 15 - 17 (Easter)
May: 6 - 8 (Bank Holiday)
May: 28 - 29 (Falconry Fair in Park, additional charge)
July: 2, 9, 16, 22,23, 29, 30
August: 6, 12, 13. 19, 20, 26 - 28
September: 3, 10, 17, 24
October: 7, 8 (Craft Fair in the park additional charge).
The House & Park will be open between 11.00am - 5.00pm on all bank holidays, April 1, 2 and October 7, 8 and between 2.00 - 5.00pm on all other days.

ADMISSION

HOUSE & GARDEN
Adult £4.50
Child (2-14yrs) . £2.50
OAP £3.50
Groups rates available.

GARDEN ONLY
Adult £2.00
Child (2-14yrs) . .£1.00
EXHIBITION
Adults £1.00
Child £0.50

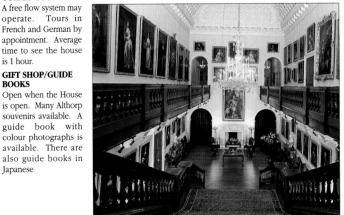

BOGHTON HOUSE
Kettering

BOUGHTON HOUSE is the Northamptonshire home of the Duke of Buccleuch and Queensberry K.T., and his Montagu ancestors since 1528.

A 500 year old Tudor monastic building gradually enlarged around seven courtyards until the French style addition of 1695, which has lead to Boughton House being described as 'England's Versailles'.

The house contains an outstanding collection of 17th and 18th Century French and English furniture, tapestries, 16th Century carpets, porcelain, painted ceilings and notable works by El Greco, Murillo, Caracci and 40 Van Dyck sketches. There is an incomparable Armoury and Ceremonial Coach.

Beautiful parkland with historic avenues and lakes, picnic area, gift shop, exciting adventure woodland play area, garden centre and tearoom.

Boughton House is administered by The Living Landscape Trust, which was created by the present Duke of Buccleuch to show the relationship between the historic Boughton House and its surrounding, traditional, working estate.

There are exhibition and lecture rooms in the Stable Block with audio/visual facilities. For details of our specialist one, three and five day Fine Art Courses run in conjunction with Sotheby's and for our schools Education Facilities (Sandford Award Winner 1988 and 1993) telephone The Living Landscape Trust.

❖

SUITABILITY FOR OTHER EVENTS
Boughton House parkland is available for film location and other events by individual negotiation.

EXTRA FACILITIES
Stables Block adjacent to House contains 120 seats. Lecture Theatre and Catering facilities.

ADVICE TO COURIERS & DRIVERS
No unaccompanied children and dogs in House and Gardens. No internal photography.

FACILITIES FOR THE DISABLED
Full disabled access and facilities - no charge for wheelchair visitors.

PARKING FOR COACHES & CARS
There is unlimited parking adjacent to the House.

CATERING
Stables Restaurant seats 100. Parties must book in advance. Varied menus of home made fayre available.

GIFT SHOP
Gift and Garden shops are open daily 2.00 - 5.00pm.

GUIDE BOOKS
New edition recently published. Also specialist book "Boughton House - The English Versailles" available - contact for further details.

GUIDED TOURS
Group visits are all guided - please contact for rates etc.

SCHOOL VISITS/CHILDREN
Heritage Education Trust Sandford Award winner 1988 and 1993. School groups admitted free, teachers pack available to cover all aspects of Estate work to show the 'living landscape' of farming, forestry and conservation.

CONTACT

Gareth Fitzpatrick
The Living Landscape Trust
Boughton House
Kettering
Northamptonshire
NN14 1BJ

Tel: (0536) 515731
Fax: (0536) 417255

LOCATION

3 miles north of Kettering on A43 - spur road from A14.

OPENING TIMES

Summer
GROUNDS
1 May - 30 Sept
Daily　1.00 - 5.00pm
(Except Fridays)
HOUSE: 1 Aug - 1 Sept
Daily　2.00 - 5.00pm

Winter
Daily by appointment for educational groups.

ADMISSION

Summer
HOUSE & GROUNDS
　Adults £4.00
　Child/OAP £3.00
GROUNDS
　Adults £1.50
　Child/OAP £1.00
Wheelchairs Free

Winter
Group Rates - contact for further details.

CONFERENCE AND FUNCTION FACILITIES

ROOM	DIMENSIONS	CAPACITY	LAYOUT	POWER POINTS	SUITABLE FOR A/VStables
Lecture		80	Buffet	10	✓
		120+	Theatre		
		80	Lunch/Dinner		
Seminar Room		30	Schoolroom	8	✓
		20	U-Shape		
		20	Boardroom		
		20	Buffet		
		30	Theatre		
Conference facilities available in stable block adjacent to House available for Countryside and Fine Art associated themes.					

CASTLE ASHBY
Northamptonshire

The lands at Castle Ashby were given to the Compton family in 1512 by Henry VIII and in 1574 Queen Elizabeth I gave William, 1st Earl of Northampton, permission to demolish the derelict 13th Century Castle and rebuild on the site. The original plan of the building was the shape of an 'E' in honour of Queen Elizabeth, and about sixty years later the courtyard was enclosed by a screen designed by Inigo Jones.

One of the features of Castle Ashby is the lettering around the House and terraces. The inscriptions when translated read "The Lord guard your coming in" and "The Lord guard your going out".

Castle Ashby belongs to the 7th Marquess of Northampton, Spencer Compton, and has been in the hands of the Compton family since it was built. The family trace their history back to the 11th Century and came to Castle Ashby from Compton Wynyates in Warwickshire. The lands and titles have descended through the male line since the 11th Century. The Comptons were created Earl of Northampton in 1618 and Marquess of Northampton in 1812.

The Compton family have played host to members of the Royal Family, at Castle Ashby, on many occasions starting with Queen Elizabeth I. James I was a regular visitor, as well as Princess Anne (later Queen Anne) and William of Orange, King George V and Queen Mary visited Castle Ashby in 1907.

GARDENS
The Extensive gardens at Castle Ashby are a combination of several styles, with a mile long avenue dating back to 1695, Victorian Terrace Gardens, the more private and romantic Italian Gardens, an elegant Conservatory, Triumphal Arch, Gloriette and Camellia House standing in a garden of its own. The carriageway continues through "Capability" Brown landscape parkland, past the Temple, round the lakes and back to the House, affording classic views on the way.

CONTACT

The General Manager
Castle Ashby House
Castle Ashby
Nr Northampton
NN7 1LQ

Tel: (01604) 696696
Fax: (01604) 696516

LOCATION

From London via M1, 90 minutes.
From Birmingham, 50 minutes.
From Chester via M6, 2¹/₂ hours.

Rail: Northampton 7 miles; Wellingborough 8 miles.

SUITABILITY FOR OTHER EVENTS
With 26 bedrooms, all with en suite bathroom, Castle Ashby is available on an exclusive basis for residential conferences, company weekends and social occasions.

There are 7 Private Function Suites available for events, for meetings for 120 people to dinners for 12. The 24 hour rate is £165 plus VAT and Day Delegate £35 plus VAT, (rates valid until Sept. 1994). Additional facilities include parkland, cricket pitch, clay shooting, archery, fishing and horse and carriage.

CATERING
All catering is provided by our team of award winning chefs. Our aim is to provide discreet service with a touch of informality thus allowing guests to experience the complete enjoyment of using the house as if it were their own.

CONFERENCE AND FUNCTION FACILITIES

ROOM	DIMENSIONS	CAPACITY	LAYOUT	POWER POINTS	SUITABLE FOR A/V
Great Hall	48' x 26' x 33'	40 - 150	Various	10	✓
Reynolds Room	47' x 22' x 11'	40 - 120	Various	12	✓
China Drawing Room	18' x 20' x 11'	15 - 40	Various	5	✓
Long Gallery	80' x 14' x 12'	30 - 60	Various	3	
Armoury	18' x 30' x 11'	16	Various	4	✓
Study	19' x 20' x 11'	12	Various	4	
There are several smaller rooms available for Syndicate Meetings					

DEENE PARK
Northamptonshire

Deene Park has been transformed by successive generations of the Brudenell family over the last four centuries into one of Northamptonshire's finest country houses and is of considerable architectural interest.

Today Deene is still a family home containing fine examples of period furniture, family portraits and beautiful paintings; the House having been carefully restored after falling into a dilapidated state during the last war.

The oldest visible part of Deene is an arch c1300, which is to the right of a chimney in the east of the House which comprises the Hall of 1450. The Great Hall was completed by the end of the 16th Century and has a magnificent sweet chestnut hammer-beam roof.

The stained glass is 17th century and depicts the arms of the Brudenells and related families.

A famous member of the family was James Brudenell, 7th Earl of Cardigan, who led the Charge of the Light Brigade at Balaklava and interesting records and historic relics about Lord Cardigan and the Charge have survived and are on show.

GARDENS
The gardens are mainly to the south of the House, with a parterre and terraced lawns to water, providing various walks with herbaceous borders, old fashioned roses, spring flowers, fine trees and shrubs.

❖

SUITABILITY FOR OTHER EVENTS
Suitable for a variety of indoor and outdoor events. Consideration given to all requests. Filming welcomed.

EXTRA FACILITIES
Specialist lectures about the house, its contents, gardens and history, can be provided by arrangement.

ADVICE TO COURIERS & DRIVERS
Access via north drive from Deene Village. No photography inside the house. Dogs allowed in car park only.

FACILITIES FOR THE DISABLED
Disabled and elderly visitors may alight at the entrance before parking in the allocated areas. Access to ground floor and garden. Toilets.

ACCOMMODATION
Residential conference facilities by arrangement.

PARKING FOR COACHES AND CARS
Unlimited parking for cars, 250 yards from the House, and space for three coaches, 10 yards from the House.

CATERING
The Restaurant/Tea Room caters for up to 60 people at any one time. Special rates are offered to groups. Bookings can be made in advance and menus are available on request. Catering facilities are available for special functions and conferences, and include buffets, lunches and dinners.

GUIDED TOURS
Tours at no additional cost are conducted for up to 70 people at any one time. Average time taken for a tour is 90 minutes. The owner will meet the groups if requested.

GIFT SHOP
Open at the same time as the House.

GUIDE BOOKS
A colour guide book is available, £1.80.

CONTACT

The House Keeper
Deene Park
Corby
Northamptonshire
NN17 3EW

Tel: (01780) 450278
(01780) 450223

Fax: (01780) 450282

LOCATION

6 miles NE of Corby off A43. From London via M1 to Junc. 15 then A43. or via A1, A14, A43 - 2 hours.

From Birmingham via M6, A14, A43 - 90 minutes

Rail: Kettering Station - 20 minutes.

OPENING TIMES

Summer

June - August

Sundays   2.00 - 5.00pm

Bank holiday Mondays only   2.00 - 5.00pm

Open Easter Sunday and Monday, Early and Late Spring Bank Holiday and August Bank Holiday   2.00 - 5.00pm

Open at all other times by arrangement, including pre-booked-parties.

Winter
(Out of season)
House and Gardens closed to casual visitors. Open by appointment for booked parties.

ADMISSION

Summer

HOUSE AND GARDENS
Adult £4.00
Child (10-14) £2.00
Child (under 10) . . Free*
GARDENS ONLY
Adult £2.50
Child (10-14) £1.25
Child (under 10) . . Free*
Groups (min 20 people)
Weekdays £3.50
(Min £70.00)
Weekends and public open days £4.00
(Min £80.00)

* Aged 10 and under free with an accompanying adult.

Winter
Groups visits only by prior arrangement.

CONFERENCE AND FUNCTION FACILITIES

ROOM	DIMENSIONS	CAPACITY	LAYOUT	POWER POINTS	SUITABLE FOR A/V
Great Hall	–	150	Theatre	✓	✓
		150	Buffet		
Tapestry Room	–	75	Theatre	✓	✓
East Room	–	18	U shape	✓	✓
		12	Boardroom		

HOLDENBY HOUSE
Holdenby

"ONE of the most pleasing sites that ever I saw" (John Evelyn 1673).

Holdenby was built in 1583 by Sir Christopher Hatton, Lord Chancellor to Queen Elizabeth I. Once the largest house in England, it was sold to the crown by Sir Christopher's heirs to repay his debts. James I paid several happy visits here but King Charles I's memories were less happy. He was imprisoned here for five months in 1647 following his defeat in the Civil War. After his execution the house was largely demolished with the remains later adapted into the existing house by the present owner's Great-Great Grandmother.

Today, Holdenby House comprises both the original Elizabethan remains and a sympathetic Victorian restoration. It also provides a splendid backdrop to Holdenby's historic garden with its fragrant border and reconstructed Elizabethan garden planted by Rosemary Verey. At the Falconry Centre visitors can see, or try flying, birds of prey. In the grounds an authentic armoury, a reconstructed 17th century homestead and a collection of rare farm animals - some dating back to Charles I's time - all enhance the sense of history at Holdenby. And for children there is the cuddle farm and play area. The major event in 1995 will be the reconstruction of the Battle of Naseby, by The Sealed Knot, on 17th and 18th June.

❖

CONTACT

Barbara Brooker
Holdenby House
Holdenby
Northamptonshire
NN6 8DJ

Tel: (01604) 770074

Fax: (01604) 770962

LOCATION

From London via M1, 90 mins. Leave at Junction 15, 15a or 16. Entrance 6 miles N/W of Northampton off the A428, or A50.

Rail: Northampton Station (London - Euston) 1 hour.

Taxi: Favell Cars (01604) 28177 / 20209.

SUITABILITY FOR OTHER EVENTS
Conferences, Seminars, Corporate Days, Weddings, Buffets and Dinners. Archery, Air Displays, Clay Pigeon Shoots, Equestrian Events, Garden Parties, Rallies, Filming etc.

EXTRA FACILITIES
Piano Museum, Falconry Displays, Croquet. A Lecture Room, Screen and Projector can all be provided.

FACILITIES FOR THE DISABLED
Disabled or elderly visitors can be left at the house prior to parking. There are toilet facilities for the disabled.

PARKING FOR COACHES & CARS
There is parking for 100 cars and 5 coaches.

CATERING
Special conference menus from finger buffets to silver service in the Dining Room. Victorian Tearoom/Restaurant seats 45 serving teas from £2.50, light meals from £4.50. Menus upon request.

GUIDED TOURS
Tours for groups of up to 80 at no additional cost. Average time for a tour is 45 minutes.

GIFT SHOP
The Gift Shop is open when the house and grounds are open or by prior arrangement. Local Gifts, Crafts and Souvenirs.

GUIDE BOOKS
Colour guide book, £1.50.

EDUCATIONAL VISITS/CHILDREN
Winner of The Sandford Award 1985 and 1990. Groups are welcome, a guide is provided and a school room is available. Of special interest to children is the Cuddle Farm.

CONFERENCE AND FUNCTION FACILITIES

ROOM	DIMENSIONS	CAPACITY	LAYOUT	POWER POINTS	SUITABLE FOR A/V
DBallroom	44' x 26'	90	Theatre	3	✓
		50	Schoolroom	3	✓
		40	Boardroom	3	✓
Pytchley	24' x 20'	30	Theatre	3	✓
		16	Boardroom	3	✓
Dining Room		48	Dinner	3	✓

LAMPORT HALL & GARDENS
Lamport

HOME of the Isham family from 1560 to 1976. The 17th and 18th Century facade is by John Webb and the Smiths of Warwick and the North Wing of 1861 by William Burn.

The Hall contains a wealth of outstanding furniture, books and paintings including portraits by Van Dyck, Kneller, Lely and others. The fine rooms include the High Room of 1655 with magnificent plasterwork, the 18th Century library with books from the 16th Century, the early 19th Century Cabinet Room containing rare Venetian cabinets with mythological paintings on glass and the Victorian Dining Room where refreshments are served.

The first floor has undergone lengthy restoration allowing further paintings and furniture to be displayed as well as a photographic record of Sir Gyles Isham, a Hollywood actor, who initiated the restoration.

The tranquil gardens were laid out in 1655 although they owe much to Sir Charles Isham the eccentric 10th Baronet who, in the mid 19th Century, created the Italian Garden and the Rockery where he introduced the first garden gnomes to England. There are also box bowers, a rose garden and lily pond and extensive walks, borders and lawns all surrounded by a spacious park.

❖

SUITABILITY FOR OTHER EVENTS
Wedding receptions, conferences, meetings, garden parties, company activity days, clay pigeon shoots, equestrian events, fashion shows, air displays, archery, rallies, filming, shows.

EXTRA FACILITIES
Parkland, Grand Piano, 2 exhibition rooms. Lectures can be arranged on the history of the property and gardens. Lecture/meeting rooms are available, seating a maximum of 50, with audio-visual equipment. Full details of costs on application. Free admission to the agricultural museum on Sundays from Easter to end of September.

ADVICE TO COURIERS & DRIVERS
Use main entrance only (on A508). No unaccompanied children. No photography inside the house.

FACILITIES FOR THE DISABLED
Disabled or elderly visitors may alight at the entrance door. Access to ground floor and gardens. Toilets.

PARKING FOR COACHES & CARS
Free for 100 cars & 3 coaches, within 20 yds of the property.

GIFT SHOP
Open as house with a range of quality gifts and souvenirs.

CATERING
The Dining/Tea Room seats 50 maximum and groups can book meals in advance. Catering available for special functions, buffets, lunches and Dinners. Guided Tours with refreshments.

GUIDED TOURS
Tours are available at no additional cost, by prior arrangement. Maximum size of party is 70, average time taken is $1^1/_2$ hours.

GUIDE BOOKS
Colour guide book, £1.70.

SCHOOL VISITS/CHILDREN
School groups welcome. A work room is available in the Study Centre. Groups are conducted round the house, gardens, church and village by specialist advisory teachers, who provide study packs. Further information contact the Education Officer 01858 462805 or the Trust Office (01604) 686272. Special guide book available for children visiting individually or with families.

CONTACT

George Drye
Executive Director
Lamport Hall
Northampton
NN6 9HD

Tel: (01604) 686272

Fax: (01604) 686224

LOCATION

From London via M1, $1^1/_4$ hours. Leave at Junction 15. Entrance on A508, 8 miles north of Northampton at junction with B576.

Rail: Kettering Station 15 miles; Northampton 8 miles.

Bus: From Northampton and Market Harborough.

OPENING TIMES

Summer
Easter - 1 October
Sundays and Bank Hol
Mons   2.15 - 5.15pm

Daily in August
1 tour at 4.30 or 5.00pm

28, 29 Oct   2.15 - 5.15pm

2, 3 Dec   2.15 - 5.15pm
Tours on other days by prior arrangement.

Winter
Group visits only by arrangement.

ADMISSION

Summer
HOUSE & GARDEN
   Adult £3.20
   Child* £1.60
   OAP £2.70
   Group** ......£POA

* Aged 5 - 16yrs.
*Min. payment £125.00 including refreshments

Winter
Group visits only by prior arrangement.

CONFERENCE AND FUNCTION FACILITIES

ROOM	DIMENSIONS	CAPACITY	LAYOUT	POWER POINTS	SUITABLE FOR A/V
Dining Room	31' x 24' 6"	80	Theatre	4	✓
		48	Schoolroom		✓
		27	U-shape		✓
		34	Boardroom		✓
		60	Lunch/Dinner		✓
		60	Buffet		✓

ROCKINGHAM CASTLE
Nr. Corby

A Royal castle until 1530, since then home of the Watson family. Rockingham Castle was built by William the Conqueror on the site of an earlier fortification and was regularly used by the early Kings of England until the 16th Century when it was granted by Henry VIII to Edward Watson whose family still live there today.

The house itself is memorable not so much as representing any particular period, but rather a procession of periods. The dominant influence in the building is Tudor within the Norman walls, but practically every century since the 11th has left its mark in the form of

architecture, furniture or works of art. The Castle has a particularly fine collection of English 18th, 19th and 20th Century paintings, and Charles Dickens, who was a frequent visitor, was so captivated by Rockingham that he used it as a model for Chesney Wold in Bleak House.

The Castle stands in 12 acres of formal and wild garden and commands a splendid view of five counties. Particular features are the 400 year old elephant hedge and the rose garden marking the foundations of the old keep. See Special Exhibition: 450 years a royal castle, 450 years a family home.

CONTACT

Miss K Barton
Rockingham Castle
Market Harborough
Leicestershire
LE16 8TH

Tel: (01536) 770240

LOCATION

2 miles north
of Corby;
9 miles from
Market Harborough;
14 miles from
Stamford on A427;
8 miles from
Kettering on A6003

SUITABILITY FOR OTHER EVENTS
Buffets, concerts, conferences, fashion shows, product launches, receptions and seminars. Air displays, clay pigeon shoots, archery, equestrian events, fairs, garden parties. Filming. Special exhibition celebrating 900 years of life in the castle from the Great Council of Rockingham in 1095 to the present day – 450 years a Royal Castle, 450 years a family home.

EXTRA FACILITIES
Grand Piano in the Long Gallery. 250 acres of parkland, grass tennis court, cricket pitch and eventing course. Strip for light aircraft 4 miles.

ADVICE TO COURIERS & DRIVERS
No photography is allowed in the Castle.

FACILITIES FOR THE DISABLED
Disabled toilets available. Elderly or disabled visitors may alight at the Castle entrance. Ramps provided.

PARKING FOR COACHES & CARS
Unlimited parking for cars up to 100 yards from the Castle. Up to 6 coaches can be parked 100 yards from the Castle.

CATERING
Home-made afternoon teas. Light lunches on Sundays and Bank Holidays. Meals on other days by arrangement. Maximum seating 86. Waitress service.

GUIDED TOURS
All pre-booked parties are given a guided tour, except on open-days, at no additional cost. By prior arrangement,

the owner may meet the groups. Duration of the tour is 45 minutes.

GIFT SHOP
Open when the castle is open to the public.

GUIDE BOOK
Colour guide £1.95. Special children's guide.

SCHOOL VISITS/ CHILDREN
Rockingham has received 3 Sandford Awards for Heritage Education. There is much of interest for schools. A special pack has been designed with the National Curriculum in mind containing 27 booklets relating to different aspects of the Castle's history, including trails for the grounds, the village and the church. This can be obtained by post, price £7.50. Special tours for schools can be arranged and covered spaces are available for work and picnics when wet.

OPENING TIMES

Summer
Easter Sunday - 30 Sept

Mons Bank Hols and
by appointment

Tuesdays in August,
following Bank Hols or
by appointment
1.30 - 5.30pm

Weds, Fris, Sats
by appointment only

Thurs, Suns
1.30 - 5.30pm

Daily by appointment
for parties.

Grounds open 11.30 on
Bank Hol. Suns & Mons.
Light refreshments available
from 12.00 Noon.

Winter
Daily by appointment for
booked parties. Closed to
casual visitors.

ADMISSION

HOUSE & GARDEN
Adult £3.80
Child (to 16 yrs.) . .£2.30
OAP £3.20
Group
Adult* £3.20
OAP £3.20
Student** £1.50
Family Ticket
2 + 2 . . . .£10.00

*Min. £64.00   **Min. £37.50

GROUNDS ONLY
Adult £2.30
Child (to 16 yrs.) . .£2.30
OAP £2.30

Prices may vary for
special events in
grounds.

CONFERENCE AND FUNCTION FACILITIES

ROOM	DIMENSIONS	CAPACITY	LAYOUT	POWER POINTS	SUITABLE FOR A/V
Great Hall	37'6" x 22'	100	Theatre	1	3
Panel Room	36' x 23'	100	Theatre	1	3
Long Gallery	87' x 16'6"	100	Theatre	2	
Walkers House 1	31' x 17'6"	60	Buffet	2	
Walkers House 2	24' x 18'	50	Buffet	2	

SULGRAVE MANOR
Northamptonshire

SULGRAVE MANOR is the early English home of the ancestors of George Washington, first mentioned in the Domesday Book in 1086. The House was the birthplace of Reverend Lawrence Washington, whose son, Colonel John Washington, left England in 1656 to take up the land which later became Mount Vernon.

In 1914 Sulgrave Manor was presented by a body of British subscribers to the peoples of Great Britain and the United States of America in celebration of the Hundred Years Peace between the two countries. Restored and refurnished, it now presents a perfect example of a small manor house and garden during the time of Shakespeare.

Of special interest is the Washington Coat of Arms (three mullets and two bars) still clearly to be seen in a spandrel of the main doorway. This is said to have inspired the Stars and Stripes of the American National Flag.

Each room in the house is furnished in the style of its period. The Great Hall and Great Chamber above have fine collections of Tudor and Early Jacobean furniture. The Queen Anne wing, added in the year 1700, displays superb examples of 18th Century craftsmanship. However it is perhaps the magnificent Kitchen with its unique collection of utensils, its perfect range and typical furniture, that is justifiably one of the great features of the house.

GARDENS
One of the attractive features of the Manor is its garden, designed in 1921 by Sir Reginald Blomfield.

---❖---

SUITABILITY FOR OTHER EVENTS
Craft fairs, Garden Parties, Receptions, Open Performances, Concerts.

EXTRA FACILITIES
Lectures can be arranged on the property and its history for up to 30 people.

ADVICE TO COURIERS & DRIVERS
Please book in advance as numbers and parking limited. No photography in house; dogs on leads in gardens only. No smoking in the House.

PARKING FOR COACHES & CARS
Parking for 40 cars and 4 coaches, 30 yards from House.

CATERING
'The Brew House' tea room (capacity 25/50 people). Parties can be booked in advance for tea and other meals.

GUIDED TOURS
Available for groups of up to 30 people at no additional cost. Average time taken to see the House 1-1¼ hours. There is a video of the 'Washington Trail', tracing the family links in this country.

GIFT SHOP
Gift Shop open at the same time as House.

GUIDE BOOKS
Colour guide book, £1.50.

SCHOOL VISITS/CHILDREN
Groups are welcome, cost £2.00 per child. A guide is provided. It is especially worthwhile for the young student as it is comparatively small. There is a special children's guide book and a paddock to play in. A teachers pack is available and preliminary visits are free.

CONTACT

Martin Sirot-Smith
Sulgrave Manor
Manor Road
Sulgrave
Banbury
Oxfordshire
OX17 2SD

Tel: (01295) 760205

LOCATION

M40 5mls, M1 15mls.
10 mins from Banbury,
Brackley, Towcester.
20 mins to Buckingham.
30 mins to N'hampton.
45 mins to Oxford,
Warwick, Stratford.
2hrs from London.

Rail: Banbury Stn 6mls.

Bus: From Banbury/
Brackley.

Taxi: Fisher's Taxis
(01295) 760797.

CONFERENCE AND FUNCTION FACILITIES

ROOM	DIMENSIONS	CAPACITY	LAYOUT	POWER POINTS	SUITABLE FOR A/V
Great Hall	24' x 18'	50	Theatre	3	
		50	Buffet	3	
		30	Schoolroom	3	
		24	Dinner	3	

OPENING TIMES

All groups and individuals are taken around the Manor House in regularly conducted tours.

Weekdays:
1 April - 31 October
Daily except Weds
2.00 - 5.30pm
Mornings by appointment only.

Bank Hols and Aug.
10.30 - 1.00pm and
2.00 - 5.30pm.

27, 28, 29 Dec
10.30am - 1.00pm and
2.00 - 4.30pm.

Weekends:
Apr - Oct
10.30am - 1.00pm and
2.00pm - 5.30pm

Mar, Nov and Dec
10.30am - 1.00pm and
2.00pm - 4.30pm

NB Last admissions 1 hour before closing times.

Special Event Days:
10.30 - 5.30pm.

Weekdays in Feb, Mar, Nov and Dec open by appointment only. Morning & evening pre-booked parties available throughout the year.

Closed Christmas Day, Boxing Day and the whole of January.

ADMISSION

Adult £3.00
Child* £1.50
OAP £3.00
Student £1.50
Family** £9.00

Groups (min 12 people)
Adult £2.50
Child* £1.25
OAP £2.50
Student £1.25

* Aged 5 - 16yrs.
** 2 adults and 2+ children.

ALTHORP HOUSE

See page 131 for full page entry.

BOUGHTON HOUSE

See page 132 for full page entry.

CASTLE ASHBY

See page 133 for full page entry.

COTON MANOR GARDEN

Tel: 01604 740219　**Fax:** 01604 740838

Guilsborough, Northampton, Northamptonshire, NN6 8RQ.
Owner: Ian Pasley-Tyler Esq　　　　**Contact:** Ian Pasley-Tyler Esq
17th century stone manor house with old English garden laid out on different levels. Water gardens, herbaceous borders, rose garden, old holly and yew hedges. Collection of ornamental waterfowl, cranes and flamingoes.
Location: 9m N of Northampton off A50 or A428.
Opening Times: Apr - Sept, Wed - Sun and Bank Hols.
Admission: Adult £2.70, Child £1.00, Conc £2.20, Family £7.00, Groups. Standard £2.20, Conc £2.00.

COTTESBROOKE HALL

OPEN

17 April - 28 Sept

Thursdays and Bank Holiday Mondays

2.00 - 5.30pm

On other weekday parties accommodated by appointment.

Tel: 01604 505808
Fax: 01604 505619

COTTESBROOKE, NORTHAMPTON NN6 8PF

Owner: Captain Macdonald-Buchanan　*Contact: The Administrator*

Architecturally magnificent Queen Anne house commenced in 1702. Renowned picture collection, particularly of sporting and equestrian subjects. Fine English and Continental furniture and porcelain. Main vista aligned on celebrated 7th century Saxon church at Brixworth. House reputed to be the pattern for Jane Austen's "Mansfield Park". Notable gardens of great variety including fine old cedars, specimen trees and herbaceous borders.
Location: 10 miles north of Northampton near Creaton on A50, near Brixworth on A508 or Kelmarsh on A14.
Admission: House & Garden: Adult £3.50. Gardens only: Adult £2.50. Children half price.

DEENE PARK

See page 134 for full page entry.

ELEANOR CROSS

Geddington, Kettering, Northamptonshire.
Owner: English Heritage　　　　**Contact:** The Administrator
One of a series of famous crosses, of elegant sculpted design, erected by Edward I to mark the resting places of the body of his wife, Eleanor, when brought for burial from Harby in Nottinghamshire to Westminster Abbey.
Location: In Geddington, off A43 between Kettering and Corby.
Opening Times: Write for details.

HOLDENBY HOUSE

See page 135 for full page entry.

KIRBY HALL

Tel: 01536 203230

Deene, Corby, Northamptonshire.
Owner: English Heritage　　　　**Contact:** The Administrator
Outstanding example of a large, stone built Elizabethan mansion, begun in 1570 with 17th century alterations. There are fine gardens, currently being restored.
Location: On unclassified road off A43 NE of Corby.
Opening Times: 1 Apr - 30 Sept Daily, 10.00am - 6.00pm. 1 Nov - 31 Mar, Wed - Sun, 10.00am - 4.00pm. (Closed 24 - 26 Dec, 1 Jan).
Admission: Adult £2.00, Child £1.50, Conc, £1.00.

LAMPORT HALL & GARDENS

See page 136 for full page entry.

NORTHAMPTON CATHEDRAL

Tel: 01604 714556　**Fax:** 01604 712066

Northampton, Northamptonshire, NN2 6AG.

Contact: Rev K Payne

Partly 19th century Pugin.
Location: ^{1}/2m from town centre on A508.
Opening Times: Daily 8.00am - 7.30pm. Sun services: 8.30am, 10.30am, 5.15pm and 7.00pm. Weekday services: 9.30am and 7.00pm.
Admission: Guided visit by priorevious application.

ROCKINGHAM CASTLE

See page 137 for full page entry.

RUSHTON TRIANGULAR LODGE

Rushton, Kettering, Northamptonshire.
Owner: English Heritage　　　　**Contact:** The Administrator
This extraordinary building symbolises the Holy Trinity, it has three sides, three floors, trefoil windows and three triangular gables on each side.
Location: 1m W of Rushton, on unclassified road 3m from Desborough on A6.
Opening Times: 1st Apr - 30 Sept daily, 10.00am - 6.00pm. Lunchtime closure from 1.00pm - 2.00pm.
Admission: Adult £1.00, Child 50p, Conc 80p.

SOUTHWICK HALL

Tel: 01832 274064

Southwick, Peterborough, Northamptonshire, PE8 5BL.
Owner: Christopher Capron Esq　　　　**Contact:** Christopher Capron Esq
Medieval building with Tudor rebuilding and 18th century additions.
Location: 3 m N of Oundle (A605). 4m W of Bulwick (A43).
Opening Times: Easter - Aug, Bank Hols (Sun and Mon). May - Aug, Wed, 2 - 5.00pm.
Admission: Adult £2.50, Child £1.50, Conc £1.80.

STOKE PARK PAVILIONS

Tel: 01604 862172

Stoke Bruerne, Towcester, Northamptonshire, NN12 7RZ.
Owner: R D Chancellor Esq　　　　**Contact:** Mrs C Cook
Two 17th century pavilions and colonnade by Inigo Jones.
Location: 7m S of Northampton.
Opening Times: Jun - Aug, Sat, Sun and BHs, 2.00pm - 6.00pm.
Admission: Adult £1.00, Child 50p.

SULGRAVE MANOR

See page 138 for full page entry.

THE MENAGERIE

Tel: 01604 870957　**Fax:** 01604 870923

Horton, Northampton, Northamptonshire NN7 2BX
Owner: Gervase Jackson Stops Esq　　　　**Contact:** Ian Kirby Esq
Folly built in the 1750s by Thomas Wright of Durham. The outstanding Rococo plasterwork in the main room includes Signs of the Zodiac. The gardens where Lord Halifax's animals were once kept, have been created by Ian Kirby and include formal ponds, wetland and bog area, herbaceous borders, two thatched arbours, one circular and classical, and the other triangular and Gothic, and a grotto featuring Orpheus playing to the animals covered in shells and minerals.
Location: 5m SE of Northampton.
Opening Times: House, Grotto and gardens open to parties of 20 or more by prior appointment £5.00 pp. Gardens only open on Thurs from Apr - Sept, 10.00am - 4.00pm.
Admission: Adult £2.50, Child £1.00. Groups of 20 or more at £5.00 a head.

SPECIAL EVENTS DIARY

- **4th March: Sulgrave Manor**
  Sophie Yates in Concert - Recital on English Virginals and Spinet celebrating the 300th anniversary of Purcell's death. Tickets £12.50 inclusive of buffet supper and wine. Booking essential.

- **1st - 2nd April: Althorp House and Park**
  Craft Fair in Park.

- **1st - 9th April: Sulgrave Manor**
  Living History 1645. For 9 days the Manor will run exactly as during the Civil War.

- **15th April: Sulgrave Manor**
  The Royal Academy of Music Quartet Tickets £12.50 inclusive of buffet supper and wine. Booking essential.

- **16th - 17th April: Lamport Hall**
  Antique Fair.

- **30th April: Lamport Hall**
  Art of Watercolour - exploring watercolour in grounds.

- **31st - 2nd May: Castle Ashby**
  Alternative Medicine & Lifestyles Weekend to include Tai Chi and Yoga, Bodyworks, Acupuncture, Aromatherapy, Message and Reflexolgy, Meditation. Gala Dinners with speakers and country pursuits.

- **6th - 8th May: Sulgrave Manor**
  Indian Rendezvous. American Indian Living History Camp.

- **7th - 8th May: Lamport Hall**
  Craft Festival & Garden Show

- **12th - 14th May: Castle Ashby**
  History and Theatre Weekend, visit to Bluebell woods, visit to Flore House and to the Menagerie.

- **14th May: Deene Park**
  Gardens Open 2-5pm under the National Gardens Scheme. Home-baked teas.

- **20th - 21st May: Sulgrave Manor**
  Herbs, Hives and History. Demonstrations stalls etc.

- **27th May - 4th June: Sulgrave Manor**
  Stars Stripes and Stitches. Annual Needlework Event. Pre-booking essential Please send for programme.

- **28th - 29th June: Lamport Hall**
  Lamport Country Festival - traditional country fair.

- **28th-29th June: Althorp House and Park**
  Falconry Fair in Park.

- **17th - 18th June: Holdenby House and Gardens**
  The Battle of Naseby will celebrate its 350th anniversary with a reconstruction by The Sealed Knot including 3,000 men and women at arms. Craft Fair, Falconry. Open 11.00am - 6.00pm both days.

- **18th June: Lamport Hall**
  East Midlands Doll Fair with Dolls Houses and Teddy Bears.

- **18th June: Sulgrave Manor**
  Gardens open as part of National Garden Scheme (+ 8 in Sulgrave village) (2pm-6pm).

- **24th June: Deene Park**
  SSAFA Military Tattoo.

- **24th - 25th June: Rockingham Castle**
  Rainbow Craft Fair

- **30th June - 2nd July: Castle Ashby**
  Horticulture and History Weekend - Tour of House, talks on conservation and gardening - Candlelit Concert and champagne buffet supper. Country fair and horse trials.

- **1st - 2nd July: Lamport Hall**
  Oil Painting Course - Richard Allen

- **1st - 2nd July: Rockingham Castle**
  Civil War Re-enactment by The Siege Group

- **1st - 9th July: Sulgrave Manor**
  Living History 1580 . For 9 days the Manor will run exactly as during the Tudor period.

- **22nd - 23rd July: Lamport Hall**
  Watercolour Painting Course - Peter Atkin

- **5th - 6th August: Cottesbrooke Hall**
  Rainbow Craft Fair

- **5th - 6th August: Sulgrave Manor**
  Tanglewood Theatre Production - Telephone for further details.

- **25th - 28th August: Deene Park**
  Greenbelt '95 - Christian Arts Festival.

- **25th - 28th August: Sulgrave Manor**
  Living History 1780 . The Manor will run exactly as during the Georgian period.

- **27th - 28th August: Lamport Hall**
  Antique Fair.

- **15th - 17th September: Castle Ashby**
  Social Graces and Hospitality - Flower arranging, etiquette, visit to Lord Northampton's wine cellar where an expert Sommelier will explain his collection.

- **2nd - 3rd September: Lamport Hall**
  Watercolour Painting Course - Peter Atkin.

- **9th - 10th September: Sulgrave Manor**
  American Civil War Camp - 55th American Civil War Infantry Unit.

- **15th - 17th September: Castle Ashby**
  Social Graces and Hospitality - Flower arranging, etiquette, visit to Lord Northampton's wine cellar where an expert Sommelier will explain his collection.

- **16th - 17th September: Lamport Hall**
  Craft Festival.

- **1st October: Lamport Hall**
  East Midlands Doll Fair with Dolls Houses and Teddy Bears

- **7th-8th October: Althorp House and Park**
  Craft Fair in Park

- **21st-22nd October: Sulgrave Manor**
  Apple Day - Apples to buy, ciders to try, demonstrations and plants for sale.

- **27th - 29th October: Castle Ashby**
  Mysteries & Curiosities weekend - Spirits, fortune tellers, Murder Mystery - tales of the unexpected.

- **28th - 29th October: Lamport Hall**
  Gift and Craft Fair.

- **Weekends in December & 27th-29th: Sulgrave Manor**
  A Tudor Christmas 10.30am - 1.00pm and 2.00pm - 4.30pm.

- **2nd-3rd December: Lamport Hall**
  Christmas Craft Fair.

- **24th - 27th December: Castle Ashby**
  Christmas Celebrations.

 THE NATIONAL TRUST    ENGLISH HERITAGE    HISTORIC HOUSES ASSOCIATION

ALNWICK CASTLE
Alnwick

Alnwick Castle, home of the Duke of Northumberland, is the second largest inhabited Castle in England after Windsor and has been in the possession of the Percys, Earls and Dukes of Northumberland, since 1309. The earliest parts of the present Castle were erected by Yvo de Vescy, the first Norman Baron of Alnwick who became the owner of the town soon after 1096.

The rugged medieval exterior belies the richness of the interior, refurbished in the classical style of the Italian Renaissance. This replaces the Gothic decoration carried out by Robert Adam in the 18th Century.

The Castle houses an exquisite collection of art treasures, including the finest examples of Italian paintings in the north of England with works by other great artists including Van Dyck and Turner. In addition to fine English and French furniture and ornately carved wooden ceilings, the Castle also houses one of the country's most important collections of early Meissen porcelain.

GARDENS
The landscape to the north, over the River Aln, was laid out by Capability Brown, and can be enjoyed from the terrace of the Castle.

CONTACT

A Fricker
Alnwick Castle
Estate Office
Alnwick
Northumberland
NE66 1NQ

Tel: (01665) 510777

Fax: (01665) 510876

LOCATION

From London 6 hours,
Edinburgh 2 hours,
Chester 4 hours,
Newcastle under 1 hour.

Bus: from bus station in Alnwick.

Rail: Alnmouth Station 5 miles.

SUITABILITY FOR OTHER EVENTS
Fashion Shows, fairs and filming. The parkland is also available for hire. Please contact the head agent.

EXTRA FACILITIES
By arrangement only.

ADVICE TO COURIERS & DRIVERS
No unaccompanied children and animals. No photography inside the castle.

FACILITIES FOR THE DISABLED
Please make enquiries prior to your visit.

PARKING FOR COACHES & CARS
Parking for 70 cars and 4 coaches adjacent to the Castle. Coach and car parking facilities are also available close by in town.

CATERING
Excellent tearoom for morning coffee, light lunches and afternoon tea. Seats up to 80.

GIFT SHOP
Open at the same time as the Castle. Items include locally made pottery, small gifts and items for children.

GUIDE BOOKS
The guide book contains full colour pictures, price £2.00. Special children's guide book.

GUIDED TOURS
During and out of opening hours. Please enquire for details.

SCHOOL VISITS/CHILDREN
A special guidebook and worksheet are available for children. Parts of particular interest include the Barbican and Gun Terrace. Special rates for children and teachers.

OPENING TIMES

Summer
Easter - mid October
Daily   11.00am - 5.00pm

Last admission 4.30pm.

Winter
October - Easter
Pre-booked parties only

ADMISSION

Summer
HOUSE & GARDEN
Adult £4.50
Child* £2.50
OAP £4.00
Family (2+2) . .£11.00

Groups (min 12 people)
Adult £4.00
Child* £2.20
OAP £3.50
*Age 5 - 16

Winter
By arrangement only.

CONFERENCE AND FUNCTION FACILITIES

ROOM	DIMENSIONS	CAPACITY	LAYOUT	POWER POINTS	SUITABLE FOR A/V
The Great Guest Hall	100' x 30'	300	Silver Service/ Buffet	✓	✓

BAMBURGH CASTLE
Bamburgh

BAMBURGH CASTLE is the home of Lady Armstrong and her family. The earliest reference to Bamburgh shows the craggy citadel to have been a royal centre by AD 547. Recent archaeological excavation has revealed that the site has been occupied since prehistoric times. The Norman Keep has been the stronghold for nearly nine centuries, but the remainder has twice been extensively restored, initially by Lord Crewe in the 1750s and subsequently by the first Lord Armstrong at the end of the 19th Century. This Castle was the first to succumb to artillery fire - that of Edward IV.

The public rooms contain many exhibits, including the loan collections of armour from HM Tower of London, the John George Joicey Museum, Newcastle-upon-Tyne and other private sources, which complement the Castle's armour. Porcelain, china, jade, furniture from many periods, oils, water-colours and a host of interesting items are all contained within one of the most important buildings of Britain's national heritage.

VIEWS
The views from the ramparts are unsurpassed and take in Holy Island, The Farne Islands, one of Northumberland's finest beaches and, landwards, the Cheviot Hills.

❖

CONTACT

P Bolam
R G Bolam & Son
Rothbury
Northumberland
NE65 7SP

Tel: (01669) 620314

Fax: (01669) 621236

LOCATION

42 miles north of Newcastle upon Tyne. 20 miles south of Berwick upon Tweed. 6 miles east of Belford B1342 from A1 at Belford.

Bus: Bus service 200 yards.

Taxi: R Aitchison (01668) 213766.

SUITABILITY FOR OTHER EVENTS
Bamburgh has been used as a location for films both interior and exterior.

ADVICE TO COURIERS & DRIVERS
No pets admitted. No cameras to be used in the interior of the building.

FACILITIES FOR THE DISABLED
Facilities for the disabled are restricted to one toilet and limited access dependant upon disability.

PARKING FOR COACHES & CARS
Capacity of the car park: approx 100 cars adjacent to the Castle. Coaches park free on tarmac drive at entrance.

CATERING
Tea Rooms for light refreshments during viewing times. Meals for organised groups can be booked in advance.

GUIDED TOURS
By arrangement at any time. Minimum charge out of hours £30.00.

GIFT SHOP
Within the Castle, offering quality merchandise. Open during public viewing hours and also for booked parties.

GUIDE BOOKS
Colour guide book, £1.30.

SCHOOL VISITS/CHILDREN
Groups of children welcome guide will be provided if requested. Of particular interest displays of arms and armour and the Armstrong naval gun. No special facilities but guides pitch tours to suit age group. Educational pack available.

OPENING TIMES

April and Sept
Daily 11.00am - 5.00pm

May and June
Daily 11.00am - 5.30pm

July and August
Daily 11.00am - 6.00pm

October
Daily 11.00am - 4.30pm

Tours by arrangement at any time.

ADMISSION

Summer

Adult £2.50
Child* £1.20
OAP £2.00

Groups**
Adult £2.00
Child* £0.90
OAP £1.60

* Up to 16
** Min payment £30

Winter
Group rates only.

BELSAY HALL, CASTLE & GDNS.
Nr. Ponteland

Belsay, with its 19th century neoclassical mansion, Jacobean manor house and medieval castle set in 30 acres of magnificent gardens, is one of the most remarkable estates in the border country. From Belsay Hall, designed with the severe elegance and symmetry of a Greek temple, it is a short walk to the landscaped gardens with massed plantings of rhododendrons and heather. Most remarkable are the wild and romantic quarry gardens, dramatically planted with evergreens and rare and exotic plants.

CONTACT

The Head Custodian
Belsay Hall
Belsay
Near Ponteland
Northumberland
NE20 0DX

Tel: 01661 881636

LOCATION

14 miles (22.4 km) north west of Newcastle-upon-Tyne on A696

OPENING TIMES

Summer

1 April - 30 September
Daily
10.00am - 6.00pm

Winter

1 October - 31 March
Daily
10.00am - 4.00pm

ADMISSION

Adults £2.60
Child* £1.30
OAP/Student/UB40
  holders £2.00

15% discount on groups of 11 or more

* 5 - 15 years.
Under 5's free

SUITABILITY FOR OTHER EVENTS
Suitable for small concerts and craft fairs.

EXTRA FACILITIES
Education Centre. An exhibition of Belsay's architectural and landscape history in stable block.

ADVICE TO COURIERS & DRIVERS
Tour leader and Coach driver have free entry. 1 extra place for every 20 additional people.

FACILITIES FOR THE DISABLED
Disabled route through garden, converted W.C..

PARKING FOR COACHES & CARS
Free coach parking available.

CATERING
Catering facilities are available. Caterers: (01661) 881033.

GUIDED TOURS
Introductory talk provided on request.

GIFT SHOP
A wide selection of souvenirs and gifts are available.

GUIDE BOOKS
Souvenir guide book available in the shop.

SCHOOL VISIT/CHILDREN
School visits are free if booked in advance. Contact the Administrator.

CHILLINGHAM CASTLE
Near Alnwick

THIS remarkable Castle, the home of Sir Humphry Wakefield Bt, with its alarming dungeons has, since the twelve hundreds, been continuously owned by the family of the Earls Grey and their relations. You will see active restoration of complex masonry, metalwork and ornamental plaster as the great halls and state rooms are gradually brought back to life with antique furniture, tapestries and arms and armour as of old and even a torture chamber.

At first a 12th Century stronghold, Chillingham became a fully fortified Castle in the 14th Century. Wrapped in the Nation's history it occupied a strategic position as fortress during Northumberland's bloody border feuds, often besieged and at many times enjoying the patronage of royal visitors. In Tudor days there were additions but the underlying Medieval character has always been retained. The 18th and 19th Centuries saw decorative refinements and extravagances including the lake, garden and grounds laid out by Sir Jeffrey Wyatville, fresh from his triumphs at Windsor Castle.

GARDENS
With romantic grounds the Castle commands breathtaking views of the surrounding countryside. As you walk to the lake you will see according to the season, drifts of snowdrops, daffodils or bluebells and an astonishing display of rhododendrons. This emphasizes the restrained formality of the Elizabethan topiary garden, with its intricately clipped hedges of box and yew. Lawns, the formal gardens and woodland walks are all fully open to the public.

SUITABILITY FOR OTHER EVENTS
Any form of corporate entertainment undertaken, we will also consider any other requests. Weddings welcome.

EXTRA FACILITIES
Chillingham is suitable for the use of light aircraft and helicopters. There is a pistol and rifle range. Salmon, sea trout and trout fishing available, also tuition from qualified shooting instructors, accommodation for up to 30 guests in the Castle. Must be arranged well in advance. Lunches, drinks and dinner for up to 150 people can be arranged at any time.

ADVICE TO COURIERS & DRIVERS
Avoid Lilburn route, gates wide enough to admit any coach. Coach parties welcome by prior arrangement. Tel: (01668)5359 or (0171) 937 7829. Fax: (01668) 5463. Sorry no dogs.

GUIDE BOOKS
There is a history of the Castle available, and a guide to the many ghosts resident at Chillingham. There will soon be a full colour guide to the Castle and its contents.

GUIDED TOURS
These can be arranged, and the owner is frequently available to take parties around personally.

GIFT SHOP
Gift/souvenir shop, also antique and curio shop.

CATERING
Tearoom for use of public, cap. 70. Booked meals for up to 100.

CONTACT

The Administrator
Chillingham Castle
Near Alnwick
Northumberland
NE66 5NJ

Tel: (01665) 215359
(0171) 937 7829

Fax: (01665) 215463
(0171) 938 3156

LOCATION

Off A1 Chatton to Berwick road or off B6346 Alnwick to Chatton Road.

Rail: Alnmouth or Berwick

OPENING TIMES

Summer
Easter Weekend
1.30pm - 5.00pm

May - September
Daily except Tues
1.30pm - 5.00pm

August
Opens at 11.00am

Winter
Open every day by appointment for booked parties. House and garden closed to casual visitors.

ADMISSION

Summer
Adult £3.30
OAP £2.80
Child* £2.20
* Up to 16 years.
Groups (min 20 people)
Per person £2.25
Pre-booking is essential.

CONFERENCE AND FUNCTION FACILITIES

ROOM	DIMENSIONS	CAPACITY	LAYOUT	POWER POINTS	SUITABLE FOR A/V
King James I Room		120			
Great Hall		100			
Minstrels' Hall		50			
2 x Drawing Room		60 each			
Museum		150			
Tea Room		100			
Lower Gallery		30			
Upper Gallery		40			

ALNWICK CASTLE

See page 141 for full page entry.

AYDON CASTLE

Tel: 01434 632450

Corbridge, Northumberland.
Owner: English Heritage   **Contact:** The Administrator
One of the finest fortified manor houses in England, dating from the late 13th century. Its survival, intact, can be attributed to its conversion to a farmhouse in the 17th century.
Location: 1m NE of Corbridge, on minor road off B6321 or A68.
Opening Times: 1 Apr - 30 Sept daily, 10am - 6pm. Lunchtime closure 1pm - 2pm.
Admission: Adult £1.80, Child 90p, Conc £1.40.

BAMBURGH CASTLE

See page 142 for full page entry.

BELSAY HALL, CASTLE & GARDENS   See page 143 for full page entry.

BERWICK BARRACKS

Tel: 01289 304493

Berwick-upon-Tweed, Northumberland.
Owner: English Heritage   **Contact:** The Administrator
Among the earliest purpose built barracks, these have changed very little since 1717. They house an exhibition 'By Beat of Drum', which recreates scenes such as a barrack room from the life of the British infantryman, the Museum of the King's Own Scottish Borderers and the Borough Museum with fine art, local history exhibition, and other collections.
Location: On the Parade, off Church Street.
Opening Times: 1 Apr - 30 Sept, daily 10.00am - 6.00pm, 1 Oct - 31 Oct, daily 10.00am - 4.00pm, 1 Nov - 31 Mar, Wed - Sun, 10.00am - 4.00pm (Closed 24 - 26 Dec, 1 Jan).
Admission: Adult £2.20, Child £1.10, Conc £1.70.

BERWICK RAMPARTS

Berwick upon Tweed, Northumberland.
Owner: English Heritage   **Contact:** The Administrator
A remarkably complete system of town fortifications consisting of gateways, ramparts and projecting bastions built in the 16th century.
Location: Surrounding Berwick Town Centre on N bank of River Tweed.
Opening Times: Any reasonable time.

BRINKBURN PRIORY

Tel: 01665 570628

Longframlington, Northumberland.
Owner: English Heritage   **Contact:** The Administrator
This late 12th century church is a fine example of early Gothic architecture, almost perfectly preserved, and is set in a lovely spot beside the River Coquet.
Location: 4¹/₂m SE of Rothbury off B6334.
Opening Times: 1 Apr - 30 Sept, daily 10.00am - 6.00pm.
Admission: Adult £1.30, Child 70p, Conc £1.00.

CHERRYBURN

Tel: 01661 843276

Station Bank, Mickley, Stocksfield, Northumberland, NE43 7DB.
Owner: The National Trust   **Contact:** The Administrator
Birthplace of Northumbria's greatest artist, wood engraver and naturalist, Thomas Bewick, b.1753. The Museum explores his famous works and life in the occasional demonstrations of hand printing from wood blocks in the printing house. Farmyard animals, picnic area, garden.
Location: 11m W of Newcastle on A695 (200yds signed from Mickley Square).
Opening Times: 1 Apr - end Oct, daily except Tues and Wed, 1.00pm - 5.30pm. Last admission 5.00pm.
Admission: Adult £2.50. No party rate.

CHESTERS ROMAN FORT & MUSEUM

Tel: 01434 681379

Walwick, Northumberland.
Owner: English Heritage   **Contact:** The Administrator
The best preserved example of a Roman cavalry fort in Britain, including remains of the bath house on the banks of the River North Tyne. The museum houses a fascinating collection of Roman sculpture and inscriptions.
Location: ¹/₂m W of Chollerford on B6318.
Opening Times: 1 Apr - 30 Sept, daily 10.00am - 6.00pm, 1 Oct - 31 Mar, daily 10.00am - 4.00pm (Closed 24 - 26 Dec, 1 Jan).
Admission: Adult £2.20, Child £1.10, Conc £1.70.

CHILLINGHAM CASTLE

See page 144 for full page entry.

CORBRIDGE ROMAN SITE

Tel: 01434 632349

Contact: The Administrator
A fascinating series of excavated remains, including foundations of granaries with a grain ventilation system. From artifacts found, which can be seen in the site museum, we know a large settlement developed around this supply depot.
Location: ¹/₂m NW of Corbridge on minor road signposted for Corstopitum, Hexham and Beaufront.
Opening Times: 1 Apr - 30 Sept, daily 10.00am - 6.00pm, 1 Oct - 31 Oct, daily 10.00am - 4.00pm, 1 Nov - 31 Mar, Wed - Sun, 10.00am - 4.00pm (Closed 24 - 26 Dec, 1 Jan).
Admission: Adult £2.20, Child £1.10, Conc £1.70.

CRAGSIDE HOUSE, GARDEN AND GROUNDS

Tel: 01669 620333

Contact: The Administrator
Designed by Richard Norman Shaw for the first Lord Armstrong and built between 1864 - 95, the house contains much of its original furniture and pre-Raphaelite paintings. It was the first house in the world to be lit by electricity generated by water power. The grounds are famous for their rhododendrons, magnificent trees and the beauty of the lakes.
Location: 5m E of Rothbury, 30m N of Newcastle-Upon-Tyne. Entrance off Rothbury/Alnwick road B6341, 1m N of Rothbury at Debdon Burn Gate.
Opening Times: House: 1 Apr - end Oct, daily except Mon (open BH Mons) 1.00pm - 5.30pm. Last admission 4.45pm. Grounds: 1 Apr - end Oct, daily except Mon (open BH Mons) 10.30am - 7.00pm. 4 Nov - 17 Dec: Tues, Sat & Sun, 10.30am - 4.00pm. Visitor Centre: 1 Apr - end Oct, daily except Mon (open BH Mons) 10.30am - 5.30pm. 4 Nov - 17 Dec: Tues, Sat & Sun 12.00pm - 4.00pm.
Admission: House, Garden, Grounds, Museum and Power Circuit: Adult £5.50. Parties £5.20. Garden and Grounds: Adult £3.50. Parties £3.20. Family ticket £14.00.

DUNSTANBURGH CASTLE

Tel: 01665 576231

Embleton, Northumberland.
Owner: English Heritage   **Contact:** The Administrator
An easy, but bracing, coastal walk leads to the eerie skeleton of this wonderful 14th century castle sited on a basalt crag, rearing up more than 100 feet from the waves crashing on the rocks below. The surviving ruins include the large gatehouse, which later became the keep, and curtain walls.
Location: 8m NE of Alnwick, on footpaths from Craster or Embleton.
Opening Times: 1 Apr - 30 Sept, daily 10.00am - 6.00pm, 1 Oct - 31 Oct, daily 10.00am - 4.00pm. 1 Nov - 31 Mar, Wed - Sun, 10.00am - 4.00pm, (Closed 24 - 26 Dec, 1 Jan).
Admission: Adult £1.30, Child 70p, Conc £1.00.

EDLINGHAM CASTLE

Edlingham, Alnwick, Northumberland.
Owner: English Heritage   **Contact:** The Administrator
Set beside a splendid railway viaduct this complex ruin has defensive features spanning the 13th and 15th centuries.
Location: At E end of Edlingham village, on minor road off B6341 6 m SW of Alnwick.
Opening Times: Any reasonable time.

HERTERTON HOUSE

Tel: 01670 774278

Cambo, Morpeth, Northumberland, NE61 4BN.
Owner: F Lawley Esq   **Contact:** F Lawley Esq
1 acre of formal garden in stone walls around a 16th century farmhouse, including a small topiary garden, physic garden and flower garden.
Location: 2m N of Cambo, just off B6342.
Opening Times: Garden only: 1 Apr - 30 Sept, Mon, Wed, Fri, Sat, 1.30pm - 5.30pm.

HOWICK HALL GARDENS

Tel: 01665 577285   **Fax:** 01665 577285

Howick, Alnwick, Northumberland, NE66 3LB.
Owner: Howick Trustees Ltd   **Contact:** Mrs D Spark
Romantically landscaped grounds surrounding the house in a little valley, with rare rhododendrons and flowering shrubs and trees.
Location: 6m NE of Alnwick
Opening Times: Apr - Oct, daily, 1.00pm - 6.00pm.
Admission: Adult £1.50, Child 75p, Senior citizen 75p.

KIRKLEY HALL COLLEGE

Tel: 01661 860808   **Fax:** 01661 860047

Ponteland, Northumberland, ME20 0AQ.
Contact: Dr R McParlin
Herbaceous Perennials, Victorian walled garden, ornamental borders, salad potager garden, sunken garden, woodland garden, greenhouses, wildlife pond.
Location: 2 ¹/₂ m NW of Ponteland on C151 to Morpeth.
Opening Times: Throughout the year, daily, 10.00am - 5.00pm
Admission: Adult £1.50, Child 70p, Child under 8 free, Family £3.00, Conc 70p, Group £1.20 per person, Guided group £2.50 per person.

LINDISFARNE CASTLE

Tel: 01289 89244

Holy Island, Berwick-upon-Tweed, Northumberland, TD15 2SH.

Owner: The National Trust   **Contact:** The Administrator

Built in 1550 to protect Holy Island harbour from attack, the castle was restored and converted into a private house for Edward Hudson by Sir Edwin Lutyens in 1903. Small walled garden was designed by Gertrude Jekyll. 19th century lime kilns in field by the castle.

Location: On Holy Island, 6m E of A1 across causeway.

Opening Times: 1 Apr - end Oct: daily except Fri (but open Good Fri) 1.00pm - 5.30pm. Last admission 5.00pm. Admission to garden only when gardener in attendance.

Admission: £3.60, Family £9.00. No party rate. Parties of 15+ must pre-book.

LINDISFARNE PRIORY

Tel: 01289 892000

Holy Island, Lindisfarne, Northumberland.

Owner: English Heritage   **Contact:** The Administrator

The site of one of the most important early centres of Christianity in Anglo-Saxon England. St Cuthbert converted pagan Northumbria, and miracles occurring at his shrine established this 11th century priory as a major pilgrimage centre. The evocative ruins, with the decorated 'rainbow' arch curving dramatically across the nave of the church, are still the destination of pilgrims today. The story of Lindisfarne is told in an exhibition which gives an impression of life for the monks, including a reconstruction of a monk's cell.

Location: On Holy Island, which can be reached at low tide across a causeway.

Opening Times: 1 Apr - end Oct, daily 10.00am - 6.00pm, 1 Oct - 31 Mar, daily 10.00am - 4.00pm. (Closed 24 - 26 Dec, 1 Jan).

Admission: Adult £2.30, Child, £1.20, Conc £1.70.

MELDON PARK

Tel: 01670 772661

Morpeth, Northumberland, NE61 3SW.

Owner: M J B Cookson Esq   **Contact:** M J B Cookson Esq

Early 19th century house by the renowned Newcastle architect, John Dobson. Fine plasterwork in Main Hall added by Lutyens in the 1920s.

Location: 7m W of Morpeth on B6343 15m N of Newcastle.

Opening Times: Last week in May and first 3 weeks of Jun, 2.00pm - 5.00pm.

Admission: Adult £3.00, Child 50p, Conc 50%.

NORHAM CASTLE

Tel: 01289 382329

Norham, Northumberland.

Owner: English Heritage   **Contact:** The Administrator

Set on a promontory in a curve of the River Tweed, this was one of the strongest of the border castles, built c.1160.

Location: Norham village, $6^1/_2$ m SW of Berwick-upon-Tweed on minor road off B6470 (from A698).

Opening Times: 1 Apr - 31 Oct daily, 10.00am - 6.00pm. 1 Nov - 31 Mar daily, 10.00am - 4.00pm. Closed 24 - 26 Dec, 1 Jan.

PRESTON TOWER

Tel: 01665 589227

Chathill, Northumberland, NE67 5DH.

Owner: Major T Baker-Creswell   **Contact:** Major T Baker-Creswell

One of the 78 Pele Towers listed in 1415. Two rooms furnished in period style.

Location: Follow Historic Property signs on A1 7m N of Alnwick.

Opening Times: Daylight hours all year.

Admission: Adult £1.00, Child 50p, Conc 50p, Groups 50p.

PRUDHOE CASTLE

Tel: 01661 33459

Prudhoe, Northumberland.

Owner: English Heritage   **Contact:** The Administrator

Set on a wooded hillside overlooking the River Tyne are the extensive remains of this 12th century castle including a gatehouse, curtain wall and keep.

Location: In Prudhoe, on minor road off A695.

Opening Times: 1 Apr - 30 Sept, daily 10am - pm, 1 Oct - 31 Oct, daily 10am - 4pm.

Admission: Adult £1.80, Child £1.35, Conc 90p.

ROMAN WALL (HOUSESTEADS FORT & MUSEUM) **Tel:** 01434 344363

Housesteads, Bardon Mill, Northumberland.

Owner: English Heritage   **Contact:** The Administrator

Perched high on a ridge overlooking open moorland, this is the best known part of the Wall. The fort covers five acres and the remains of many buildings, such as granaries, barrack blocks and gateways, can be seen. A small exhibition displays altars, inscriptions and models.

Location: $2^3/_4$m NE of Bardon Mill on B6318.

Opening Times: 1 Apr - 30 Sept, daily 10.00am - 6.00pm, 1 Oct - 31 Mar, daily 10.00am - 4.00pm. (Closed 24 - 26 Dec, 1 Jan).

Admission: Adult £2.30, Child £1.20, Conc £1.70.

SEATON DELAVAL HALL

OPEN

1 May - 30 Sept

Weds, Suns and Bank Holidays

2 - 6.00pm

Tel: 0191 237 3040
or 0191 237 1493

SEATON SLUICE, WHITLEY BAY, NORTHUMBERLAND NE26 4QR

Owner: The Lord Hastings   *Contact: F. Hetherington*

A splendid English baroque house, regarded by many as Sir John Vanbrugh's masterpiece. The playwright who turned so successfully to Architecture began the great house in 1718 for Admiral George Delaval. Building on the central block (Vanbrugh's Palladian Villa) ceased about 1728. The wings which are arcaded and pedimented include the East Wing containing the magnificent stables, built by Sir Francis Delaval (great nephew of the builder) in1768. In the grounds are extensive gardens. There is also a coach house and an ice house. For refreshment there is a tea room.

Location: Half mile from coast at Seaton Sluice between Blyth and Whitley Bay. Ten miles from Newcastle upon Tyne.

Admission: Adults £2.00, Child (with adult) 50p.

THE LADY WATERFORD HALL & MURALS

Tel: 01890 82524

Ford Village, Berwick-upon-tweed, Northumberland.

Contact: The Caretaker

Formerly the village school, built in 1862 by Louisa, Marchioness of Waterford, a friend of John Ruskin. She painted a series of murals using local children and their parents as models for Biblical scenes.

Location: $2^3/_4$m NE of Bardon Mill on B6318.

Opening Times: Daily 10.30am - 5.30pm. Easter - Oct, by appointment in winter.

VINDOLANDA

Tel: 01434 344277 **Fax:** 01434 344060

Bardon Mill, Hadrian's Wall, Hexham, Northumberland, NE47 7JN.

Contact: Mrs P Birley

Recent excavations have uncovered some of the most unusual and well preserved objects to come from the Roman world.

Location: 8m W of Hexham off A69.

Opening Times: Feb-Nov, Daily from 10am. Closes: 4pm in winter & 6.30pm in summer.

Admission: Adult £3.25, Child £2.00, Conc £2.50, 10% discount for groups of 15 plus.

WALLINGTON

Tel: 01670 774283

Cambo, Morpeth, Northumberland, NE61 4AR.

Owner: The National Trust   **Contact:** The Administrator

Built 1688, altered in 18th Century. Central Hall added in 19th Century, decorated by William Bell Scott, Ruskin and others. Fine porcelain, furniture and pictures in series of rooms including a late Victorian nursery and dolls' houses. Coach display in West Coach House. Woodlands, lakes, walled terraced garden and conservatory with magnificent fuchsias.

Location: Access from N 12m W of Morpeth on B6343, access from S, A696 from Newcastle. 6m NW of Belsay, B6342 to Cambo.

Opening Times: House: 1 Apr - end Oct, daily except Tues 1pm - 5.30pm. Last admission 5.00pm. Walled Garden: daily 1 Apr - 30 Sept 10.30am - 7pm, Oct 10.30am - 6pm, Nov - Mar 10.30am - 4pm or dusk if earlier. Grounds: all year during daylight hours.

Admission: House, Walled Garden and Grounds: Adult £4.60. Parties £4.10. Walled Garden and Grounds only: Adult £2.30. Parties £1.80.

WARKWORTH CASTLE

Tel: 01665 711423

Warkworth, Northumberland.

Owner: English Heritage   **Contact:** The Administrator

The great towering keep of this 15th century castle, once the home of the mighty Percy family, dominates the town and River Coquet.

Location: $7^1/_2$m S of Alnwick on A1068.

Opening Times: 1 Apr - 30 Sept, daily 10.00am - 6.00pm, 1 Oct - 31 Mar, daily 10.00am - 4.00pm. (Closed 24 - 26 Dec, 1 Jan).

Admission: Adult £2.00, Child £1.00, Conc £1.50.

WARKWORTH HERMITAGE

Warkworth, Northumberland.

Owner: English Heritage   **Contact:** The Administrator

Upstream by boat from the castle this curious hermitage cuts into the rock of the river cliff.

Location: $7^1/_2$m S of Alnwick on A1068.

Opening Times: Telephone Warkworth Castle 01665 711423, for opening arrangements.

SPECIAL EVENTS DIARY

- **17th March: Wallington**
  Early Music Demonstration & lecture by Peter Trevelyan, 8.00pm.

- **15th May: Cragside**
  Piano Recital - Young Choon Park 7.30pm

- **16th June: Wallington**
  Outdoor Concert with lasers and fireworks - 'Voulez Vous' and the 'Cavern Beatles' perform live. Bring a picnic, rugs and wear gear of the time! 7.30pm

- **28th June - 2nd July: Wallington**
  Open Air Shakespeare with Theatre Set-Up "A Midsummer Night's Dream" 7.30pm

- **22nd 23rd July: Cragside**
  Craft Weekend

- **29th July: Wallington**
  Concert with Guitar and Flute Duo 7.30pm

- **12th August: Wallington**
  Open Air Classics with Fireworks 8.00pm

- **20th August: Wallington**
  Wallington Family Funday

- **10th September: Wallington**
  Gardeners' Open Day

- **12th November: Wallington**
  Concert - Jacques Loussier Play Bach Trio with a French Winter Buffet contact Northumbria Regional Office 01670 774691 12.30pm.

Belsay Hall, Northumberland

Belsay Castle, Northumberland

HOLME PIERREPONT HALL

OPEN

June: Suns
July: Thurs & Suns
August: Tues, Thurs, Fris & Suns

Easter spring and summer holidays Suns, Mons & Tues 2 - 6.00pm

Groups by appointment throughout the year including evening visits.

Tel: 01602 332371

HOLME PIERREPONT, NOTTINGHAM NG12 2LD

Owner: Mr and Mrs Robin Brackenbury   *Contact:* Mr Robin Brackenbury

Visited by Henry VII in 1487, the house is peaceful and welcoming with splendid mediaeval rooms, a Charles II staircase and fine 17th to 20th century English country furniture and family portraits. The courtyard garden, 1875 is planted with roses, herbaceous beds and an elaborate box parterre. **The Long Gallery seats 100 for business or charity functions or the Lodgings 30.**

Location: Five miles from Central Nottingham. Follow signs to the National Water Sports Centre and continue on for 1¹/₂ miles.
Admission: Adults £3.00, Child £1.00. Gardens only £1.50.

CARLTON HOUSE

Tel: 01636 821421

Carlton-on-Trent, Nottinghamshire, NG23 6NW.
Owner: Lt. Col & Mrs Vere-Laurie   **Contact:** Lt. Col & Mrs Vere-Laurie
Mid 18th century house by Joseph Pocklington of Newark. Stables attributed to Carr of York.
Location: 7 m N of Newark off A1.
Opening Times: By appointment only.
Admission: House and Garden £2.50, Minimum charge for a party £15.00.

CASTLE MUSEUM & ART GALLERY

Tel: 01602 483504   **Fax:** 01602 350988

Nottingham, Nottinghamshire, NG1 6EL.
     Contact: The Curator
17th century with 13th century gateway, now a museum and art gallery.
Location: Centre of Nottingham.
Opening Times: Daily, 10.00am - 5.00pm. Closed Christmas Day and Boxing Day.
Admission: Weekdays free. Weekends: Adult £1.00, Child 50p, Conc for Passport to Leisure Holders. Joint ticket to Brewhouse Yard Museum.

CLUMBER PARK

Tel: 01909 476592

Clumber Park, Worksop, Nottinghamshire, S80 3AZ.
Owner: The National Trust   **Contact:** Visitor Liaison Officer
3,800 acres of parkland, farmland, lake and woodlands. The mansion was demolished in 1938, but the fine Gothic Revival Chapel, built 1886 - 89 for the 7th Duke of Newcastle, survives. Park includes the longest double lime avenue in Europe and a superb 80 acre lake. Also, classical bridge, temples, lawned Lincoln Terrace, pleasure grounds and stable block. Walled Garden including Victorian Apiary. Vineries and Tools exhibition.
Location: 4¹/₂m SE of Worksop, 6¹/₂m SW of Retford, 1m from A1/A57, 11m from M1 Junction 30.
Opening Times: Park: open all year during daylight hours. Walled Garden, Victorian Apiary, Fig House, Vineries & Garden Tools Exhibition: 1 Apr - end Sept: Sat, Sun & BH Mon 10.00am - 5.00pm, last admission 4.30pm. Conservation Centre: 1 Apr - 24 Sept: Sat, Sun & BH Mon 1.00pm - 5.00pm. Chapel: daily 10.00am - 4.00pm (closed Christmas Day).
Admission: Walled Garden, Victorian Apiary, Vineries & Garden Tools 60p.

HODSOCK PRIORY GARDENS

Tel: 01909 591204   **Fax:** 01909 591578

Blyth, Worksop, Nottinghamshire, S81 OTY.
Owner: Sir Andrew and Lady Buchanan   **Contact:** Lady Buchanan
A 5 acre private garden including a Domesday snowdrop site, daffodils and bluebell wood. Grade I listed gatehouse c.1500. Italianate terraces surrounding Victorian house (not open).
Location: Off B6045 Worksop to Blyth road.
Opening Times: Feb, Mon - Fri, 1.00pm - 4.00pm. Sat/Sun, 10.00am - 4.00pm. 2 April - 30 Jul, Sun, Tues, Wed, Thur, 2.00pm - 5.00pm (except late May BH w/e).
Admission: Adult £2.00, Child free, Groups 20 plus £1.80, 40 plus £1.60.

NEWSTEAD ABBEY

Tel: 01623 793557   **Fax:** 01623 797136

Linby, Nottinghamshire, NG15 8GE.
     Contact: Ms S Boiling
Historic home of the poet, Lord Byron, set in grounds of over 300 acres. Mementoes of Byron and decorated rooms from medieval to Victorian times.
Location: 12m N of Nottingham along A60 Mansfield Rd.
Opening Times: 1 Apr - 30 Sept, 12.00pm - 6.00pm, last admission 5.00pm. Grounds open all year except 24 Nov. Apr - Sept, 9.00am - 8.00pm. Oct - Mar, 9.00am - 5.00pm.
Admission: House & Grounds: Adult £3.50, Child £1.00, Conc £2.00. Grounds Only: Adult £1.60, Child £1.00, Conc £1.00.

NORWOOD PARK

Tel: 01636 812762   **Fax:** 01636 815649

Nottinghamshire, NG25 OPF.
Owner: Sir John Starkey   **Contact:** Lady Starkey
18th century family house, with private cricket ground.
Location: W of Southwell off Halam Rd.
Opening Times: Groups by appointment all year round.
Admission: Groups £3.00.

RUFFORD ABBEY

Tel: 01623 823148

Ollerton, Nottinghamshire.
Owner: English Heritage   **Contact:** The Administrator
A 12th century Cistercian abbey once largely concealed by a 17th century country house. Its demolition revealed the remains of the lay brothers' quarters.
Location: 2 m S of Ollerton off A614.
Opening Times: 1 Apr - 31 Oct daily, 10.00am - 5.00pm. 1 Nov - 31 Mar daily, 10.00am - 4.00pm. Closed 24 - 26 Dec, 1 Jan.

WINKBURN HALL

Tel: 01636 636465   **Fax:** 01636 636717

Winkburn, Newark, Nottinghamshire, NG22 8PQ.
Owner: Richard Craven-Smith-Milnes Esq   **Contact:** Richard Craven-Smith-Milnes Esq
A fine Carolean house recently restored, nestles besides a charming church.
Location: 8m W of Newark off A617.
Opening Times: Throughout the year by appointment only.
Admission: Standard £3.50.

WOLLATON HALL NATIONAL HISTORY MUSEUM

Tel: 01602 284602

Wollaton Park, Nottingham, Nottinghamshire, NG8 2AE.
Owner: Nottingham City Council   **Contact:** The Administrator
Flamboyant Elizabethan house built by Robert Smythson in a park, which despite being surrounded by Nottingham suburbs, remains attractively wild. Now used as a museum.
Location: Apr - Sept, Mon - Sat, 10.00am - 5.00pm. Sun 1.00pm - 5.00pm. Oct - Mar 10.00am - 4.30pm. Sun 1.30pm - 4.30pm.
Opening Times: Throughout the year by appointment only.
Admission: Weekdays free. Weekends & Bank holidays, Adults £1.00, Children 50p. Joint ticket for Wollaton Hall & Industrial Museum. Grounds 50p per car. Free orange badge holders.

SPECIAL EVENTS DIARY

- **24th-25th June: Holme Pierepont Hall**
  Flower & Garden Festival

 THE NATIONAL TRUST    ENGLISH HERITAGE   HISTORIC HOUSES ASSOCIATION

BLENHEIM PALACE
Oxfordshire

BLENHEIM PALACE, home of the 11th Duke of Marlborough and birthplace of Sir Winston Churchill, was built between 1705-1722 for John Churchill, 1st Duke of Marlborough, in grateful recognition of his magnificent victory at the Battle of Blenheim in 1704. One of England's largest private houses, Blenheim was built in the Baroque style by Sir John Vanbrugh and is considered his masterpiece. The land and £240,000 were given by Queen Anne and a grateful nation.

Blenheim's wonderful interior reveals striking contrasts - from the lofty Great Hall to gilded State rooms and the majestic Long Library. The superb collection includes fine paintings, furniture, bronzes and the famous Marlborough Victories tapestries. The five room Churchill Exhibition includes his birth room.

GARDENS
The Palace grounds reflect the evolution of grand garden design. Of the original work by Queen Anne's gardener. Henry Wise, only the Walled Garden remains; but dominating all is the superb landscaping of 'Capability' Brown. Dating from 1764, his work includes the lake, Park and Gardens. Achille Duchêne, employed by the 9th Duke, subsequently recreated the Great Court and built the Italian Garden on the east and The Water Terraces on the west of the Palace. Recently the Pleasure Gardens complex has been developed. This includes The Marlborough Maze, Herb Garden, Adventure Playground, Butterfly House and Putting Greens.

SUITABILITY FOR OTHER EVENTS
Corporate hospitality, including dinners and receptions, filming, equestrian events, craft fairs. Will consider any proposals.

EXTRA FACILITIES
Lake (rowing boats for hire), motor launch trips, train rides. Private tours may be pre-booked.

ADVICE TO COURIERS & DRIVERS
Advise Administrator of special requirements for groups over 100. Coaches/groups welcome without pre-booking. 'Notes for Party Organisers' available by post. Dogs on leash in Park. (Guide dogs only in House and Garden). Photography inside (no flash). Unlimited parking for cars and coaches.

CATERING
2 Restaurants, 2 Cafeterias. Group capacity 150. Groups can book for afternoon tea, buffets, lunches or dinners, menus available on request. Catering for private groups.
Further information/bookings: Catering Manager, (01993) 811274.

FACILITIES FOR THE DISABLED
Disabled or elderly visitors may alight at the Palace entrance and vehicles are then parked in allocated area. Toilet facilities in both the Palace and Park.

GUIDED TOURS
Tours included in the cost of entry. Guide Book £3.00.

GIFT SHOPS
Open 10.30am - 5.30pm also a Bookshop, Souvenir Stall and Garden Shop.

EDUCATION SERVICE
Welcome during normal hours. Full education service available, including visits to Palace, Park, Farm and Saw Mill. Also nature trail, lecture room and picnic hut. Holder of Sandford Award for Heritage Education since 1982. For details: Education Officer, (01993) 811091.

CONTACT

Paul F D Duffie FTS
Blenheim Palace
Woodstock
Oxon
OX20 1PX

Tel: (01993) 811091
Fax: (01993) 813527

LOCATION

From London, M40, A44
(1¹/₂ hrs), 8 mls N of
Oxford. London 63mls
Birmingham 54mls

Air: Heathrow Airport
60mls (1hr)

Coach: From London
(Victoria) to Oxford

Rail: Oxford Station

Bus: Oxford
(Cornmarket) -
Woodstock

OPENING TIMES

Summer
Mid March - 31 October

OPEN DAILY
10.30am-5.30pm
Last admission 4.45pm

Winter
1 Nov - Mid March
Park Only

The Duke of Marlborough reserves the right to close the Palace or Park or to amend admission prices without notice.

ADMISSION

• Palace Tour & Churchill Exhibition, Park, Garden, Butterfly House, Adventure Play Area, Motor Launch, Train, Car or Coach Parking, but not entry to the maze or rowing boat hire.

1995/6 Rates

Adult	£7.00
Child (5 - 15 yrs.)	£3.50
Child (16 & 17 yrs.)	£5.10
OAP	£5.10

Groups
Adult	£5.90
OAP	£4.90
Child (5 - 15 yrs.)	£4.90
Child (16 & 17 yrs.)	£3.00

• Blenheim Park, Butterfly House, Adventure Play Area, Train, Parking, but not entry to the Marlborough Maze or Rowing Boat Hire.

Coaches*	£17.50
Cars*	£4.00
Adult**	£1.00
Child**	£0.50

* Including occupants.
** Pedestrians.

• Private visits* . . £14.00
* By appointment only.
Min. charge of £280 (mornings and £420 (evenings)

CONFERENCE AND FUNCTION FACILITIES

ROOM	DIMENSIONS	CAPACITY	LAYOUT	POWER POINTS	SUITABLE FOR A/V
Spencer Churchill		80	Theatre	✓	✓
		60	Schoolroom		
		40	U-shape		
		40	Boardroom		
Great Hall	70' x 40'	150	Dinner	✓	✗
Saloon	50' x 30'	72	Dinner	✓	✗
(with Great Hall)		450	Reception		
Library	180' x 40'	300	Dinner	✓	✗

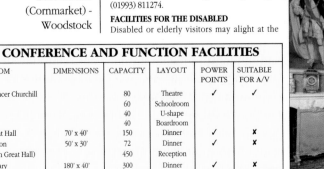

BROUGHTON CASTLE
Banbury

BROUGHTON CASTLE is essentially a family home lived in by Lord and Lady Saye and Sele and their family.

The original medieval Manor House, of which much remains today, was built in about 1300 by Sir John de Broughton. It stands on an island site surrounded by a 3 acre moat. The Castle was greatly enlarged between 1550 and 1600, at which time it was embellished with magnificent plaster ceilings, splendid panelling and fine fireplaces.

In the 17th Century William 8th Lord Saye and Sele, played a leading role in national affairs. He opposed Charles I's efforts to rule without Parliament and Broughton became a secret meeting place for the King's opponents.

During the Civil War William raised a regiment and he and his 4 sons all fought at the nearby Battle of Edgehill. After the battle the Castle was besieged and captured.

Arms and armour for the Civil War and from other periods are displayed in the Great Hall. Visitors may also see the Gatehouse, Gardens and Park together with the nearby 14th Century Church of St Mary, in which there are many family tombs, memorials and hatchments.

GARDENS
The garden areas consists of mixed herbaceous and shrub borders containing many old roses. In addition, there is a formal walled garden with beds of roses surrounded by box hedging and lined by more mixed borders.

❖

SUITABILITY FOR OTHER EVENTS
Broughton offers a most unusual setting for filming, product launches, advertising features, corporate events in Park.

ADVICE TO COURIERS & DRIVERS
Photography permitted for personal use. No dogs inside House. At busy times avoid Banbury and bring the group via Bloxham.

FACILITIES FOR THE DISABLED
Disabled visitors allowed vehicle access to main entrance

PARKING FOR COACHES & CARS
Capacity of the car park: 60 cars with unlimited overflow and 6 coaches with ample overflow. Both areas are 300 yards from the Castle.

CATERING
Tea Room available on open days. Tea/Coffee available for guided groups if pre-booked. Other meals by arrangement.

GUIDED TOURS
Available to pre-booked groups at no extra charge. Guided tours not available on open days.

GIFT SHOP
Open on public open days and also for pre-booked guided groups.

GUIDE BOOKS
Colour guide book, £1.00. Children's guide book, 50p. Brief notes are available in French, Spanish, Dutch, Italian, Japanese and German.

SCHOOL VISITS/CHILDREN
School visits welcomed. Children's guide books available. Children may try on armour, and look at household items of yesteryear.

CONTACT

Ms. J. Perkins
Broughton Castle
Banbury
Oxfordshire
OX15 5EB

Tel: (01295) 720041

LOCATION

Broughton Castle is 2 miles west of Banbury Cross on the B4035, Shipston on Stour - Banbury Road. Easily accessible from Stratford-on-Avon, Warwick, Oxford, Burford and the Cotswolds. M40 exit 11.

Rail: From London/ Birmingham to Banbury.

Bus: Local bus service to Banbury. At busy times the approach from the South through Bloxham may be preferable.

OPENING TIMES

Summer
18 May - 14 September

Weds   2.00 - 5.00pm

July & August
Thurs   2.00 - 5.00pm

Mon, Tues, Fri, Sat
Groups by appointment.

Sun   2.00 - 5.00pm

Bank Hol Sundays and Mondays, including Easter
2.00 - 5.00pm

Winter
Any time for pre-booked groups. Closed Christmas & New Year.

ADMISSION

Adult £3.50
Child (0-16) £1.50
OAP £3.00
Groups*
  Adult £3.00
  Child (0-16) £1.50
  OAP £3.00

* Min payment: adults £50.00 children £30.00.

KINGSTONE LISLE PARK
Wantage

KINGSTONE LISLE is a sensational Palladian House, home of the Lonsdale Family. The house is set in 140 acres of parkland. Superb views are enjoyed up to the Lambourn Downs where the Roman Ridgeway marks the southern boundary, Three spring-fed lakes beside the house complete this very attractive landscape.

The House built in 1677, is on the site of a fortified Castle which burnt down in 1620 (the original 12th century church is all that remains), The nearby Blowing Stone which according to legend was blown by King Alfred to muster his armies on the Downs is still in the village and can be blown by visitors during daylight hours.

The hall is in the style of Sir John Soane and there is a strong impression of entering an Italian Palazzo with beautiful ornate plaster ceilings, columns and figurines. By complete contrast the inner hall becomes the classical English country house, the most exciting feature being the Flying Staircase winding its way up, totally unsupported.

A fine collection of art, furniture, clocks, glass and needlework together with the architecture inspire visitors with admiration for the craftsmanship that has existed in Britain over the centuries.

GARDENS
Twelve acres of gardens include a shrubbery, pleached limes, an avenue leading up to an ornamental pond and a replica of Queen Mary's rose garden in Regents Park.

❖

OPENING TIMES

17 April, 8 May, 29 May 28 August

1.30pm - 5.00pm

ADMISSION

Summer
Adult £5.00
Child (Under 16) . . .Free
Fishing only £5.00
Groups of 20 or more 10% discount by prior arrangement only.

CONTACT

The Secretary
Kingstone Lisle Park
Wantage
Oxfordshire
OX12 9QG

Tel: (01367) 820599

Fax: (01367) 820749

LOCATION

From London 76 miles, M4 Junct. 14.
From Oxford A420, 20 miles

Air: Heathrow Airport approx 1 hour via M4.

Rail: To Didcot where taxis are available.

SUITABILITY FOR OTHER EVENTS
Filming and photography; shooting parties; exclusive house parties; dinner bed and breakfast by arrangement.

EXTRA FACILITIES
Holiday Accomodation. Trout fishing all year round. Coarse fishing (seasonal). Private 9 hole golf practice course.

ADVICE TO COURIERS & DRIVERS
Alternative accommodation available at the Blowing Stone Inn in the village.

FACILITIES FOR THE DISABLED
Disabled and elderly visitors may alight at the entrance to the property. There are no toilets for the disabled.

PARKING FOR COACHES & CARS
Capacity of the car park: 25 cars, 30 yards from the House, and 3 coaches, 10 yards from the House.

CATERING
Lunch and dinner parties available strictly by arrangement for up to 30 people in the superb formal dining room.

GUIDED TOURS
On the hour at 2, 3 and 4.00pm on open days.

GUIDE BOOKS
Colour guide book, £2.00.

CONFERENCE AND FUNCTION FACILITIES

ROOM	DIMENSIONS	CAPACITY	LAYOUT	POWER POINTS	SUITABLE FOR A/V
Dining Room	22' x 35'	22	Boardroom	✓	✓
		100	Buffet		
		40	Lunch/Dinner		
Ballroom	34' x 21'	150	Theatre	✓	✓
Hall	22' x 38'	130	Theatre	✓	✓
Drawing Room	35' x 21'	150	Theatre	✓	✓

STONOR
Henley-on-Thames

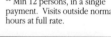

Stonor, family home of Lord and Lady Camoys and the Stonor family for over 800 years, is set in a valley in the beautiful woods of the Chiltern Hills and surrounded by an extensive deer park.

The earliest part of the house dates from the 12th Century, whilst most of the house was built in the 14th Century. Early use of brick in Tudor times resulted in a more uniform facade concealing the earlier buildings, and changes to the windows and the roof in the 18th Century reflect the Georgian appearance still apparent today.

Inside, the house shows strong Gothic decoration, also from the 18th Century, and contains many items of rare furniture, sculptures, bronzes, tapestries, paintings and portraits of the family from Britain, Europe and America.

The Catholic Chapel used continuously through the reformation is sited close by a pagan stone circle. In 1581, Stonor served as a sanctuary for St Edmund Campion, and an exhibition at the house features his life and work.

GARDENS

Extensive gardens enclosed at the rear of the house face South and have fine views over the park. The springtime display of daffodils is particularly outstanding.

For 1995 the garden will feature a display of stone sculpture from Zimbabwe

❖

SUITABILITY FOR OTHER EVENTS
Grounds available for filming, craft fairs, car displays, product promotion, clay pigeon shooting.

EXTRA FACILITIES
Coffee for morning tours, by arrangement. There are also a limited number of evening tours and buffet suppers, also by prior arrangement. Lectures can be given on the property, its contents and history.

ADVICE TO COURIERS & DRIVERS
Admissions from groups must be by single payment on arrival unless prior arrangements are made for payment with vouchers. No dogs except on leads and not allowed within the House, tearoom or shop. No smoking in House, tearoom or shop. No photography in House.

FACILITIES FOR THE DISABLED
Disabled and elderly visitors may be left at the entrance to the house before parking. There are no toilets for the disabled, although access to the toilets is level. Ramp access to gardens, tearoom and shop.

PARKING FOR COACHES & CARS
Capacity of the Car Park: unlimited area for cars and space for 30 coaches, 100 yards from the House.

CATERING
Groups can book lunch or supper. Afternoon Teas are available during all open times without prior booking. Menus available upon request.

GUIDED TOURS
Guided tours are available outside normal public hours. From 20 to 60 people can be taken round at any one time. Tour takes $1\frac{1}{4}$-$1\frac{1}{2}$ hours.

GIFT SHOP
Open for same hours as the House. Selection of Stonor and general souvenirs.

GUIDE BOOKS
Colour guide book, with separate handlist of contents, price £2.00

SCHOOL VISITS/CHILDREN
School groups are welcome, cost £2.00 per head. Lectures and guided tours by arrangement.

CONTACT

D Boddy
Stonor Park
Henley-on-Thames
Oxfordshire
RG9 6HF

Tel: (01491) 638587

Fax: (01491) 638587

LOCATION

1 hour from London, M4 to Junct. 8/9. A4130 to Henley-on-Thames, then A4130/B480 to Stonor.

Bus: 3 miles along the Oxford - London route.

Rail: Henley-on-Thames Station 5 miles.

OPENING TIMES

Summer
April - September
Sunday: 2.00 - 5.30pm
Mons: Bank Hols only
12.30 - 5.30pm
Tues: Groups by appointment
Weds: April, only by appointment
May - Sept 2.00 - 5.30pm
Thurs: Jul & Aug
2.00 - 5.30pm
Other times by appointment
Fris: Closed
Sat: Aug: 2.00 - 5.30pm

Winter
October - March
Closed

ADMISSION

HOUSE & GARDEN
Adult £4.00
Child (under 14) . . .Free
Concessions* . . .£3.65
Groups** £3.40

GARDENS ONLY
Adult £2.00

* National Trust and English Heritage members,. HHA FREE.
** Min 12 persons, in a single payment. Visits outside normal hours at full rate.

ARDINGTON HOUSE
Tel: 01235 833244

Wantage, Oxfordshire, OX12 8QA.
Owner: Mrs D C N Baring   **Contact:** Mrs D C N Baring
Early 18th century exceptionally fine brickwork hall with imperial staircase, panelled dining room with plasterwork ceiling. Attractive garden and stable yard. Guided tours by members of the family.
Location: 12m S of Oxford, 12m N of Newbury, 2$\frac{1}{2}$m E of Wantage.
Opening Times: May to Sept, Mons and all Bank Hols 2.30pm - 4.30pm. Parties welcomed by appointment.
Admission: House and Gardens £2.00, Small supper parties, coffee & tea by arrangement.

BLENHEIM PALACE
See page 149 for full page entry.

BROUGHTON CASTLE
See page 150 for full page entry.

BUSCOT OLD PARSONAGE
Tel: 01494 528051

Buscot, Faringdon, Oxfordshire, SN7 8DQ.
Owner: The National Trust   **Contact:** The Tenant
An early 18th century house of Cotswold stone on the bank of the Thames with a small garden.
Location: 2m from Lechlade, 4m from Faringdon on A417.
Opening Times: Apr - end Oct, Wed only 2.00pm - 6.00pm by appointment.
Admission: £1.00. Not suitable for parties.

BUSCOT PARK
Tel: 01367 242094

Buscot, Faringdon, Oxfordshire, SN7 8DQ.
Owner: The National Trust   **Contact:** Lord Faringdon
A late 18th century house with pleasure gardens, set within a park.
Location: Between Lechlade and Faringdon on A417.
Opening Times: Apr - end Sept (including Good Fri, Easter Sat & Sun): Wed to Fri 2.00pm - 6.00pm. Also open every 2nd and 4th weekend 2.00pm - 6.00pm.
Admission: House & Grounds £4.00, Grounds only £3.00. No reduction for parties, which must book in advance.

CHRIST CHURCH CATHEDRAL
Tel: 01865 276154

The Sacristy, The Cathedral, Oxford, OX1 1DP.
    Contact: Jim Godfrey
12th century Norman Church, formerly an Augustinian monastery, given Cathedral status in 16th century by Henry VIII. Also the college chapel for Christ Church, the largest of the Oxford Colleges.
Location: City centre, off St Aldates. Entry via Meadow Gate visitors entrance on south side of college.
Opening Times: Mon - Sat 9.00am - 5.00pm. Sun 1.00pm - 5.00pm, closed Christmas Day. Services: weekdays 7.20am, 6.00pm. Sun 8.00am, 10.00am, 11.15am, 6.00pm.
Admission: Adult £2.50, Child £1.00, Child under 10 free, Concessions £1.00.

COGGES MANOR FARM MUSEUM
Tel: 01993 772602   **Fax:** 01993 703056

Church Lane, Witney, Oxfordshire, OX8 6LA.
    Contact: Ms C Mason
The manor house and farm buildings with walled gardens are run as a museum to show life at the turn of this century. Daily cooking demonstrations on the kitchen range.
Location: Just off A40 Oxford - Burford Road.
Opening Times: Tues - Fri 10.30am - 5.30pm. Sat and Sun, 12.00pm - 5.30pm. Open BH Mons. Closed Good Fri. Early closing in Oct.
Admission: Adult £3.00, Child £1.50, Family £8.00, Conc £1.75.

DEDDINGTON CASTLE

Deddington, Oxfordshire.
Owner: English Heritage   **Contact:** The Administrator
Extensive earthworks concealing the remains of a 12th century castle which was ruined as early as the 14th century.
Location: S of B4031 on E side of Deddington, 17m N of Oxford on A423.
Opening Times: Any reasonable time.

DITCHLEY PARK
Tel: 01608 677346

Enstone, Oxfordshire, OX7 4ER.
Owner: Ditchley Foundation   **Contact:** Brigadier Michael Willis
The most important house by James Gibbs with most distinguished interiors by Henry Flitcroft and William Kent. Ditchley was a regular weekend retreat for Churchill during the Second World War.
Location: 2m from Charlbury.
Opening Times: Telephone for further details.
Admission: Adult £3.00, Child £1.50, Family £8.00, Conc £1.75.

GREAT COXWELL BARN
Tel: 01494 528051

Great Coxwell, Faringdon, Oxfordshire.
Owner: The National Trust   **Contact:** The Administrator
A 13th century monastic barn, stone built with stone tiled roof, which has an interesting timber construction.
Location: 2m SW of Faringdon between A420 and B4019.
Opening Times: All year, daily at reasonable hours.
Admission: 50p.

GREYS COURT
Tel: 01491 628529

Rotherfield Greys, Henley-on-Thames, Oxfordshire, RG9 4PG.
Owner: The National Trust   **Contact:** The Custodian
Rebuilt in the 16th century and added to in the 17th, 18th and 19th centuries, the house is set amid the remains of the courtyard walls and towers of a 14th century fortified house. A Tudor donkey wheel well-house and an ice house are still intact, and the garden contains Archbishop's Maze, inspired by Archbishop Runcie's enthronement speech in 1980.
Location: 3m W of Henley-on-Thames, E of B481.
Opening Times: Apr - end Sept. House: Mon, Wed & Fri 2pm - 6pm (closed Good Fri). Garden: daily except Thur & Sun 2pm - 6pm (closed Good Fri) Last admission 5.30pm.
Admission: House & Garden: £4.00, Family £10.00. Garden only: £3.00, Family £7.50. No reduction for coach parties who must book.

KINGSTON BAGPUIZE HOUSE

OPEN

1 Apr - 30 Sept
Sun & Bank
Hol. Mons.
2.30 - 5.30pm

Groups by
written
appointment on
Weekdays only

Tel: 01865 820259

ABINGDON, OXFORDSHIRE OX13 5AX

Owner: The Lord & Lady Tweedsmuir   *Contact:* The Lady Tweedmuir
This Charles II manor house was built before 1670 in the style of Inigo Jones. It has a fine cantilevered staircase, and panelled rooms with some good furniture and pictures. The large garden contains many unusual trees and shrubs. There are attractive 17th century stables and outbuildings. Visitors are shown round the House by the family and their friends.
Location: In Kingston Bagpuize village, off A415 Abingdon Road near A415/A420 bypass intersection. Abingdon 5 miles, Oxford 9 miles.
Admission: House & Garden: Adult £3.00. OAP £2.50, Child £2.00.
Garden only: £1.00 (child under 5 - Free to garden but not House).
Group rates on request.

KINGSTON LISLE PARK
See page 151 for full page entry.

MAPELDURHAM HOUSE
Tel: 01734 723350

Reading, Oxfordshire, RG4 7TR.
Owner: J J Eyston Esq   **Contact:** J J Eyston Esq
A beautiful late 16th century Elizabethan Manor House set in tranquil surroundings alongside the River Thames. Original plasterwork ceilings and grand oak staircases.
Location: 4 m NW of Reading.
Opening Times: Opening times not available at time of going to press.

MILTON MANOR

OPEN

Easter - 30 Sept
Sundays only plus
Bank Holiday
Weekends
(Sat, Sun Mons)

August
Daily except Mondays
12 Noon - 5.00pm

House open for
guided tours only at
12 Noon, 2.30pm
& 3.30pm

Tel: 01235 831287
Fax: As phone

MILTON MANOR, OXFORDSHIRE

Owner: *Anthony Mockler-Barrett*   **Contact:** *Lady Grayson*

Extraordinarily attractive Restoration house, traditionally designed by Inigo Jones with a celebrated Gothick library and a beautiful chapel. Seat of the Barrett family for six generations. Pleasing and relaxed atmosphere, maturely wooded grounds, stables, walled garden, dovecote, animals, woodland walk, picturesque little temple by the back lake. Plenty to see and enjoy for all ages.
Location: Off A34 signposted; 9 miles south of Oxford.
Admission: House & Gardens: Adult £3.00, Child £1.50.
Grounds only: Adult £1.50, Child 75p. Free parking.
Groups by arrangement throughout year.

MINSTER LOVELL & DOVECOTE

Tel: 01993 775315

Witney, Oxfordshire.
Owner: English Heritage   **Contact:** The Administrator
The ruins of Lord Lovell's 15th century manor house stand in a lovely setting on the banks of the River Windrush.
Location: Adjacent to Minster Lovell Church, 3m W of Witney off A40.
Opening Times: 1 Apr - 30 Sept, daily 10am - 6pm. 1 Oct - 31 Mar, daily 10am - 4pm.
Admission: Free. (Keykeeper).

PRIORY COTTAGES

Tel: 01494 528051

1 Mill Street, Steventon, Abingdon, Oxfordshire, OX13 6SP.
Owner: The National Trust   **Contact:** The Tenant
Former monastic buildings, converted into two houses. South Cottage contains the Great Hall of the original priory.
Location: 4m S of Abingdon, on B4017 off A34 at Abingdon West or Milton interchange on corner of The Causeway and Mill Street, entrance in Mill Street.
Opening Times: The Great Hall in South Cottage only: Apr - end Sept: Wed, 2.00pm - 6.00pm by written appointment.
Admission: £1.00, no reduction for parties.

ROUSHAM HOUSE

Tel: 01869 347110 / 360407

Steeple Aston, Oxfordshire, OX5 3QX.
Owner: Charles Cotterell-Dormer Esq   **Contact:** Charles Cotterell-Dormer Esq
Rousham represents the first stage of English landscape design and remains almost as William Kent (1685 - 1748) left it. One of the few gardens of this date to have escaped alteration. Includes Venus' Vale, Townesend's Building, seven arched Praeneste, the Temple of the Mill and a sham ruin known as the 'Eyecatcher'. The house was built in 1635 by Sir Robert Dormer.
Location: E of A4260 S of B4030.
Opening Times: House; Apr - Sept, Wed, Sun and BHs 2.00pm - 4.30pm. Garden; All year, daily, 10.00am - 4.30pm.
Admission: Garden: Adult £2.50. **No children under 15.**

STANTON HARCOURT MANOR

OPEN

Thurs, Sun and
Bank Hol Mon.
April: 16, 17, 27, 30.
May: 1, 7, 8, 11, 14,
25, 28, 29
June: 8, 11, 22, 25
July: 6, 9, 20, 23
Aug: 10, 13, 24,
27, 28
Sept: 7, 10, 21, 24
2.00 - 6.00pm

Tel: 01865 881928

STANTON HARCOURT, NR. WITNEY, OXFORDSHIRE OX8 1RJ

Owner: *Mr Crispin & The Hon Mrs Gascoigne*   **Contact:** *Mrs. S. J. Pauling*

12 acres of garden with Great Fish Pond and Stew Ponds provide tranquil surroundings for the unique mediaeval buildings - old Kitchen (Alexander) Pope's Tower and domestic Chapel. The House, a fine example of a very early unfortified house built to house the Harcourt family and its retainers, is still maintained as the family home.
Location: 9 miles west of Oxford, 5 miles south east of Witney off B4449, between Eynsham and Standlake.
Admission: House & Gardens: Adult £3.00, Child (under 12) /OAP £2.00
Gardens: Adult £1.50, Child (under 12) /OAP £1.00
Coaches by prior arrangement.

STONOR

See page 152 for full page entry.

RYCOTE CHAPEL

Tel: 01869 347110 / 360407

Rycote, Oxfordshire.
Owner: English Heritage   **Contact:** The Administrator
A 15th century chapel with exquisitely carved and painted woodwork.
Location: 3 m SW of Thame, off A329.
Opening Times: 1 Apr - 30 Sept 2.00pm - 6.00pm, Sat & Sun only.
Admission: Adult £1.30, Child 70p, Conc £1.00.

UNIVERSITY OF OXFORD BOTANIC GARDENS

Tel: 01865 276920

Rose Lane, Oxford, Oxfordshire, OX1 4AX.

Contact: Timothy Walker Esq
Location: E end of High St, on the banks of River Cherwell.
Opening Times: 9.00am - 5.00pm (4.30pm in winter). Greenhouses 2.00pm - 6.00pm.
Admission: £1.00 during summer months per person, otherwise free. Guided tours by appointment only at £2.35 per person.

WATERPERRY GARDENS

Tel: 01844 339254/226 **Fax:** 01844 339883

Wheatley, Oxford, Oxfordshire, OX33 1JL.
Owner: W Piercel Esq   **Contact:** W Piercel Esq
Location: Junction 8 on M40, 3m from Wheatley.
Opening Times: Mar - Oct, Mon - Fri 10.00am - 5.30pm. Sat and Sun, 10.00am - 6.00pm. Nov - Feb, 10.00am - 5.00pm. 13 - 16 Jul open only for visitors to Art in Action.
Admission: Adult £2.20, Child 10 - 16 £1.00 (under 16 free), Family of 2+2 £5.00, Senior citizens £1.70, Groups of 20+ £1.60.

SPECIAL EVENTS DIARY

- **6th - 8th May: Blenheim Palace**
  Craft Fair.
- **28th June: Blenheim Palace**
  Charity Cricket Match.
- **4th June: Stonor**
  VW Car Rally (9am-6pm) Display of VW cars especially Beetles. Trade Stands. Contests for cars and drivers.
- **8th - 9th July: Blenheim Palace**
  Courtyard Concert.
- **14th July: Blenheim Palace**
  Stately Homes Festival Concert (Palace).

- **29th - 30th: Blenheim Palace**
  Music & Fireworks Concerts (Park).
- **11th - 13th July: Blenheim Palace**
  Outdoor Concerts (Park)
- **25th - 28th July: Stonor**
  Chilterns Craft Show (daily 10am-6pm) 250 exhibitors demonstrating and selling.
- **26th - 28th July: Blenheim Palace**
  Craft Fair.
- **14th - 17th: Blenheim Palace**
  Blenheim International Horse Trials.

HAWKSTONE PARK
Nr Shrewsbury

HAWKSTONE PARK, with its well hidden pathways, concealed grottos, secret tunnels and magical collection of follies is truly unique. It is a forgotten masterpiece; originally one of the most visited landscapes in Britain and now the only Grade 1 landscape in Shropshire.

Sir Roland Hill started it all in the 18th century with his son Richard 'The Great Hill', arranging for some 15 miles of paths and some of the best collections of follies in the world to be constructed in the grounds of their ancestral home. At the turn of the 19th century the Hills could no longer accommodate the growing number of sightseers to the Hall. As a result an Inn, which is now Hawkstone Park Hotel, was opened and guided tours were organised. Little has changed since then. The Park is full of attractions, surprises and features. You can see dramatic cliffs and rocks, towers, monuments, tunnels. passageways, precipice rocks, paths, rustic sofas, romantic secret valleys. It takes around three hours to complete the whole tour of the Park. From the Green House you embark upon a unique experience. Paths, steps, walls, even the Greek Urn, were put in place during the busy period at Hawkstone Park. Caves and seats, handy resting places for the weary visitor, were hewn into the rock face.

At the top of the Terrace sits a folly, the White Tower. Close by is the Monument, a 112 foot column, at the top of which stands the new statue of Sir Roland Hill, the first protestant Lord Mayor of London. The seemingly endless numbers of tracks leading from the Terrace will tempt visitors off the straight and narrow perhaps to the Swiss Bridge or to St. Francis' Cave or the Fox's Nob.

The tour then continues from the bottom of the Terrace to Grotto Hill via Gingerbread Hall and the magnificent Serpentine Tunnel and cleft which leads to the longest grotto passageway in Europe.

After admiring the breathtaking view from the top of Grotto Hill you slowly make your way back towards the entrance but not before passing the Hermits Cave. One admission price covers entrance to the entire Park.

CONTACT

K Darville-Smith
Hawkstone Park
Weston-under-Redcastle
Nr Shrewsbury
Shropshire
SY4 SUY

Tel: (01939) 200300

Fax: (01939) 200311

LOCATION

12 miles north of Shrewsbury off A49
3 miles from Hodnet off A53/A442
M6 to M54 either A49, A41, A442

Rail: Shrewsbury Station, 12 miles

Wem Station, 7 miles

OPENING TIMES

Summer
1 April - 31 October

PARK
Daily from 10.00am
10.00am - 6.00pm in July and August.

Winter
Park Closed. Except for December weekends for Father Christmas visits in the caves.

Hotel open all year round.

ADMISSION

Adult £4.00
Child £2.00
OAP/Student £3.00
Family £11.00
(2 adults + 3 children)

Groups discounts
(min 12 people)
Adult, Child and OAP
50p off normal admission prices.

SUITABILITY FOR OTHER EVENTS
Suitable for a wide variety of events including golf tournaments, film/TV location work, festivals, musical events and craft fairs.

EXTRA FACILITIES
Golf courses (2 x 18 hole) and academy course and practice ground, driving range, residential golf school, video analysis room, clay pigeon shooting, archery.

ADVICE TO COURIERS & DRIVERS
Parking/ refreshments free for drivers. Dogs on a lead. and cameras permitted. Bring sensible shoes.

FACILITIES FOR THE DISABLED
Limited. Disabled toilets. The walk is not suitable for frail or disabled.

CATERING
Tea Room open all day tea/coffee sandwiches, snacks, salads, cakes. Restaurant available at Hotel (adjacent) serving snacks, grills and a full a la carte menu.

GUIDED TOURS
By arrangement only. Maps are provided.

GIFT SHOP
Open daily. Excellent range of souvenirs traditional Gifts/Toys.

GUIDE BOOKS
Maps Free. Guide Books £3.50.

SCHOOL VISITS / CHILDREN
Very welcome. £1.50 per child, teacher free in 1:10 ration **OR** £2.00 per child with free use of classroom and picnic area and free monument cut out, teachers free in 1:10 ratio.

CONFERENCE AND FUNCTION FACILITIES

ROOM	DIMENSIONS	CAPACITY	LAYOUT	POWER POINTS	SUITABLE FOR A/V
Waterloo	15.45 x 10m	200	Theatre/ reception	10	✓
Wellington	6.1 x 7.62m	50	Theatre/ reception	4	✓
Redcastle	12.2 x 8.8m	100	Theatre/ reception	16	✓
Hill	8.5 x 7m	50	Theatre/ reception	8	✓

OAKLEY HALL
Market Drayton

OAKLEY HALL is situated in magnificent countryside on the boundary of Shropshire and Staffordshire. The present Hall is a fine example of a Queen Anne mansion house and was built on the site of an older dwelling mentioned in the Domesday Survey of 1085. Oakley Hall was the home of the Chetwode family until it was finally sold in 1919.

GARDENS

Set in 100 acres of rolling parkland, the Hall commands superb views over the surrounding countryside and the gardens include wild areas in addition to the more formal parts.

Oakley Hall is a privately owned family house and since it is not open to the general public it provides a perfect location for exclusive private or corporate functions. The main hall can accommodate 120 people comfortably and has excellent acoustics for concerts. The secluded location and unspoilt landscape make Oakley an ideal setting for filming and photography.

The surrounding countryside is rich in historical associations. St. Mary's Church at Mucklestone, in which parish the Hall stands, was erected in the 13th Century and it was from the tower of this Church that Queen Margaret of Anjou observed the Battle of Blore Heath in 1459. This was a brilliant victory for the Yorkist faction in the Wars of the Roses and the blacksmith at Mucklestone was reputed to have shod the Queen's horse back to front in order to disguise her escape.

❖

SUITABILITY FOR OTHER EVENTS
Concerts, conferences, wedding receptions, fashion shows, product launches, seminars, clay pigeon shooting, garden parties and filming.

EXTRA FACILITIES
Grand piano, hard tennis court, croquet lawn, horse riding.

CONFERENCE FACILITIES
See below for rooms available. Slide projector, word processor, fax and secretarial assistance are all available by prior arrangement.

ACCOMMODATION
3 double and one twin bedroom with baths.

ADVICE TO COURIERS & DRIVERS
No stiletto heels. No dogs.

FACILITIES FOR THE DISABLED
Disabled and elderly visitors may alight at the entrance to the Hall, before parking in the allocated areas. There are toilet facilities for the disabled at the newly-refurbished stable block.

PARKING FOR COACHES & CARS
Parking for 100 cars, 100/200 yds from the Hall.

CATERING
Buffets, lunches and dinners can all be arranged for large or small groups, using high quality local caterers.

GROUP VISITS
By prior arrangement groups will be met and entertained by members of the Fisher family.

CONTACT

Mrs Ann E Fisher
Oakley Hall
Market Drayton
Shropshire
TF9 4AG

Tel: (01630) 653472
Fax: (01630) 653282

LOCATION

From London 3hrs: M1, M6 to exit 14, then A5013 to Eccleshall, turn right at T-junction, 200 yards, then left onto B5026. Mucklestone is 1³/₄ mls from Logger-heads on B5026. Turn left before Church, to end of lane then right. 200 yards turn left into small lane opposite telephone kiosk. Bear left between two lodges.

OPENING TIMES

All Year

Not open to the public. The house is available all year round for private or corporate events.

ADMISSION

Please telephone for details.

CONFERENCE AND FUNCTION FACILITIES

ROOM	DIMENSIONS	CAPACITY	LAYOUT	POWER POINTS	SUITABLE FOR A/V
Hall	50' x 30'	130	Theatre	10	✓
		130	Buffet		
		150	Lunch/Dinner		
Dining Room	40' x 27'	80	Theatre	6	✓
		30	U-shape		
		20	Boardroom		
		60	Buffet		
		80	Lunch/Dinner		
Ballroom	40' x 27'	80	Theatre	6	✓
		30	U-shape		
		20	Boardroom		
		60	Buffet		

WESTON PARK
Near Shifnal

WESTON PARK has been the home of successive generations of the Earls of Bradford since the 12th Century and is today owned by a charity, 'The Weston Park Foundation'.

The present House was built on the site of the original medieval Manor House in 1671 and was designed by Lady Elizabeth Wilbraham. It boasts a fine collection of paintings with works by Stubbs, Van Dyck, Holbein, Gainsborough and Lely. The contents of the House, brought together by the family over the centuries, include some fine examples of 18th Century English and European furniture, rare Parisian tapestries from the Gobelin factory and porcelain collections.

The House stands in 1,000 acres of formal gardens, arboretum and parkland designed by the 'Capability' Brown. Particular features are the Italian Broderie and the Rose Garden of the South Terrace.

The Park now houses numerous visitor attractions, including a Woodland Adventure Playground, Miniature Railway and Pets Corner.

An extensive programme of events is held each season, and includes Classical Concerts, Horse Trials and the Midland Game & Country Sports Fair. Further details available from Weston Park.

❖

SUITABILITY FOR OTHER EVENTS
Residential parties, special dinners, wedding receptions, conferences, product launches, outdoor concerts and events, filming location.
Weston Park offers a full event organisation service.

EXTRA FACILITIES
Helipad and airstrip. Wide variety of sporting activities organised for private groups eg Clay Pigeon Shooting, Archery, Hovercrafts, Rally Driving..

ACCOMMODATION
Weston Park offers 19 delightful bedrooms with bathrooms, 15 doubles/twins, 3 singles and 1 three-bedded suite.

ADVICE TO COURIERS & DRIVERS
Dogs must always be kept on leads. Interior photography by prior arrangement only.

PARKING FOR COACHES & CARS
There is unlimited parking at the front door for cars and coaches containing private parties. There is a public car and coach park 100 yards from the property.

FACILITIES FOR THE DISABLED
House and part of the grounds accessible by wheelchair. There are toilets for the disabled.

CATERING
The Old Stables Restaurant & Tea Room provides meals and snacks on public open days.
Dine and Stay arrangements in the House on selected dates.

GIFT EMPORIUM
Open at the same time as the Park.

GUIDE BOOKS
Colour guide book, £1.00.

SCHOOL VISITS/CHILDREN
Weston Park is open on Tuesdays, Wednesdays and Thursdays in the latter half of June and all July. Advance booking is essential. Cost per child £1.50. Teachers' guidance notes and National Curriculum related Workpacks available.

CONTACT

Park: Helen Howat
House: Andy Sinclair
Weston Park
Nr Shifnal
Shropshire
TF11 8LE

Tel: (01952) 850207

Fax: (01952) 850430

LOCATION

Birmingham 30 minutes. Manchester 1 hour. Motorway access - Junct. 12 M6 or Junct. 3 M54. House situated on A5.

Rail: Nearest Railway Stations - Wolverhampton or Stafford.

Air: Birmingham

OPENING TIMES

Summer
Easter - mid June
Bank Hols & Weekends

Mid June - End July
Daily, except Mon & Fri.

August Daily

September
Weekends only

HOUSE   1.00 - 5.00pm
PARK   11am - 7.00pm

Winter
October - Easter
Closed

NB Visitors are advised to telephone first to check this information.

ADMISSION

HOUSE & GARDEN
Adult £5.00
Child (3 - 16yrs.) . .£3.50
OAP £3.75

GARDEN ONLY
Adult £3.00
Child (3 - 16yrs.) . .£2.00
OAP £2.50

CONFERENCE AND FUNCTION FACILITIES

ROOM	DIMENSIONS	CAPACITY	LAYOUT	POWER POINTS	SUITABLE FOR A/V
Dining Room	52' x 23'	40 - 150	Various	15	
Orangery	51' x 20'	40 - 150	Various	12	
Music Room	50' x 20'	30 - 100	Various	24	✓
The Old Stables	58' x 20'	30 - 95	Various	4	✓
Conference Room	40' x 7'6"	20 - 60	Various	14	✓

ACTON BURNELL CASTLE

Acton Burnell, Shrewsbury, Shropshire.
Owner: English Heritage   **Contact:** The Administrator
The warm red sandstone shell of a fortified 13th century manor house.
Location: In Acton Burnell, on unclassified road 8m S of Shrewsbury.
Opening Times: Any reasonable time.

ADCOTE
Tel: 01939 260202   **Fax:** 01939 261300

Little Ness, Shrewsbury, Shropshire, SY4 2JY.
Owner: Arlcote School Educational Trust Ltd   **Contact:** Mrs S Cecchet
Designed by Norman Shaw. The most controlled, coherent and masterly of his big country houses. Now used as a school.
Location: 7m NW of Shrewsbury.
Opening Times: 19 Apr - 7 Jul, (except 28 May - 1 Jun), 2.00pm - 5.00pm. Re-opens 5 Sept - 15 Oct.
Admission: Free, but the Governors reserve the right to make a charge.

ATTINGHAM PARK
Tel: 01743 709203

Shrewsbury, Shropshire, SY4 4TP.
Owner: The National Trust   **Contact:** The Administrator
An elegant neo-classical mansion of the late 18th century with magnificent state rooms, Italian furniture, Regency silver and impressive picture collection. The deer park was landscaped by Humphry Repton. There are good walks along the river and through the park all year.
Location: 4m SE of Shrewsbury, on N side of Telford road B4380, formerly A5, from M54 B5061, then B4380.
Opening Times: House: 1 Apr - 27 Sept, Sat to Wed, 1.30pm - 5.00pm.; BH Mon 11.00am - 5.00pm; also Oct: Sat & Sun 1.30pm - 5.00pm. Last admission 4.30pm. Deer Park & Grounds: daily (except Christmas Day) dawn to dusk.
Admission: House & Park: Adult £3.50, Family £8.70. Park & Grounds only £1.40. Pre-booked parties £2.50.

BENTHALL HALL
Tel: 01952 882159

Shrewsbury, Shropshire, SY4 4TP.
Owner: The National Trust   **Contact:** Mr & Mrs J Benthall
A 16th century stone house with mullioned windows and moulded brick chimneys. The interior includes intricately carved oak staircase, decorated plaster ceilings and oak panelling, also family collections of furniture, ceramics and paintings. Carefully restored plantsman's garden. Restoration church.
Location: 1m NW of Broseley (B4375), 4m NE of Much Wenlock, 6m S of Wellington.
Opening Times: 2 Apr - 27 Sept: Wed, Sun & BH Mon, 1.30pm - 5.30pm. Last admission 5.00pm. Parties by prior arrangement.
Admission: £3.00, reduced rates for booked parties. Garden £2.00.

BUILDWAS ABBEY
Tel: 01952 433274

Shropshire
Owner: English Heritage   **Contact:** Mr & Mrs J Benthall
Extensive remains of a Cistercian abbey built in 1135. The remains include the church which is almost complete except for the roof.
Location: On S bank of River Severn on B4378, 2 m W of Iron Bridge.
Opening Times: 1 Apr - 30 Sept, daily, 10.00am - 6.00pm.
Admission: Adult £1.30, Child 70p, Conc £1.00. Lunchtime closure 1.00pm - 2.00pm.

CLIVE HOUSE MUSEUM
Tel: 01743 354811

College Hill, Shrewsbury, Shropshire, SY1 1LT.
Owner: Shrewsbury and Atcham Borough Council   **Contact:** Mrs M White
Period room settings and displays in a town house briefly associated with Robert, Lord Clive (Clive of India).
Location: Town centre, close to TIC.
Opening Times: Tues - Sat: 10.00am - 4.00pm, Summer Suns: 11.00am - 4.00pm.
Admission: Adult £1.00, Child 50p, OAP/Student £1.00, parties 10% discount.

CLUN CASTLE

Clun, Ludlow, Shropshire.
Owner: English Heritage   **Contact:** The Administrator
Remains of a four storey keep and other buildings of this border Castle are set in outstanding countryside. Built in the 11th century.
Location: In Clun, off A488, 18m W of Ludlow.
Opening Times: Any reasonable time.

DUDMASTON HALL

OPEN

29 Mar - 1 Oct
Weds & Suns
2.00 - 5.30pm
Thursdays booked
parties by
arrangement
2.00 - 5.30pm

Tea room
1.00 - 2.00pm
Light lunches
2.00 - 5.30pm teas

Tel: 01746 780866

QUATT, BRIDGNORTH, SHROPSHIRE WV15 6QN
Owner: National Trust   *Contact:* The Property Manager
Late 17th century Manor house, home of Sir George & Lady Labouchere. Contains furniture and china, Dutch flower paintings, watercolours, botanical art and modern pictures and sculpture, family and natural history. 9 acres of lakeside gardens and Dingle walk.
Location: 4 miles south-east of Bridgnorth on A442.
Admission: House & Garden: Adult £3.50, Party £2.10.
     Garden only: £2.50. Family £8.00.

COMBERMERE ABBEY
Tel: 01948 871637   **Fax:** 01948 871293

Whitchurch, Shropshire, SY13 4AJ.
Owner: Mrs P Callander Beckett   **Contact:** Mrs P Callander Beckett
Location: 5m E of Whitchurch, off A530.
Opening Times: By arrangement for groups.
Admission: Groups: £5.00 per person inclusive of refreshments.

HAUGHMOND ABBEY

Shrewsbury, Shropshire.
Owner: English Heritage   **Contact:** The Administrator
Extensive remains of a 12th century Augustinian abbey, including the Chapter House which retains its late medieval timber ceiling.
Location: 3 m NE of Shrewsbury off B5062.
Opening Times: 1 Apr - 30 Sept, Wed - Sun, 10.00am - 6.00pm, also Bank Hols. Lunchtime closure 1.00pm - 2.00pm.
Admission: Adult £1.30, Child 70p, Conc £1.00.

HAWSTONE PARK
See page 155 for full page entry.

HODNET HALL GARDENS

OPEN

1 April - 30 Sept
Tues - Sat
(closed Mons)
2.00 - 5.00pm

Sundays & Bank
Holiday Mondays
12. Noon - 5.30pm

Tel: 01630 685202
Fax: 01630 685853

HODNET, MARKET DRAYTON, SHROPSHIRE TF9 3NN
Owner: Mr and the Hon Mrs A Heber-Percy   *Contact:* Mrs M. A Taylor

Beautiful woodland walks through trees and shrubs in 60 acres of flowering lakeside gardens. Tea Rooms (with animal trophy display). Gift Shop. Kitchen Garden sales. Free car park. Dogs allowed (on leash). Parties catered for. Contact the Secretary.
Location: 12 miles north east of Shrewsbury on A53; M6 Junction 15; M54 junction 3.
Admission: Adults £2.60, Child £1.00, OAP £2.10.

IRON BRIDGE

Ironbridge, Shropshire.
Owner: English Heritage   **Contact:** The Administrator
The world's first iron bridge and Britain's best known industrial monument. Cast in Coalbrookdale by local ironmaster, Abraham Darby, it was erected across the River Severn in 1779.
Location: In Ironbridge, adjacent to A4169.
Opening Times: Any reasonable time.

IRONBRIDGE GORGE MUSEUM

Tel: 01952 433522   **Fax:** 01952 432204

Ironbridge, Telford, Shropshire TF8 7AW

Contact: Mr K Foster

Opening Times: Summer; 10.00am - 5.00pm daily; except Jul and Aug 10.00am - 6.00pm. Phone for winter details.
Admission: Passport ticket which allows admission to all sites; Adult £8.00, Child £5.00, Family £25.00, Senior citizens £7.00, Local UB40s 50%, Students £5.00, Group discounts vary from 10% - 30% depending on the time year. Single site tickets also available. Verify with administrator.

LANGLEY CHAPEL

Acton Burnell, Shrewsbury, Shropshire.
Owner: English Heritage   **Contact:** The Administrator
A delightful medieval chapel, standing alone in a field, with a complete set of early 17th century wooden fittings and furniture.
Location: 1$^{1}/_{2}$m S of Acton Burnell, on unclassified road off A49 91/2m S of Shrewsbury.
Opening Times: 1 Apr - 31 Oct: daily, 10.00am - 6.00pm. 1 Nov - 31 Mar: daily, 10.00am - 4.00pm. Closed 24 - 26 Dec, 1 Jan.

LILLESHALL ABBEY

Oakengates, Shropshire.
Owner: English Heritage   **Contact:** The Administrator
Extensive ruins of an abbey of Augustinian canons including remains of the 12th and 13th century church and the cloister buildings..
Location: On unclassified road off A518, 4 m N of Oakengates.
Opening Times: Any reasonable time.

LUDLOW CASTLE

Tel: 01584 873355

Castle Square, Shropshire, SY8 1EG.
Owner: Trustees of Powis Castle Estate   **Contact:** Jean Nicholas
Dating from about 1086. Circular nave in Norman chapel. 16th century Judges lodgings. Contemporary performances of Shakespeare in the Castle during the Ludlow Festival.
Location: 30m S Shrewsbury. Centre of Ludlow.
Opening Times: 1 Feb - 30 April, 10.30am - 4.00pm, 1 May - 30 Sept, 10.30am - 5.00pm. 1 Oct - Christmas, 10.30am - 4.00pm.
Admission: Adult £2.50, Child £1.50, Family £7.50, Conc £2.00, Groups 10% discount.

MORETON CORBET CASTLE

Moreton Corbet, Shrewsbury, Shropshire
Owner: English Heritage   **Contact:** The Administrator
A ruined medieval castle with the substantial remains of a splendid Elizabethan mansion, captured in 1644 from Charles I's supporters by Parliamentary forces.
Location: In Moreton Corbet off B5063, 7 m NE of Shrewsbury.
Opening Times: Any reasonable time.

MOREVILLE HALL

Bridgenorth, Shropshire, WV16 5BN.
Owner: The National Trust   **Contact:** Mrs J K Norbury
An Elizabethan house of mellow stone, converted in the 18th century. The Hall is in a fine setting, with three attractive gardens.
Location: 30m S Shrewsbury. Centre of Ludlow.
Opening Times: By written appointment only.

PREEN MANOR GARDENS

Tel: 01694 771207

Church Preen, Church Stretton, Shropshire.
Owner: P Trevor Jones Esq   **Contact:** P Trevor Jones Esq
6 acre garden on site of Cluniac monastery, with walled, terraced, wild, water, kitchen and chess gardens. 12th century monastic church with a yew tree reputedly the oldest in Europe.
Location: 30m S Shrewsbury. Centre of Ludlow.
Opening Times: Coach parties by appointment in Jun & Jul.

OAKLEY HALL

See page 156 for full page entry.

ROWLEY'S HOUSE MUSEUM

Tel: 01743 361196

Barker Street, Shrewsbury, Shropshire, SY1 1QH.
Owner: Shrewsbury and Atcham Borough Council   **Contact:** Mrs M White
Impressive timber framed building and attached 17th century brick mansion with costume, archeological and natural history displays.
Location: Tues - Sat: 10.00am - 5.00pm, Suns: Jun-Sept 11.00am - 4.00pm.
Opening Times: Adult £2.00, Child 50p, Conc £1.00, parties 10% discount.

SHIPTON HALL

Tel: 01746 785225

Much Wenlock, Shropshire, TF13 6JZ.
Owner: Mrs M J Bishop   **Contact:** Mrs M J Bishop
Elizabethan stone house with profusion of Tudor panelling. Plasterwork on the ceilings and chimney pieces is especially noteworthy.
Location: 6m SW of Much Wenlock on B4378.
Opening Times: Easter - 30 Sept, Thurs 2.30pm - 5.30pm. BH Sun and Mon, 2.30pm - 5.00pm. Groups of 20 or more at any time of day or year.
Admission: Adult £2.50, Child £1.50, Groups less 10% for 20 plus.

SHREWSBURY CASTLE & SHROPSHIRE REGIMENTAL MUSEUM

Tel: 01743 358516

Castle Street, Shrewsbury, Shropshire, SY1 2AT.
Owner: Shrewsbury & Atcham Borough Council   **Contact:** Mrs M White
Location: Town centre, adjacent BR and Bus stations.
Opening Times: Tues-Sat: 10.00am - 5.00pm. Summer Sun: 11.00am - 4.00pm.
Admission: Adult £2.00, Child 50p, OAP/Student £1.00, parties 10% discount.

SHREWSBURY CATHEDRAL

Tel: 01743 232723

Shrewsbury, Shropshire, SY2 6BS.

Contact: T C Bumford

Benedictine Abbey founded in 1083, tomb of Roger de Montgomerie and remains of tomb of St Winedride, 7th century Welsh Saint. The Abbey was part of the monastery and has also been a parish church since 12th century. Now made popular by Ellis Peters author of Brother Cadfael novels. Historical exhibition from Saxon times to present.
Location: Signposted from Shrewsbury bypass (A5 and A49).
Opening Times: Easter - Oct 9.30am - 5.30pm, Nov - Easter 10.00am - 4.00pm.
Admission: Donation.

STOKESAY CASTLE

NEAR CRAVEN ARMS, SHROPSHIRE SY7 9H

Owner: English Heritage
Contact: The Head Custodian

Tel: 01588 672544

Set in peaceful countryside, Stokesay Castle is one of the most perfectly preserved examples of an early fortified manor houses in England. It stands in a picturesque group with its own Jacobean gatehouse and parish church. Inside, the buildings are still remarkably intact, offering a fascinating insight into medieval life at Stokesay.

Location: Near Craven Arms, Shropshire.

Admission: Adults £2.50 OAP/Student/UB40 £1.90 Child £1.30
15% discount on parties of 11 or more.

OPEN
1 April - 30 Sept: Daily   10.00am - 6.00pm
1 Oct - 31 Oct: Daily   10.00am - 4.00pm
1 Nov - 31 Mar: Wed - Sun 10.00am - 4.00pm

UPTON CRESSETT HALL

Tel: 01746 714506   **Fax:** 01746 714506

Bridgenorth, Shropshire, WV16 6UH.
Owner: William Cash Esq   **Contact:** William Cash
The Gatehouse is available for accommodation / renting. Medieval manor house in red brick, magnificent gatehouse in beautiful countryside, 14th century Great Hall.
Location: 4 m from Bridgenorth off A458.
Opening Times: May - Sept, 2.30pm - 5.00pm. Parties any time by appointment.
Admission: Adult £2.50, Child £1.00, Parties over 12 £2.00.

WROXETER ROMAN CITY

Tel: 01743 761330

Wroxeter, Shrewsbury, Shropshire.
Owner: English Heritage   **Contact:** The Administrator
The excavated centre of the fourth largest city in Roman Britain, with impressive remains of the 2nd century municipal baths. The museum has finds from the town and earlier legionary fortress.
Location: At Wroxeter, 5m E of Shrewsbury, 1m S of A5.
Opening Times: 1 Apr - 30 Sept: daily 10.00am - 6.00pm, 1 Oct - 31 Oct: daily 10.00am - 4.00pm, 1 Nov - 31 Mar: Wed - Sun 10.00am - 4.00pm (Closed 24 - 26 Dec, 1 Jan).
Admission: Adult £2.00, Child £1.00, Conc £1.50.

WALCOT HALL

OPEN

House & Garden
May - Sept.
Bank Hol Suns
& Mons
(except Xmas &
New Year)
May: Sun, Wed, & Fri
June: Wed & Fri
July & Aug: Suns
Sept: Wed.
2.15 - 4.30pm.

Tel: 0171 5812782
Fax: 0171 589 0195

LYDBURY NORTH, NR BISHOP'S CASTLE, SHROPSHIRE SY7 8AZ

Owner: C.R.W. Parish   *Contact: C.R.W. Parish*

Georgian home of Lord Clive of India who commissioned Sir William Chambers to re-design it, and the Stable Block in 1763. His son added the free-standing Ballroom and developed 30 acres of Arboretum and Pools to the rear, with mile-long Lakes in the front. Suitable Film Locations; Balls, Corporate Events; Holiday Accommodation, Receptions, Parties and Shows.
Location: On the edge of the Clun Forest. 3 miles east of Bishop's Castle on B4385; 1/2 mile outside Lydbury North. The drive is adjacent to the Powis Arms Pub.
Admission: Adult £2.50, Child under 15 free. Groups of 10+ by arrangement. Teas when available.

WENLOCK PRIORY

OPEN
1 April - 30 Sept: Daily 10.00am - 6.00pm
1 Oct - 31 Oct: Daily 10.00am - 4.00pm
1 Nov - 31 Mar: Wed - Sun 10.00am - 4.00pm

**MUCH WENLOCK,
SHROPSHIRE TF13 6HS**

Owner: English Heritage
Contact: The Head Custodian

Tel: 01952 727466

The magnificent remains of the Cluniac monastery of Wenlock Priory are set among smooth lawns and ornamental topiary in Much Wenlock, a picturesque market town lying in some of the most attractive countryside in Shropshire. There is plenty to explore, including the priory church and the Norman chapter with its superb decorative arcading.

Location: In Much Wenlock.
Admission: Adult £2.00
OAP/Student/UB40 £1.50
Child £1.00
15% discount on parties of 11 or more.

WESTON PARK

See page 157 for full page entry.

WILDERHOPE MANOR

Tel: 01694 771363

Longville, Much Wenlock, Shropshire, TF13 6EG.
Owner: The National Trust   **Contact:** The Administrator
This limestone house stands on southern slope of Wenlock Edge in remote country with views down to Corvedale. Dating from 1586, it is unaltered but unfurnished. Features include remarkable wooden spiral stairs, unique bow rack and fine plaster ceilings. Circular walk through farmland and woods.
Location: 7m SW of Much Wenlock. 7m E of Church Stretton, 1/2m S of B4371.
Opening Times: Apr - end Sept: Wed & Sat 2.00pm - 4.30pm. Oct - end Mar 1996: Sat only 2.00pm - 4.30pm.
Admission: £1.00, no reduction for parties.

SPECIAL EVENTS DIARY

- **16th - 17th April: Weston Park**
  Festival of Transport.

- **29th April: Weston Park**
  Albrighton "Point to Point".

- **6th - 8th May: Weston Park**
  Craft Fair.

- **13th - 14th May: Weston Park**
  Weston Park Horse Trials.

- **28th - 29th: Weston Park**
  Spring Spectacular.

- **28th - 29th: Walcot Hall**
  National Gardens Scheme Garden & Arboretum open.

- **5th June: Dudmaston**
  Open Air Theatre - The Merry Wives of Windsor

- **10th June: Walcot Hall**
  Shropshire Game Fair

- **24th - 25th June: Weston Park**
  German Shepherd Dog Show

- **29th June: Dudmaston**
  Open Air Theatre - The Merry Wives of Windsor

- **9th July: Weston Park**
  Napoleonic Battle Spectacular

- **16th - 20th August: Weston Park**
  Music Festival

- **22nd - 24th August: Weston Park**
  Pony Club Championships

- **27th - 28th August: Weston Park**
  Town & Country Fayre

- **9th - 10th September: Weston Park,**
  Hovercraft Rally

- **16th - 17th September: Weston Park,**
  Midland Game and Country Sports Fair

- **7th - 8th October: Weston Park**
  Autumn Horse Trials

- **5th November: Weston Park**
  Bonfire and Firework Spectacular

HATCH COURT
Taunton

HATCH COURT is a distinctive and most attractive Bath Stone Palladian mansion built in 1755 by Thomas Prowse of Axbridge. It is surrounded by parkland with its historic herd of fallow deer, in the midst of the Somerset countryside, and yet is one of the most accessible houses in the South West, being but six miles from the motorway.

The house, now occupied by the fifth generation of the same family is a much loved and lived in family home. It has a magnificent stone staircase, fine plasterwork and a good collection of furniture and paintings from the 17th to 20th centuries. There is a small museum commemorating the founding by a member of the family of one of the Empire's last privately raised regiments, and beyond this lies an unique semi-circular China Room with a fine display of porcelain and glass.

THE GARDENS
The gardens and parkland have undergone extensive redevelopment. In particular, there is a magnificent two acre walled kitchen garden, now fully restored in an original style, which supplies the house and the locality with fruit, vegetables and herbs, whilst remaining a fine visual spectacle. Further large plantings of trees, roses and herbaceous borders have been achieved in recent years and 1995 sees the extended opening of the gardens for the first time.

Hatch Court is available as a private and exclusive venue where great attention is paid to the impeccable presentation of a lovely house, full of history and tradition.

❖

SUITABILITY FOR OTHER EVENTS
Private and corporate receptions, lunches and dinners for up to 120 people. Conferences, seminars and training days. Filming, promotional events, car rallies. Any event sympathetic to the house and its surroundings will be considered.

ADVICE TO COURIERS & DRIVERS
Pre booked groups are particularly welcome at anytime when the house is not open to the public. Guided tours by the owner. Refreshments and full catering by arrangement.

FACILITIES FOR THE DISABLED
The gardens are completely and easily accessible to wheelchairs. There are no specific disabled toilets.

PARKING FOR COACHES AND CARS
Unlimited, free parking.

CATERING
Full catering, home-made and often home grown is available by request. Menus can easily be tailored to suit any requirement. Teas usually available on public open days.

GIFT SHOP
Plants and produce in the walled garden. Guide books, postcards etc. in the house.

CONTACT

Mrs Jane Odgers /
Dr Robin Odgers
Hatch Court
Hatch Beauchamp
Taunton
TA3 6AA

Tel: (01823) 480120

Fax: (01823) 480058

LOCATION

Hatch Court is situated just off the A358 six miles South East of Taunton and Junction 25 off the M5 motorway.

From Bristol and Exeter: 45 - 60 minutes.

Rail: Taunton

Air: Bristol and Exeter

OPENING TIMES

Summer
HOUSE
15 June - 14 Sept
Thurdays and Bank
Hol Mons 2.30 - 5.30pm
Last admission 5.00pm

GARDEN
1 May - 28 Sept
Tues, Weds, Thurs and
Bank Hol Mons
(1, 29 May & 28 August)
2.30 - 5.30pm

The house and gardens are open at all other times of the year to groups by prior appointment.

ADMISSION

HOUSE
Adult £3.00
Child £1.50
Child (under 12) . . .Free
OAP £3.00

GARDEN
Adult £2.00
Child £1.00
Child (under 12) . . .Free
OAP £1.50

CONFERENCE AND FUNCTION FACILITIES

ROOM	DIMENSIONS	CAPACITY	LAYOUT	POWER POINTS	SUITABLE FOR A/V
Long Room	16' x 30'	24	Boardroom	6	✓
		60	Theatre		··
Dining room	18' x 30'	24	Boardroom	2	✓
		70	Theatre		
		50	Banqueting		
Hall	24' x 40'	100	Reception	2	✓
Orangery	14' x 32'	50	Reception	2	✓

BARFORD PARK

Tel: 01278 671269

Spaxton, Bridgewater, Somerset, TA4 2AJ.

Owner: Col M Stancomb   **Contact:** Col M Stancomb

Handsome, Queen Anne, red-brick family house, with walled flower garden in parkland setting.

Location: Spaxton, Somerset.

Opening Times: By appointment only.

BARRINGTON COURT

Tel: 01460 241938

Barrington, Ilminster, Somerset, TA19 ONQ.

Owner: The National Trust   **Contact:** The Administrator

The best example of a Gertrude Jekyll garden. A beautiful garden laid out in a series of rooms, including the White Garden, the Rose and Iris Garden and the Lily garden. The working kitchen garden has apple, pear & plum trees trained along high stone walls. The Tudor manor house was restored in the 1920s by the Lyle family.

Location: In Barrington village, 5m NE of Ilminster, on B3168.

Opening Times: Barrington Court Garden: 1 Apr - 1 Oct: daily, except Fri, 11.00am - 5.30pm. Last admission 5.00pm. Court House: 5 Apr - 27 Sept: Wed only, 11.00am - 5.30pm. Last admission 5.00pm.

Admission: Adult £3.10, Child £1.50, Parties £2.60, Child £1.20. Court House: Adult £1.00, Child 50p.

CLEEVE ABBEY

Tel: 01984 40377

Washford, Somerset.

Owner: English Heritage   **Contact:** The Administrator

There are few monastic sites where you will see such a complete set of cloister buildings, including the refectory with its magnificent timber roof. Built in the 13th century, this Cistercian abbey was saved from destruction at the Dissolution by being turned into a house and then a farm.

Location: In Washford, 1/4m S of A39.

Opening Times: 1 Apr - 30 Sept: daily 10.00am - 6.00pm, 1 Oct - 31 Oct: daily 10.00am - 4.00pm, 1 Nov - 31 Mar: Wed - Sun 10.00am - 4.00pm (Closed 24 - 26 Dec, 1 Jan).

Admission: Adult £2.00, Child £1.00, Conc £1.50.

COLERIDGE COTTAGE

Tel: 01278 732662

35 Lime Street, Nether Stowey, Bridgwater, Somerset, TA5 1NQ

Owner: The National Trust   **Contact:** The Custodian

Coleridge's home for three years from 1797. It was here that he wrote the Rime of the Ancient Mariner, part of Christabel and Frost at Midnight.

Location: At W end of Nether Stowey, on S side of A39, 8m W of Bridgwater.

Opening Times: Parlour & Reading room only: 2 Apr - 3 Oct: Tues to Thur & Sun, 2.00pm - 5.00pm. In winter by written application.

Admission: Adult £1.50, Child 80p, no reduction for parties which must book.

CROWE HALL

Tel: 01225 310322

Widcombe Hill, Bath, Somerset, BA2 6AR.

Owner: John Barratt Esq   **Contact:** John Barratt Esq

10 acres of romantic hillside gardens. Victorian grotto, classical Bath villa with good 18th century furniture and paintings.

Location: 1m SE of Bath.

Opening Times: Gardens only open 26 Mar, 23 Apr, 14 & 28 May, 18 Jun, 16 Jul. House and Gardens by appointment.

Admission: House & Gardens: Adult £3.00, Child £1.00. Gardens only: Adult £1.50, Child 30p.

DUNDSTER CASTLE

Tel: 01643 821314

Dunster, Minehead, Somerset, TA24 6SL.

Owner: The National Trust   **Contact:** The Administrator

The fortified home of the Luttrell family for 600 years, with a 13th century castle building below a Norman motte. The 17th century mansion was remodelled by Salvin in 1870 but retains its fine staircase and plasterwork. There is a terraced garden of rare shrubs, and a 28 acre park.

Location: In Dunster, 3m SE of Minehead.

Opening Times: Castle: 1 Apr - 1 Oct, open daily except Thur & Fri (closed Good Fri), 11.00am - 5.00pm, also 2 Oct - 31 Oct: daily except Thur & Fri, 11.00am - 4.00pm. Garden & Park: 1 Feb - 10 Dec, daily Feb, Mar, Oct, Nov, Dec, 11.00am - 4.00pm; Apr - Sept, 11.00am - 5.00pm (open Good Fri). Last admission 1/2 hour before closing.

Admission: Castle, garden & park: Adult £4.80, Child (under 16) £2.40, Pre-booked parties £4.30. Castle & park only: Adult £2.70, Child £1.30, Family £6.50.

DUNSTER WORKING WATERMILL

Tel: 01643 821759

Mill Lane, Dunster, Minehead, Somerset, TA24 6SW.

Owner: The National Trust   **Contact:** The Administrator

Built on the site of a mill mentioned in the Domesday Survey of 1086, the present mill dates from the 18th century and was restored to working order in 1979.

Location: On River Avill, beneath Castle Tor, approach via Mill Lane or Castle Gardens on foot.

Opening Times: Apr - end Jun, daily, except Sat (open Easter) 11.00am - 5.00pm. Jul & Aug: daily 11.00am - 5.00pm. Sept & Oct: daily, except Sat 11.00am - 5.00pm.

Admission: £1.50. Family tickets available. Party rates by prior arrangement.

EAST LAMBROOK MANOR

Tel: 01460 240763   **Fax:** 01460 242344

South Petherton, Ilminster, Somerset, TA13 5HL.

Owner: A Norton Esq   **Contact:** A Norton Esq

Cottage style garden created post 1937 by Margery Fish and described in her well known book "We Made a Garden". Now restored by the present owners with the help of one of the original gardeners.

Location: 7m E of Ilminster, signed off A303 at South Petherton.

Opening Times: 1 Mar - 30 Oct, Mon - Sat, 10.00am - 5.00pm.

Admission: Adult £2.00, Child 50p, Conc £1.80, Groups by prior arrangement £1.80 pp.

FARLEIGH HUNGERFORD CASTLE

Tel: 01225 754026

Farleigh Hungerford, Somerset.

Owner: English Heritage   **Contact:** The Administrator

Extensive ruins of a 14th century castle with a splendid chapel containing wall paintings, stained glass and the fine tomb of Sir Thomas Hungerford, builder of the castle.

Location: In Farleigh Hungerford 3 1/2m W of Trowbridge on A366.

Opening Times: 1 Apr - 30 Sept: daily 10.00am - 6.00pm, 1 Oct - 31 Oct: daily 10.00am - 4.00pm, 1 Nov - 31 Mar: Wed - Sun 10.00am - 4.00pm (Closed 24 - 26 Dec, 1 Jan).

Admission: Adult £1.30, Child 70p, Conc £1.00.

FORDE ABBEY

OPEN

Gardens:
Daily all year
10 am - 4.30pm

House:
1 April - end Oct.
Suns, Weds & Bank
Holidays
1 - 4.30pm
Last admission.

Tel: 01460 220231
Fax: 01460 220296

CHARD, SOMERSET TA20 4LU

Owner: *Mark Roper Esq.*   **Contact:** *Mark Roper Esq.*

"Winners of Christies/HHA Garden of Year Award 1993"

Founded by Cistercian monks almost 900 years ago. Today it remains a genuine family, home unchanged since the middle of the 17th century. Situated in some of the most beautiful countryside in west Dorset. 30 acres of gardens with herbaceous borders, arboretum, magnificent trees and shrubs, 5 lakes, Bog garden. Here you can enjoy the peace and beauty of a past age. There are no ropes or barriers in the house and no sideshows in the gardens.

Location: Just off the B3167 4 miles south of Chard.

Admission: House & Gardens - Adult £4.50, OAP £4.00, Groups £3.50, Child Free. Gardens only - Adult £3.25, OAP £2.75, Groups £2.75, Child Free.

GAULDEN MANOR

Tel: 01984 7213

Tolland, Lydeard St Lawrence, Taunton, Somerset, TA4 3PN.

Owner: James Le Gendre Starkie Esq   **Contact:** James Le Gendre Starkie Esq

Small stone manor house with Great Hall having fine plaster ceiling. Good antique furniture. Attractive garden.

Location: 9m NE of Taunton. 1m E of Tolland Church.

Opening Times: Easter Sun and Mon and all summer BHs, then from 7 May - 3 Sept, Thurs and Sun, 2.00pm - 5.30pm. By appointment on other days.

Admission: Adult £3.00, Child £1.50, Group £2.80.

GLASTONBURY TRIBUNAL

Tel: 01458 832954

Glastonbury High Street, Glastonbury, Somerset.

Owner: English Heritage   **Contact:** The Administrator

A well preserved medieval town house, reputedly once used as the courthouse of Glastonbury Abbey.

Location: In Glastonbury High Street.

Opening Times: 1 Apr - 30 Sept daily, 10.00am - 5.00pm (6.00pm on Fri & Sat) 1 Oct - 31 Mar daily, 10.00am - 4.00pm.

HATCH COURT

See page 161 for full page entry.

HESTERCOMBE HOUSE

Tel: 01823 413030   **Fax:** 01823 337222

Hestercombe Gardens, Cheddon Fitzpaine, Taunton, Somerset, TA2 8LQ.
Owner: Somerset County Council Fire Brigade   **Contact:** D M Usher Esq
Designed in 1904, the garden has been restored in recent years by Somerset County Council using Miss Jekyll's original planting plans as a guide.
Location: 4m from Taunton, close to the village Cheddon Fitzpaine.
Opening Times: All year, Mon - Fri, 9.00am - 5.00pm. 1 May - 30 Sept, Sat and Sun 2.00pm - 5.00pm.
Admission: Adult £2.00. Child under 16 free, Conc £1.50, Coach parties by arrangement.

KING JOHN'S HUNTING LODGE

Tel: 01934 732012

The Square, Axbridge, Somerset, BS26 2AP.
Owner: The National Trust   **Contact:** The Administrator
An early Tudor merchant's house, extensively restored in 1971.
Location: In the Square, on corner of High Street.
Opening Times: Easter - end Sept, daily 2.00pm - 5.00pm.
Admission: £1.00. School parties by arrangement.

LYTES CARY MUSEUM

Tel: 01985 843600

Charlton Mackrell, Somerset, TA11 7HU.
Owner: The National Trust   **Contact:** The Administrator
A manor house with a 14th century chapel, 15th century hall and 16th century great chamber. The home of Henry Lyte, translator of Niewe Herball (1578). Hedged gardens with long herbaceous border.
Location: 1m N of Ilchester bypass A303, signposted from roundabout at junction of A303. A37 take A372.
Opening Times: 1 Apr - 28 Oct: Mon, Wed & Sat, 2.00pm - 6.00pm or dusk if earlier. Last admission 5.30pm.
Admission: £3.70, no reduction for parties.

MAUNSEL HOUSE

OPEN

Weddings, Private Parties, Conferences, Functions, Filming, Fashion Shows, Archery, Clay Pigeon Shooting, Equestrian Events, Garden Parties, Coach & Group Parties welcome by appointment.

Tel: 01278 663413
Fax: 01278 661074

NORTH NEWTON, NR. BRIDGWATER, SUFFOLK CO10 6EQ

Owner: Sir Benjamin Slade   *Contact: Sir Benjmin Slade*

Imposing 13th century manor house, partly built before the Norman Conquest but mostly built around a Great Hall erected in 1420. Geoffrey Chaucer wrote part of "The Canterbury Tales" whilst staying at the house. Maunsel House is the ancestral seat of the Slade family and is now the home of the 7th baronet, Sir Benjamin Slade.
Location: Bridgwater 4 miles, Bristol 20 miles, Taunton 7 miles, junct. 24 M5, turn left North Petherton 1¹/₂ miles North Newton, ¹/₂ mile south St. Michael Church.
Admission: For further info tel: 01895 272929 during office hours or 01278 661075.

MIDELNEY MANOR

OPEN

1 May - 28 Sept
Every Thursday and all Bank Holiday Mondays

2.30 - 5.30pm

Last Tour 4.30 pm

Tel: 01458 251229

LANGPORT, SOMERSET TA10 0LW

Owner: J. M. R. Cely Trevilian Esq.   *Contact: J. M. R. Cely Trevilian Esq.*

Originally the Island Manor of the Abbots of Muchelney, the 16th-18th century Manor House situated in the middle of the Somerset Levels and Moors was built by and has been the property of the Trevilian family since the 16th century. 17th century falcons mews, gardens, woodland walks, Heronry.
Location: Signposted from A378 at Bell Hotel Curry Rivel or from B3168 Hambridge/ Curry Rivel road.
Admission: Adult £2.50, Child £1.00. Parties, Weddings & Private functions by appointment.

MONTACUTE HOUSE

Tel: 01935 823289

Montacute, Martock, Somerset, TA15 6XP.
Owner: The National Trust   **Contact:** The Administrator
A magnificent Elizabethan house, with an H-shaped ground plan and many Renaissance features, including contemporary plasterwork, chimneypieces and heraldic glass. The house contains fine 17th and 18th century furniture, an exhibition of samplers dating from the 17th century, Elizabethan and Jacobean portraits from the National Portrait Gallery displayed in the Long Gallery and adjoining rooms. The formal garden includes mixed borders and old roses and a landscaped park.
Location: In Montacute village, 4m W of Yeovil, on S side of A3088, 3m E of A303.
Opening Times: House: 1 Apr - 30 Oct: daily except Tues 12.00pm - 5.30pm. Last admission 5.00pm. Closed Good Fri. Garden & Park: 1 Apr - Mar 1996, daily except Tues 11.30am - 5.30pm or dusk if earlier.
Admission: House, garden & park: Adult £4.80, Child £2.50, Pre-booked parties (15+) £4.40, Child £2.20. Garden & park only: Adult £2.70 (Apr - Oct), Child £1.20. No reduction for parties; from Nov - Apr 1996 £1.30.

MUCHELNEY ABBEY

Muchelney, Somerset.
Owner: English Heritage   **Contact:** The Administrator
Well preserved ruins of the cloisters, with windows carved in golden stone, and abbot's lodging of the Benedictine abbey, which survived by being used as a farmhouse after the Dissolution.
Location: In Muchelney 2 m S of Langport.
Opening Times: 1 Apr - 30 Sept daily, 10.00am - 6.00pm. Lunchtime closure 1.00pm - 2.00pm.
Admission: Adults £1.30, Child 70p, Conc £1.00.

NUNNEY CASTLE

Nunney, Somerset.
Owner: English Heritage   **Contact:** The Administrator
A small 14th century moated castle with a distinctly French style. Its unusual design consists of a central block with large towers at the angles.
Location: In Nunney 3¹/₂ m SW of Frome, off A361.
Opening Times: Any reasonable time.

PRIEST'S HOUSE

Tel: 01458 252621

Muchelney, Langport, Somerset, TA10 0DQ.
Owner: The National Trust   **Contact:** The Administrator
A late medieval hall house with large Gothic windows, originally the residence of priests serving the parish church across the road. Lived in and recently repaired.
Location: 1m S of Langport.
Opening Times: 1 Apr - 1 Oct: Sun & Mon 2.00pm - 5.00pm..
Admission: £1.50, no reductions.

 THE NATIONAL TRUST    ENGLISH HERITAGE   HISTORIC HOUSES ASSOCIATION

STEMBRIDGE TOWER MILL

Tel: 01458 250818

High Ham, Somerset, TA10 9DJ.
Owner: The National Trust   **Contact:** The Tenant
The last thatched windmill in England, dating from 1822 and in use until 1910.
Location: 2m N of Langport, ¹/₂m E of High Ham.
Opening Times: 2 Apr - 1 Oct: Sun, Mon & Wed, 2.00pm - 5.00pm.
Admission: Adult £1.50, Child 80p, parties by prior arrangement.

STOKE-SUB-HAMDON PRIORY

Tel: 01985 843600

North Street, Stoke-sub-Hamdon, Somerset, TA4 6QP.
Owner: The National Trust   **Contact:** The Administrator
A complex of buildings, begun in the 14th century for the priests of the chantry chapel of St Nicholas, which is now destroyed.
Location: Between A303 and A3088. 2m W of Montacute between Yeovil and Ilminster.
Opening Times: All year, daily 10.00am - 6.00pm or dusk if earlier.

THE BISHOP'S PALACE

Wells, Somerset, BA5 2PD.
Owner: The Church Commissioners   **Contact:** Mr Edwards
Moated palace, the earliest parts of which date from the 13th century. Several state rooms with portraits of former Bishops. In the grounds are the wells from which the place derives its name.
Location: Wells.
Opening Times: The Henderson Rooms, Bishop's Chapel and Grounds: 1 Apr - 31 Oct; Sun, 2.00pm - 6.00pm. Tues, Wed, Thurs and BH Mon. Aug, daily, 10.00am - 6.00pm. Also for exhibitions as advertised. The Trustees reserve the right to change times on occasions. Guided and educational tours by arrangement.

TINTINHULL HOUSE GARDEN

Tel: 01935 822545

Farm Street, Tintinhull, Somerset, BA22 9PZ.
Owner: The National Trust   **Contact:** The Gardener
A 20th century formal garden surrounding a 17th century house. The garden layout, divided into areas by walls and hedges, has border colour and plant themes, including shrub roses and clematis, there is also a kitchen garden.
Location: 5m NW of Yeovil, ¹/₂m S of A303, on E outskirts of Tintinhull.
Opening Times: 1 Apr - 2 Oct: Wed, Thur, Sat, Sun & BH Mon 12.00pm - 6.00pm.
Admission: Adult £3.50, Child £1.60, no reduction for parties.

WELLS CATHEDRAL

Tel: 01749 674483   **Fax:** 01749 677360

Wells, Somerset, BA5 2PA.

                     Contact: Mr J Shillingford
Fine medieval Cathedral. The Quire with tapestries and stained glass, Chapter House and clock should not be missed.
Location: 20m from both Bath & Bristol.
Opening Times: Summer 7.15am - 8.30pm or dusk. Winter 7.15am - 6.00pm.
Admission: Donation. Groups should book in advance.

SPECIAL EVENTS DIARY

- **16th April: Barrington Court,**
  Easter Egg Hunt.

- **29th April: Montacute House**
  8pm Recital - Catherine Bott and Friends - English 17th century - Purcell and his contemporaries, Tickets £10.00 incl. wine. Pre-concert suppers extra.

- **24th June: Barrington Court**
  Gala Evening with Opera Brava - Adults £10.00, child £4.00.

- **8th July: Wells Cathedral**
  National Trust Centenary Service and Garden Party in Bishop's Palace.

- **2nd - 3rd September: Montacute House**
  Joust and Ox Roast - afternoon.

SANDON HALL
Sandon

CONTACT

Michael Bosson
Sandon Hall
Stafford ST18 OBZ
Tel: (01889) 508004
Fax: (01889) 508586

LOCATION

A51. 10 miles north of Rugeley and 4 miles south of Stone. Entrance through double lodges opposite Sandon village War Memorial. From south (incl. Birmingham Airport): M42, exit 9, Lichfield, Rugeley. London 2³/₄ hrs, 151 miles. From north (incl. Manchester Airport) 1 hr: M6, exit 14. Stafford ringroad B5066

Rail: Stafford station
Taxi: (01785) 48548
Chauffeur Service: Carriage Call (01785) 819489

SANDON HALL, the home of the Earl and Countess of Harrowby, is in the heart of Staffordshire. The Estate has been in the family since 1776 when an earlier house designed by Joseph Pickford of Derby was bought by Nathaniel Ryder, 1st Baron Harrowby, son of Sir Dudley Ryder, Lord Chief Justice of England. After damage by fire in 1848 the house was re-built by William Burn, the most proven Country House architect of the day.

The family has been prominent in legal and parliamentary affairs for 250 years, with seven generations in parliament, three successive ones in the Cabinet.

Visitors are struck by the atmosphere and by the elegant ambience . Sandon however, for all its grandeur, is first and foremost a home. The grounds and park are equally impressive, while the hall itself provides a wonderful backdrop for marquees.

Special events include Antiques Fairs, Veteran Car Rally, Craft Show, Home Decor Exhibition, Masked Ball, Country Sports Fair.

Sandon has recently been the subject of a Central/Carlton TV feature, and offers excellent possibilities for filming.

MUSEUM
The new museum comprises the State Drawing Room and Dining Room, and upstairs many items of unusual and varying interest including early costumes, childhood toys and photographs of early 20th century house parties. Also manuscript letters, albums and prints. There are political objets d'art, and the famous duelling pistols of Pitt the Younger. There is a complete room decorated with very rare hand-painted Chinese wallpaper of the 18th century and a probably unique collection of First World War Recruitment Posters.

GARDENS AND GROUNDS
The 47 acre garden is landscaped and especially beautiful at azalea/rhododendron time and in the autumn. There is a notable arboretum with many magnificent trees, and a network of paths for enjoyable walks. Pre-booking normally essential.

❖

OPENING TIMES
Throughout the year, with some exceptions, for events/functions both indoors and outdoors. Likewise for visits to the museum and/or gardens by pre-booked parties. Tours may be arranged outside normal opening hours by special agreement.

ADMISSION

MUSEUM
Adult £3.00
Child £2.00
OAP £2.50
Guided group tours by appointment only. Max. No. 20. Groups of 40 may be accommodated by combining museum and garden tours.

GARDENS & GROUNDS
Self-guided tour (guide booklet at extra cost) by appointment only - except during some public events.
Adult £1.50
Child £1.00
OAP £1.00
Guided tours may be arranged at certain times. Please enquire.

SUITABILITY FOR EVENTS
The state rooms are ideally suited for a variety of functions with the fine Conservatory being a perfect spot for light catering. The Saloon with excellent acoustics, a grand piano and an organ, is suitable for musical events, balls, cocktail parties, literary evenings etc. Trade exhibitions, promotional events and fashion shows can easily be accommodated. A large Dining Room provides an ideal setting for prestige dinner parties, while the elegant Library offers the tranquility required for important business meetings/lectures.

EXTRA FACILITIES
The 400 acre rolling parkland is exceptionally attractive. It was laid out in the mid-18th century and can be booked for many types of outdoor events, including product launches and caravan rallies.

ADVICE TO COURIERS AND DRIVERS
No smoking indoors. No photography inside the House without advance permission. Dogs only in Park on lead.

PARKING FOR COACHES AND CARS
Unlimited free parking available on grass, adjacent to the Hall. No parking on the forecourt.

CATERING
Organised by approved and recommended outside caterers. Internally several rooms can be hired out for lunch and dinner.

GUIDED TOURS
All visits to the museum are guided and last on average about 1¹/₄ hrs. Pre-booking essential. Refreshments may be available if requested in advance.

SCHOOL VISITS/ CHILDREN
Accompanied groups welcome. The museum has great historical interest while the parkland is particularly suitable for rural studies, including forestry and agriculture.

CONFERENCE AND FUNCTION FACILITIES
Subject to prior arrangement most state rooms can be made available for functions/meetings; by the way of example the saloon measures 84' x 23' and the main library is 820 sq. ft. Please telephone for further details.

SHUGBOROUGH ESTATE
Stafford

SHUGBOROUGH is the ancestral home of the fifth Earl of Lichfield, who as Patrick Lichfield is known worldwide as a leading photographer.

The 18th century Mansion House contains a fine collection of ceramics silver, paintings and French furniture. Part of the House continues to be lived in by the Earl and his family. Nothing could be more English!

Visitors can enjoy the 18 acre Grade I Historic Garden and a unique collection of neo-classical monuments by James Stuart.

Other attractions include the original servants'

quarters. The working laundry, kitchens, brewhouse and coach houses have all been lovingly restored. Costumed guides can show how the servants lived and worked over 100 years ago.

Shugborough Park Farm is a Georgian farmstead that features an agricultural museum, working corn mill and rare breeds centre.The livestock are all historic breeds and in the farmhouse visitors can see brick bread ovens in operation and butter and cheese making in the dairy.

The Estate is set in 900 acres of park and woodland with many walks and trails

CONTACT

Anne Wood,
Promotions and
Events Manager,
Shugborough
Milford
Stafford
ST17 0XB

Tel: (01889) 881388

Fax: (01889) 881323

LOCATION

From London M1, M6 from junct. 19, leave M6 junct. 13, follow signs.

Rail: British rail intercity trains at Stafford.

Taxi: Anthony's Stafford (01785) 52255

SUITABILITY FOR OTHER EVENTS
Private and corporate entertainment, conferences, product launches and dinner parties. Catering can be arranged . Filming and event location.

EXTRA FACILITIES
Over 900 acres of parkland and gardens available for hire. Themed activities, tours and demonstrations.

FACILITIES FOR THE DISABLED
Disabled and elderly visitors may alight at the entrance to the property before parking in the allocated areas.. Toilets for the disabled. Stair climber to House. Batricars available. Disabled friendly picnic tables available. Taped tours..

ADVICE TO COURIERS & DRIVERS
Discounted vouchers for drivers meals available. Please advise clients that there is no photography allowed within the property.

PARKING FOR COACHES & CARS
Capacity of car park - 200 cars and 28 coaches, 150 yards from the House. Additional parking on the grass.

CATERING
Licensed Tea Room/Cafe seating 95 also tearoom at Farm seats 30. Prior notice for large groups. Catering for special functions/conferences.

GUIDED TOURS
Pre-booked tours of approx. 1 hour duration. Themed tours as required. Minimum size of each groups - 15 Please telephone for full adult group and educational package details.

GIFT SHOP/GUIDE BOOKS
National Trust Shop at main site open at the same time as the property. Selection of colour guide books available.

SCHOOL VISITS/CHILDREN
Variety of award winning educational packages and demonstrations available all year in all areas. Curriculum related. Pre-visits for teachers. Please contact education officer.

OPENING TIMES

Summer
25 March - 27 October
Daily   11am - 5.00pm
Booked parties from 10.30 am throughout the year.

Winter
Pre-booked parties only.
28 October - 22 Dec
& 2 January - 22 March
Daily   10.30am - 4.00pm

ADMISSION

ALL ATTRACTIONS
Adults £7.50
Concessions* . . .£5.00
Family 3 Sites . .£15.00

GARDENS & PARK
Cars £1.50
Coaches . . . . . . .Free

SINGLE SITES
(House, Museum or Farm)
Per site
Adult £3.50
Concessions* . . .£2.00

* Concessions for children (under 5's FREE), OAPs, Students, unemployed & groups.

**Nat. Trust Members free to Mansion House, reduced rate to Museum and Farm.

CONFERENCE AND FUNCTION FACILITIES

ROOM	DIMENSIONS	CAPACITY	LAYOUT	POWER POINTS	SUITABLE FOR A/V
Saloon	60' x 24'	80	Theatre	✓	✓
Conference Suite	35' x 24'	40	Lunch/Dinner Theatre	✓	✓
		40	U-shape		
		40	Boardroom		
		40	Buffet		

ANCIENT HIGH HOUSE

Tel: 0785 223181

Stafford, Staffordshire, ST16 2HS.
Owner: Stafford Borough Council　　　**Contact:** R Halliwell
The largest timber framed town house in England. Built in 1595 by wool merchant, John Dorrington. Permanent collection displayed in period room settings which relate to the house's history. Staffordshire Yeomanry exhibition on top floor.
Location: Stafford.
Opening Times: Jan - Apr 10.00am - 3.00pm, April onwards 10.00am - 4.00pm.
Admission: Adults £1.35, Child 70p.

BIDDULPH GRANGE GARDEN

OPEN
1st Apr - 29 October
Weds - Fri
12 Noon - 6.00pm
Sat, Suns & Bank
Holiday Monday
11.00am - 6.00pm
(Closed Good Friday)
Also open
4 Nov - 17 Dec
Sat, Sun
12 Noon - 4.00pm

Tel: 01782 517999

GRANGE ROAD, BIDDULPH, STOKE-ON-TRENT ST8 7SD
Owner: The National Trust　　　*Contact: The Head Gardener*
A rare and exciting survival of a high Victorian garden - recently restored by the National Trust. The Garden is divided into a series of themed gardens within a garden, with a Chinese temple, Egyptian Court, Pinetum, Dahlia Walk, Glen and many other settings.
Location: Off A527, 3½ mls south of Congleton, 8 mls north of Stoke-on-Trent.
Admission: Adult £3.90, Child £1.95, Family (2 adults & 2 children) £9.75.

BOSCOBEL AND THE ROYAL OAK

BREWOOD, STAFFORDSHIRE ST19 9AR

Owner: English Heritage
Contact: The Head Custodian

Tel: 01902 850244

Fully refurnished and restored, the panelled rooms and pretty gardens give this house a truly romantic character. King Charles II hid in the house and nearby Royal Oak to escape detection by Cromwell's troops after the battle of Worcester.

Location: 8 miles north-west of Wolverhamton. 4 miles east of Tong.

Admission: Adult £3.30 OAP/Student/UB40 £2.50 Child £1.70
15% discount on parties of 11 or more.

OPEN
1 April - 30 Sept: Daily 10.00am - 6.00pm
1 Oct - 31 Oct: Daily 10.00am - 4.00pm
1 Nov - 31 Mar: Wed - Sun 10.00am - 4.00pm
Closed in January

CHILLINGTON HALL

Tel: 01902 850236

Codsall Wood, Wolverhampton, Staffordshire, WV8 1RE.
Owner: Mr & Mrs P Giffard　　　**Contact:** Mr & Mrs P Giffard
Georgian red brick house with fine saloon set in "Capability Brown" park having the largest lake created by Brown.
Location: 2 m S of Brewood off A449.
Opening Times: Jun - 14 Sept, Thurs. Easter Sun. Suns prior to May Bank Hol and Suns in Aug.
Admission: Adult £2.50, Child £1.25.

ECCLESHALL CASTLE

Tel: 01785 850151

Stafford, Staffordshire, ST21 6LS.
Owner: T M Carter Esq　　　**Contact:** The Curator
Location: ¼m N of Eccleshall on A519.
Opening Times: Gardens only, 2.00pm - 5.30pm Easter Sun. Sun and Wed from Jun - 31 Aug.
Admission: Donations to local charities.

LICHFIELD CATHEDRAL

Tel: 01543 250300

Lichfield, Staffordshire, WS13 7LD.

Contact: Canon A Barnard
800 year old Gothic Cathedral with three spires on a 1300 year old Christian site. 8th century gospel manuscript, 16th century Flemish glass, silver collection - a worshipping community.
Location: Approach from A38 and A51, N from M42 and M6.
Opening Times: All day, everyday.
Admission: Donation.

SAMUEL JOHNSON BIRTHPLACE MUSEUM

Tel: 01543 264972　　**Fax:** 01543 254562

Breadmarket Street, Lichfield, Staffordshire, WS13 6LG.
Owner: Lichfield City Council　　　**Contact:** Dr G Nicholls
The house where Samuel's father had a bookshop is now a museum with many of Johnson's personal relics.
Location: Breadmarket Street, Lichfield.
Opening Times: Daily 10.00am - 5.00pm.
Admission: Adult £1.00, Child 60p, Family £2.70, Conc 60p, Groups 60p.

TAMWORTH CASTLE

Tel: 01827 63563

The Holloway, Tamworth, Staffordshire, B79 7LR.
Owner: Tamworth Borough Council　　　**Contact:** Mrs E Ballard
Norman motte and bailey castle with fifteen period rooms spanning 800 years of history.
Location: Town centre off A453.
Opening Times: All year, Mon - Sat, 10.00am - 5.30pm. Sun 2.00pm - 5.30pm. Last admission 4.30pm.
Admission: Adult £3.00, Child £1.50, Family £7.50, Conc £1.50. Groups of 10 plus: Adults £2.40, Children £1.00, School children 60p.

WOLSELEY GARDEN PARK

Tel: 01889 574888　　**Fax:** 01889 574888

Wolseley Bridge, Stafford, Staffordshire, ST17 0YT.

Contact: D Harper Esq
45 acres of gardens on a variety of themes, recently created by Sir Charles and Lady Wolseley. Scented garden for the blind.
Location: At junction of A51 and A513 (2m N of Rugeley in Staffordshire).
Opening Times: Apr - Oct, 10.00am - 6.00pm. Nov - Mar, 10.00am - 4.00pm. Open every day except Christmas.
Admission: Adult £2.00, Child £1.00, Conc £1.50, Group of 20 plus 50p discount.

SPECIAL EVENTS DIARY

- **8th - 9th April: Shugborough Estate**
  BASC Gamekeepers Fair.

- **29th - 30th April: Shugborough Estate**
  Shugborough in Bloom - Spectacular displays in the Georgian Mansion House 11am - 5pm (Bonsai Festival).

- **13th - 14th May: Sandon Hall**
  Stafford County Antiques Fair

- **13th - 14th May: Shugborough Estate**
  Shugborough in Bloom - Spectacular displays in the Georgian Mansion House 11am - 5pm (Orchid Festival).

- **27th - 29th May: Sandon Hall**
  Living Heritage Craft Show.

- **27th - 29th May: Shugborough Estate**
  National Trust Centenary Craft Fair.

- **11th June: Shugborough Estate**
  National Trust Centenary Victorian Street Market.

- **11th June: Biddulph Grange Garden**
  Gilbert and Sullivan - The Mikado.

- **16th - 18th June: Sandon Hall**
  Home and Garden Design Exhibition.

- **23rd June: Shugborough Estate**
  Viennese Evening Concert. Bookings tel: 01625 573477.

- **9th July: Shugborough Estate**
  Doll and Teddy Bear Show.

- **15th - 16th July: Shugborough Estate**
  Shugborough Gardening Event in conjunction with Central TV.

- **15th - 16th July: Shugborough Estate**
  Shugborough in Bloom - Spectacular displays in the Georgian Mansion House 11am - 5pm (Rose Festival).

- **22nd July: Shugborough Estate**
  National Trust Centenary Firework & Laser Symphony Concert (gates open 6pm). Bookings tel: 01625 573477.

- **23rd July: Shugborough Estate**
  Goose Fair.

- **29th - 30th July: Shugborough Estate**
  Shugborough in Bloom - Spectacular displays in the Georgian Mansion House 11am - 5pm (Sweet Pea Festival).

- **12th - 13th July: Shugborough Estate**
  Shugborough in Bloom - Spectacular displays in the Georgian Mansion House 11am - 5pm (Fuchsia Festival).

- **19th-20th July: Sandon Hall**
  Living Heritage Country Sports Fair

- **26th - 28th July: Shugborough Estate**
  Summer Craft Festival

- **23rd - 24th September: Shugborough Estate**
  Shugborough in Bloom - Spectacular displays in the Georgian Mansion House 11am - 5pm (Dahlia Festival).

- **30th September - 1st Oct: Sandon Hall**
  Living Heritage Craft Show

- **21st - 22nd Oct: Sandon Hall**
  Stafford County Antiques Fair

- **28th - 29th October: Shugborough Estate**
  Halloween at Shugborough 5.00 - 8.00pm

- **4th November: Shugborough Estate**
  Bonfire Night

- **4th - 5th November: Sandon Hall**
  Christmas Gift Fayre

- **5th - 7th December: Shugborough Estate**
  Victorian Christmas Evenings 5.00 - 9.00pm

The Maze at Somerleyton Hall, Suffolk

KENTWELL HALL
Long Melford

KENTWELL HALL is a beautiful redbrick Tudor Manor House surrounded by a broad moat.

Built by the Clopton Family, from wealth made in the wool trade, Kentwell has an air of timeless tranquillity. The exterior is little altered in 450 years. The interior was remodelled by Hopper in 1825 and his work has been embellished and enhanced in restoration by the present owners. Hopper's interiors, notably the Great Hall and Dining Room, emphasise their Tudor provenance, but the Drawing Room and Library are simply and restrainedly classical; all are eminently habitable.

Kentwell, as well as being a family home, conveys a deep feeling of the Tudor period with the service areas: Great Kitchen, Bakery, Dairy and Forge always fully equipped in 16th century style. Kentwell's unique 16th century atmosphere and large collection of 16th century artifacts make it an ideal location for films and videos.

The gardens are part of Kentwell's delight. Intimate yet spacious, you are seldom far from a moat, clipped yews (some 30 ft high) or mellow brick wall. There is a fine walled garden with original 17th Century layout and a well established large Herb Garden and Potager.

The farm is run organically and is set around timber framed buildings and stocked with rare breed farm animals.

Home to the **Award -Winning Re-Creations of Tudor Domestic Life** when visitors meet numerous 'Tudors' with dress, speech, activities and locations appropriate for the 16th century. These take place on selected weekends between April and September.

❖

CONTACT

Mrs J G Phillips
Kentwell Hall
Long Melford
Suffolk
CO10 9BA

Tel: (01787) 310207
Fax: (01787) 379318

LOCATION

Off the A134. 4 miles north of Sudbury, 14 miles South of Bury St Edmunds.

Rail: Sudbury Stn 4 miles, Colchester Stn 20 miles.

Air: Stanstead 30 miles.

Taxi: Felix (01787) 310574.

SUITABILITY FOR OTHER EVENTS
Kentwell specialises in: Genuine Tudor Style Banquets, Wedding Receptions, formal but friendly luncheons and dinners and particularly 'Company Days' when the whole company, or a division, come to Kentwell for a specially devised one-day programme of fun, stimulation and challenge.

EXTRA FACILITIES
A wide variety of 'Tudor-style' activities can be arranged for visitors, including longbow shooting, working bakery, dairy and stillroom, spinning etc. Clay pigeon shooting in Park. Airstrip suitable for light aircraft and microlites.

ADVICE TO COURIERS & DRIVERS
No dogs or unaccompanied children. No photography in the House.

FACILITIES FOR THE DISABLED
Disabled or elderly visitors may alight at house, with prior notice. New disabled toilet.

PARKING FOR COACHES & CARS
There is parking for several hundred cars and coaches.

CATERING
Kentwell provides its own catering, often from produce home grown or raised from Kentwell's own organic farm. Home-made teas and lunches on open days up to full catering for grander functions. The undercroft can comfortably seat 96.

GIFT SHOP
Open at the same time as the House and selling a variety of local and 'Tudor-style' items. New range of colour guide books will be introduced.

SCHOOL VISITS/CHILDREN
School groups are encouraged: Kentwell has a highly developed schools' programme dealing with 700 parties per year. Schools can visit a Re-Creation of Tudor Life, themselves re-create Tudor life in the Moat House or take one of our tours conducted by a qualified teacher on the House, Garden, Farm or aspects of each.

OPENING TIMES

Spring
14 Apr- 21 Apr
Daily: 12 noon - 5.00pm

22 April - 11 June
Suns: 12 noon - 5.00pm

6 - 8, & 27 May - 2 June
12 noon - 5.00pm
Except Bank Hol weekends
11.00 - 6.00pm

Summer
18 Jun - 16 Jul
Open only for Re-Creation of Tudor Life.
(See Below)

19 Jul - 24 Sept.
Daily 12 noon - 5.00pm
Except Bank Hol weekends
11.00 - 6.00pm

October Suns only.

Re-creation of Tudor Life
Weekends only
• 14 Apr - 17 Apr
• 6 May - 8 May
• 27 May - 29 May
• 5 Aug - 6 Aug
• 25 Aug - 28 Aug
• 23 Sept - 24 Sept
Daily - usually 11am - 6.00pm

Great annual Re-Creation
(Sats & Suns only)
• 18 Jun - 16 Jul
• 14 July
11.00am - 5.00pm

ADMISSION

"(Subject to variation in VAT) but not during Re-Creations when special prices apply".
FULL TICKET
   Adult £4.50
   Child (5-15) £2.75
   OAP £3.75
GARDEN & FARM
   Adult £2.50
   Child (5-15) £1.75
   OAP £2.25
Groups
20% discount for groups of 25 or more if pre-booked.

OWNERS TOURS
   Standard £5.50
   Extended £6.50
(min 30 people per tour)

CONFERENCE AND FUNCTION FACILITIES

ROOM	DIMENSIONS	CAPACITY	LAYOUT	POWER POINTS	SUITABLE FOR A/V
Great Hall	40' x 24'	100	Buffet	✓	✓
		120	Theatre		
		30	Boardroom		
		60	Lunch/Dinner		
Main Dining Room	24' x 24'	75	Buffet	✓	
		40	Lunch/Dinner		
Drawing Room	35' x 24'	75	Buffet	✓	
		50	Lunch/Dinner		
Library	36' x 20'	20	Boardroom	✓	

SOMERLEYTON HALL
Lowestoft

SOMERLEYTON HALL is a perfect example of a House built to show off the wealth of the new Victorian aristocracy. The house was remodelled from a modest 17th Century Manor House by the rich railwayman Sir Morton Peco. When he was declared bankrupt in 1863, his extravagant concoction of red brick, white stone and lavish interiors was sold to another hugely successful businessman, carpet manufacturer Sir Francis Crossley. The present owner Lord Somerleyton, is his great-grandson.

No expense was spared in the building or the fittings. Stone was brought from Caen and Aubigny and the magnificent carved stonework created by John Thomas (who worked on the houses of Parliament) has been recently restored.

In the state rooms there are paintings by Landseer, Wright of Derby and Stanfield, together with fine wood carvings by Willcox of Warwick and from the earlier house, Grinling Gibbons.

The Oak Room retains its carved oak panelling and Stuart atmosphere: the rest is lavishly Victorian. Grandest of all is the Ballroom with its crimson damask walls reflected in rows of long white and gilt mirrors.

GARDENS

Somerleyton's 12 acre gardens are justly renowned. The 1846 yew hedge maze is one of the few surviving Victorian mazes in Britain. The stable tower clock by Vuilliamy made in 1847 is the original model for a great clock to serve as the Tower Clock in the new Houses of Parliament, now world famous as Big Ben. Colour is added to the gardens by rhododendrons, azaleas and a long pergola trailing mauve, pink and white wisteria. Special features include: a sunken garden; the Loggia Tea Room; glasshouses by Sir Joseph Paxton; an aviary; fine statuary.

❖

SUITABILITY FOR OTHER EVENTS
Somerleyton Hall is suitable for conferences, receptions, fashion shows, archery, clay pigeon shooting, equestrian events, garden parties, shows, rallies, filming, wedding receptions.

EXTRA FACILITIES
The Winter Gardens, Loggia, Conference Rooms and Ballroom can be hired throughout the year.

ADVICE TO COURIERS & DRIVERS
No dogs or photography in the House.

FACILITIES FOR THE DISABLED
If visitors are badly disabled they may alight at the entrance to the house, before parking in the allocated areas. Wheelchair and ramps are available. There are toilets for the disabled.

PARKING FOR COACHES & CARS
Capacity of the Car Park: 100 cars and 10 coaches, 20 yards from Garden entrance.

CATERING
Loggia Tea Room, fresh home baked cooking light lunches and the ever popular cream teas.

GUIDED TOURS
By prior arrangement. If requested, the owner may meet groups. Average time for tour 3/4 hour.

GIFT SHOP
Open at same time as the Hall and Gardens.

GUIDE BOOKS
Colour guide book, £2.00.

SCHOOL VISITS/CHILDREN
Groups of children welcome during the season every morning, by prior arrangement, from 9.30am to 2.30pm. A guide is provided. Areas of particular interest include: Maze and garden trail, aviary, dolls house.

CONTACT

Lord Somerleyton
Estate Office
Somerleyton Hall
Nr Lowestoft
Suffolk
NR32 5QQ

Tel: (01502) 730224
Fax: (01502) 732143

LOCATION

5 miles north-west
Lowestoft off B1074: 7
miles Yarmouth (A143)

Rail: Somerleyton
Station 1¹/₂ miles.
Taxi: St Olaves'
Service Station,
Great Yarmouth 488278.

OPENING TIMES

Summer
Easter Sunday - 1 Oct
inclusive

HOUSE, MAZE &
GARDENS
Thurs, Suns and
Bank holidays with the
addition of Tues, and
Weds in July and August

House: 2.00 - 5.00pm
Garden: 12.30 - 5.00pm

Winter
Closed except by
appointment.

ADMISSION

Adult £3.75
OAP £3.25
Child £1.75
Family (2+2) . .£10.50

Groups rates on application. The house and gardens are available for guided tours for private parties or school groups. Details on application.

Somerleyton Hall is ideal for a wide range of events. Details on application.

CONFERENCE AND FUNCTION FACILITIES

ROOM	DIMENSIONS	CAPACITY	LAYOUT	POWER POINTS	SUITABLE FOR A/V
Conference Suite	34'3" x 22'	75	Theatre	4	✓
The Loggia	47'4" x 10'2"	80	Various	3	✓
Winter Garden	99' x 16'	80	Various	3	✓

ABBEY VISITOR CENTRE

Tel: 01284 763110   **Fax:** 01284 757079

Samson Tower, Abbey Precinct, Bury St Edmunds, Suffolk, IP33 1RS.
Owner: St Edmondsbury Borough Council   **Contact:** T Meakin
Location: Town centre off A14.
Opening Times: Apr and Oct, daily, 10.00am - 5.00pm. May and Sept, daily, 10.00am - 6.00pm. Jun - Aug, daily, 10.00am - 8.00pm. Nov - Mar, Wed, Sat, 10.00am - 4.00pm, Sun 12.00pm - 4.00pm.
Admission: Adult 80p, Child 60p, Conc 60p, Groups 20% discount, Free for locals.

BELCHAMP HALL

Tel: 01787 372744

Belchamp Walter, Sudbury, Suffolk, CO10 7AT.
Owner: M M J Raymond Esq   **Contact:** M M J Raymond Esq
Queen Anne period house with period furniture and 17th and 18th century family portraits. Gardens..
Location: 5 m SW of Sudbury.
Opening Times: By appointment only. May to Sept - Tues & Thurs and Easter, Spring & Summer Bank Hol Mons 2.30pm - 6.00pm.
Admission: Adult - £3.00, Child £1.50. Reduction for parties. Ploughman's lunches, teas, by arrangement.

BLAKENHAM WOODLAND GARDEN

Tel: 0171 4112000   **Fax:** 0171 4112399

Little Blakenham, Nr. Ipswich
Owner: Lord Blakenham   **Contact:** Rosalind Wild
Location: 4m NW of Ipswich.
Opening Times: 1 Mar - 30 Jun, every day except Sat, 1.00pm - 5.00pm.
Admission: Standard £1.00.

FRAMLINGHAM CASTLE

Tel: 01728 72330

Framlingham, Suffolk.
Owner: English Heritage   **Contact:** The Administrator
A superb 12th century castle which, from the outside, looks almost the same as when it was built. From the continuous curtain wall, linking 13 towers, there are excellent views of Framlingham and the charming reed fringed mere. At different times, the castle has been a fortress, an Elizabethan prison, a poor house and a school. The many alterations over the years have led to a pleasing mixture of historical styles.
Location: In Framlingham on B1116.
Opening Times: 1 Apr - 30 Sept: daily 10.00am - 6.00pm, 1 Oct - 31 Mar: daily 10.00am - 4.00pm (Closed 24 - 26 Dec, 1 Jan).
Admission: Adult £2.00, Child £1.00, Conc £1.50.

GAINSBOROUGH'S HOUSE

OPEN

All year
Tues - Sat
10.00am - 5.00pm.

Sun & Bank Hol
Mons 2 - 5.00pm
Closes at 4.00pm
Nov to Easter
Closed: Mondays.
Good Friday and
Christmas to
New Year.

Tel: 01787 372958

46 GAINSBOROUGH ST, SUDBURY, SUFFOLK CO10 6EU

Owner: Gainsborough's House Society   *Contact: Hugh Belsey*

Birthplace of Thomas Gainsborough RA (1727-88). Georgian fronted town house, with attractive walled garden, displays more of the artist's work than any other Gallery. The collection is shown together with eighteenth century furniture and memorabilia. Varied programme of contemporary exhibitions organised throughout the year includes; fine art, craft, photography, printmaking, sculpture and highlights the work of East Anglian Artists.

Location: 46 Gainsborough Street, Sudbury town centre.
Admission: Adult £2.50, OAP £2.00. Children and students £1.25.

HELMINGHAM HALL

OPEN

Gardens only
30 Apr - 10 Sept
Sundays only
2.00 - 6.00pm

Wednesdays
between the
above dates for
prior arranged
groups for 30+.

Tel: 01473 890363
Fax: 01473 890776

STOWMARKET, SUFFOLK IP14 6EF

Owner: The Lord and Lady Tollemache   *Contact: Mrs A Newman*

The Tudor Hall surrounded by its wide moat is set in a 400 acre deer park. Two superb gardens, one surrounded by its own moat and walls extends to several acres. One has wide herbaceous borders and an immaculate kitchen garden. The second enclosed within yew hedges has a special rose garden with a Herb and Knot garden containing plants grown in England before 1750.

Location: B1077 9 miles north of Ipswich.
Admission: Adult £2.80, Concessions £2.60, Child (5 - 15) £1.50. Groups 30+ £2.30. Safari rides: Adult £1.90 Child £1.30

ICKWORTH

Tel: 01284 735270

The Rotunda, Horringer, Bury st Edmunds, Suffolk, IP29 5QE.
Owner: The National Trust   **Contact:** The Administrator
The eccentric Earl of Bristol (also Bishop of Derry) created this equally eccentric house, started in 1795 to display his collections. The paintings include works by Titian, Gainsborough and Velasquez and the magnificent Georgian Silver Collection is displayed in the oval Rotunda which is linked by curved corridors to flanking wings. The house is surrounded by an Italianate garden and is set in a 'Capability' Brown park with several waymarked woodland walks and a deer enclosure with hide.
Location: In Horringer, 3m SW of Bury-St-Edmunds on W side of A143.
Opening Times: House: 25 Mar - 5 Nov, Tues, Wed, Fri, Sat, Sun & BH Mon 1.00pm - 5.00pm. Park: all year, daily 7.00am - 7.00pm. Garden: 25 Mar - 5 Nov, daily 10.00am - 5.00pm; 6 Nov - end Mar 1996, daily 10.00am - 4.00pm. Whole property closed Good Fri.
Admission: House, Garden & Park: Adult £4.30, Child £2.00, Pre-booked parties £3.50. Park & Garden only: Adult £1.50, Child 50p.

KENTWELL HALL

See page 169 for full page entry.

LANDGUARD FORT

Tel: 01394 286403

Felixstowe, Suffolk.
Owner: English Heritage   **Contact:** The Administrator
Impressive 18th century fort with later additions built on a site originally fortified by Henry VIII and in use until after World War II.
Location: 1 m S of Felixstowe near docks.
Opening Times: Museum open 29 May - 25 Sept, Wed & Sun only, 2.30pm - 5.00pm. Guided tours of fort Wed & Sun 2.45pm & 4.00pm.
Admission: Adults £1.00, Child 60p, EH members 80p.

LAVENHAM GUILDHALL

Tel: 01787 247646

Felixstowe, Suffolk.
Owner: The National Trust   **Contact:** The Administrator
This early 16th century timber framed Tudor building, originally the hall of the Guild of Corpus Christi, overlooks and dominates the market place. Within the nine rooms of the Guildhall are displays of local history, farming, industry and the development of the railway, and a unique exhibition of 700 years of the medieval woollen cloth trade. There is a delightful walled garden with a 19th century lock up and mortuary.
Location: A1141 and B1071.
Opening Times: 25 Mar - 5 Nov daily, 11.00am - 5.00pm (closed Good Fri).
Admission: Adult £2.50, Child first two free then 60p, Parties £2.10, School parties 50p by prior arrangement. All children free during school summer holidays.

LEISTON ABBEY

Leiston, Suffolk.
Owner: English Heritage   **Contact:** The Administrator
The remains of this abbey for Premonstratensian canons, including a restored chapel, are amongst the most extensive in Suffolk.
Location: 1 m N of Leiston off B1069.
Opening Times: Any reasonable time.

LITTLE HALL

Tel: 01787 247179   **Fax:** 01787 248341

Market Place, Lavenham, Suffolk, CO10 9QZ.
Owner: Suffolk Preservation Society   **Contact:** B W Forgham
Little Hall, a Grade II Listed Building with a Crown Post roof, reveals five centuries of change. Its history mirrors the rise and fall of Lavenham's cloth trade. Restored by the Gayer-Anderson twins in the 1930s.
Location: Market Place, Lavenham.
Opening Times: Easter - Oct, Wed, Thurs, Sat, Sun, 2.30pm - 5.30pm. Bank Hols.

MANOR HOUSE MUSEUM

Tel: 01284 757072   **Fax:** 01284 757079

Honey Hill, Bury St Edmunds, Suffolk, IP33 1HF.
Owner: St Edmondsbury Borough Council   **Contact:** T Meakin
Georgian mansion with displays specialising in horology from 17th to 20th century.
Location: Bury town centre off A14.
Opening Times: Mon - Sat, 10.00am - 5.00pm. Sun 2.00pm - 5.00pm.
Admission: Adult £2.50, Child £1.50, Family £7.00, Conc £1.50, Groups 20% discount.

MELFORD HALL ✿

Tel: 01787 880286

Long Melford, Sudbury, Suffolk, CO10 9AH.
Owner: The National Trust   **Contact:** The Administrator
A turreted brick Tudor mansion, little changed since 1578 with the original panelled banqueting hall, an 18th century drawing room, a Regency library and a Victorian bedroom, showing fine furniture and Chinese porcelain. There is also a special Beatrix Potter display and a garden.
Location: In Long Melford on E side of A134, 14m S of Bury St Edmunds, 3m N of Sudbury.
Opening Times: Apr: Sat, Sun & BH Mon 2.00pm - 5.30pm, May - end Sept, Wed, Thur, Sat, Sun & BH Mon 2.00pm - 5.30pm, Oct: Sat & Sun 2.00pm - 5.30pm. Last admission 5.00pm.
Admission: Principal rooms & garden £2.70, pre-arranged parties £2.30 Wed & Thur only.

MOYSES HALL MUSEUM

Tel: 01284 757488   **Fax:** 01284 757079

Cornhill, Bury St Edmunds, Suffolk, IP33 1DX.
Owner: St Edmondsbury Borough Council   **Contact:** T Meakin
Very early 12th century flint house, now a museum of Suffolk history.
Location: Town centre off A14.
Opening Times: 10.00am - 5.00pm daily except Sun 2.00pm - 5.00pm.
Admission: Adult £1.25, Child 75p, Concessions 75p, Groups 20% discount, Free for local residents.

ORFORD CASTLE ▣

Tel: 01394 450472

Orford, Suffolk.
Owner: English Heritage   **Contact:** The Administrator
A royal castle built for coastal defence in the 12th century. A magnificent keep survives almost intact with three towers reaching to 90 feet. Inside there are many rooms to explore.
Location: In Orford on B1084 20 m NE of Ipswich.
Opening Times: 1 Apr - 30 Sept: daily 10.00am - 6.00pm, 1 Oct - 31 Mar: daily 10.00am - 4.00pm (Closed 24 - 26 Dec, 1 Jan).
Admission: Adult £2.00, Child £1.00, Conc £1.50.

OTLEY HALL

OPEN

Apr: 16, 17
May: 28, 29
August: 27, 28

2.00 - 6.00pm

Cream Teas

(See also below)

Tel: 01473 890264
Fax: 01473 890803

OTLEY, SUFFOLK IP6 9PA

Owner: Mr. J Mosesson   *Contact:* The Secretary

A stunning 15th century Moated Hall (Grade I), still a family home set in 10 acres of gardens and grounds. Frequently referred to as "one of the loveliest mediaeval moated houses in England". Rich in history and architectural features. Also open by appointment for private guided tours, corporate hospitality, wedding receptions and film/photography location. Voted by AA Publications 1994 'One of the top 20 historic houses in Britain"

Location: From A14 take Norwich/Diss junction (A410), then follow B1078 signs.
Admission: On open days Adult £4.00, Child £2.50.

SAXTEAD GREEN POST MILL ▣

Tel: 01728 685789

Saxtead Green, Suffolk.
Owner: English Heritage   **Contact:** The Administrator
The finest example of a Suffolk Post Mill. Still in working order, you can climb the wooden stairs to the various floors, full of fascinating mill machinery.
Location: 2½ m NW of Framlington on A1120.
Opening Times: 1 Apr - 30 Sept, daily, 10.00am - 6.00pm, 1 Oct - 31 Oct, 10.00am - 4.00pm. Lunchtime closure 1.00pm - 2.00pm.
Admission: Adult £1.30, Child 70p, Conc £1.00.

SOMERLEYTON HALL 🏛

See page 170 for full page entry.

THE PRIORY, LAVENHAM 🏛

OPEN

Easter - 31 October

Daily

10.30am - 5.30pm

Tel: 01787 247003

WATER STREET, LAVENHAM, SUFFOLK CO10 9RW

Owner: Mr and Mrs Alan Casey   *Contact:* Mr and Mrs Alan Casey

Beautiful medieval timber-frame house in the heart of Lavenham, yet backing on to rolling countryside. Once the home of Benedictine monks, rich cloth merchants and an Elizabethan Rector. Superbly restored and furnished with a blend of antique and modern furniture, paintings and stained glass by Ervin Bossanyi (1891-1975); aromatic herb garden with culinary, medicinal and dyers herbs; kitchen garden, orchard and pond.

Location: The Priory is in the centre of Lavenham in Water Street.
Admission: Adult £2.50, Child £1.00

WINGFIELD COLLEGE 🏛

Tel: 01379 384888   **Fax:** 01379 384034

Wingfield Eye, Suffolk, IP21 5RA.
Owner: Ian Chance Esq   **Contact:** Ian Chance Esq
Founded in 1362 on the 13th century site of the Manor House by Sir John de Wingfield, a close friend of the Black Prince. Magnificent Medieval Great Hall. Surrendered to Henry VIII in 1542 and seized by Cromwell's Parliament in 1649. Mixed period interiors with 18th century neo-classical facade. Walled gardens and Topiary. Teas. Celebrated Arts and Music Season. Adjacent church with tombs of College founder and Benefactors, the Earls and Dukes of Suffolk.
Location: Signposted off B1118, 7m SE of Diss.
Opening Times: East Sat to 26 Sept - Sat, Suns and Bank Hols 2.00pm - 6.00pm.
Admission: Adult £2.50, Conc £1.00.

WYKEN HALL

Tel: 01359 250287   **Fax:** 01359 250240

Stanton, Bury St Edmunds, Suffolk, IP31 2DW.
Owner: Sir Kenneth Carlisle   **Contact:** Sir Kenneth Carlisle
Romantic 4 acre garden with rose, herb, knot and wild gardens, and maze. Cafe and country store in 16th century barn selling Wyken wine. Woodland walk to vineyard.
Location: 9m NE of Bury St Edmunds off A143. Follow brown tourist signs to Wyken Vineyard from Isworth.
Opening Times: 1 Feb to 24 Dec on Thurs, Fri, Sun and Bank Hol Mons 10.00am - 6.00pm.
Admission: Garden only: Adult £2.00, Child under 12 free, OAP £1.50.

SPECIAL EVENTS DIARY

- **25th March - 21st May: Gainsborough's House**
  Exhibition of Contemporary portraits of East Anglians. Sculpture in the Garden: Andrew Burton.

- **14th - 17th April: Kentwell**
  Great Easter Egg Hunt and Quiz and Re-Creation of Tudor Life at Eastertide. 11am-6pm.

- **28th - 30th May: Kentwell**
  1945 Re-Lived - will take the visitor back to the week before VE Day when Kentwell was requisitioned as a large transit camp. The collection of 1945 Forces and Weapons (including Sherman Tanks and artillery) may be the largest of its type in Europe for any of the VE day celebrations. 10am-6pm.

- **6th - 8th May: Kentwell**
  Re-Creation of Tudor Life with May Queen, Jack O Green and Tudor Maypole showing May Day Celebrations Tudor style. 11am-6pm.

- **27th May - 29th July: Kentwell**
  Re-Creation of Tudor Life at Whitsuntide. 11am-6pm

- **27th May - 23rd July: Gainsborough's House**
  John Dodgson, Desmond MacCarthy: Views of Long Melford.

- **27th May - 9th July: Wingfield College**
  Mini-Print International Exhibition - over 600 original prints by artists worldwide.

- **18th June - 16th July: Kentwell**
  'Kentwell 1546' Great Annual Re-Creation of Tudor Life. 11am-5pm (Sats, Suns & 14th July only).

- **28th - 29th July: Kentwell**
  Open Air Shakespeare "A Midsummer Night's Dream". 7.45pm.

- **29th July - 17th Sept: Gainsborough's House**
  Sculpture in the Garden: Oliver Barratt Exhibition - Printmaker in Residence.

- **5th - 6th August: Kentwell**
  Annual Longbow Shoot and Re-Creation of Tudor Life at Lammas, 11am-6pm.

- **25th - 28th: Kentwell**
  High Summer Re-Creation of Tudor Life 11am-6pm

- **23rd - 24th September: Kentwell**
  Michaelmas Re-creation of Tudor Life. 11am-6pm

Helmingham Hall, Suffolk

CLANDON PARK/ HATCHLANDS
Guildford

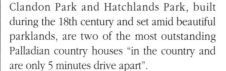

Clandon Park and Hatchlands Park, built during the 18th century and set amid beautiful parklands, are two of the most outstanding Palladian country houses "in the country and are only 5 minutes drive apart".

Clandon Park - Clandon is a house of dramatic contrasts; from the neo-classical marble hall to the Maori Meeting House in the garden; the opulent saloon to the old kitchen - complete with original range - below stairs. All this adds up to a fascinating insight into the different lifestyles of the ruling and serving classes in the 18th century. Today the house is rightly acclaimed for its remarkable collection of ceramics, textiles and furniture and its excellent restaurant.

Hatchlands Park - was built in 1757 for Admiral Boscawen, one of the great Naval Heroes. The house has the earliest known decorative plasterwork by Robert Adam in an English country house. The Cobbe collection of early keyboard instruments, paintings and furniture was introduced in 1988 when the house was extensively re-decorated. In the keyboard collection is an Evard pianoforte, one of the most beautiful square pianos to survive the 18th century and almost certainly made for Queen Marie Antoinette.

❖

SUITABILITY FOR OTHER EVENTS
Clandon House available for non-residential private and commercial functions; the administrator welcomes enquiries.

EXTRA FACILITIES
National Trust concerts during the season at both properties.

FACILITIES FOR THE DISABLED
Clandon Park - Parking near front of house for disabled visitors only or less-able visitors may be set down in front of house. WC on lower ground floor difficult for wheelchairs. Ramp to garden. The first floor is completely level but has 3 steps up to it. Restaurant is accessible. Braille Guide.

Hatchlands Park - Access to ground floor, terrace and part of garden. WC, Wheelchair available.
New for 1995: Braille Guide for Gertrude Jekyll garden.

PARKING FOR COACHES & CARS
Available 300 yards from the house.

CATERING
Clandon - Licensed Restaurant open same days as house 12.30 - 5.30pm. Tel: 01483 222502.

Hatchlands - open as house 12.30 - 5.00pm.
Tel: 01483 211120

GUIDED TOURS
Clandon - Parties and morning tours by arrangement with the Administrator. Connoisseur Tours - please ring for information.

GIFT SHOP
Both open as house. Clandon Park shop also open for Christmas Shopping and weekends in March. Tel: 01483 211412.

GUIDE BOOKS
Available at both properties.

CHILDREN
Changing facilities. Sorry, backpacks not admitted.

CONTACT

The Administrator
Clandon Park/
Hatchlands Park
West Clandon
Guildford
Surrey
GU4 7RQ

Tel: (01483) 222482

LOCATION

Clandon
At West Clandon on
the A247, 3 miles
east of Guildford.
Rail: Clandon
BR 1 mile.

Hatchlands
East of East Clandon
on the A246 Guildford -
Leatherhead road.
Rail: Clandon BR
2 1/2 miles,
Horsley 3 miles.

OPENING TIMES

Clandon

1 April - 29th October
Daily except Thurs & Fri.
(open Good Fri.)

1.30 - 5.30pm

Bank Hol. Mons.
11.00am - 5.30pm

Garden open
weekends in March.

Hatchlands

2 April - 31 October

Tues, Weds, Thurs,
Suns & Bank Hol. Mons.
Fridays in August only.
2.00 - 5.30pm

Park Walks
Daily (Apr - Oct)
12.30 - 6.00pm

ADMISSION

Clandon

Adults £4.00
Child £2.00
Fam. ticket £10.00
Groups (Mons - Weds. only)
Adult £3.50

Hatchlands

Adults £4.00
Grounds only . .£1.50
Child £2.00
Grounds only 75p
Fam. ticket £10.00
Groups
(Tues-Thurs only)
Adult £3.50

HAM HOUSE
Richmond

Ham House, on the banks of the River Thames between Richmond and Kingston, is perhaps the most remarkable Stuart house in the country. Apart from the fact that its architectural fabric has survived virtually unchanged since the 1670's (when the building was enlarged by the Duke and Duchess of Lauderdale), it still retains many of the furnishing from that period - an extraordinary survival. The gardens have been restored to their original guise using plans and images which were found in the house. Ham is presented today principally as the late 17th century Lauderdale residence with overlays of the 18th and 19th centuries. Visitors view the rooms in the sequence intended at the time, progressing through a hierarchy of apartments towards the Queen's Closet - the culmination of the sequence. The gardens were laid out in compartments, reflecting the ordered symmetry of the house and together they present the modern visitor with a complete picture of the 17th century aristocratic life. *Please note: The house has recently been re-opened to the public after a programme of refurbishment.*

CONTACT

The Administrator
Ham House
Ham
Richmond
Surrey
TW10 7RS

Tel: (0181) 940 1950

Fax: (0181) 332 6903

LOCATION

Ham is 1 $\frac{1}{2}$ miles from Richmond and 2 miles from Kingston. On the south bank of the River Thames, west of A307 at Petersham.

Rail: Richmond or Kingston BR and underground.

Bus: LT65 Ealing Broadway - Kingston; 371 Richmond - Kingston. London and Country 415 Victoria - Guildford; London & Country 427 Richmond - Addlestone; all passing BR Richmond and Kingston Tel (0171) 222 1234

SUITABILITY FOR OTHER EVENTS
Orangery and Rose Garden available for functions. Tel: (0181) 940 0735

EXTRA FACILITIES
Picnics in Rose Garden. National Trust Summer Concerts in garden.

ADVICE TO COURIERS & DRIVERS
Please advise that there is no photography allowed inside.

FACILITIES FOR THE DISABLED
Parking near house for drivers or disabled/elderly visitors may be set down and collected near house. Access to house by ramps; lift access to 1st floor on request. NB The grounds do include some deep gravel paths. Staff trained in sympathetic hearing scheme. 2 wheelchairs available. WC. Braille Guide.

PARKING FOR COACHES & CARS
Free parking within 400 yards (not NT)

CATERING
Orangery Restaurant (licensed) open same days as house, waitress service, lunches from 12.30, teas 3.00 - 5.00pm, booking welcome.

GUIDED TOURS
Include "focus" tours, these are available for parties by prior arrangement.

GIFT SHOP
April - end October. days and times as house. Also open for Christmas shopping Tel: (0181) 948 2035 for details.

GUIDE BOOKS
Available from the house and gift shop.

CHILDREN
Baby changing facilities, highchairs in restaurant. House unsuitable for backpacks or pushchairs.

OPENING TIMES

Summer

HOUSE:
1 April - 31 October
Mons - Weds
1.00 - 5.00pm

Sats 1.00 - 5.30pm

Suns 11.30 - 5.30
(Open Good Fri
1.00 - 5.00pm but closed
Tues following)

GARDEN:
Daily except Fri. (open Good Friday)
Closed 25th - 26th December and 1 January
10.30am - 6.00pm
(or dusk if earlier)

Winter

HOUSE & GARDEN

4 Nov - 17 Dec
Sats & Suns only
1.00 - 4.00pm
Last admission $\frac{1}{2}$ hour before closing.

ADMISSION

Adult £4.00
Child £2.00
Fam. Ticket . . .£10.00
Gardens . . . . . . free

Groups
Pre-booked 15 or more.
Rates on application

LOSELEY PARK
Guildford

LOSELEY PARK, built in 1562 by Sir William More, is a fine example of Elizabethan architecture, its mellow stone brought from the ruins of Waverley Abbey now over 850 years old. The House is set amid magnificent parkland grazed by the Loseley Jersey herd. Many visitors comment on the very friendly atmosphere of the House - it is a country house, the family home of descendants of the builder.

Furniture has been acquired by the family and includes an early 16th Century Wrangelschrank beautifully inlaid with many different woods, a Queen Anne cabinet, Georgian arm chairs and settee, a Hepplewhite four-poster bed, King George IV's coronation chair. The King's bedroom has Oudenarde tapestry and a carpet commemorating James I's visit.

The Christian pictures include the Henri Met de Bles triptych of the Nativity and modern mystical pictures of the living Christ, St Francis and St Bernadette. The Christian Trust Centre is in the Oak Room and a small Chapel is available for use by visitors. A Christian Cancer Help Centre meets twice monthly

GARDEN

A magnificent Cedar of Lebanon presides over the front lawn. Parkland adjoins the lawn and a small lake adds to the beauty of Front Park.

In the Walled Garden are mulberry trees, yew hedges, a grass terrace and the Moat Walk with herbaceous borders including a newly planted rose garden, herb, fruit and vegetable garden.

❖

SUITABILITY FOR OTHER EVENTS
Ideal for wedding receptions. Business launches and promotions. A 12 acre field adjoining can also be hired for events in addition to the lawns. Fashion shows, air displays, archery, garden parties, shows, rallies, filming.

EXTRA FACILITIES
These include: Parkland, moat walk and terrace. Lectures can be arranged on the property, its contents, gardens and history. Loseley Christian Trust Exhibition.

ADVICE TO COURIERS & DRIVERS
Coaches approach Loseley from B3000 only, as other roads too narrow. No dogs, except on leads in the car park, no unaccompanied children, no photography in the House, no videos on Estate. All party visits to the House and Farm must be booked in advance. Children's play area. Picnic area.

FACILITIES FOR THE DISABLED
Disabled and elderly visitors may alight at the entrance to the property. Vehicles can then be parked in the allocated area. There are toilet facilities for the disabled. Wheelchair access to ground floor of the House.

PARKING FOR COACHES & CARS
Capacity of the car park - 150 cars, 100 yards from the House and 6 coaches. Summer overflow car park.

CATERING
Health, and wholeness are in the forefront at Loseley. The Barn Restaurant has a capacity of up to 150 people. For special functions, banquets and conferences catering can be arranged by Alexander Catering. Permanent marquee (70'x40') capable of seating 250 people. Additional marquees can also be hired. A new tea room in the house for 1995 plus Loseley Shop.

GUIDED TOURS
Average time for a tour of the House $3/4$ hour. Guided group farm tours take up to 2 hrs and must be prebooked.

GUIDE BOOKS
Colour guide book, £1.50.

SCHOOL VISITS/CHILDREN
School Groups are welcome and by prior arrangement a guide can be provided. Prices: House £2.00, Farm Trailer Ride £2.00 and Farm Walk £2.00. Special rates for school groups. Of particular interest is the farm, where milking can be seen at the appropriate time. Also a 30 minute Nature Trail, which proved very popular in 1994.

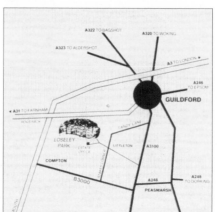

CONTACT

Ms. Rachel Hutt
Loseley Park
Guildford
Surrey
GU3 1HS

Tel: (01483) 304440
Telex: 859972 LOSELG
Fax: (01483) 302036

LOCATION

From London (30miles) A3, leave at Compton, South of Guildford, on B3000 for 2 miles, signposted.
Bus: $1^{1}/4$ miles from House.
Rail: Guildford Stn 2 miles, Godalming 3 miles.
Air: Heathrow 30 miles, Gatwick 30 miles.

OPENING TIMES

Summer
3 May - 30 September
Wed - Sat & Bank Hol
Mons 2.00pm - 5.00pm
Last entry 4.30pm

Tues pre-booked parties only.
Closed Suns.

NB. Group Farm tours, April - October must be pre-booked.

Winter
Tithe Barn available for weddings and private/business functions all year.

ADMISSION

HOUSE & GARDEN
Adult £3.50
Child* £2.00
Group** £2.75

GARDEN ONLY
Adult £1.50
Child* £0.50
Group** £1.20

FARM TOUR & GRDS
Adult £4.00
Child* £2.00
Group** £2.50

* 3 - 16 yrs. Under 3's Free.
**Min. payment 20 people.

ABOVE: THE GREAT HALL

THE TITHE BARN AT LOSELEY PARK

The Tithe Barn (originally 1635) is situated on the sweeping lawns of Loseley House and offers unrivalled views of the surrounding parkland and magnificent Cedar of Lebanon.

It is adaptable for a wide range of functions and will comfortably accommodate 50-150 people for a full sit-down meal, or up to 200 for a cocktail reception. Should a larger group be envisaged, our permanent marquee may be used and further marquees erected. The South Room of the Tithe Barn is ideal for small meetings and private lunches.

The location is ideal for business and corporate hospitality events and is in easy reach of the A3 and M25, an hour from London and some 40 minutes from Heathrow and Gatwick Airports. Ample car parking is available.

CONFERENCE AND FUNCTION FACILITIES

ROOM	DIMENSIONS	CAPACITY	LAYOUT	POWER POINTS	SUITABLE FOR A/V
C17th Tithe Barn	100' x 18'	200 Theatre Schoolroom U-shape Boardroom Buffet Lunch/Dinner	Reception	3	3
South Room	30' x 15'	40 Syndicate Room	Private Parties		
Marquee	70' x 40'	250	Various		

BELOW: THE TITHE BARN

BELOW: THE TITHE BARN

CAREW MANOR

Tel: 0181 770 4781   **Fax:** 0181 770 4777

Church Road, Beddington, Croydon, Surrey, SM6 7NH.
Owner: London Borough of Sutton   **Contact:** Ms V Murphy
Late Medieval Great Hall with hammer-beam roof. Early 18th century dovecote also shown.
Location: Off A232 on edge of Beddington Park.
Opening Times: Sun and BH Mon during summer. Ring for details.
Admission: Guided tour £2.30, Adults 90p, Child 45p, Groups ring for details.

CLANDON PARK/HATCHLANDS

See page 174 for full page entry.

CLAREMONT LANDSCAPE GARDEN

Tel: 01372 469421

Portsmouth Road, Esher, Surrey, KT10 9JG.
Owner: The National Trust   **Contact:** The Administrator
One of the earliest surviving English landscape gardens, restored to its former glory. Begun by Sir John Vanbrugh and Charles Bridgeman before 1720, the gardens were extended and naturalised by William Kent. 'Capability' Brown also made improvements. Features include a lake, island with pavilion, grotto, turf amphitheatre, viewpoints and avenues.
Location: On S edge of Esher, on E side of A307 (no access from Esher bypass).
Opening Times: Jan - 31 Mar, daily (except Mon) 10.00am - 5.00pm or sunset if earlier. Apr - 31 Oct; Mon - Fri, 10.00am - 6.00pm. Sat and Sun and BH Mon 10.00am - 7.00pm. 12 - 16 Jul garden closes. 4 Nov - end Mar, daily (except Mon), 10.00am - 5.00pm or sunset if earlier. Last admission 1/2 an hour before closing. Closed 25 Dec & 1 Jan.
Admission: Sun & BH Mon £2.60, Mon to Sat £1.80, no reduction for parties. Coach parties must book; no coach parties on Sun.

FARNHAM CASTLE KEEP

Castle Hill, Farnham, Surrey, GU6 0AG.
Owner: English Heritage   **Contact:** N Bray Esq
Used as a fortified manor by the medieval Bishops of Winchester, this motte and bailey castle has been in continuous occupation since the 12th century. You can visit the large shell-keep enclosing a mound in which are massive foundations of a Norman tower.
Location: 1/2m N of Farnham town centre on A287.
Opening Times: 1 Apr - 30 Sept daily 10.00am - 6.00pm.
Admission: Adult £2.00, Child, £1.00, Conc £1.50.

GODDARDS

Tel: 01306 730487

Abinger Lane, Abinger Common, Dorking, Surrey, RH5 6JH.
Owner: The Lutyens Trust   **Contact:** Capt Anthony Smith
Edwardian country house by Sir Edwin Lutyens with Gertrude Jekyll garden, in beautiful setting on slopes of Leith Hill.
Location: Half way between Guildford and Dorking. 2m South of A25.
Opening Times: Apr to Oct by telephoning the Administrator.
Admission: £3.50 for guided tour.

GREATHED MANOR

Tel: 01342 832577

Ford Manor Road, Dormansland, Lingfield, Surrey, RH7 6PA.
Owner: Country Houses Association   **Contact:** The Administrator
Victorian Manor House.
Location: 1 1/2 m SE of Lingfield off the B2028.
Opening Times: May - Sept, Wed and Thurs, 2.00pm - 5.00pm.
Admission: Adult £2.50, Child £1.00, Groups by arrangement.

HAMPTON COURT PALACE

Tel: 0181 781 9787   **Fax:** 0181 781 9794

East Molesey, Surrey, KT8 9AU.
Owner: Historic Royal Palaces
Location: On the A309 which is just off A3 at Kingston.
Opening Times: 30 Mar - Oct, Mon, 10.15am - 6.00pm, Tues - Sun 9.30am - 6.00pm. Nov - 1 Mar, Mon, 10.15am - 4.30pm. Tues - Sun, 9.30am - 4.30pm.
Admission: Adult £7.00, Child under 16 £4.70, Child under 5 free, Family £19.30, Conc £5.30.

HAM HOUSE

See page 175 for full page entry.

HERITAGE CENTRE

Tel: 0181 773 4555   **Fax:** 0181 770 4777

Honeywood Walk, Carshalton, Surrey, SM5 3NX.
Owner: London Borough of Sutton   **Contact:** Ms J Howard
17th century listed building with permanent and changing displays of various aspects of local life.
Location: Carshalton.
Opening Times: Wed - Fri, 10.00am - 5.00pm. Sat, Sun and BH Mons, 10.00am - 5.30pm.
Admission: Adult 80p, Child 40p, Groups call to verify rates.

LITTLE HOLLAND HOUSE

Tel: 0181 770 4781   **Fax:** 0181 770 4777

40 Beeches Avenue, Carshalton, Surrey, SM5 3LW.
Owner: London Borough of Sutton   **Contact:** Ms V Murphy
Home of Frank Dickinson (1874 - 1961) follower of Arts and Crafts movement, who built the house to his own design.
Location: On B278 1m S of junction with A232.
Opening Times: First Sun of each month and BH Sun And Mon, 1.30pm - 5.30pm. Closed Christmas and New Year.
Admission: Free. Groups outside normal opening hours - £2.00 pp (includes guided tour).

LOSELEY PARK

See page 176-177 for full page entry.

OAKHURST COTTAGE

Tel: 01428 684733

Hambledon, Godalming, Surrey.
Owner: The National Trust   **Contact:** Mrs E Hardy
A very small 16th century timber-framed cottage, restored and furnished as a simple cottager's dwelling. Delightful cottage garden with contemporary plant species. Some restriction may be necessary on access to upper floor.
Location: Hambeldon, Surrey
Opening Times: 30 Mar - end Oct; Wed, Thur, Sat, Sun & BH Mon 2.00pm - 5.00pm. *Strictly appointment only.*
Admission: Adult £2.20, Child £1.10, no reduction for parties.

PAINSHILL PARK

Tel: 01932 864674   **Fax:** 01932 868001

Portsmouth Road, Cobham, Surrey, KT11 1JE.
Owner: Painshill Park Trust   **Contact:** Mrs E Fox
Undiscovered for 200 years, this is one of the finest 18th century landscapes created by the Hon Charles Hamilton (1704 - 86), an artist and brilliant designer. He recreated scenes, a series of set pieces with architectural features around a 14 acre lake.
Location: W of Cobham on A245, 2m N of junction 10 on M25. 100 metres E of A3/A245 junction.
Opening Times: 9 Apr - 15 Oct, Sun only. Pre-booked groups of 10 or more may be arranged on any other day throughout the year.
Admission: Adult £3.50, Child £2.50, under 5 free, Family £10.00, Conc £3.00, Groups £2.80 pp.

POLESDEN LACEY

Tel: 01372 458203

Dorking, Surrey, RH5 6BD.
Owner: The National Trust   **Contact:** Administrator
Originally an elegant 1820s Regency villa, the house was remodelled after 1906 by the Hon Mrs Ronald Greville, a well-known Edwardian hostess. Her collection of fine paintings, furniture, porcelain and silver are still displayed in the reception rooms, plus photographs from Mrs Greville's albums. Extensive grounds, walled rose garden, lawns and tree lined walks. King George VI and Queen Elizabeth spent part of their honeymoon here.
Location: 5m NW of Dorking, 2m S of Great Bookham, off A246.
Opening Times: House: Mar, Sat & Sun only, 1.30pm - 4.30pm. 30 Mar - 30 Oct, Wed - Sun (inc. Good Fri), 1.30pm - 5.30pm; also open BH Mon & preceding Sun, 11.00am - 5.30pm. Gardens: daily all year 11.00am - 6.00pm or dusk if earlier. Last admissions to house 1/2 an hour before closing.
Admission: Garden & Grounds: open all year round £2.50. House: £3.00, Pre-booked parties £4.50 (house & garden).

RAMSTER GARDENS

Tel: 01428 644422

Ramster, Chiddingfold, Surrey, GU8 4SN.
Owner: Mrs M Gunn   **Contact:** Mrs M Gunn
20 acres of woodland and flowering shrub garden laid out in 1904. Well groomed but not over-disciplined appearance.
Location: 1 1/2m S of Chiddingfold on A283.
Opening Times: 15 Apr - 30 Jul, 2.00pm - 6.00pm.
Admission: Adult £2.00, Child free, Conc £2.00, Group £2.00 pp.

RHS GARDEN WISLEY

OPEN

All year

Mon through Sat

(except Christmas Day)

10.00am - sunset or 7.00pm during the summer

Tel: 01483 224234
Fax: 01483 211750

NR. WOKING, SURREY

Owner: The Royal Horticultural Society   *Contact:* The Royal Horticultural Society

A world famous garden which extends to 240 acres and provides the chance to glean new ideas and inspiration. Highlights include the azaleas and rhododendrons in spring, the glasshouses, and the Model Gardens. The visitor centre offers the world's best selection of gardening books and over 8.500 varieties of plants for sale. Delightful restaurant facilities are open throughout the year.

Location: Off the A3 Nr. Woking, Surrey.
Admission: Adults £4.70, Child under 6 free, Child from 6-16 £1.75.
         Groups of 20+ £3.75

ROYAL BOTANIC GARDENS

Tel: 0181 940 1171   **Fax:** 0181 332 5197

Kew, Richmond, Surrey, TW9 3AB.

Contact: The Administrator
Location: A307 / junction A305 and A205 (1m Chiswick roundabout M4).
Opening Times: 9.30am daily except Christmas Day and New Year's Day.
Admission: Adult £4.00, Child / Conc £2.00, Family £10.00, Groups 20% discount when pre-booked and payed.

SHALFORD MILL

Shalford, Guildford, Surrey.
Owner: The National Trust   **Contact:** The Administrator
18th century watermill on the Tillingbourne, given in 1932 by "Ferguson's Gang".
Location: 1^1/2m S of Guildford on A281, opposite Sea Horse Inn.
Opening Times: Daily 10.00am - 5.00pm.

WHITEHALL

Tel: 0181 643 1236   **Fax:** 0181 770 4777

1 Malden Road, Cheam, Surrey, SM3 8QD.
Owner: London Borough of Sutton   **Contact:** P Jackson Esq
Early 16th century timber framed house with displays on Nonsuch Palace, medieval Cheam pottery.
Location: On A243 just N of junction with A232.
Opening Times: Apr - Sept, Tues - Fri and Sun, 2.00pm - 5.30pm. Sat 10.00am - 5.30pm. BH Mons Oct - Mar, Wed, Thurs and Sun 2.00pm - 5.30pm; Sat 10.00am - 5.30pm. Also open Mons 2.00pm - 5.30pm. Closed Christmas and New Year.
Admission: Adult 80p, Child 40p. Outside open hours: Groups £1.50pp inc guided tour. 35p per school child in organised groups. 1 teacher free per 10 children.

WINKWORTH ARBORETUM

Tel: 01483 208477

Hascombe Road, Godalming, Surrey, GU8 4AD.
Owner: The National Trust   **Contact:** Head of Arboretum
Hillside woodland with two lakes, many rare trees and shrubs and fine views. The most impressive displays are in spring for bluebells and azaleas, autumn for colour and wildlife.
Location: Near Hascombe, 2m SE of Godalming on E side of B2130.
Opening Times: All year, daily, during daylight hours.
Admission: Adult £2.00, Child (5-17) £1.00, no reduction for parties.

SPECIAL EVENTS DIARY

- **1st-2nd July:**   **Ham House**
  Open Air Concerts to celebrate the National Trust's Centenary

- **29th September:**   **Ham House**
  Concert - The Amsterdam Baroque Orchestra

One part of the R.H.S. Garden, Wisley, Surrey.

Salsburys Marquee Hire

For your special occasion

Weddings, Dances, Corporate Hospitality, Exhibitions and more ...

We can supply:

- *Marquees*
- *Range of Linings*
- *Dance Floors*
- *Carpeting*
- *Tables and gilt chairs*
- *Heaters and other marquee furniture*

Just phone or fax us for a free quotation.

Avenue Farmhouse, 1 Little Street, Yardley Hastings, Northants NN7 1EZ
Tel: (01604) 696715   Fax: (01604) 696302

ARUNDEL CASTLE
Arundel

This great castle, home of the Dukes of Norfolk, dates from the Norman Conquest, containing a very fine collection of furniture and paintings, Arundel Castle is still a family home, reflecting the changes of nearly a thousand years.

In 1643, during the Civil War, the original castle was very badly damaged and it was later restored by the 8th, 11th and 15th Dukes in the 18th and 19th Centuries. It has amongst its treasures personal possessions of Mary Queen of Scots and a selection of historical, religious and heraldic items from the Duke of Norfolk's collection.

The Duke of Norfolk is the Premier Duke, the title having been conferred on Sir John Howard in 1483 by his friend King Richard III. The Dukedom also carries with it the hereditary office of Earl Marshal of England. Among the historically famous members of the Howard family are Lord Howard of Effingham who, with Drake, repelled the Spanish Armada; the Earl of Surrey, the Tudor poet and courtier and the 3rd Duke of Norfolk, uncle of Anne Boleyn and Catherine Howard, both of whom became wives of King Henry VIII.

❖

CONTACT

The Administrator
Arundel Castle
Arundel
West Sussex
BN18 9AB

Tel: (01903) 883136
or (01903) 882173
Fax: (01903) 884581

LOCATION

Brighton 40 minutes,
Worthing 15 minutes,
Chichester 15 minutes.
From London A3 or A24,
1¹/₂ hours.

Bus: Bus stop 100 yards.

Rail: Station 1/2 mile.

Air: Gatwick 25 miles.

Motorway: M25,
30 miles.

SUITABILITY FOR OTHER EVENTS
Fashion shows and filming.

ADVICE TO COURIERS & DRIVERS
No unaccompanied children, dogs or photography inside the Castle.

FACILITIES FOR THE DISABLED
Disabled and elderly visitors may alight at the entrance to the property, before parking in the allocated areas. There are toilets for the disabled.

PARKING FOR COACHES & CARS
Capacity of the car park: 200 cars within the grounds, 200 yards from the Castle with further space for cars elsewhere. Coaches can park opposite the Castle entrance.

CATERING
Groups need to book in advance for afternoon tea, lunch or dinner. The Restaurant seats 140 people and prices range from £1.95 for tea and £3.75 for lunch. Special rates are offered to pre-booked groups only. Self Service Restaurant within the Castle serves home-made food for lunch and afternoon tea.

GUIDED TOURS
These are available for pre-booked parties only at £7.00 per head. Tours are also available in French and German. Average time taken for a tour 1¹/₂ hours.

GIFT SHOP
The shop sells many items chosen by the Countess of Arundel and is always open at the same time as the Castle.

GUIDE BOOKS
Colour guide book, published in English, French, and German.

SCHOOL VISITS/CHILDREN
A special guide book can be purchased for children. Items of particular interest include a Norman Keep and Armoury. Special rates for schoolchildren (aged 5-15) and teachers.

OPENING TIMES

Summer
2 April - 27 October.
Daily except Sats
12 noon - 5.00pm
Last admission 4.00pm
Good Fri. closed

Winter
28 October - 31 March
Pre-booked parties only

ADMISSION

Summer
Adult £5.00
Child (5-15) £3.50
OAP £4.50
Fam. Ticket . .£14.00
Groups (min 20 people)
Adult £4.50
Child (5-15) £3.00
OAP £4.00

Winter
PRE-BOOKED PARTIES
Mornings £7.00
Min Fee £350.00
Evenings, Sats &
Sundays £8.00
Min Fee £400.00
* Sats & Suns only

CHARLESTON FARMHOUSE
Lewes

A mile or so from Firle village, near the end of a track leading to the foot of the Downs, lies Charleston Farmhouse. It was discovered in 1916 by Virginia and Leonard Woolf when Virginia's sister, the painter Vanessa Bell, was looking for a place in the country. Here Vanessa moved with fellow artist Duncan Grant, the writer David Garnett, her two young sons, and an assortment of animals. It was an unconventional and creative household which became the focal point for artists and intellectuals later to be known as the Bloomsbury set - among them Roger Fry, Lytton Strachey and Maynard Keynes.

Over the years the artists decorated the walls, furniture and ceramics with their own designs, influenced by Italian fresco painting and post-impressionist art. Creativity extended to the garden too. Mosaics were made in the piazza, sculpture was cleverly positioned to intrigue, and subtle masses of colour were used in the planting.

After Duncan Grant's death in 1978, the Charleston Trust was formed to save and restore the house to its former glory. The task has been described as "one of the most difficult and imaginative feats of restoration current in Britain".

❖

SUITABILITY FOR OTHER EVENTS
Filming.

EXTRA FACILITIES
Small lecture room available by special arrangement.

ADVICE TO COURIERS & DRIVERS
No dogs, no photography. It is essential to arrange visits in advance and out of public hours. Please telephone the office. Details on restriction of coach size shown under 'parking'.

FACILITIES FOR THE DISABLED
Disabled and elderly visitors may alight at the entrance. Wheelchair visitors by prior arrangement, outside public hours. There is no access beyond the ground floor for wheelchairs. Special toilets are available.

PARKING FOR COACHES & CARS
There is car parking for 30 cars, 50 yards from the property. Mini coaches only (up to 26 seats) may use the lane to the property. Large coaches may set down at the end of the lane - 10 minutes walk - or effect a Mini-Bus transfer. Details from office.

FUNCTION FACILITIES
The New Studio is available for hire by small groups. Full details available from the administrator.

CATERING
There is no restaurant at Charleston but refreshments are made available to groups by prior booking.

GUIDED TOURS
Tours are available on Wednesdays, Thursdays, Fridays and Saturdays. The maximum size of each group is 12. Groups of up to 50 can be arranged with prior notification, out of public hours. Tours available in French if booked in advance. There is no charge for the tour and the average time taken is 1 hour.

GIFT SHOP
The Gift Shop is open whilst the house is open.

GUIDE BOOKS
'Charleston Past and Present' contains photographs and reminiscences of family members and friends together with full details of the house and gardens, price £8.99. Guide notes are available at £2.00.

SCHOOL VISITS/CHILDREN
Charleston is particularly suitable for 6th Form and art groups. A guide is provided and at times a schoolroom is available for hire.

ADDITIONAL INFORMATION
Changing series of Exhibitions in Shop Gallery. The Charleston Festival is held in May every year. For Summer School details contact office. Special openings for Friends of Charleston.

CONTACT

Mrs Christina Jeffrey
Charleston Farmhouse
Firle
Lewes
East Sussex
BN8 6LL

Tel: (01323) 811265
(Visitor information)
(01323) 811626
(Admin.)

LOCATION

6mls east of Lewes on A27 between Firle and Selmeston. The lane to Charleston leads off the A27, 2 miles beyond the Firle turning.
London 60 miles,
Brighton 15 miles,
Monk's House, Rodmell (Leonard and Virginia Woolf's house) 11 miles.
Air: Gatwick 20 miles.
Rail: London (Victoria) hourly to Lewes (65 minutes). Occasional train to Berwick.
Bus: Route on A27.
Taxi: George and Graham, Lewes 473692.

OPENING TIMES

Summer
OFF PEAK PERIOD
1 April - 16 July
13 Sept - 29 Oct

Guided Tours:
Wed - Sat   2 - 6.00pm
Last admission   5.00pm

Fridays are on a Connoisseur basis only (see below)

Kitchen open Thursday and Friday only.

Unguided tours:
Suns. & Bank Hols.
2.00 - 6.00pm
Last admission   5.00pm

PEAK PERIOD
19 Jul - 10 Sept
As off-peak times except Fridays are not connoisseur days. Kitchen Thurs. only.

Shop and gardens open 11.00am - 2.00pm

'Accompanied' tours from 11.45 every open day except Sundays and Bank Hol Mons.

Winter
Nov - Christmas.
Weekends only.
Mini-Tours   2 - 4.00pm
Christmas
Shopping   2 - 5.00pm

ADMISSION

Summer
Adult £4.50
Concessions* . . .£3.00
Connoisseur Days   £6.00

Winter
Short tours
Per person £2.50

* Children (5-16), Concessions mid-week throughout season, also weekends April, May & October

GOODWOOD HOUSE
Chichester

GOODWOOD has been the country home of the Dukes of Richmond and Gordon for more than three centuries. The first Duke was the son of King Charles II and his French mistress, Louise de Keroualle. He was famous for his love of life and his brilliance at entertaining, a tradition which has continued at Goodwood to this day.

The third Duke not only built the great house but also collected many of its magnificent treasures. Paintings by Stubbs, Canaletto and Van Dyck, and a porcelain collection of exceptional excellence make this one of England's most important historic houses.

No other estate can offer the unique attraction of 19 days' racing on its own racecourse from May to October. Glorious Goodwood week in July is a renowned sporting and social event of international stature. Goodwood also offers the Festival Of Speed, held annually in June and now one of the most successful historic motor racing events in the world. The Festival attracts top cars and drivers for two days of classic motor sport.

Whether it is to reward the achievements of your sales team or to launch a new product, choosing Goodwood as the place to celebrate reflects the stature and style of your company. The estate is the essence of English life at its best with the famous racecourse, the historic motor circuit, the aerodrome and the secluded hotel, all within a mile of the house itself.

Simply, there is no better place to celebrate your success.

Goodwood House is used throughout the year for all kinds of corporate and social events. The State Apartments can be used for Product Promotions, Company Entertaining, One-Day Seminars, Conference Dinners, Luncheon and Dinner Parties including a private tour of the art collections, Wedding Receptions, Fashion Shows and as a location for filming.

All catering is planned and prepared by Goodwood chefs. Buffets, lunches, dinners and receptions can be arranged all year round.

CONFERENCE AND FUNCTION FACILITIES

ROOM	DIMENSIONS	CAPACITY	LAYOUT	POWER POINTS	SUITABLE FOR A/V
Ball Room	79' x 23'	74 - 350	Various	✓	✓
Yellow Drawing Room	50' x 20'	40 - 90	Various	✓	✓
Front Hall	38' x 35'	40 - 90	Various	✓	✓
NINE OTHER ROOMS ALSO AVAILABLE.					

LEONARDSLEE GARDENS
Horsham

LEONARDSLEE GARDENS represent one of the largest and most spectacular woodland gardens in England with one of the finest collections of mature rhododendrons, azaleas, choice trees and shrubs to be seen anywhere. It is doubly fortunate in having one of the most magnificent settings, within easy reach of London, only a few miles from the M23. Laid out by Sir Edmund Loder since 1889 the gardens are still maintained by the Loder family today. The 240 acre (100 hectare) valley is world-famous for its spring display of azaleas and rhododendrons around the 6 lakes, giving superb views and reflections.

The delightful Rock Garden - a photographers paradise - is a kaleidoscope of colour in May. The superb exhibition of Bonsai in a walled courtyard shows the fascinating living art-form of Bonsai to perfection. The Alpine House has 400 different alpine plants growing in a natural rocky setting. Wallabies (used as mowing machines!) have lived wild in part of the garden for over 100 years, and deer (Sika, Fallow & Axis) may be seen in the parklands.

Many superb rhododendrons have been raised as Leonardslee. The most famous is Rhododendron loderi raised by Sir Edmund Loder in 1901. The original plants are still to be seen in the garden. In May the fragrance of their huge blooms pervades the air throughout the valley.

With many miles of paths to enjoy, visitors return frequently to savour a paradise in spring, serene in summer and mellow in autumn.

❖

SUITABILITY FOR OTHER EVENTS
Photography - Landscape and fashion, film location.

EXTRA FACILITIES
Clock Tower Restaurant available for private or corporate function in the evenings and out of season

ADVICE TO COURIERS & DRIVERS
Parking and refreshments free to drivers. Average length of visit 2- 4 hours.

FACILITIES FOR THE DISABLED
Not suitable for the disabled.

PARKING FOR COACHES & CARS
Ample free parking.

CATERING
Clock Tower Restaurant and Garden Cafe. Morning coffee, lunches, teas.

GIFT SHOP
Large range of quality goods.

PLANTS FOR SALE
Good selection, especially Rhododendrons and Azaleas,

GUIDE BOOKS
Colour guide book £1.50.

SCHOOL VISITS/CHILDREN
So as to maintain the peace and tranquillity of the gardens, school visits are not encouraged.

CONTACT

R Loder
Leonardslee Gardens
Lower Beeding
Horsham
West Sussex
RH13 6PP

Tel: (01403) 891212

LOCATION

M23 to Handcross then A279 (signposted Cowfold) for 4 miles. From London: 1 hour 15 mins.

Rail: Horsham Station 4^1/$_2$ miles.

Bus: No. 107 from Horsham and Brighton

OPENING TIMES

Summer
1 April - 31 October
Daily 10.00am - 6.00pm
May 10.00am - 8.00pm

Winter
1 November - 31 March
Closed to the general public. Available for functions.

ADMISSION

May
    Adults £4.00
    Child £2.00
April, June - October
    Adult £3.00
    Child £2.00
Season Tickets . .£10.00

Groups
May Mon - Fri . . .£3.50
Sat, Sun &
Bank Hol Mons: . .£4.00

April, June - October
    Adult £2.50
    Child (any time) . .£2.00

CONFERENCE AND FUNCTION FACILITIES

ROOM	DIMENSIONS	CAPACITY	LAYOUT	POWER POINTS	SUITABLE FOR A/V
Clock Tower		80 100	Dinner Buffet	4	

PETWORTH HOUSE
Petworth

Everything about Petworth is on a grand scale. More of a palace than a conventional country house, this magnificent late 17th century mansion is set within a beautiful 700 acre deer park, landscaped by 'Capability' Brown and immortalised in Turner's paintings.

Originally the seat of the ancient and powerful Percy family, the medieval Earls of Northumberland, the house was acquired through marriage by Charles Seymour, 6th Duke of Somerset, in 1682. It was he who was responsible for transforming Petworth House into the superb stately home that we see today.

Later owners left their own distinctive marks on the property and most notable then was the 3rd Earl of Egremont, a distinguished agriculturalist and patron of the arts, who embellished the house with the great collections of paintings and sculpture for which Petworth is rightly famed. One of his closest friends, and a regular visitor to the house, was J M W Turner, who has left many memorable paintings of the rooms and parkland that can be enjoyed by visitors today. *New for 1995 is the opening of the restored kitchens in the servants block - a fascinating contrast to the grandeur and magnificence of the State Rooms.*

CONTACT

The Administrator
Petworth House
Petworth
West Sussex
GU28 OAE

Tel: (01798) 342207

Fax: (01798) 342963

LOCATION

In the centre of
Petworth town
(approach roads
A292/A285);
Car park signposted.

Rail: Pulborough
BR 5 ¼ miles

EXTRA FACILITIES
Programme of events throughout the year. Large musical concerts in the park.

ADVICE TO COURIERS & DRIVERS
Coach parties alight at Church Lodge entrance, coaches then park in NT car park.

FACILITIES FOR THE DISABLED
As carpark is 800 yards from house there is a vehicle available to take less able visitors to house.

PARKING FOR COACHES & CARS
Car park 800 yards from house.

CATERING
Light lunches and teas in licensed restaurant from 12.30pm - 5.00pm, open same days as house.

GUIDED TOURS
Available by arrangement with the administrator on variety of subjects - tailor-made to suit your group (additional charge).

GIFT SHOP
Open same days as house 1.00pm - 5.00pm. Also open for Christmas shopping. Telephone for details.

GUIDE BOOKS
Available from the house and gift shop. Also Children's quiz and Children's guide book.

SCHOOL VISITS/CHILDREN
Pre-arranged school visits welcome. Baby feeding and changing facilities, highchairs. Pushchairs admitted in house but no prams please.

OPENING TIMES

House and Park:

1 April - 31 October
Daily except
Mons & Fri
1.00 - 5.30pm
(Open Good Fri and
Bank Hol Mondays)

Last admissions 5.00pm

Extra rooms shown,
Tues, Weds and Thurs.

Park Only: All year
Daily
8.00am - Sunset

Closed 23rd - 25th June
from 12.00 Noon.

ADMISSION

Adult £4.00
Child £2.00
Fam. Ticket . . .£10.00

Park Only . . . . . Free

Groups
(pre-booked 15 or more)
Adult £3.50

ST. MARY'S
Bramber

CONTACT

Peter Thorogood or
Roeger Linton (Curator)
St Mary's House
Bramber
West Sussex
BN44 3WE
Tel: (01903) 816205

LOCATION

Bramber village off A283
via M23/A23 or A24.
From London 56 miles,
via M23/A23 or A24.

Bus: From Shoreham to
Steyning, alight
Bramber.

Taxi: Southern Taxis
(01273) 461655, Access
Cars (01273) 452424.

Train: To Shoreham-by-
Sea with connecting
bus 20 (4 miles).

FAMOUS historic house in the downland village of Bramber. Built in 1470 by William Waynflete, Bishop of Winchester, founder of Magdalen College, Oxford. Classified (Grade I) as "the best example of late 15th Century timber-framing in Sussex." Fine panelled rooms, including the unique trompe l'oeil 'Painted Room', decorated for the visit of Elizabeth I. The 'Kings Room' has connections with Charles II's escape to France in 1651. Rare 16th Century painted wall leather. English furniture, ceramics, manuscripts and fine English costume-doll collection.. The Library houses important private collection of works by Victorian poet and artist Thomas Hood. Still a lived in family home, St. Mary's was awarded the 'Warmest Welcome' Commendation by the S.E. Tourist Board.

GARDENS

Charming gardens with amusing Topiary as seen on BBC TV. Features include an exceptional example of the Living Fossil Tree, Ginkgo Biloba, a magnificently tall Magnolia Grandiflora, and the mysterious ivy-clad Monk's Walk.

❖

SUITABILITY FOR OTHER EVENTS
Exclusive corporate or private functions, promotional product launches, wedding receptions Atmospheric film-location.

EXTRA FACILITIES
Lecture/demonstration facilities for up to 70 people. Projector/screen available. Grand piano

ADVICE TO COURIERS & DRIVERS
Parties must be booked in advance. Please allow 2½ hours for your visit. Free tour and tea for coach driver. Dogs on leads in car park only. No photography in House.

PARKING FOR COACHES & CARS
Pull-in gravel car park - 30 cars or 2 coaches, 20 yards from House. Also a village car park 50 yds.

CATERING
Superb Victorian Music Room seats up to 70.. Groups can book in advance for morning coffee or afternoon teas. Quality catering for functions by in-house and top London caterers..

GIFT SHOP
Souvenirs of the House.

GUIDED TOURS
The owner and/or family usually meet groups visiting the House. Larger parties, maximum 60, divided into smaller groups. Average time taken for tour 1 hour. Allow extra time for refreshments.

SCHOOL VISIT/CHILDREN
Groups welcome by prior arrangement.

CONFERENCE AND FUNCTION FACILITIES

ROOM	DIMENSIONS	CAPACITY	LAYOUT	POWER POINTS	SUITABLE FOR A/V
Music Room	60' x 30'	80	Theatre	3	3
		30	U-shape		
		30	Boardroom		
		80	Buffet		
Monks' Parlour	26' x 22'	25	Buffet	3	3
Painted Room	26' x 15'	20		3	3

OPENING TIMES

Summer

General Public:
Easter - End September
Suns, Mons. 2 - 6.00pm

During August also
Weds., & Thurs.
2 - 6.00pm

Groups:
Easter - End October.
Daily by appointment
avoiding public opening
times.

Winter
November - March
By appointment only.

ADMISSION

HOUSE & GARDEN
Adult £3.50
Child £2.00
OAP £3.20
Student £2.50

Groups
Adult/OAP
25 or more £3.00
Less than 25 . . .£3.50
Child* £2.00
Student £2.50

Winter
Groups only
Per person £5.50

THE ROYAL PAVILION
Brighton

CONTACT

Anne Burrill
Head of Public Services
The Royal Pavilion
Brighton
East Sussex
BN1 1EE
Tel: (01273) 603005
Fax: (01273) 779108

LOCATION

The Royal Pavilion is in the centre of Brighton easily reached by car and road.
From London M25, M23, A23 - 1 hr. 30 mins.
Rail: Victoria to Brighton station 55 mins.

15 mins. walk from Brighton station

Air: Gatwick 20 mins.

Justifiably termed "the most extraordinary palace in Europe," The Royal Pavilion, the famous seaside palace of King George IV, is one of the most exotically beautiful buildings in the British Isles.

First built as a simple, classical villa by Henry Holland in 1787, it was transformed into its current Indian style by John Nash between 1815-1822. The interiors are decorated in the Chinese taste, here carried to unique heights of splendour.

Extensive restoration has revealed the magnificent decorations and fantastic furnishings, from the opulence of the State rooms to the beauty of the recently restored apartments of Queen Victoria.

In the Banqueting Room, with its spectacular central lamp, is exhibited one of the most important collections of Regency silver gilt on public view. In the Great Kitchen with its cast-iron palm trees is displayed a superb collection of copper containing over 500 pieces

Experience the fantasy of the Music Room, a sight which moved George to tears when he first saw it, wander through the King's private apartments, promenade along the corridor with its real and imitation bamboo furniture, including the famous cast-iron staircases ... and much much more. Furniture and works of art include many original pieces on loan from H M the Queen .

A recent restoration programme has transformed the surrounding gardens to their original Regency design. New additions to the Upper Floor are the Royal Bedrooms of the Dukes of York and Clarence.

As a tourist attraction or a venue for corporate hospitality this Regency Palace is breathtaking.

OPENING TIMES

Summer
June - September
Daily 10.00am - 6.00pm
Last entry at 6.00pm

Winter
Oct - May
Daily 10.00am - 5.00pm
Last entry at 5.00pm
Closed 25th and 26th December only.

ADMISSION

Adult £3.75
Child £2.10
OAP £2.75
Student £2.75
GROUPS (20+)
Adult £3.25
Prices valid until 31.3.95

SUITABILITY FOR OTHER EVENTS
Ideal for prestigious entertaining: Dinners, buffets, drinks receptions, concerts, presentations and Weddings. Also available for filming and photography.

EXTRA FACILITIES
Surrounding gardens relaid to the original regency designs. Special events programme. Slide lecture presentations can be arranged in house and out.

ADVICE TO COURIERS & DRIVERS
Free entry and refreshments for drivers. Please advise clients that there is no photography inside.

FACILITIES FOR THE DISABLED
Disabled toilet. Wheelchair access ground floor. Admission free. Tactile tours offered, hearing sets available for specialist tours. Tours available for all those with special needs.

PARKING FOR COACHES & CARS
Close to NCP car parks, town centre voucher parking. Coach drop-off point in New Road, parking in Madeira Drive.

CATERING
Superb Queen Adelaide tea-rooms - from coffees to light lunches. Balcony terrace with sweeping views across the Pavilion lawns.

GUIDED TOURS
By arrangement with public services section (01273 - 713232) available also in French and German, General Interest to specialist Art Tours. Special Needs also.

GIFT SHOP
'The most unusual shop in Brighton'. Everything from reproduction Pavilion furniture to Regency jams and teas.

GUIDE BOOK
Colour Guide £1.99. Furniture catalogue 99p. Spanish, German and French translations.

SCHOOL VISITS
Specialist tours relating to all levels of national curriculum. Must be booked in advance.

CONFERENCE AND FUNCTION FACILITIES

ROOM	DIMENSIONS	CAPACITY	LAYOUT	POWER POINTS	SUITABLE FOR A/V
Banqueting Room		90 - 200	Various	✓	
Great Kitchen		40 - 90	Various	✓	
Music Room		180	Various	✓	
Queen Adelaide Suite		60 - 100	Various	✓	
Small Adelaide		35 - 40	Various	✓	
William IV		70 - 80	Various	✓	✓

ALFRISTON CLERGY HOUSE

Tel: 01323 870001

The Tye, Alfriston, Polegate, Sussex, BN26 5TL.

Owner: The National Trust   **Contact:** The Administrator

This 14th century Wealden hall house is half-timbered and thatched, and contains a medieval hall, exhibition room and two other rooms open to the public, plus a charming cottage garden.

Location: 4m NE of Seaford, just E of B2108, in Alfriston village, adjoining the Tye and St Andrews Church.

Opening Times: Apr - end Oct, daily 10.30am - 5.00pm or sunset if earlier. Last admission 1/2 hour before closing.

Admission: Adult £2.00, Child £1.00, pre-booked parties £1.50.

ANNE OF CLERVES HOUSE

Lewes High Street, Lewes, Sussex, BN7 1YE.

Owner: Sussex Archeological Society   **Contact:** A Freeman Esq

16th century town house given to Anne of Cleves by her ex-husband Henry VIII as part of her divorce settlement. Now a museum of Sussex industrial and domestic life.

Location: 4m NE of Seaford, just E of B2108, in Alfriston village, adjoining the Tye and St Andrews Church.

Opening Times: All year, daily 10am - 5.30pm, except Sundays when it closes at 2.00pm.

Admission: Adult £1.80, Student £1.50, Child 90p, Family £4.50.

ARUNDEL CASTLE

See page 181 for full page entry.

ARUNDEL CATHEDRAL

Tel: 01903 882297

Parsons Hill, Arundel, Sussex, BN18 9AY.

Contact: Rev A Whale

Cathedral church of the RC Diocese of Arundel and Brighton built by Henry, 15th Duke of Norfolk and opened 1873. Architectural style - French Gothic. Carpet of Flowers and Floral Festival held each year on the Feast of Corpus Christi and day preceding (Wed and Thur). Corpus Christi occurs 60 days after Easter.

Location: Above junction of A27 and A284

Opening Times: Summer: 9.00am - 6.00pm Winter: 9.00am - dusk. Mass at 10.00am each day. Sunday Masses: 6.30pm Vigil Saturday evening, 8.00am, 9.30am and 11.00am. Shop opened after services and on special occasions and otherwise at request.

BATEMAN'S

Tel: 01435 882302

Burwash, Etchingham, Sussex, TN19 7DS.

Owner: The National Trust   **Contact:** The Administrator

Home of Rudyard Kipling from 1902 - 36, the house was built by a local ironmaster in 1634. Kipling's rooms and study are as they were during his lifetime. At the bottom of the garden, the watermill grinds corn for flour (Sat pm only). Alongside is one of the oldest working water-driven turbines in the world, installed by Kipling to generate electricity for the house. Kipling's 1928 Rolls-Royce. Gardens maintained much as they were in Kipling's time.

Location: 1/2m S of Burwash A265.

Opening Times: House, mill & garden: Apr - end Oct; Sat to Wed 11.00am - 5.00pm (open Good Fri). Last admission 4.30pm.

Admission: Adult £4.00, Child £2.00, Pre-booked parties £3.00. Sun, Mon & Good Fri £4.00 (no reduction for parties).

BAYHAM ABBEY

Tel: 01892 890381

Lamberhurst, Sussex.

Owner: English Heritage.   **Contact:** The Administrator

These riverside ruins are of a house of 'white' canons, founded c.1208 and preserved in the 18th century, when its surroundings were landscaped to create the delightful setting in which you will find the ruins today.

Location: 1 3/4m W of Lamberhurst off B2169.

Opening Times: 1 Apr - 30 Sept, daily 10.00am - 6.00pm, 1 Oct - 31 Oct: daily 10.00am - 4.00pm.

Admission: Adult £2.00, Child £1.00, Conc £1.50.

BENTLEY HOUSE

Tel: 01825 840573   **Fax:** 01825 840573

Halland, Lewes, Sussex, BN8 5AF.

Owner: East Sussex County Council   **Contact:** Barry Sutherland Esq

Brick Tudor farmhouse with a large reception room of Palladian proportions added on either end in the 1960s by the architect Raymond Erith, each lit by large Venetian windows. Furnished to form a grand 20th century evocation of a mid Georgian house.

Location: A26 and B2192 signposted off A22.

Opening Times: Summer: 21 Mar - 31 Oct, daily, 10.30am - 4.30pm (last admissions). 5.00pm in Jul and Aug. House: open 12 Noon daily from 1 Apr. Winter; open w/ends only 10.30am - 4.00pm (last admissions). House closed Dec and estate closed throughout Jan.

Admission: Family £9.95, Adult £3.60 (£2.80 in winter), Senior citizens £2.80, Students £2.80, Child (4-15 years) £2.00, Child under 4 free, Coach drivers free admission and refreshment ticket 10% discount for parties of 11 or more. Call to verify prices.

BODIAM CASTLE

OPEN

18 Feb - end of Oct
Daily
10.00am - 6.00pm or dusk if earlier
Nov - 2 Jan
Tues - Sun
10.00am - Dusk
(closed Christmas holiday)
Open New Years Day.

Tel: 01580 830436
Fax: 01580 830436

BODIAM, NR ROBERTSBRIDGE, EAST SUSSEX TN32 5UA

Owner: The National Trust   *Contact:* The Administrator

Bodiam Castle was built in 1385 for comfort and defence. Surrounded by a moat and with its exterior virtually complete it is recognised as one of the finest examples of Medieval military architecture in the country. Although a ruin inside, the floors have been replaced in some of the towers and impressive views can be enjoyed from the battlements. Shop and restaurant.

Location: 3 miles south of Hawkhurst, 2 miles east of A21 Hurst Green.

Admission: Adult £2.50, Child £1.30

BORDE HILL GARDEN

Tel: 01444 450326   **Fax:** 01444 440427

Balcombe Road, Haywards Heath, Sussex, RH16 1XP.

Owner: Borde Hill Garden Ltd   **Contact:** Mrs J Wilkinson

Large informal woodland garden, some formal areas with herbaceous borders. Woodland walk.

Location: 1 1/2m N of Haywards Heath.

Opening Times: 18 Mar - 1 Oct, 10.00am - 6.00pm.

Admission: Adult £3.50, Child £1.50, Family £7.50, Groups of 15 plus £3.00.

BOXGROVE PRIORY

Boxgrove, Chichester, Sussex.

Owner: English Heritage   **Contact:** The Administrator

Remains of the Guest House, Chapter House and church of this 12th century priory, which was the cell of a French abbey until Richard II confirmed its independence in 1383.

Location: N of Boxgrove, 4 m E of Chichester on minor road off A27.

Opening Times: Any reasonable time.

BATTLE ABBEY

BATTLE, EAST SUSSEX

Owner: English Heritage
Contact: The Head Custodian
Tel: 01424 773792

Lies on the historic site of the Battle of Hastings which, in 1066 changed the course of England's history forever. It was founded by William the Conqueror c.1070 to atone for the terrible slaughter of the battle, and the high alter is built where King Harold fell mortally wounded. Visitors can explore the actual battlefield, and the 14th century Great Gatehouse, with its impressive battlemented walls and turrets and a fascinating exhibition which brings the site's history alive.

Location: Off A2100 in Battle, 7 miles from Hastings.

Admission: Adults £3.20 OAP/Student/UB40 £2.40 Child £1.60 15% discount on parties of 11 or more.

OPEN

1 April - 30 Sept: Daily   10.00am - 6.00pm
1 Oct - 31 Mar: Daily   10.00am - 4.00pm

BRAMBER CASTLE

Bramber, Sussex.

Owner: English Heritage   **Contact:** The Administrator

The remains of a Norman castle gatehouse, walls and earthworks in a splendid setting overlooking the Adur valley.

Location: On W side of Bramber village off A283.

Opening Times: Any reasonable time.

BRICKWALL HOUSE

Tel: 01797 223329

Northiam, Rye, Sussex.

Owner: Frewen Educational Trust   **Contact:** The Administrator

Impressive timber framed house. 17th century drawing room with magnificent plaster ceilings and good portraits including by Lely, Kneller and Vereist. Topiary, chess garden.

Location: S side of Northiam village at junction of A28 and B2088.

Opening Times: Apr - 31 Sept, Sat And Bank Hol Mons, 2.00pm - 5.00pm

Admission: £2.00.

CHARLESTON FARMHOUSE

See page 182 for full page entry.

CHICHESTER CATHEDRAL

Tel: 01243 782595   **Fax:** 01243 526190

Chichester, Sussex, PO19 1PX.

Contact: Mrs S E Papworth

The beauty of the 900 year old cathedral, site of the Shrine of St Richard, is enhanced by many art treasures, ancient and modern.

Location: West Street, Chichester.

Opening Times: Summer: 7.30am - 7.00pm Winter: 7.30am - 5.00pm Sun services: 8.00am, 10.00am, 11.00am and 3.30pm Weekday services: 7.00am, 8.00am and 5.30pm.

Admission: Donation.

DANNY

Tel: 01273 833000

Hurstpierpoint, Sussex, BN6 9BB.

Owner: Country Houses Association   **Contact:** J Gran Esq

A late Elizabethan E shaped house in red brick, part modernised in 1728.

Location: Just outside Hurstpierpoint on the Hassocks road..

Opening Times: May - Sept, Wed and Thurs, 2.00pm - 5.00pm

Admission: Adult £2.50, Child under 16 £1.00, Groups by arrangement.

FIRLE PLACE

OPEN
May - Sept
Tours Wed, Thurs,
Suns and Bank
Holiday Mondays
2.00 - 5.00pm
Connoisseurs
unguided tours with
additional rooms
shown 1st Wed in
each month.
Exclusive private
viewing 25+ by
arrangement.

Tel: 01273 858335

NR. LEWES, EAST SUSSEX BN8 6LP

Owner: Viscount Gage   *Contact:* Showing Secretary

Home of the Gage family since the 15th century, the original Tudor house was largely altered c1730. House contains a magnificent collection of European and British Old Masters. Also fine French and English furniture together with notable Sévre porcelain. A House for connoisseurs. American connections.

Location: On A27 equidistant Brighton/Eastbourne, Lewes 5 miles.

Admission: Adult £3.50, Pre-booked Group 25+ £3.00. Connoisseurs Day £4.50 Private Viewing 25+ £5.50 by arrangement.

GOODWOOD HOUSE

See page 183 for full page entry.

GREAT DIXTER

Tel: 01797 253107

Northiam, Sussex, TN31 6PH.

Owner: C Lloyd   **Contact:** The Administrator

15th century manor hall house restored by Lutyens, who designed the gardens which contain a wide range of unusual plants.

Location: Signposted off the A28 in Northiam village.

Opening Times: House & garden - 1 Apr to 8 Oct daily but closed on ordinary Mon, also 14/15 and 21/22 Oct 2.00pm - 5.00pm. Gardens open 11.00am on 27/28/29 May, Suns in Jul and Aug and 28 Aug.

Admission: House & garden: Adult £3.50, Child 50p. Gardens: Adult £2.50, Child 25p.

HAMMERWOOD PARK

OPEN
Easter Monday -
September
Weds, Sats & Bank
Holiday Mondays
2.00 - 5.30pm
Guided tour starts
2.05pm
Coaches strictly by
appointment. Small
groups at any time
throughout the year
by appointment.

Tel: 01342 850594
Fax: 01342 850864

HAMMERWOOD PARK, EAST GRINSTEAD, SUSSEX RH19 3QE

Owner: David Pinnegar   *Contact:* David Pinnegar

Built in in 1792 as an Apollo's hunting lodge by Benjamin Latrobe, architect of the Capitol and the White House, Washington D.C. Owned by Led Zepplin in the 1970's, rescued from dereliction in 1982. Cream Teas in the Organ Room, the work of French artists in the hall, whilst a derelict dining room still shocks the unwary. Guided tours by the family, said by many to be the most interesting in Sussex. Accommodation available.

Location: 3$\frac{1}{2}$ miles east of East Grinstead on A264 to Tunbridge Wells; 1 mile west of Holtye.

Admission: House & Park: Adult £3.50, Child £1.50. Private Viewing by arrangement.

HIGH BEECHES GARDENS

Tel: 01444 400589

High Beeches House, Handcross, Sussex, RH17 6HQ.

Owner: High Beeches Gardens Conservation Trust   **Contact:** Ms S Bray

Created by the Loder family at the turn of the century. 20 acre of woodland garden with wonderful autumn colour. Wildflower meadow.

Location: 1 m S of M23.

Opening Times: Apr - Jun, 6 afternoons a week. Sept - Oct closed Wed.

Admission: Adult £3.00, Child free, Groups by appointment at any time.

HIGHDOWN GARDENS

Tel: 01903 501054

Littlehampton Road, Goring by Sea, Worthing, Sussex, BN12 6PE.

Owner: Worthing Borough Council   **Contact:** C Beardsley Esq

Unique gardens in disused chalk pit, begun in 1909.

Location: Littlehampton Road, Goring by Sea, Worthing, Sussex, BN12 6PE.

Opening Times: 1 Apr - 30 Sept; Mon - Fri, 10.00am - 6.00pm. Sat and Sun including Bank Hols, 10.00am - 8.00pm. 1 Oct - 30 Nov, Mon - Fri, 10.00am - 4.30pm. 1 Dec - 31 Jan 10.00am - 4.00pm. 1 Feb - 31 Mar , Mon - Fri, 10.00am - 4.30pm.

Admission: Free.

LAMB HOUSE

Tel: 01892 890651

West Street, Rye, Sussex, TN31 7ES.

Owner: The National Trust   **Contact:** The Administrator

The home of the writer Henry James from 1898 to 1916 where he wrote the best novels of his later period. The walled garden, staircase, hall and three rooms on the ground floor containing some of James's personal possessions are on view. Also once home to the author E F Benson.

Location: In West Street, facing W end of church.

Opening Times: Apr - end Oct: Wed & Sat only 2.00pm - 6.00pm. Last admission 5.30pm.

Admission: £2.00, no reductions.

LEONARDSLEE GARDENS

See page 184 for full page entry.

LEWES CASTLE
Tel: 01273 486290   **Fax:** 01273 486290

169 High Street, Lewes, Sussex, BN7 1YE.
Owner: Sussex Archeological Society   **Contact:** Mrs H E Poole
One of the earliest Norman castles. 16th - 17th century Barbican houses displays on pre-historic Roman, Saxon and medieval Sussex.
Location: Central Lewes.
Opening Times: Mon - Sat, 10.00am - 5.30pm. Sun and BHs, 11.00am - 5.30pm.
Admission: Adult £2.90, Child £1.50, Family £7.70, Conc £2.40, Pre-booked groups over 20 £2.40 per person.

MICHELHAM PRIORY
Tel: 01323 844224   **Fax:** 01323 844224

Upper Dicker, Hailsham, Sussex, BN27 3QS.
Owner: Sussex Archeological Society   **Contact:** A Jenkinson
14th century gatehouse and 16th century house with interesting furniture. 6 acre garden .
Location: 8m NW Eastbourne off A22 & A27.
Opening Times: 25 Mar - 31 Oct, daily and Suns in Nov and Mar 11.00am - 5.00pm; Apr - Jul and Sept 11.00am - 5.00pm, Aug 10.30am - 5.30pm.
Admission: Adult £3.60, Child £2.00, Family £9.50, OAP/student £2.90, Groups £2.80.

MOORLANDS
Tel: 01892 652474

Friar's Gate, Crowborough, Sussex, TN6 1XF.
Owner: Dr Steven Smith   **Contact:** Dr Steven Smith
3 acres set in lush valley adjoining Ashdown forest; water garden with ponds and streams; primulas, rhododendrons, azaleas, many unusual trees and shrubs. New river walk.
Location: 8m NW Eastbourne off A22 & A27.
Opening Times: Wed 1 Apr - 31 Oct, 11.00am - 5.00pm. Sun - 7 and 28 May, 4 and 11 Jun and 23 Jul 2.00pm - 6.00pm.
Admission: Adult £2.00, Child free, OAP £1.50.

NYMANS GARDEN
Tel: 01444 400321

Handcross, Haywards Heath, Sussex, RH17 6EB.
Owner: The National Trust   **Contact:** The Administrator
One of the great gardens of the Sussex Weald, with rare and beautiful plants, shrubs and trees from all over the world. Walled garden, hidden sunken garden, pinetum, laurel walk and romantic ruins. Woodland walks.
Location: On B2114 at Handcross, 4 ¹/₂m S of Crawley, just off London-Brighton M23 / A23.
Opening Times: Wed 1 Apr - 31 Oct, 11.00am - 5.00pm. Sun - 7 and 28 May, 4 and 11 Jun and 23 Jul 2.00pm - 6.00pm.
Admission: Adult £2.00, Child free, OAP £1.50.

PALLANT HOUSE
Tel: 01243 774557   **Fax:** 01243 536038

9 North Pallant, Chichester, Sussex, PO19 1TJ.
Owner: Pallant House Gallery Trust   **Contact:** David Coke
Lovingly restored Queen Anne townhouse with historic rooms in Georgian style, fine antique furniture and formal garden. Highly important collection of Bow porcelain and displays of modern British art (Nicholson, Nash, Moore, Sutherland, Piper etc). Georgian style walled garden.
Opening Times: All year Tues - Sat 10.00am - 5.30pm. Last admission 4.45pm. Closed Sun, Mon and Bank Hols.

PASHLEY MANOR
Tel: 01580 200692   **Fax:** 01580 200102

Ticehurst, Wadhurst, Sussex, TN5 7HE.
Owner: James A Sellick Esq   **Contact:** James A Sellick
8 acres of formal garden from 18th century with recent new plantings, waterfalls, pond and moat.
Location: On B2099 between A21 and Ticehurst.
Opening Times: Garden only: Apr - 30 Sept, Tues, Wed, Thur, Sat, 11am - 5pm and BHs.

PETWORTH HOUSE
See page 185 for full page entry.

PEVENSEY CASTLE
Tel: 01323 762604

Pevensey, Sussex.
Owner: English Heritage   **Contact:** The Administrator
This medieval castle includes the remains of an unusual keep enclosed within its walls which originally date back to the 4th century Roman fort Anderida.
Location: In Pevensey.
Opening Times: 1 Apr - 30 Sept, daily 10.00am - 6.00pm, 1 Oct - 31 Oct: daily 10.00am - 4.00pm, 1 Nov - 31 Mar: Wed - Sun 10.00am - 4.00pm (Closed 24 - 26 Dec, 1 Jan).
Admission: Adult £2.00, Child £1.00, Conc £1.50.

PRESTON MANOR

OPEN

Mon 1.00 - 5.00pm
(10.00am - 5.00pm
Bank Holidays)

Tues - Sat
10.00am - 5.00pm

Sunday
2.00 - 5.00pm

Closed:Good Friday,
25/26 December

Tel: 01273 603005

BRIGHTON, EAST SUSSEX BN1 6SD

Owner: Brighton Borough Council

The beautifully preserved historic home of the Stanford family. Notable collections of fine furniture, portraits and antiquities show life upstairs and down, including the superbly renovated servants' quarters, day nursery and toy collection & Butler's Pantry. The beautiful lawns surrounding the manor also contain a walled and scented garden, Pets Cemetery and the 13th century Parish Church of St. Peter. The manor is also available for hire - the perfect setting for select entertaining, combining elegance and tradition. Also used for filming and photographic work.

Location: Within easy reach of Brighton town centre in Preston Park.
Admission Adults £2.60. Student/OAP £2.10. Groups of 20 adults £2.25. Child £1.50.
Prices valid until 31.3.95.

PARHAM HOUSE & GARDENS

OPEN

Easter Sunday to first Sunday in October Weds, Thurs, Suns and Bank Holiday Monday afternoons.

Gardens: 1 - 6.00pm
House: 2 - 6.00pm
Last entry 5.00pm

Tel: 01903 744888
Fax: 01903 746557

PARHAM PARK, PULBOROUGH, WEST SUSSEX RH20 4HS

Tenants: Parham Park Ltd. Reg. Charity   *Contact: Pat Kennedy*

This peaceful Elizabethan house contains an important collection of furniture, paintings, needlework and carpets. The flowers for the arrangements in the beautifully panelled rooms are grown in the four acre walled garden. The 18th century pleasure Grounds with their fine trees, statuary and lake are the setting for an annual garden weekend every July.
Location: Mid-way between Pulborough & Storrington on A283.
Admission: House & Gardens: Adult £4.25, OAP £3.75, Child £2.50.
     Garden only: Adult/OAP £3.00, Child £1.50.

SHEFFIELD PARK GARDEN

DANE MILL, NR. UCKFIELD, EAST SUSSEX TN22 3QV

Owner: The National Trust
Contact: The Property Manager

Tel: 01825 790231

A magnificent 100 acre landscape garden, with 5 lakes linked by cascades, laid out in the 18th century by Capability Brown. Carpeted with bluebells in spring, its rhododendrons, azaleas and stream garden are spectacular in early summer. In autumn its collection of rare tree and shrubs are ablaze with colour. Shop.

Location: 5 miles north-west of Uckfield, on east side of A275.

Admission: Mar, Apr & Jun to the end Sept, Nov & Dec:
Adult £3.70, Child £1.80

May & Oct:
Adult £4.00, Child £2.00.

OPEN

March: Sat & Sun only   11.00am - 4.00pm
Apr - 5 Nov: Tues - Sun & Bank Hol Mon
   11.00am - 6.00pm or sunset if earlier.
8 Nov - 16 Dec: Wed - Sat 11.00 - 4.00pm
Last adm. 1 hr before closing.

STANDEN

OPEN

Special weekend openings on 18/19 and 25/26 March
1.30 - 4.30pm

1 Apr - end of Oct
Wed - Sun and Bank Holiday Mons

Gardens:
12.30 - 6.00pm

House:
1.30 - 5.30pm

Tel: 01342 323029

EAST GRINSTEAD, WEST SUSSEX, RH19 4NE

Owner: *The National Trust*   **Contact:** *Jane Grundy, the Administrator*

Dating from the 1890's and containing original Morris & Co. furnishings and decorations, Standen survives today as a remarkable testimony to the ideals of the Arts and Crafts movement. The property was built as a family home by the influential architect Phillip Webb and retains a warm, welcoming atmosphere. Details of Webb's designs can be found everywhere from the fireplaces to the original electric light fittings.

Location: 2 miles south of East Grinstead, signposted from B2110.

Admission: House & Garden: Weekdays £4.00, Sats & Suns, Good Friday and Bank Hol Mons £4.80. Garden only: £2.50 and £3.00 respectively. Children Half price. Family Ticket £10.00 or £12.00.

ST MARY'S

See page 186 for full page entry.

THE ROYAL PAVILION

See page 187 for full page entry.

UPPARK

Tel: 01730 825317

South Harting, Petersfield, Sussex, GU31 5QR.

Owner: The National Trust   **Contact:** The Administrator

Fine late 17th century house situated high on the South Downs with magnificent views towards the Solent. Important collection of paintings and decorative art formed by members of Fetherstonhaugh family. Interesting below stairs servants' rooms, links with H G Wells whose early years were spent here, dairy and new exhibition on restoration. Harting Down, with one of the finest stretches of the South Downs Way, is within one mile of Uppark.

Location: 5m SE of Petersfield on B2146.

Opening Times: 1 Jun - end Oct: Sun to Thur, House: 1.00pm - 5.30pm. Last admission 5.00pm. Car Park, Garden, Exhibition & Woodland Walk: 12.00pm - 5.30pm. Print room open on a limited basis first Mon each month.

Admission: House, Garden & Exhibition: £5.00, Family £12.50, Parties (no reduction) must be pre-booked weekdays only.

WAKEHURST PLACE

Tel: 01444 892701

Ardingly, Haywards Heath, Sussex, RH17 6TN.

Owner: The National Trust   **Contact:** The Administrator

A superb collection of exotic trees, shrubs and other plants, many displayed in a geographic manner. Extensive water gardens, a Winter Garden, a Rock Walk and many other features including a find Elizabethan mansion. The Loder Valley Nature Reserve can be visited by prior arrangement.

Location: 1½m NW of Ardingly, on B2028.

Opening Times: All year: daily (except 25 Dec & 1 Jan).Nov - end Jan: 10.00am - 4.00pm, Feb & Oct: 10.00am - 5.00pm, March: 10.00am - 6.00pm, Apr - end Sept: 10.00am - 7.00pm, Last admission 1/2 hour before closing. Mansion closes 1 hour before gardens.

Admission: Adult £4.00, Child (16 -) £1.50, Conc £2.00, reductions for pre-booked and pre-paid parties.

WEALD & DOWNLAND OPEN AIR MUSEUM

Tel: 01243 811348   **Fax:** 01243 811475

Singleton, Chichester, Sussex, PO78 0EV.

Contact: Richard Pailthorpe Esq

Collection of over 35 historic buildings rescued from destruction, including working watermill and various timber framed houses.

Location: 6m N of Chichester.

Opening Times: 1 Mar - 31 Oct, daily, 11am -5pm. Nov - Feb, Weds & weekends only.

Admission: Adult £4.20, Child £2.10, Family £11.00, Senior Citizen £3.70.

WEST DEAN GARDENS

OPEN

1 Apr - 29 Oct
Daily
11.00am - 5.00pm
Last entry 4.30pm

Parties by arrangement.
House not open.

Tel: 01243 811301
Fax: 01243 811342

WEST DEAN, CHICHESTER, WEST SUSSEX PO18 0QZ

Owner: *The Edward James Foundation*   **Contact:** *Jim Buckland*

Historic 35 acre garden in tranquil downland setting. Noted for its 300' long Harold Peto pergola, mixed and herbaceous borders, rustic summerhouses, water garden and specimen trees. Restored walled garden, 2.5 acres, contains a fruit collection, 13 Victorian glasshouses, apple store, large working kitchen garden and tool and mower collection. Circuit Walk (2.25 miles) climbs through parkland to the beautiful 45 acre St Roches Arboretum. Plant Centre, garden shop and restaurant in new Prince of Wales Institute of Architecture designed Visitor Centre.

Location: 6 miles north of Chichester on A286, Nr. Weald and Downland open air museum.

Admission: Adult £3.00, OAP £2.50, Child £1.50. Pre-booked parties 20+ £2.50.

SPECIAL EVENTS DIARY

- **9th April: Firle Place**
  Hunter Trials.

- **21st - 23rd April: Goodwood House**
  Home Design & Interiors Exhibition.

- **29th - 30th April: Bodiam Castle**
  Medieval Fair.

- **2nd, 30th May: Goodwood House**
  Antiques Market in grounds.

- **6th - 8th May: Leonardslee Gardens**
  Bonsai demonstrations.

- **12th - 14th May: Goodwood House**
  Antiques Fair.

- **17th June: Sheffield Park Garden**
  Open Air Concert with Fireworks - 1920's evening.

- **23rd - 25th June: Petworth Park**
  Open Air Concerts 8pm (Sun. matinée 1.30pm).

- **24th June: Bodiam Castle**
  Open Air Jazz Concert.

- **24th - 25th June: Leonardslee Gardens**
  Country Craft Fair (6th year).

- **24th - 25th June: Goodwood House**
  Festival of Speed.

- **26th Jun, 29th Aug, 16th Oct, 27th Nov: Goodwood House**
  Antiques Market in grounds.

- **2nd July: Firle Place**
  Southdown Country Fair.

- **7th July: Goodwood House**
  Fireworks Concert (at Racecourse).01243 780192 from Mid-May.

- **15th July - 16th July: Parham House**
  Garden Weekend

- **3rd September: Firle Place**
  Horse and Pony Endurance Ride.

- **17th September: Firle Place**
  British Horse Society Horse Trials

- **17th - 19th November: Goodwood House**
  Antiques Fair.

- **2nd - 3rd December: Goodwood House**
  Craft Fair.

ARBEIA ROMAN FORT
Tel: 0191 4561369 **Fax:** 0191 4276862

Baring Street, South Shields, Tyne & Wear, NE33 2BB.
Owner: Tyne & Wear Museums Service   **Contact:** The Curator
Extensive remains of 2nd century Roman fort, including fort defences, stone granaries, gateways, and latrines. Full scale simulation of Roman gateway and museum.
Location: Near Town Centre.
Opening Times: Tues - Sat, 10.00am - 5.30pm. Easter - Oct, Sun, 2.00pm - 5.00pm. Open Bank Hol Mons.
Admission: Free.

BEDE MONASTERY MUSEUM
Tel: 0191 4892106 **Fax:** 0191 4282361

Church Bank, Jarrow, Tyne & Wear, NE32 3DY.
Owner: St Paul's Jarrow Development Trust   **Contact:** Miss Susan Mills
Little remains of the original monastery where the Venerable Bede lived AD673 - 735 and which is now considered "The Cradle of English Learning". The museum in a Georgian house, has a model of the monastery and an AV display about the life of a monk.
Location: Just off A19 - S end of Tyne Tunnel.
Opening Times: Tues - Sat, 10.00am - 5.30pm. Sun 2.30pm - 5.30pm.
Admission: Adult £2.50, Child £1.25, Conc £1.25, Groups by arrangement.

BESSIE SURTEES HOUSE ⛶
Tel: 0191 2611585

41 - 44 Sandhill, Newcastle, Tyne & Wear.
Owner: English Heritage   **Contact:** The Administrator
Two 16th and 17th century merchant's houses stand on the quayside near the Tyne Bridge. One is a rare example of Jacobean domestic architecture.
Location: 41- 44 Sandhill, Newcastle.
Opening Times: Weekdays only 10.00am - 4.00pm. Closed Bank Hols, 24 - 26 Dec, 1 Jan

CATHEDRAL CHURCH OF ST NICHOLAS
Tel: 0191 2321939 **Fax:** 0191 2300735

Newcastle upon Tyne, Tyne & Wear, NE1 1GF.

Contact: Rev Canon Peter Strange
Mostly 14th century surmounted by 15th century lantern spire, one medieval window, two renaissance memorials, one large 15th century Flemish brass.
Location: City centre $^1/_2$ m from A167 signposted from Swan House roundabout.
Opening Times: Sun 7.00am - 12.00pm, 4.00pm - 7.00pm, Mon - Fri 7.00am - 6.00pm, Sat 8.30am - 4.00pm.

GIBSIDE 🌿
Tel: 01207 542255

Nr Rowlands Gill, Burnopfield, Newcastle upon Tyne, Tyne & Wear, NE16 6BG.
Owner: The National Trust   **Contact:** The Administrator
Gibside is one of the finest 18th Century designed landscapes in the north of England. The Chapel was built to James Paine's design soon after 1760. Outstanding example of Georgian architecture approached along a terrace with an oak avenue. Walk along river Derwent through woodland.
Location: 6m SW of Gateshead, 20m NW of Durham. Entrance on B6314 between Burnopfield and Rowlands Gill.
Opening Times: 1 Apr - end Oct: daily except Mon (open BH Mon), 11.00am - 5.00pm. Last admission 4.30pm.
Admission: Chapel and Grounds: Adult £2.80, Child half price. Pre-booked parties £2.50.

HYLTON CASTLE ⛶

Sunderland, Tyne & Wear.
Owner: English Heritage   **Contact:** The Administrator
This is a 15th century keep-gatehouse set in wooded parkland with a fine display of medieval heraldry adorning the facades.
Location: 3³/₄ m W of Sunderland.
Opening Times: Any reasonable time. (Access to grounds only).

SOUTER LIGHTHOUSE 🌿
Tel: 0191 5293161

Coast Road, Whitburn, Tyne & Wear, SR6 7NR.
Owner: The National Trust   **Contact:** The Administrator
Shore based lighthouse and associated buildings, built in 1871, the first to be powered by an alternative electric current.
Location: 2¹/₂m S of Southshields on A183. 5m N of Sunderland on A183.
Opening Times: 1 - 30 Apr and 1 - 29 Oct: Sat, Sun and Wed, Good Fri and Easter Mon, 11.00am - 5.00pm. Last admission 4.30pm. 1 May - 30 Sept: daily except Fri, weekdays 10.30am - 4.30pm. Last admission 4.00pm, Sat and Sun 11.00am - 5.00pm. Last admission 4.30pm.
Admission: Adult £2.30, Child half price. Pre-booked parties £1.70.

ST PAUL'S MONASTERY ⛶
Tel: 0191 4892106

Jarrow, Tyne & Wear.
Owner: English Heritage   **Contact:** The Administrator
The home of the Venerable Bede in the 7th and 8th centuries, partly surviving as the chancel of the parish church. It has become one of the best understood Anglo-Saxon monastic sites.
Location: In Jarrow, on minor road N of A185.
Opening Times: Monastery ruins - any reasonable time. Nearby museum open 1 Apr - 31 Oct, Tue - Sat & Bank Hols, 10.00am - 5.30pm. 1 Nov - 31 Mar, Tue - Sat, 11.00am - 4.30pm, Sun 2.30pm - 5.30pm. Closed Christmas, New Year.
Admission: Museum charge: Adults £1.00, Child 50p.

TYNEMOUTH CASTLE AND PRIORY ⛶
Tel: 0191 2541090

Jarrow, Tyne & Wear.
Owner: English Heritage   **Contact:** The Administrator
The castle walls and gatehouse enclose the substantial remains of a Benedictine priory founded c.1090 on a Saxon monastic site. Their strategic importance has made the castle and priory the target for attack for many centuries. In World War I, coastal batteries in the castle defended the mouth of the Tyne.
Location: In Tynemouth, near North Pier.
Opening Times: 1 Apr - 30 Sept: daily 10.00am - 6.00pm, 1 Oct - 31 Oct: daily 10.00am - 4.00pm, 1 Nov - 31 Mar: Wed - Sun 10.00am - 4.00pm (Closed 24 - 26 Dec, 1 Jan).
Admission: Adult £1.30, Child 70p, Conc £1.00.

WASHINGTON OLD HALL 🌿
Tel: 0191 4166879

The Avenue, Washington Village, Tyne & Wear, NE38 7LE.
Owner: The National Trust   **Contact:** The Property Manager
Jacobean manor house incorporating portions of 12th century house of the Washington family.
Location: In Washington on E side of Avenue. 5m W of Sunderland (2m from A1); S of Tyne Tunnel, follow signs for Washington New Town District 4 and then village.
Opening Times: 1 Apr - end Oct: daily (closed Fri and Sat but open Good Fri), 11.00am - 5.00pm. Last admission 4.30pm.
Admission: Adult £2.30, Child half-price, Parties (15 +) £1.80, by prior arrangement only.

SPECIAL EVENTS DIARY

- **1st April: Gibside**
  Triple Celebration: Talk, Buffet, Music.
- **27th May: Gibside**
  Family Funday - Creepy Crawlies.
- **29th May: Gibside**
  Craft Fair and Exhibition.
- **10th June: Gibside**
  Country and Western Barbeque.
- **17th June: Gibside**
  Young Musicians' Festival 2pm-10pm - Jazz, Folk, Wind, Choir, Big Band and Rock.
- **24th June: Gibside**
  Midsummer Music Concert with Fireworks Finale - Northern Sinfonia perform popular classics tel: 01670 774691.
- **14th-16th July: Gibside**
  Flower Festival and Country Fair.
- **30th July: Souter Lighthouse**
  Family Fun Day - 11am-5pm.
- **28th August: Gibside**
  Craft Fair.
- **15th September: Gibside**
  Hair, Face and Fashion Day.
- **16th October: Gibside**
  Halloween BBQ and Final Fling.
- **4th November: Souter Lighthouse**
  Centenary Bonfire Party.
- **26th November: Washington Old Hall**
  Thanksgiving Supper.

ARBURY HALL
Nuneaton

Built on the site of the Augustinian Priory of Erdbury, Arbury Hall has been the seat of the Newdegate family for over 400 years. This Tudor/Elizabethan house was 'gothicised' by Sir Roger Newdigate, the 5th Baronet in the 18th Century to become "The Gothick Gem of the Midlands".

The saloon and dining room ceilings are especially spectacular, the former modelled on the Henry VII Chapel in Westminster Abbey. Portraits include works by Lely, Romney, Reynolds and Devis, and furniture includes Hepplewhite and Gothick Chippendale. A collection of porcelain consists of oriental and Chelsea pieces amongst others, and there is a particularly

splendid display of Jacobite Toasting Glasses.

The Hall stands in secluded parkland and the delightful landscaped garden of rolling lawns, winding paths and beautiful trees and lakes are mainly the result of the 2nd Baronet's influence. Spring flowers, especially daffodils are profuse, and seen at their glorious best in June as is the vista of rhododendrons and the giant wisteria. North of the house lies the haven of the Rose Garden.

The Stables portico was designed by Wren.

George Eliot, the novelist was born on the estate and Arbury and Sir Roger were immortalised by her in her book, 'Scenes of Clerical Life'.

❖

CONTACT

Maj. W D Morris-Barker
Arbury Hall
Nuneaton
Warwickshire
CV10 7PT

Tel: (01203) 382804
Fax: (01203) 641147

LOCATION

London, M1, M6 exit 3
(A444-Nuneaton),
$1^3/4$ hours.

Chester A51, A34, M6
(from exit 14 to exit 3),
$2^1/2$ hours.
Nuneaton 10mins.

Bus: Nuneaton 3 miles.

Rail: Nuneaton Station
3 miles.

Air: Birmingham Int'l
17 miles.

SUITABILITY FOR OTHER EVENTS
Corporate Hospitality, Film Location, small conferences. product launches and promotion. marquee functions.

EXTRA FACILITIES
Clay pigeon shooting, archery and other sporting activities. Grand piano in Saloon. Helicopter Landing Site.

ADVICE TO COURIERS & DRIVERS
Follow tourist signs. Approach map available for coach drivers. Dogs on leads only in gardens. No cameras or video recorders allowed.

FACILITIES FOR THE DISABLED
Ramp access to main hall. Disabled visitors may alight at the Hall main entrance before parking in allocated areas.

PARKING FOR COACHES AND CARS
Parking for 200 cars and 3 coaches 250 yards from house. Other parking available.

GIFT SHOP
Open during opening hours and for private parties.

CATERING
Stables Tearooms for teas and light meals. Menus available for pre-booked parties. Exclusive lunches and dinners for

corporate parties in Dining Room, max. 50, buffets 120.

GUIDE BOOKS
Colour guide, £1.50.

GUIDED TOURS
All tours are guided. Duration of private tours, $1^1/2$ hours.

SCHOOL VISITS
Pre-arranged school parties are welcome, school room available. Children's guide book 25p.

Summer
16 April - 24 Sept.

Hall: Suns and Bank
Holiday Mons.
2.00 - 5.30pm.

Gardens: Suns & Mons.
2.00 - 6.00pm.

Last admissions to halls and gardens 5.00pm.

Open for pre-booked parties on most dates. Minimum 25 persons.

Winter
October - Easter
Corporate functions only.

Summer
Hall, Park & Gardens
  Adult £3.50
  Child (up to 14 yrs.) . .£2.00

Garden Only
  Adult £2.00
  Child (up to 14 yrs.) . .£1.00

GROUPS
  Adult £3.00
Special rates for pre-booked parties of 25 or more persons.

CONFERENCE AND FUNCTION FACILITIES

ROOM	DIMENSIONS	CAPACITY	LAYOUT	POWER POINTS	SUITABLE FOR A/V
Dining Room	35' x 28'	50	Lunch/Dinner		
		120	Buffet		
Saloon	35' x 30'	70	Theatre	4	
		18	Schoolroom		
Drawing Room	38' x 21'	40	Theatre	3	✓
		24	Schoolroom		
Long Gallery	48' x 11'	40	Theatre	4	✓
Stables Tea Rooms	31' x 18'	60	Cafeteria	3	✓
		80	Theatre		

COUGHTON COURT
Alcester

COUGHTON COURT has been the home of the Thockmortons since the 15th century and the family still live there today. The magnificent Tudor gatehouse was built around 1530 with the north and south wings completed ten or twenty years later. The gables and the first storey of these wings are of typical mid-sixteenth century half-timber work.

Of particular interest to visitors is the Thockmorton family history from Tudor times to the present generation. On view are family portraits through the centuries, together with other family memorabilia and recent photographs. Also furniture, tapestries and porcelain.

A long-standing Roman Catholic theme runs through the family history as the Thockmortons have maintained their Catholic religion until the present day. The house has a strong connection with the Gunpowder Plot and also suffered damage during the Civil War. Exhibitions on the Gunpowder Plot as well as Childrens Clothes open in 1995 (included in admission price).

GARDENS
The house stands in 25 acres of gardens and grounds along with two churches and a lake. A formal garden was constructed in 1992 with designs based on an Elizabethan knot garden in the courtyard. Visitors can also enjoy a specially created walk beside the River Arrow, returning to the house alongside the lake.

SUITABILITY FOR OTHER EVENTS
Coughton is suitable for receptions, special dinners in the panelled dining room, filming, buffets, business meetings, fairs and garden parties. The excellent acoustics of the Saloon make it ideal for concerts, especially chamber music concerts.

EXTRA FACILITIES
Marquees can be erected on the large lawn area and there is a Grand Piano in the Saloon.

ADVICE TO COURIERS & DRIVERS
Coughton Court is located on the A435, 2 miles north of Alcester. Dogs allowed in car park only. No photography or stiletto heels in house. Unlimited parking for coaches and cars.

FACILITIES FOR THE DISABLED
Only the ground floor of the house is suitable for disabled visitors. Toilet partially adapted for the disabled.

CATERING
There is a licensed restaurant open 11.30 - 5.30pm on days when the house is open. Capacity: 100 inside and 60 outside. Buffet or sit down meals can be provided, by arrangement, in the Dining Room and Saloon. Also in-house catering can be arranged for other events.

GUIDED TOURS
By arrangement.

GIFT SHOP AND PLANT CENTRE
Open when house is open.

GUIDE BOOKS
Guide book, £2.50.

CONTACT

Mr A McLaren
Coughton Court
Alcester
Warwickshire
B49 5JA

Tel: (01789) 400777
Fax: (01789) 765544

LOCATION

Located on A435, 2 miles north of Alcester, 10 miles N-W of Stratford-on-Avon. 16 miles from Birmingham City Centre.

OPENING TIMES

Summer
HOUSE
April and October
Sat & Sun
12 Noon - 5.00pm

Easter
Sat - Wed (inclusive)
12 Noon - 5.00pm

May - September
Daily except Thurs & Fri
12 Noon - 5.00pm

GROUNDS
11.00 - 5.30pm

Winter
Closed

ADMISSION

HOUSE & GROUNDS
Adult £4.50
Child £2.25
Family* £12.00
* 2 adults and up to 4 children.

GROUNDS ONLY
Adult £2.50
Child £1.25
Family* £6.60

CONFERENCE AND FUNCTION FACILITIES

ROOM	DIMENSIONS	CAPACITY	LAYOUT	POWER POINTS	SUITABLE FOR A/V
Dining Room	45' x 27'	40	Schoolroom	4	✓
		25	U-shape		
		20	Boardroom		
		55	Buffet		
		60	Theatre		
		46	Lunch/Dinner		
Saloon	60' x 36'	60	Schoolroom	6	✓
		35	U-shape		
		30	Boardroom		
		90	Buffet		
		90	Theatre		
		60	Lunch/Dinner		
THE SALOON, WHICH HAS PARTICULARLY GOOD ACOUSTICS, IS OFTEN USED FOR MUSIC RECORDING.					

RAGLEY HALL
Alcester

RAGLEY HALL, home of the Earl & Countess of Yarmouth was designed by Robert Hooke in 1680 and is one of the earliest and loveliest of England's great Palladian country houses. The perfect symmetry of its architecture remains unchanged except for the massive portico added by Wyatt in 1780.

The present interior is almost entirely due to two widely separated generations: in 1750, when Francis Seymour owned Ragley, James Gibbs designed the magnificent baroque plasterwork of the Great Hall. On completion, Francis filled the Hall with French and English furniture and porcelain and had portraits of himself and his sons painted by Sir Joshua Reynolds.

The present owners are the Earl and Countess of Yarmouth who are continuing the ongoing task of restoration and renovation to maintain Ragley in its present glory. Notable also is the mural, by Graham Rust, in the South Staircase Hall which was completed in 1983.

GARDENS

The main formal garden descends in a series of wide rose covered terraces. The rest of the 27 acre garden consists of shrubs and trees interspersed with spacious lawns providing vistas across the 400 acre park.

Other features are the lake created in 1625, the cricket pitch, still in regular use and the Adventure Playground and Maze.

CONTACT

Michael Barbour
Ragley Hall
Alcester
Warwickshire
B49 5NJ

Tel: (01789) 762090
Fax: (01789) 764791

LOCATION

From London 100 miles,
M40 via Oxford and
Stratford-on-Avon.

Bus: Birmingham -
Evesham, from
Lodge gates.

Rail: Evesham Station
9 miles.

Air: Birmingham Int'l
20 miles.

Taxi: 007 Taxi
(01789) 414007

SUITABILITY FOR OTHER EVENTS
Private and corporate entertainment. Conferences and seminars, product launches, dinner parties and activity days can all be arranged. A comprehensive service is provided Film and photographic location..

EXTRA FACILITIES
The park, lake and picnic area are also available for use.

ADVICE TO COURIERS & DRIVERS
Please advise in advance, especially if catering is required. Coach drivers admitted free and receive information pack and luncheon voucher. No dogs; no photography in house please. Guide book in in French and German.

FACILITIES FOR THE DISABLED
Disabled and elderly visitors may alight at the entrance to the property, before parking in the allocated areas. Toilets for the disabled and lifts to the first and main floor for wheelchairs at the north side of the house.

CATERING
The licensed Terrace Tea Rooms are open 11.30 - 5pm for light lunches, snacks, afternoon teas and cakes. Groups must book. Supper and private tours can be arranged, as can Private Luncheons and Dinners in the State Dining

Room or Great Hall for 2-150 people. Please contact the Business Manager for full details.

GIFT SHOP
Open same time as the Hall, with an excellent selection of unusual and traditional gifts.

SCHOOL VISITS/CHILDREN
School groups are welcome, £2.00 per head. Teachers packs and work modules available on request. Children can enjoy the Adventure Wood and Farm and Woodland Walk. Childrens Guide Book.

GUIDED TOURS
Private tours by Lord Yarmouth are available outside opening hours. The maximum size for the party is 100. For a guided tour there is a cost of £9.00 per head, plus VAT. Duration of the tour is approximately 1 hour.

OPENING TIMES

Summer
April - October

HOUSE
11.00am - 5.00 pm

GARDEN & PARK
10.00am - 6.00pm

Mon Bank Hols Only
(July & Aug: Park &
Gardens open.)

OPEN Tues, Wed, Thur,
Sat, & Sun

Fri Closed, except July &
Aug, when Park &
Gardens open.

Winter
2 October - 31 March
Open any time by prior
arrangement.

ADMISSION

Summer
HOUSE & GARDEN
Adult £4.50
Child* £3.00
OAP £4.00
Groups**
Adult £4.00
Schoolchild* . . .£2.00
OAP £4.00

* Aged 5-16.
** Min. payment £80.00 for parties of 20 or more.

Winter
HOUSE & GARDEN
Private conducted tour
By arrangement.

CONFERENCE AND FUNCTION FACILITIES

ROOM	DIMENSIONS	CAPACITY	LAYOUT	POWER POINTS	SUITABLE FOR A/V
Great Hall	70' x 40'	up to 150	Various	✓	✓
Red Saloon	30' x 40'	150	Reception	✓	
Green Drawing	20' x 30'	150	Reception	✓	
Supper	45' x 22'	up to 100	Various	✓	✓

ARBURY HALL

See page 193 for full page entry.

CHARLECOTE PARK

OPEN

Apr to end of Oct
Fri to Tues
closed Good Fri
11.00am - 6.00pm
House Closed
1.00 - 2.00pm
Last admissions
5.00pm
Group rate &
Introductory talk
available week
days only by
appointment.

Tel: 01789 470277

WARWICK, WARWICKSHIRE CV35 9ER

Owner: The National Trust   *Contact:* The Administrator

Home of the Lucy family since 1247; present house built in 1550's and later visited by Queen Elizabeth I; part landscape by "Capability' Brown, supports herds of red and fallow deer, reputedly poached by Shakespeare, and a flock of Jacob Sheep, first introduced in 1756; principal rooms altered in the 1830's in Elizabethan Revival style.

Location: 1 mile west of Wellesbourne, 5 miles east of Stratford-Upon-Avon 6 miles south of Warwick on north side of B4086. Signed from the A429.

Admission: Adult £4.00, Child £2.00, Family (2 + 4) £11.00

COUGHTON COURT

See page 194 for full page entry.

Warwick Castle, Warwickshire

FARNBOROUGH HALL

OPEN

House Grounds and
Terrace Walk
April to end of Sept.
Wed and Sat
also 7 & 8 May
2.00 - 6.00pm

Terrace Walk only
Thur and Fri
2.00 - 6.00pm
Last Adm. 5.30pm

Tel: 01295 690202

BANBURY, OXFORDSHRE OX17 1DU

Owner: The National Trust   *Contact:* The Administrator

A classical mid 18th century stone house, home of the Holbech family for 300 years; notable plasterwork, the entrance hall, staircase and 2 principal rooms are shown; the grounds contain charming 18th century temples, a $^2/_3$ mile terrace walk and an obelisk.

Location: 6 miles north of Banbury, $^1/_2$ mile west of A423.

Admission: House, Grounds & Terrace Walk: £2.70, Garden & Terrace Walk: £1.50. Terrace walk only (Thur & Fri) £1.00. Children Half price.

HONINGTON HALL

OPEN

June to August
Wednesdays only

Bank Holiday
Mondays

2.30 - 5.00pm

Parties at other
times by
appointment.

Tel: 01608 661434

SHIPSTON-ON-STOUR, WARWICKSHIRE CV36 5AA

Owner: Benjamin Wiggin Esq.   *Contact:* Benjamin Wiggin Esq.

This fine Caroline manor house was built in the early 1680's for Henry Parker in mellow brickwork and stone quoins and window dressings. Modified in 1751 when an octagonal saloon was inserted. The interior was also lavishly restored around this time and contains exceptional mid-Georgian plasterwork. Set in 15 acres of grounds.

Location: 10 miles south of Stratford-upon-Avon. $1^1/_2$ miles north of Shipston-on Stour. Take A3400 towards Stratford, then signed right to Honington.

Admission: Adult £2.75, Child £1.00.

KENILWORTH CASTLE

OPEN

1 Apr - 30 Sept
Daily
10.00am - 6.00pm

1 Oct - 31 Mar
Daily
10.00am - 4.00pm

Tel: 01926 52078

KENILWORTH, WARWICKSHIRE CV8 1NE

Owner: English Heritage   *Contact:* The Head Custodian

One of the grandest castle ruins in England, with red sandstone walls up to 20 feet thick and a 12th century keep, Kenilworth Castle was once home to Robert Dudley, a favourite of Queen Elizabeth I. There are impressive remains of the state rooms built and furnished for the Queen's visit in 1575.

Location: On Western Edge of Kenilworth, off B4103.

Admission: Adult £2.00, OAP/Student/UB40 £1.50, Child £1.00. 15% discount for parties of 11 or more.

LORD LEYCESTER HOSPITAL

Tel: 01926 491422

High Street, Warwick, Warwickshire, CV34 4BH.

Owner: The Governors of Lord Leycester Hospital   **Contact:** Capt D I Rhodes

Location: 1m N of M40, J15 on A429.

Opening Times: Tues - Sun, 10.00am - 5.00pm (Oct - Mar 10.00am - 4.00pm). Closed Good Fri and Christmas Day.

Admission: Adult £2.25, Child £1.00, Conc £1.50, Groups of 20 plus 5% discount.

PACKWOOD HOUSE

OPEN

Apr to end of Sept.
Wed to Sun and
Bank Holiday
Monday
2.00 - 6.00pm

Closed Good Friday
Oct: Wed - Sun
12.30 - 4.30pm

Last adm. half hour
before closing.

Tel: 01564 782024

LAPWORTH, SOLIHULL, B94 6AT

Owner: The National Trust   *Contact: The Administrator*

A fascinating timber framed Tudor house containing a wealth of fine tapestries and furniture, superb gardens noted mainly for their yew topiary and Carolean garden.

Location: 2 miles east of Hockley Heath (on A3400), 11 miles south east of Central Birmingham (139: SP174722).

Admission: Adult £3.50, Child £1.75, Family £9.60. Garden only: £2.00.

RAGLEY HALL

See page 195 for full page entry.

UPTON HOUSE

OPEN

1 Apr to 31 Oct
Sat to Wed
including
Bank Hol. Mon.
2.00 - 6.00pm

Last adm. 5.30pm

Closed Thurs & Fri
(inc. Good Friday)

Tel: 01295 670266

BANBURY, OXFORDSHIRE OX15 6HT

Owner: The National Trust   *Contact: The Administrator*

The house contains an outstanding collection of paintings by English and continental old masters, Brussels tapestries, Sévres porcelain, Chelsea figures and 18th century furniture. The famous garden has terraces descending into a deep valley; herbaceous borders, the national collection of Asters, over an acre of kitchen garden laid out in the 1930's and pools with ornamental fish.

Location: On A422, 7 miles north west of Banbury, 12 miles south east of Stratford upon-Avon. (151: SP371461).

Admission: Adult £4.60. OAP £2.30, Family £12.60. Garden only: £2.30.

WARWICK CASTLE

Tel: 01926 495421   **Fax:** 01926 401692

Warwick, Warwickshire, CV34 4QU.

Owner: Warwick Castle Ltd / Madam Tussaud's   **Contact:** Ms Joy Frowde

Warwick Castle is the finest medieval castle in England set on the picturesque banks of the River Avon. There are few buildings that are as steeped in history and as marvellously preserved.

Location: Centre of Warwick.

Opening Times: Open every day except Christmas Day, 10.00am - 6.00pm (1 Apr - 28 Oct). 10.00am - 5.00pm (29 Oct - 31 Mar). NB last admission half an hour earlier. On August Weekends and August Bank Hol Mon the Castle will be open until 7.00pm.

Admission: Adult £8.25, OAP £5.95, Student £6.25, Child £4.95, Family Ticket (2 x 2) £22.00. Groups (min of 20): Adult £6.50, OAP £5.25, Student £5.50, Child £4.25. Two special tours are available of the Castle and the grounds.

SPECIAL EVENTS DIARY

- **18th - 19th March:** Ragley Hall
  Craft Fair

- **7th - 8th May:** Ragley Hall
  Ragley Horse Trials

- **1st June:** Charlecote Park
  Family Day

- **3rd - 4th June:** Ragley Hall
  Gardens and Craft Fair (season tickets NOT valid)

- **15th - 21st June:** Charlecote Park
  Midsummer Music Festival

- **24th June:** Ragley Hall
  Hamlet - Outdoors (Evening Event)

- **25th June:** Ragley Hall
  Mountain Bike Championship

- **30th June:** Baddesley Clinton
  Outdoor Opera with Opera Brava

- **1st July:** Baddesley Clinton
  Outdoor Opera with Opera Brava

- **9th - 10th July:** Coughton Court
  Open Air theatre in garden "The Taming of the Shrew" production of Shakespeare's play by New Pilgrim Players.

- **15th July:** Coughton Court
  Arthritis & Rheumatism Council Open Air Fair in the gardens.

- **16th July:** Ragley Hall
  Transport Show

- **29th July:** Ragley Hall
  Newfoundland Dog Water Trials

- **5th August:** Ragley Hall
  Fireworks & Laser Concert (Evening Event)

- **19th - 20th August:** Ragley Hall
  Warwickshire & Worcestershire Game Fair (season tickets NOT valid)

- **1st September:** Ragley Hall
  Last Night of the Proms (season tickets NOT valid)

- **10th September:** Ragley Hall
  Mini Rally

- **16th - 24th September:** Ragley Hall
  Warwickshire & Worcestershire Artists Exhibition

- **7th - 8th October:** Ragley Hall
  Craft Fair

Honington Hall, Warwickshire

ASTON HALL

Tel: 0121 327 0062

Trinity Road, Aston, Birmingham, West Midlands, B6 6JD.

Owner: Birmingham City Council   **Contact:** Ms L Flanaghan

Fine Jacobean mansion with panelled long gallery, and outstanding plasterwork. Jacobean kitchen and nursery and 20 period rooms.

Location: 2 1/2m N of Birmingham near Villa Park.

Opening Times: 1 April - 29 Oct, 2.00pm - 5.00pm.

Admission: No charge at present.

BADDESLEY CLINTON

OPEN

4 Mar to end of Sept
Wed to Sun &
Bank Hol Mons
(Closed Good Fri)
2.00 - 6.00 pm
Oct: Wed to Sun
12.30 - 4.30pm
March '96
Wed to Sun
2.00 - 6.00pm
Grounds open
from 12.30pm

Last admission to
house, shop and
Restaurant 1/2 hr
before closing

Tel: 01564 783294

LAPWORTH, KNOWLE, SOLIHULL B93 QDQ

Owner: *The National Trust*   **Contact:** *The Administrator*

A romantically sited medieval moat manor house, dating from 14th century; little changed since 1634; family portraits, priest holes; garden; ponds and lake walk.

Location: 3/4 miles west of A4141 Warwick/Birmingham road at Chadwick End.

Admission: Adult £4.20, Child £2.10, Family £11.60
Grounds, Restaurant & Shop: £2.10.

THE BIRMINGHAM BOTANICAL GARDENS AND GLASSHOUSES

OPEN

Daily

9.00am - Dusk
(8.00pm latest)

Sundays opening
time 10.00 am.

Tel: 0121 454 1860

WESTBOURNE ROAD, EDGBASTON, BIRMINGHAM B15 3TR

Owner: *Birmingham Botanical & Horticultural Society*   **Contact:** *Miss. N. Bate*

Tropical, Mediterranean and Desert Glasshouses contain a wide range of exotic and economic flora. 15 acres of beautiful gardens with the finest collection of plants in the Midlands. Home of the National Bonsai Collection. Children's adventure playground, Aviaries, Gallery, Gift Shop and Plant Centre. Refreshments.

Location: 2 miles west of city centre. Follow signs to Edgbaston then brown tourist signs.

Admission: Adult £3.00 (£3.30 on Suns & Bank Hols), Concessions £1.70 Children under 5 Free.

BLAKESLEY HALL

Tel: 0121 783 2193

Yardley, Birmingham, West Midlands.

Owner: Birmingham City Council   **Contact:** The Administrator

Late 16th century timber framed yeoman's house furnished according to an inventory of 1684. Displays of building methods and a pottery.

Location: 2 1/2m N of Birmingham near Villa Park.

Opening Times: 2.00pm - 5.00pm throughout the summer.

Admission: Free.

SPECIAL EVENTS DIARY

Birmingham Botanical Gardens and Glasshouses

- **19th April:** *Birmingham and Midland Orchid Show 11am - 4pm*
- **21st May:** *Friends Plant Market, 10.30am - 4.30pm*

COVENTRY CATHEDRAL

Tel: 01203 227597

Coventry, West Midlands.

Owner: Provost & Canons of Coventry Cathedral   **Contact:** The Dean

The remains of the blackened medieval Cathedral, bombed in 1940, stand beside the new Cathedral by Basil Spence, constructed in 1962. Modern works of art include huge tapestry by Graham Sutherland, stained glass window by John Piper and bronze sculpture by Epstein.

Location: 2 1/2m N of Birmingham near Villa Park.

Opening Times: All year, daily. Easter - Sept 9.30am - 7pm. Oct - Easter 9.30am - 5pm.

Admission: Donation £2.00 for Cathedral.

HALESOWEN ABBEY

Tel: 01203 227597

Halesowen, Birmingham, West Midlands

Owner: English Heritage   **Contact:** The Administrator

Remains of an abbey founded by King John in the 13th century, now incorporated into a 19th century farm. Parts of the church and the monk's infirmary can still be made out.

Location: Off A456 Kidderminster road, 6 miles W of Birmingham City Centre.

Opening Times: 1 Apr - 30 Sept 10.00am - 6.00pm, Jul - Aug, weekends only. Lunchtime closure 1.00pm - 2.00pm

Admission: Adult £1.00, Child 50p, Conc 80p.

MOSELEY OLD HALL

OPEN

1 Apr - 29 Oct
Wed, Sat, Sun &
Bank Hol. Mons;
also Tues in
July & Aug
2.00 - 5.30pm

Bank Holiday Mon
11.00am - 5.00pm
Pre-booked parties
at other times
including
evening tours
by appointment.

Tel: 01902 782808

FORDHOUSES, WOLVERHAMPTON WV10 7HY

Owner: *The National Trust*   **Contact:** *The Property Manager*

An Elizabethan House with later alterations. Charles II hid here after the battle of Worcester and the bed in which he slept is on view, as well as the hiding place he used. The small garden has been reconstructed in 17th century style with formal box parterre; 17th century plants only are grown. The property is a Sandford Education Award Winner.

Location: 4 miles north of Wolverhampton between A449 and A460.

Admission: Adult £3.30, Child £1.65, Family ticket (2 adults/2 children) £8.00.

RYTON ORGANIC GARDENS

Tel: 01203 303517   **Fax:** 01203 303517

Ryton-on-Dunsmore, Coventry, West Midlands, CV8 3LG.

Owner: Henry Doubleday Research Association   **Contact:** J Gear / P Clark

The Midlands' most talked about gardens. 8 acres of beautiful and informative gardens including herbs, shrubs, flowers, rare and unusual vegetables, all organically grown. Enlarged award-winning restaurant and shop.

Location: 5m Southeast of Coventry off A45 on the road to Wolston.

Opening Times: Every day except during Christmas week, 10.00am - 5.30pm

Admission: Adult £2.50, Child (5 - 16) £1.25, OAP £1.75, Family £6.50.

WIGHTWICK MANOR

Tel: 01902 761108

Wightwick Bank, Wolverhampton, West Midlands, WV6 8EE.

Owner: The National Trust   **Contact:** The Administrator

Begun in 1887, the house is a notable example of the influence of William Morris, with many original Morris wallpapers and fabrics. Also of interest are Pre-Raphaelite pictures, Kempe glass and de Morgan ware. The Victorian/Edwardian garden has yew hedges and topiary, terraces and two pools.

Location: 3m W of Wolverhampton, up Wightwick Bank (A454), beside the Mermaid Inn.

Opening Times: House: 1 Mar - 31 Dec and Mar 1996: Thur & Sat 2.30pm - 5.30pm. Also open BH Sat, Sun & Mon 2.30pm - 5.30pm. Garden: Wed & Thur 11.00am - 6.00pm; Sat, BH Sun & BH Mon 1.00pm - 6.00pm.

Admission: Adult £4.50, Student £2.25 Garden only: £2.00.

- **11th June:** *Midland Bonsai Society Show 11am - 4pm*
- **16th July:** *Bonsai Fair 10.30am - 4.30pm*
- **17th September:** *Birmingham Dahlia Society Show 11am - 4pm*
- **1st October:** *Cactus Society Show 11am - 4pm*
- **20th November:** *Friends Craft Fair 11am - 4.pm*

BOWOOD HOUSE
Calne

BOWOOD is the family home of the Earl and Countess of Shelburne, the Earl being the eldest son of the Marquess of Lansdowne. Begun c.1720 for the Bridgeman family, the House was purchased by the 2nd Earl of Shelburne in 1754 and completed soon afterwards. Part of the House was demolished in 1955, leaving a perfectly proportioned Georgian home, over half of which is open to visitors. Robert Adam's magnificent Diocletian wing contains a splendid library, the Laboratory where Joseph Priestly discovered oxygen gas in 1774, the Orangery - now a Picture Gallery, the Chapel and a Sculpture Gallery in which some of the famous Lansdowne Marbles are displayed. Among the family treasures shown in the numerous Exhibition Rooms are Georgian costumes, including Lord Byron's Albanian dress; Victoriana; Indiana (the 5th Marquess was Viceroy 1888-94); and superb collections of watercolours, miniatures and jewellery. The House is set in one of the most beautiful parks in England. Over 2,000 acres of gardens and grounds were landscaped by Capability Brown between 1762 and 1768, and are embellished with a Doric Temple, a cascade, a pinetum and an arboretum. The Rhododendron Gardens are open for six weeks during May and June. All the walks have seats.

❖

SUITABILITY FOR OTHER EVENTS
Receptions, film location.

EXTRA FACILITIES
Internationally renowned Garden Centre, 2,000 acre park, 40 acre lake, massive adventure playground, golf course and Country Club.

ADVICE TO COURIERS & DRIVERS
2-3 hours should be allowed to visit the house, gardens and grounds. We recommend parties who require lunch or tea to book in advance. No dogs allowed. Parking for over 1,000 cars and unlimited parking for coaches, 400 yards from the House.

FACILITIES FOR THE DISABLED
Disabled and elderly visitors may alight at the House before parking in the allocated area. There are toilet facilities for the disabled in the House and in the Garden Centre.

CATERING
Both The Bothy (self-service light snacks, capacity 50) and the Restaurant (waitress-service, capacity 85) are available. Pre-booked prices range from £5.95 to £7.25 for a two course lunch and coffee; £6.65 to £10.30 for the daily buffet, dessert and coffee; £2.80 for a cream tea. Catering facilities can be provided for functions, for 45 to 85 persons.

GUIDED TOURS
Groups can be met and given an introductory talk, and if requested can be given a guided tour, for which there is an additional charge. Average time for tour of House 1¼ hrs.

GIFT SHOP
Garden centre open throughout the year, selling Bowood souvenirs, china, toiletries etc. as well as a wide range of plants. Kitchen Shop open in the House.

GUIDE BOOKS
Colour guide book, £2.50. Translation sheets available in French, German, Japanese and Dutch. Comprehensive guide to Bowood's trees and shrubs £1.50, Catalogue of the Collection of paintings £1.50.

SCHOOL VISITS/CHILDREN
School parties are welcome. Special guide books for children. Educational visit with teacher's notes for pre-, during and post-school visit, for both primary and secondary schools. Many picnic areas. Exciting and unique Adventure Playground.

GOLF COURSE & COUNTRY CLUB
In May 1992, the Bowood Golf and Country Club opened. The 18 hole course and practice area covers two hundred acres in the western corner of Capability Brown's park. Access to the course and club house is through Sir Charles Barry's famous 'golden gates' in Derry Hill. The course is open to all players holding a current handicap.

CONTACT

The Administrator
Bowood House and
Gardens
Calne
Wiltshire
SN11 0LZ

Tel: (01249) 812102

LOCATION

From London M4,
Junct. 17, 2 hours.

Swindon 17 miles,
Bristol 26 miles and
Bath 16miles.

Bus: to the gate,
1½ miles through
park to House.

Rail: Chippenham
Station 5 miles,

Taxi: AA Taxis,
Chippenham 657777.

OPENING TIMES

Summer
1 April - 29 October

Daily 11.00am - 6.00pm
NB Open Bank Hols

Winter
30 October - 29 March
House closed.
Garden Centre Open.

ADMISSION

Summer
Adult £4.70
Child* £2.50
OAP £4.00

Groups (min 20 people)
Adult £4.20
Child* £2.20
OAP £3.50

RHODODENDRON
GARDENS
Open for six weeks in
May and June.
Adult £2.50
Child* . . . . .F.O.C.
OAP £2.50

* Aged 5-15.

CORSHAM COURT
Corsham

CORSHAM COURT is an Elizabethan house of 1582 that was bought by Paul Methuen in the mid-18th Century, to house a collection of 16th and 17th Century Italian and Flemish master paintings and statuary. In the middle of the 19th Century, the House was enlarged to receive a second collection, purchased in Florence, principally of fashionable Italian masters, rare Italian primitives and stone inlaid furniture.

Paul Methuen (1723-95) was a great-grandson of Paul Methuen of Bradford-on-Avon and cousin of John Methuen, ambassador and negotiator of the Methuen Treaty of 1703 with Portugal which permitted export of British woollens to Portugal and allowed a preferential $33^1/_3$% duty discount on Portuguese wines - bringing about a major change in British drinking habits.

The architects involved in the alterations to the House and Park were Lancelot Capability Brown in the 1760s, John Nash in 1800 and Thomas Bellamy in 1845-9. Brown set the style by retaining the Elizabethan Stables and Riding School, but rebuilding the Gateway, retaining the gabled Elizabethan stone front and doubling the gabled wings at either end and, inside, by designing the East Wing as Stateroom-Picture Galleries. Nash's work has now largely disappeared, but Bellamy's stands fast, notably in the Hall and Staircase.

The State Rooms, including the Music Room and Dining Room, provide the setting for the outstanding collection of over 150 paintings, statuary, bronzes and furniture. The collection includes work by such names as Chippendale, the Adams brothers, Carvaggio, Reni, Rosa, Rubens, Lippi, Reynolds, Romney and a pianoforte by Clementi.

GARDENS
Capability Brown planned to include a lake, avenues and specimen trees such as the Oriental Plane now with a 200 yard perimeter. The Gardens, designed not only by Brown but also by Repton, contain a Ha-ha, herbaceous borders, secluded gardens, lawns, rose gardens, a lily pool, a stone bath house and the Bradford Porch.

SUITABILITY FOR OTHER EVENTS
Corsham is suitable for filming.

ADVICE TO COURIERS & DRIVERS
Bring coach parties up to the front door. PLEASE BOOK coach parties in advance. No photography, no umbrellas, dogs must be kept on leads in the garden.

FACILITIES FOR THE DISABLED
Disabled and elderly visitors may alight at the entrance to the property, before parking in the allocated areas.

PARKING FOR COACHES & CARS
Capacity of the Car Park: 400 cars, 120 yards from the House and coaches may park at the door to the House.

CATERING
No catering is provided. Audrey's Tea Rooms are recommended. Tel: Corsham (01249) 714931.

GUIDED TOURS
These are offered for up to 50-55 people on any one tour. If requested the owner may meet the group visiting the House. Approximate duration of the tour is $1^1/_2$ hours.

GIFT SHOP
There is a sales area, stocking postcards, slides and books.

GUIDE BOOKS
Colour guide book, for sale or hire.

SCHOOL VISITS/CHILDREN
School visits can be arranged: rate negotiable. A guide will be provided.

CONTACT

Corsham Court
Corsham
Wiltshire
SN13 0BZ
Tel: (01249)701610/
701611

LOCATION

Corsham is sign posted from the M4.
From Edinburgh, A1, M62, M6, M5, M4, 8 hrs.
From London, M4, $2^1/_4$ hrs.
From Chester, M6, M5, M4, 4 hours.

Motorway: M4 Junct. 17, 9 miles.

Rail: Chippenham Station 6 miles.

Taxi: (01249) 715959.

OPENING TIMES

Summer
Good Friday - 30 Sept

Daily except Mons
2.00 - 6.00pm
Last Admission 5.30pm

Open Bank Hol Mons only.

Winter
1 Oct - Good Friday
Daily except Mons
and Fris   2.00 - 4.30pm
Last admission 4pm.

NB. Closed December

ADMISSION

All Year

HOUSE & GARDEN

Adult £3.50
Child* £2.00
OAP(U.K) £3.00
Student £3.50

Groups**
Adult £3.00
Child* £1.50
OAP(U.K) £2.50
Student £3.00

GARDEN ONLY
Adult £2.00
Child* £1.00
OAP £1.50
Student £2.00

Groups**
Per person. £1.50

* Aged 5 - 16yrs.
** Min payment £40.00

LONGLEAT HOUSE
Warminster

LONGLEAT HOUSE lies in a sheltered valley amidst rolling parkland, landscaped by Capability Brown in the late 18th century. The magnificent Elizabethan property, built by Sir John Thynne with the help of the celebrated mason-architect Robert Smythson was completed in 1580 and has been the home of the same family ever since.

The house contains many treasures, including paintings by Titian, Tintoretto, Wootton, a fine Louis XV1 desk and a fabulous silver table centrepiece weighing 1,000 ounces. Between 1801 and 1811 the architect Jeffrey Wyatville designed the magnificent stable block and also carried out many alterations to the House. However, the Great Hall was not altered and remains the same fine Elizabethan room as Sir John left it in 1580.

The formal gardens contain a beautiful Orangery and a delightful boathouse. In 1949 Longleat became the first Stately Home to open to the public thus starting a new industry in Britain. The first Safari Park outside Africa in 1966. The Life and Times of Henry Lord Bath – A Memorial Exhibition - shows the long and active life of the 6th Marquess and is told through this personal collection from early childhood memories on the Estate, through World War Two to his twilight years. Following his fascination for Churchill, he amassed one of the finest collections of Churchill memorabilia, which is housed in this moving and nostalgic exhibition. Lord Bath's Murals are a recent addition to the House continuing the tradition of each generation adding to and embellishing their family home.

CONTACT

Customer Services Dept.
The Estate Office
Longleat
Warminster
Wiltshire
BA12 7NW

Tel: (01985) 844400

Fax: (01985) 844885

LOCATION

London 2 hrs.
M3, A303, A36, A362.
Midway between
Warminster and Frome
or from North
West M4 exit 18.

Rail: mainline
Paddington to
Westbury 12 miles.

Air: Bristol airport 30
miles.

Taxi: Beeline Taxis
(01985) 212215

SUITABILITY FOR OTHER EVENTS
Fashion shows, concerts, archery, equestrian events, garden parties, shows, rallies, filming, promotions, product launches.

EXTRA FACILITIES
Also available for use: Grand Piano, Parkland, Helicopter Pad. Specialist Lectures can be arranged by prior appointment on the property and its history for up to 50 people. Rooms can be hired.

ADVICE TO COURIERS & DRIVERS
Facilities available for coach drivers.

CATERING
There is a cellar Café (capacity 80). Parties can be booked in advance for tea and other meals. Menus are available on request. Cream Teas are available, as well as lunch from £5.00 and sandwiches and snacks from £1.20.

GUIDED TOURS
For groups of up to 20 people. Please pre-book tours when required in French, Spanish or German. Average time per tour is one hour.

GIFT SHOP
The gift shop is open daily except 25th December from 10am to 6pm. in Summer and 10am to 4pm. in winter. There is a range of souvenirs available.

GUIDE BOOKS
A full-colour guide book with photographs is available. French and German material on request.

SCHOOL VISITS / CHILDREN
Groups are welcome with 1 teacher given free entry per 10 children. Full group and education pack available on request.

CONFERENCE AND FUNCTION FACILITIES

ROOM	DIMENSIONS	CAPACITY	LAYOUT	POWER POINTS	SUITABLE FOR A/V
Green Library	42' x 22'	90	Various	✓	✓
		80	Dinner/Dance (with Great Hall)		
Great Hall	48' 9" x 27'	150	Various	✓	✓

OPENING TIMES

Summer
11 March - 29 October
House, Grounds and
Safari Park only
Daily 10.00am - 6.00pm
Last admission 5.30pm
or sunset if earlier.

Other attractions:
11.00am - 6.00pm.

Winter
November - April
(except Christmas Day)
House, Grounds only
Daily 10.00am - 4.00pm
by guided tour.
Times will vary.

ADMISSION

Summer
1995 prices -
phone for further info.

HOUSE ONLY
Adult £4.80
Child* £3.00
OAP £3.80
Groups (min 15 people)
Adult £3.00
Child* £1.50
OAP £2.50

GROUNDS ONLY
Adult £2.00
Child* £0.50
OAP 1.50

Groups of over 15 Free.

PASSPORT TICKETS
Apr - Sept. includes Safari Park, Longleat House, Dolls Houses, Boat Ride, Lord Bath's Bygones, VIP Vehicles, Dr. Who, Maze, Butterfly Garden, Postman Pat's Village, Railway, Pets Corner, Simulator, Adventure Castle, Memorial Exhibition, Grounds and Garden.

Adult £11.00
Child* £9.00
OAP £9.00
Groups (min 15 people)
Adult £8.50
Child* £7.00
OAP £7.00

*Age 4 -14.

Winter
House only open.
Rates as summer.

SHELDON MANOR
Chippenham

The surviving manorhouse of a long-gone medieval village has a great Porch described by Pevsner as 'astounding'. The parvise is late 13th Century, the east wing dates from 1431 and the west wing was rebuilt in 1659. The oak staircase with carved open finials and dog-gate is contemporary with this. The Hall and Dining Room are oak-panelled and the main bedroom has William and Mary panelling.

The stone cistern in the thickness of the Plantagenet wall, fed by a wooden pipe from the roof, is unique. The Priest's Room has its original oak waggon roof and carved wallplates. The Chapel was built c.1450, and has three original windows and windbraces in the roof. The apple-house of half-timbered brick and thatch stands on staddle-stones. Visitors often remark on the welcoming 'feel' of the house, and its atmosphere, warm, serene and timeless.

Inside are collections of early oak furniture,

Nailsea glass, Persian rugs and saddle bags, porcelain and American Revolutionary War Memorabilia; a warm welcome, and no 'ropes'.

GARDENS
The forecourt probably comprises the medieval garden, with two exceptional yew trees. The terraces descending southwards to a long swimming pool in natural stone contain many old fashioned roses. -- a connoisseur collection - trees, and flowering shrubs, some planted in old Dutch cheese vats. Newly-established, a maze of edible plants.

National Winner of the first Historic House Awards, given by the AA and the NPI, in co-operation with the Historic Houses Association, for the privately-owned historic house open to the public which has best preserved its integrity and the character of its architecture and furniture while remaining a lived-in family home.

❖

CONTACT

Mrs M Gibbs
Sheldon Manor
Chippenham
Wiltshire
SN14 0RG

Tel: (01249) 653120

Fax: (01249) 461097

LOCATION

From London: M4 to Exit 17, 4 miles. A429 towards Chippenham, A420 towards Bristol. Follow sign posts.

Rail: Chippenham Station 3 miles.

Bus: Chippenham Bus Station 3 miles.

Taxi: Webbs, (01249) 660022.

SUITABILITY FOR OTHER EVENTS
Wedding receptions, birthday celebrations, garden parties, clay-pigeon shooting, archery, shows, rallies, filming are a speciality

EXTRA FACILITIES
Video, upright piano. Talks on the property, contents, garden and history can be arranged for up to 100 people. No extra charge for this Projector and screen can be hired.

ADVICE TO COURIERS & DRIVERS
No dogs or photography indoors. Facilities tailored to suit any function, always with a personal touch. Pre-booked coaches welcome. Parking for 200 cars, 100 yards from Manor. Area for coaches nearer house.

FACILITIES FOR THE DISABLED
Disabled and elderly visitors may alight at the entrance to the property, before parking in the allocated areas. Toilet facilities for the disabled on request.

CATERING
The Restaurant/Tea Room, which has won much praise from visitors, seats up to 84. The adjoining Cockloft (3 rooms) may be hired for private functions. Buffet

lunches/dinners, cream teas, medieval/17th century meals, garden barbecues are all bookable for groups. Menus/prices on request.

GUIDED TOURS
Leisurely tours of the house can be arranged, usually with the owners (in French/Italian also). Average tour lasts 1 hour.

SCHOOL VISITS/CHILDREN
School groups are welcome out of normal opening hours. Cost dependent on age and length of visit, guide and schoolroom available. Teachers welcome on familiarisation visit. Items of interest: dolls' house, Jacob sheep, parrot. Swimming is available for school visits provided there is a life saver in the party.

OPENING TIMES

Summer
Public Days, Sundays, Thursdays and Bank Holidays from Easter Day to 2nd October 12.30 - 6.00pm

House opens 2pm.

Private parties at anytime by prior arrangement

Winter
Closed.
Private day groups anytime by arrangement.

ADMISSION

Summer

HOUSE & GARDEN
Adult £3.00
Child* £1.00
OAP £2.75
Student £2.75

GARDEN ONLY
Adult £2.00
Child* £0.35
OAP £1.50
Student £1.50
Children free in family group.

Groups**
Adult
Private days £3.50
Open days £2.75
Child* . . . .Dependent on
. . . . . . .age/length of visit.
OAP . . . . .No private day
. . . . .concessions.

*Free under 11, £1 11-16 House & Garden. Free Garden only.

* *Min. Payment 20 people. If no catering required, extra charge made.

Winter
Same as Summer.
Groups only.

CONFERENCE AND FUNCTION FACILITIES

ROOM	DIMENSIONS	CAPACITY	LAYOUT	POWER POINTS	SUITABLE FOR A/V
Great Hall	21' x 30'	100	Various	1	✓
Stables	21' x 38'	150	Various	6	✓
	21'x24'	50			
Cockloft	3 rooms	50	Various	4	✓
Reception Room	21' x 21'		Various		
Library	18' x 15'		Various		

WILTON HOUSE
Wiltshire

CONTACT

Mr Alun Williams
Wilton House
Wilton
Salisbury
SP2 OBJ

Tel: (01722) 743115
Fax: (01722) 744447

LOCATION

3 miles west of
Salisbury on the A30.
Rail: Salisbury Station
(3 miles)
Bus: Every 10 minutes
from Salisbury.
Taxi: Sarum Taxi
(01722) 334477

The 17th Earl of Pembroke and his family live in Wilton House which has been the ancestral home for 450 years. In 1544 Henry VIII gave the Abbey and lands of Wilton to Sir William Herbert who had married Anne Parr, sister of Catherine, sixth wife of King Henry.

The Tudor Tower, in the centre of the east front, is the only part of the original building to survive a fire in 1647. Inigo Jones and John Webb were responsible for the rebuilding of the House in the Palladian style, whilst further alterations were made by James Wyatt from 1801. The chief architectural features are the magnificent 17th century state apartments (including the famous Single and Double Cube rooms) and the 19th century cloisters.

The House contains one of the finest art collections in Europe, with over 230 original paintings on display, including works by Van Dyck, Rubens, Joshua Reynolds and Breughel. Also on show - Greek and Italian statuary, a lock of Queen Elizabeth's I hair, Napoleon's despatch case, and Florence Nightingale's sash.

The visitor centre houses a dynamic introductory film (narrated by Anna Massey), the reconstructed Tudor kitchen and Victorian Laundry. It also provides a new home for the 'Wareham Bears', a unique exhibition of some 200 miniature teddy bears displayed with their own house, stables and other scenes.

21 acres of landscaped parkland and gardens beside the River Nadder. Palladian Bridge. Adventure playground.

❖

SUITABILITY FOR OTHER EVENTS
Film location, Fashion Shows, Product Launches, Equestrian Events, Garden Parties, Antiques Fairs, Concerts, Vehicle Rallies, Exclusive Banquets.

ADVICE TO COURIERS & DRIVERS
Free coach parking. Group rates (Min 15 pax), meal vouchers, drivers lounge. No photography /dogs in House.

FACILITIES FOR THE DISABLED
Toilets for the disabled. Excellent wheelchair access. Visitors may alight at the Entrance Guide dogs admitted..

PARKING FOR COACHES & CARS
Car (200+) and coach (12) park adjacent to visitor entrance.

CATERING
Self-service restaurant open 11am-1730. Advance booking required for groups (waitress service available for coffee, lunch and tea).

GIFT SHOP
Open as House. Stocks a wide variety of quality souvenirs. New for 1995 'The Wilton Collection', plus specialist teddy bear shop.

GUIDE BOOKS
24 page full colour guide book £2. French, German, Spanish, Italian, Japanese and Dutch information sheets.

GUIDED TOURS
Pre-booking a necessity

SCHOOL VISITS/CHILDREN
Teachers handbook for National Curriculum and worksheets. EFL students welcome. Free preparatory visit for group leaders.

OPENING TIMES

Summer
11 April - 29 October

Daily 11.00am - 6.00pm
Last admission 5.00pm

Winter
Closed, except for private parties.

ADMISSION

Summer
HOUSE, GROUNDS & EXHIBITION.

Adults £5.75
Child £3.75
OAP £4.75
Family (2+2) . .£15.25
Groups   (min 15 people)
Adult £4.50
OAP £4.50
Child £3.25

Winter
Prices on application

CONFERENCE AND FUNCTION FACILITIES

ROOM	DIMENSIONS	CAPACITY	LAYOUT	POWER POINTS	SUITABLE FOR A/V
Double Cube	60' x 30'	120	Dinner	12	
		150	U-Shape		
Exhibition Centre	50' x 40'	140	Dinner	6	
Film Theatre	34' x 20'	67	Theatre	2	✓

AVEBURY MANOR GARDEN

Tel: 01672 539388

Marlborough, Wiltshire, SN8 1RF.

Owner: The National Trust   **Contact:** The Administrator

A regularly altered house of monastic origin, the present buildings date from the early 16th century, with notable Queen Anne alterations and Edwardian renovation by Col Jenner. The topiary and flower gardens contain medieval walls, ancient box and numerous compartments.

Location: 6m W of Marlborough, 1m N of the A4 on A4361 and B4003.

Opening Times: 1 Apr - 31 Oct: daily except Mon & Thur (open BH Mon) 11.00am - 5.30pm.

Admission: Adult £2.20, Child £1.40, Parties £2.00, Child £1.20.

AVEBURY MUSEUM

Avebury, Marlborough, Wiltshire

Owner: The National Trust (E.Heritage Management)   **Contact:** The Administrator

The investigation of Avebury Stone Circles was largely the work of Alexander Keiller in the 1930s. He put together one of the most important prehistoric archaeological collections in Britain which can be seen at Avebury Museum.

Location: In Avebury 7 m W of Marlborough.

Opening Times: 1 Apr - 31 Oct daily, 10.00am - 6.00pm. 1 Nov - 31 Mar, Wed - Sun, 10.00am - 4.00pm. Closed 24 - 26 Dec, 1 Jan.

Admission: Adult £1.35, Child £1.00, Conc 65p. National Trust members Free.

AVEBURY STONE CIRCLES

Tel: 01672 539555

Marlborough, Wiltshire, SN8 1RF.

Owner: The National Trust   **Contact:** The Administrator

One of the most important Megalithic monuments in Europe, this 281/2 acre site with stone circles enclosed by a ditch and external bank is approached by an avenue of stones. The site also includes the Alexander Keiller Museum and the Wiltshire Life Society's display of Wiltshire rural life in the Great Barn. The site is managed by English Heritage and owned by the National Trust.

Location: 6m W of Marlborough, 1m N of the A4 on A4361 and B4003.

Opening Times: Stone Circle: open daily. Great Barn: telephone for details.

BOWOOD HOUSE 🏛

See page 199 for full page entry.

BRADFORD-ON-AVON TITHE BARN 🔲

Tel: 0117 9750700

Bradford-on-Avon, Wiltshire.

Owner: English Heritage   **Contact:** The Administrator

A magnificent medieval stone-built barn with a slate roof and wooden beamed interior.

Location: 1/4 m S of town centre, off B3109.

Opening Times: Keykeeper (telephone 01272 750770 for details).

BROADLEAS GARDENS

Tel: 01380 722035

Devizes, Wiltshire, SN10 5JQ.

Owner: Broadleas Gardens Trust   **Contact:** Lady A Cowdray

A delightful garden on green sand where magnolias, camellias, and rhododendrons flourish with underplantings of erythroniums, trilliums and sanguinarias. Many roses and rare perennials in other areas. Plants for sale.

Location: Signposted from town centre or 1m south of Devizes on A360 (not suitable for coaches).

Opening Times: Apr - Oct, Sun, Wed, Thur 2 - 6pm or by arrangement for groups.

Admission: Adult £2.00, Child £1.00, Groups over 10 £1.70.

CORSHAM COURT 🏛

See page 200 for full page entry.

GREAT CHALFIELD MANOR

Tel: 01985 8436005

Melksham, Wiltshire, SN2 8NJ.

Owner: The National Trust   **Contact:** Mrs R Floyd

Dating from 1480, the manor house is set across a moat between parish church and stables. Restored early this century by Major R Fuller, whose family still lives here.

Location: 3m SW of Melksham via Broughton Gifford Common.

Opening Times: 4 Apr - 31 Oct: Tues, Wed, Thur by guided tours only, starting 12.15pm, 2.15pm, 3.00pm, 3.45pm and 4.30pm. Guided tours of the manor take 45 minutes and numbers are limited to 25. It is suggested that visitors arriving when a tour is in progress visit the church and garden first. Closed on public holidays.

Admission: £3.50, no reductions.

HAMPTWORTH LODGE

Tel: 01794 390215   **Fax:** 01794 390700

Landford, Salisbury, Wiltshire, SP5 2EA.

Owner: N J M Anderson Esq   **Contact:** N J M Anderson

Timber framed house, modelled on early 18th century house, built in 1912 to the designs of Guy Dawber, a member of the Art Workers Guild.

Location: 10 m SE of Salisbury.

Opening Times: Groups by arrangement at any time from 1 Apr to 30 Oct.

Admission: Standard £3.00, under 11 free.

HEALE GARDEN 🏛

OPEN

Garden, Shop & Plant Centre

throughout the year

10.00am - 5.00pm

Tours of the house, lunches/teas for parties of over 20 by arrangement.

Tel: 01722 782504

WOODFORD, SALISBURY, WILTSHIRE SP4 6NT

Owner: Mr Guy and Lady Anne Rasch   *Contact: Lady Anne Rasch*

First winner of Christie's/HHA Garden of the Year award. Grade I Carolean manor house where King Charles II hid during his escape in 1651. In January great drifts of snowdrops and aconites bring early colour and the promise of Spring. The garden provides a wonderfully varied collection of plants, shrub, musk and other roses, growing in the formal setting of clipped hedges and mellow stonework. Particularly lovely in Spring and Autumn is the water garden surrounding an authentic Japanese Tea House and Nikko Bridge which create an exciting focus in this part of the garden.

Location: 4 miles north of Salisbury on the Woodford Valley road between A345 and A360.

Admission: Adult £2.50, accompanied child under 14 free.

IFORD MANOR GARDENS 🏛

OPEN

April & Oct.
Suns only &
Easter Mon.
2.00 - 5.00pm
May - Sept.
Tue, Wed, Thurs,
Sat, Suns & Bank
Holiday Mons.
2.00 - 5.00pm
Coaches by
appointment at
other times

Tel: 01225 863146
Fax: 01225 862364

IFORD MANOR, BRADFORD-ON-AVON, WILTSHIRE BA15 2BA

Owner: Mrs. E. A. J. Cartwright-Hignett   *Contact: Mrs. E. A. J. Cartwright-Hignett*

An enchanted garden. Iford Manor, a Tudor house with a classical facade, was once a busy centre of the woollen industry. Set in a romantic river valley it is now surrounded by a peaceful terraced garden of unique character. Designed by the Edwardian architect Harold Peto, it has pools, statuary, a colonnade, terraces and a cloister. Featured in Gardeners World in 1993.

Location: 7 miles S.E. from Bath via A36, signposted Iford.

Admission: Adult £2.00, OAP/Student/Child £1.50. Free car parking. Picnic area by river.

LACOCK ABBEY

Tel: 01249 730227

Lacock, Chippenham, Wiltshire, SN15 2LG.

Owner: The National Trust   **Contact:** The Administrator

13th century abbey converted into a house in 1540, with 18th century Gothic alterations. 19th century home of William Fox-Talbot , inventor of photography. Fine trees, spring flowers and rose gardens.

Location: In the village of Lacock, 3m N of Melksham, 3m S of Chippenham, just E of A350.

Opening Times: House: 1 Apr - end Oct daily (except Tues), 1.00pm - 5.30pm. Cloisters and grounds: daily 12.00pm - 5.30pm. Last admission 5.00pm. Closed Good Fri.

Admission: House, Grounds and Cloisters: Adult £4.20, Child £2.20. Parties (15 or more) £3.70, Child £1.90. Cloisters and Grounds only: Adult £2.10, Child £1.00.

LITTLE CLARENDON

Tel: 01985 843600

Dinton, Salisbury, Wiltshire, SP3 5OZ.
Owner: The National Trust   **Contact:** The Tenant
A Tudor house, but greatly altered in the 17th century.
Location: ¼m E of Dinton Church.
Opening Times: By prior written appointment.
Admission: £1.50, no reductions.

LONG HALL GARDENS

Tel: 01985 850424

Stockton, Warminster, Wiltshire, BA12 0SE.
Owner: N H Yeatman-Biggs Esq   **Contact:** N H Yeatman-Biggs
4 acre mainly formal garden with herbaceous gardens, shrub rose gardens, spring bulbs and fine hellebore walk.
Location: Stockton 7m SE of Warminster, off A36, W of A303 Wylye interchange.
Opening Times: 6 May - 5 Aug, first Sat in the month, 2.00pm - 6.00pm.
Admission: Adult £2.00, Child free, Groups by appointment at £5.00 including cream teas.

LONGLEAT HOUSE

See page 201 for full page entry.

LUCKINGTON COURT

Tel: 01794 390215

Chippenham, Wiltshire, SN14 6PQ.
Owner: The Hon Mrs Trevor Horn   **Contact:** The Hon Mrs Trevor Horn
3 acre garden with walled flower gardens, shrubberies, young arboretum attached to Queen Anne manor house (not open).
Location: B4040 near Sherston.
Opening Times: Gardens, Weds 2.00pm - 6.00pm (Sun 14 May for NGS).
Admission: Adult £1.00, Child free.

LYDIARD HOUSE

Tel: 01793 770401

Lydiard Park, Lydiard Tregoze, Swindon, Wiltshire, SN5 9PA.
Owner: Borough of Thamesdown   **Contact:** Ms S Finch-Crisp
Georgian house in attractive parkland, once dilapidated, but now fully restored with fine furniture and paintings.
Location: 4m W of Swindon, close to J16/M4.
Opening Times: Mon - Sat, 10.00am - 1.00pm, 2.00pm - 5.30pm. Sun 2.00pm - 5.30pm. Closes at 4.00pm Nov - Feb.
Admission: Adult 60p, Child 25p.

MOMPESSON HOUSE

Tel: 01722 335659

The Close, Salisbury, Wiltshire, SP1 2EL.
Owner: The National Trust   **Contact:** The Custodian
Fine Queen Anne town house, furnished as the home of a Georgian gentleman, with a walled garden. Art exhibition throughout the season.
Location: On N side of Choristers' Green in Cathedral Close, near High Street Gate.
Opening Times: 1 Apr - 31 Oct: daily except Thur and Fri, 12. Noon - 5.30pm. Last admission 5.00pm.
Admission: Adult £3.00, Child £1.50. Parties £2.70.

NEWHOUSE

Tel: 01725 510055

Redlynch, Salisbury, Wiltshire, SP5 2NX.
Owner: George Jeffreys Esq   **Contact:** George Jeffreys
Brick Jacobean "Trinity House", c. 1619, with two Georgian wings. Contents include costume collection, documents and the "Hare" picture.
Location: 9m S of Salisbury, 3m from Downtow, off B3080.
Opening Times: 1 - 31 Aug excluding Sun, 2.00pm - 5.30pm. By arrangement between May & Sept for groups of 25 plus.
Admission: Adult £2.00, Child under 15 £1.00.

OLD SARUM

Tel: 01722 335398

Salisbury, Wiltshire.
Owner: English Heritage   **Contact:** The Administrator
First an Iron Age fort, later inhabited by Romans, Saxons, Danes and Normans, there is much to disentangle from the 56 acres of ruins at this fascinating site. The Normans created a castle, the first Salisbury Cathedral and the Bishop's Palace. From the castle ramparts there are fine views of the surrounding countryside.
Location: 2m N of Salisbury off A345.
Opening Times: 1 Apr - 30 Sept: daily 10.00am - 6.00pm, 1 Oct - 31 Mar: daily 10.00am - 4.00pm, (Closed 24 - 26 Dec, 1 Jan).
Admission: Adult £1.50, Child 80p, Conc £1.10.

OLD WARDOUR CASTLE

Tel: 01747 870487

Tisbury, Wiltshire.
Owner: English Heritage   **Contact:** The Administrator
In a picture book setting, the unusual hexagonal ruins of this 14th century castle stand on the edge of a beautiful lake, surrounded by landscaped grounds which include an elaborate rockwork grotto.
Location: Off A30 2m SW of Tisbury.
Opening Times: 1 Apr - 30 Sept: daily 10.00am - 6.00pm, 1 Oct - 31 Oct: daily 10.00am - 4.00pm, 1 Nov - 31 Mar: Wed - Sun 10.00am - 4.00pm, (Closed 24 - 26 Dec, 1 Jan).
Admission: Adult £1.50, Child 80p, Conc £1.10.

PHILLIPS HOUSE

Tel: 01722 176208

Dinton, Salisbury, Wiltshire, SP3 5HJ.
Owner: The National Trust   **Contact:** YWCA Warden
A neo-Grecian house by Jeffry Wyattville, completed in 1816.
Location: 9m W of Salisbury, on N side of B3089.
Opening Times: On Sat only, by prior written arrangement.
Admission: £1.50, no reductions.

SALISBURY CATHEDRAL

Tel: 01722 328726   Fax: 01722 323569

Salisbury, Wiltshire, SP1 2EF.

Contact: Mrs P Hellewell
Majestic medieval cathedral with the tallest spire in England. Treasures include an original Magna Carta and Europe's oldest working clock.
Location: Off M3 - London / West Country.
Opening Times: Cathedral: daily Mon - Sat, 8.00am - 6.30pm (8.30pm May - Aug) Sun : 8.00am - 9.00am, 12.30pm - 2.30pm and 4 - 6.30pm. Chapter House: daily, except Dec.
Admission: Cathedral: Adult £2.50, Child 50p, Conc £1.00, Family £5.00. Chapter House: Adult 30p, Child free, Conc 20p.

SHELDON MANOR

See page 202 for full page entry.

STONEHENGE

Tel: 01980 624715

Amesbury, Wiltshire.
Owner: English Heritage   **Contact:** The Administration
One piece of magic that never fails to cast a spell over the traveller is the awe inspiring sight of this famous prehistoric monument as one crosses Salisbury Plain. Started 5,000 years ago, we can only really apply supposition and guess work to interpret the reasons for its existence, but we do know that the prehistoric builders went to incredible lengths to construct such a monument. The massive stone lintels are mortice-and-tenoned to the uprights upon which they rest, and are curved to follow a circle. Some of the stones weigh over 50 tons each, with some brought from the Preseli Mountains in Wales. Even if we remain unclear about its purpose, we can admire this extraordinary achievement of the earliest inhabitants of these islands.
Location: 2m W of Amesbury on junction A303 and A344/A360.
Opening Times: Open all year, daily from 9.30am (9.00am 1 Jul - 31 Aug). Closing times vary between 4.00pm and 7.00pm depending on season. Please check before travelling to avoid disappointment.
Admission: Adult £3.00, Child, £1.50, Conc £2.30. National Trust members admitted free.

STOURHEAD

Tel: 01747 840417

Stourton, Warminster, Wiltshire BA12 6QD
Owner: The National Trust   **Contact:** The Adminstrator
Landscape garden laid out from 1741-80, with lakes and temples, rare trees and plants. The house, begun in 1721 by Colen Campbell, contains furniture by the younger Chippendale, and fine paintings. King Alfred's Tower, a red-brick folly built in 1772 by Flitcroft at the edge of the estate, is 160ft high, giving fine views over the neighbouring counties of Somerset, Dorset and Wiltshire.
Location: At Stourton off B3092, 3 m NW of Mere (A303).
Opening Times: 1 April to 29 Oct, daily 11am - 6pm. 30 Oct - 24 Dec 11am - 4pm. Jan - end of March 1996, 11am - 4pm.
Admission: House: Adult £4.30, Child £2.20, Group £3.60 by written appointment only, Family £10.00. Garden: March - Oct, Adult £4.20, Child £2.10, Group £3.60, Family £8.00. No reduction for parties. Combined House and Garden: Adult £7.50, Child £3.50, Group £7.20, Family £20.00. King Alfred's Tower: £1.50 Child (5-16 yrs) 70p.

THE NATIONAL TRUST   ENGLISH HERITAGE   HISTORIC HOUSES ASSOCIATION

STOURTON HOUSE FLOWER GARDEN

Tel: 01747 840417

Zeals, Warminster, Wiltshire, BA12 6QF.
Owner: Mrs E Bullivant   **Contact:** Mrs E Bullivant
4 acres of beautifully maintained gardens. Many unusual plants. Plants for sale. No dogs. Wheelchair friendly.
Location: 3m N of Mere next to Stourhead., A303.
Opening Times: Apr - 30 Nov, Wed, Thur, Sun, and BH Mons 11.00am - 6.00pm.
Admission: Adult £2.00, Child 50p, Groups; Open days £1.50, Other days £2.00 by appointment. Parking free.

THE COURTS

Tel: 01225 782340

Holt, Trowbridge, Wiltshire, BA14 6RR.
Owner: The National Trust   **Contact:** Head Gardener
A 7 acre garden of mystery flanking an 18th century house (not open to the public), with an ornamental facade.
Location: 3m SW of Melksham, 3m N of Trowbridge, 2¹/₂m E of Bradford-on-Avon, on S side of B3107.
Opening Times: Garden only: 2 Apr - 31 Oct: daily except Sat 2.00pm - 5.00pm. Out of season by appointment.
Admission: £2.80, Child £1.40, parties by arrangement.

THE KING'S HOUSE

Tel: 01722 332151

65 The Close, Salisbury, Wiltshire, SP1 2EN.
Owner: P R Saunders   **Contact:** P R Saunders
Location: In Salisbury Cathedral Close, west side.
Opening Times: Mon - Sat, 10.00am - 5.00pm. Suns Jul, Aug and Salisbury Festival 2.00pm - 5.00pm.
Admission: Adult £2.50, Child 50p, Conc £1.75, Groups £1.75.

WILTON HOUSE

See page 203 for full page entry.

WESTWOOD MANOR

Tel: 01225 863374

Bradford-on-Avon, Wiltshire, BA15 2AF.
Owner: The National Trust   **Contact:** The Tenant
A 15th century stone manor house, altered in the late 16th century, with late Gothic and Jacobean windows and Jacobean plasterwork. There is a modern topiary garden.
Location: 1¹/₂m SW of Bradford-on-Avon, in Westwood village, beside the church.
Opening Times: 2 Apr - 1 Oct: Sun, Tues & Wed 2.00pm - 5.00pm.
Admission: £3.30, no reductions.

SPECIAL EVENTS DIARY

- **24th - 26th March: Wilton House**
  18th Annual Wilton House Antiques Fair
  10.30am-5.00pm daily, Adult £3, Child £1.50

- **16th - 17th April: Iford Manor Gardens**
  Demonstrations/skirmish by The Sealed Knot - Lord Robards Regiment.

- **15th - 17th April: Longleat**
  Easter Balloon Fiesta

- **16th April: Wilton House**
  Children's Easter Egg Treasure Hunt Quiz around the House

- **22nd April: Wilton House**
  London-Mexico Rally: Spectator stages (Wilton Estate)

- **23rd April: Wilton House**
  Shakespeare celebrations

- **6th - 7th May: Wilton House**
  May Day Folk Singers: Wilton House

- **6th - 8th May: Wilton House**
  Wessex Craft Fayre: Wilton Park (01425) 272711

- **13th - 14th May: Longleat**
  Cycling Festivals - courses for all abilities, trade stands, mountain bike trails, treasure hunt, toddlers obstacle course.

- **21st May: Wilton House**
  Salisbury Festival: Chamber Music Concert (01722) 323888

- **27th May - 4th June: Longleat**
  "Friends of Thomas The Tank Engine" various activities associated with this classic character.

- **3rd - 4th June: Longleat**
  Longleat Horse Trials

- **13th June: Lacock Abbey**
  Open Air Theatre - A Midsummer Night's Dream by Theatre Set-Up 7.30pm

- **17th June: Stourhead**
  Viennese Symphony Concert with fireworks and lasers 8pm £13.

- **24th June: Wilton House**
  National Music Days

- **25th June: Longleat**
  Radio Rally - gathering of radio ham enthusiasts.

- **8th July: Longleat**
  Proms Concert. Outdoor music concert with fabulous fireworks. Robert Hardy as guest speaker.

- **19th - 27th July: Stourhead**
  Fête Champêtre to celebrate the National Trust's Centenary £11-£18 dependent on the night.

- **28th July: Wilton House**
  Bournemouth Sinfonietta: Open Air Classical Spectacular with fireworks. Tickets £14.50 with early booking and group discounts.

- **29th - 30th July: Longleat**
  Wiltshire Balloon Festival

- **19th August: Longleat**
  Jazz on a Summer Evening

- **19th - 20th August: Wilton House**
  Wilton Horse Trials: Wilton Park (01722) 77321

- **20th August: Wilton House**
  Teddy Bears Picnic

- **9th - 10th September: Longleat**
  Dog Agility

- **9th - 10th September: Wilton House**
  Spiders Web Lacemakers (Cloisters)

- **7th - 8th October: Wilton House**
  Themed flower arranging competition (Cloisters)

- **18th November: Stourhead**
  Centenary Concert £11 including wine 8pm

- **18th - 19th November: Longleat**
  Craft Fayre

HANBURY HALL
Worcestershire

Hanbury Hall is every Englishman's idea of a substantial squire's house, tucked away in a large park free from reminders of the modern world. The home of the Vernon family for more than three centuries, it was entirely remodelled by 1701.

The magnificent staircase paintings were an afterthought (about 1710) painted by Sir James Thornhill, famous for the Painted Hall at Greenwich. The Dining Room has a most spectacular ceiling incorporating more Thornhill.

Emma Vernon created two further imposing rooms in the 1770's - the Library and the Drawing Room - this time in a light neo-classical style. She had married a selfish and extravagant man (who later became the Marquess of Exeter), who drove her to "Norris's drops and Madeira" and divorce in 1791. Luckily the splendid collection of family portraits survived these difficult times.

As well as the two family armorial dinner services, (c.1725 & c.1850), the house is now the permanent home of the Watney collection of porcelain and Dutch flower paintings. In the Blue bedroom can be found the Angel bed c.1725 with its original hangings in fine condition .

GARDENS AND PARKLAND

With changing fashion a fairly elaborate formal layout was swept away in the mid 18th century. However, 1993 saw the start of the re-creation of principal elements of the original scheme by re-introducing the sunken parterre, topiary/fruit garden and formal wilderness. In addition the handsome Orangery (c.1740), an excellent example of the 18th century ice house and the orchard remain with gentle walks across 400 acres of parkland.

❖

SUITABILITY FOR OTHER EVENTS

To use Hanbury Hall is no skirmish with illusion, it is genuine elegant country living. The house garden and parkland may be hired exclusively. Everything can be organised in distinctive style. Help given with:

- Activity days and other such country pursuits.
- Location filming.
- Hotel accommodation..
- Various meeting facilities for up to 50 people.
- Lunch and/or dinner for up to 68 people.
- Receptions for up to 100 people.
- Marquee events linked to the house for large numbers.

ADVICE TO COURIERS & DRIVERS

Coach parties welcome by prior arrangement only. Driver admitted free.No dogs, photography, limited space in tea room.

FACILITIES FOR THE DISABLED

Disabled may alight at the entrance before parking in the allocated area. Ramp to ground floor with level access to principal rooms & tea room. Toilets for the disabled, wheelchairs available.

PARKING FOR COACHES & CARS

General public car park: 120 cars, 2 coaches 300 yds (disabled 30 yds) from Hall. Unlimited private use extending onto grass.

CONTACT

Property Manager,
Hanbury Hall
Droitwich
Worcestershire
WR9 7EA

Tel: (01527) 821214

Fax: (01527) 821251

LOCATION

Hanbury's central location gives easy access form all parts of the country.

10 minutes from the M5 at junction 5 - follow Droitwich/Hanbury Hall signs.

Birmingham: City Centre, Airport, N.E.C., I.C.C. all within 30 minutes.

OPENING TIMES

Summer
1 Apr - 30 Oct
Sat. Sun & Mon.
2.00 - 5.30pm

In addition:
Tues & Wed afternoons during August

Winter
Available throughout the year for private use. Closed to the general public.

ADMISSION

Adult £3.70
Child £1.80
Family £10.00

GUIDED TOURS
Private guided tours by prior arrangement with Administrator. Max 60 people, min. charge £74.00.

GIFT SHOP
National Trust gift shop when house open to the general public.

CONFERENCE AND FUNCTION FACILITIES

ROOM	DIMENSIONS	CAPACITY	LAYOUT	POWER POINTS	SUITABLE FOR A/V
Dining Room	11m x 5.5m	28	Dinner	2	✓
Drawing Room	7.4m x 8.3m	50	Various	4	✓
Hall	6.7m x 13.5m	70	Various	6	✓
Library	8.1m x 5.8m	40	Reception	2	
Meetings	7.6m x 5.6m	1 - 24	Boardroom/	12	✓
Suite	3.4m x 5.6m	12-25	Theatre	6	

AVONCROFT MUSEUM OF HISTORIC BUILDINGS

OPEN

June - August
11.00am - 5.30pm
April, May, Sept
11.00am - 5.00pm
closed Mondays
March - Nov
10.30am - 4.00pm
closed Mons & Fris
but open Bank Hols.

Tel: 01527 831886
01527 831363

STOKE HEATH, BROMSGROVE, WORCESTER B60 4JR

Owner: Council of Management   *Contact: Mr. Peter J Rex*

Historic Houses rescued and restored in 15 acres of Worcestershire countryside. Exhibits include the magnificent 14th century roof of the Guesten Hall of Worcester Cathedral, a 1946 prefab. timber framed buildings, chainshop, nailshop, toll house, and a working windmill. New in 1994 - the National Telephone Kiosk Collection with examples from 1922 to today. Car/coach park, refreshments, picnic site and gift shop.

Location: 2 miles south of Bromsgrove off A38 by-pass.

Admission: Adults £3.50, OAP £2.80, Child £1.75, Family Ticket (2+2) £9.40. Booked parties at reduced rates.

BURFORD HOUSE GARDENS

Tel: 01584 810777   **Fax:** 01584 810673

Burford, Tenbury Wells, Worcestershire, WR15 8HQ.
Owner: Treasures Of Tenbury Ltd   **Contact:** Mrs Patricia Cox
Gardens created by John Treasure over past 35 years with numerous interesting plants.
Location: 3/4m W of Tenbury Wells.
Opening Times: All year, daily, 10.00am - 5.00pm.
Admission: Adult £2.50, Child £1.00, Family £15.00, Conc £2.00, Groups £2.00.

ELGAR'S BRITHPLACE MUSEUM

Tel: 01905 333224

Crown East Lane, Lower Broadheath, Worcester, WR2 6RH.
Owner: Elgar's Birthplace Trust   **Contact:** The Administrator
The cottage, where the composer Sir Edward Elgar was born in 1857, now houses a unique collection of priceless manuscripts and press cuttings.
Location: 3m W of Worcester off A44.
Opening Times: 1 May - 30 Sept, 10.00am - 6.00pm. 1 Oct - 15 Jan, 1.30 - 4.30pm. 16 Jan - 15 Feb closed. 16 Feb - 30 Apr, 1.30 - 4.30pm. Closed on Wed throughout the year.
Admission: Adult £3.00, Child 50p, Senior citizens £2.00, Conc £1.00. Groups on application.

HANBURY HALL

See page 207 for full page entry.

HARTLEBURY CASTLE

Tel: 01299 250416

Kidderminster, Worcestershire.
Owner: The Church Commissioners   **Contact:** The Secretary
Historic House of the Bishops of Worcestershire since 850. State rooms include medieval Great Hall, and 18th century Gothic interiors with fine plaster work.
Location: 5m S of Kidderminster.
Opening Times: State Rooms: Easter Mon - 3 Sept, first Sun in every month (but telephone to check), Easter hols and Tues following BHs, 2.00pm - 5.00pm. Also every Wed during this period, 2.00pm - 4.00pm. County Museum: Mar - Nov, Mon - Thurs, 10.00am - 5.00pm. Fri and Sun 2 - 5.00pm. Closed Sat and Good Fri. Open BHs 10am - 5.00pm.
Admission: State Rooms: Adult 75p, Child 25p, Senior citizens 50p, Guided tours for parties of 30 or more on weekdays by arrangement. County Museum: Standard £1.50, Conc 75p, Family ticket £4.20. Call to verify.

HAWFORD DOVECOTE

Tel: 01684 850051

Hawford, Worcestershire.
Owner: The National Trust   **Contact:** The Administrator
A 16th century half-timbered dovecote.
Location: 3m N of Worcester, 1/2m E of A449.
Opening Times: Apr - end Oct, daily 9.00am - 6.00pm or sunset if earlier. Closed Good Fri, other times by prior appointment.
Admission: 60p.

LEIGH COURT BARN

Worcester.
Owner: English Heritage   **Contact:** The Administrator
Magnificent 14th century timber framed barn built for the monks of Pershore. It is the largest of its kind in Britain.
Location: 5m W of Worcester on unclassified road off A4103.
Opening Times: 1 Apr - 30 Sept: Thur - Sun 10.00am - 6.00pm.

LITTLE MALVERN COURT

Tel: 01684 892988   **Fax:** 01684 893057

Malvern, Worcestershire, WR14 4JN.
Owner: T M Berrington Esq   **Contact:** T M Berrington
14th century Priors Hall once part of Benedictine Priory, attached to 19th century family house with 10 acre gardens.
Location: 5 1/2m S of Great Malvern on Upton on Severn Road A4104.
Opening Times: 19 Apr - 20 Jul, Wed and Thur, 2.15pm - 5.00pm.

LOWER BROCKHAMPTON

Tel: 01885 488099

Malvern, Worcestershire, WR14 4JN.
Owner: The National Trust   **Contact:** The Administrator
A late 14th century moated manor house, with an attractive detached half timbered 15th century gatehouse, a rare example of this type of structure. Also, the ruins of a 12th century chapel.
Location: 2m E of Bromyard on A44, reached by a narrow road through 1 1/2m of woods and farmland.
Opening Times: 19 Apr - 20 Jul, Wed and Thur, 2.15pm - 5.00pm.
Admission: £1.60, family £4.40.

MADRESFIELD COURT

Tel: 01684 573024   **Fax:** 01684 573024

Madresfield, Malvern, WR13 5AU.
Owner: The Trustees   **Contact:** Sir Charles Morrison
Elizabethan and Victorian house with medieval origins. Fine contents. Extensive wild garden.
Location: 8m of M5 J7.
Opening Times: Limited, by appointment. Apr to Sept.
Admission: £5.00.

SPETCHLEY PARK GARDEN

Tel: 01905 345213 / 224

Spetchley , Worcester, WR5 1RS.
Owner: R J Berkeley Esq   **Contact:** R J Berkeley
30 acre private garden containing large collection of trees, shrubs and plants, many rare and unusual. Deer Park close by with herds of red and fallow deer. Teas.
Location: 2m E of Worcester on A422.
Opening Times: Apr - Sept - Tues - Fri 11.00am - 5.00pm. Sun 2.00pm - 5.00pm. Bank Hols Mons 11.00am - 5.00pm. Closed on Sat and all other Mons.
Admission: Adult £2.20, Child £1.10. Reduced rates for parties on application.

THE GREY FRIARS

WORCESTER

Owner: The National Trust
Contact:

Tel: 01905 23571

Built in 1480, with early 17th and late 18th century additions, this timber-framed house was rescued from demolition at the time of the Second World War and has been restored and refurbished; interesting textiles and furnishings add character to the panelled rooms; an archway leads through to a delightful garden.

Location: Centre of Worcester.

Admission: Adult £2.10, Child £1.00, Family Ticket £5.70 (2 + up to 4 children).

OPEN
April to end Oct
Wed. Thu. & Bank Hol Mons.
2.00 - 5.30pm
Also 21 May 11am - 3pm
Last admissions 30 mins before closing.

 THE NATIONAL TRUST   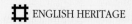 ENGLISH HERITAGE    HISTORIC HOUSES ASSOCIATION

WICHENFORD DOVECOTE

Tel: 01684 850051

Wichenford, Worcestershire.
Owner: The National Trust   **Contact:** The Administrator
A 17th century half timbered dovecote.
Location: 5½m NW of Worcester, N of B4204.
Opening Times: Apr - end Oct: daily 9.00am - 6.00pm or sunset if earlier. Closed Good Fri, other times by appointment.
Admission: 60p.

WITLEY COURT

GREAT WITLEY, WORCESTER WR6 6ST

OPEN

1 Apr - 30 Sept
Daily
10.00am - 6.00pm

1 Oct - 31 Oct
Daily
10.00am - 4.00pm

1 Nov - 31 Mar
Wed - Sun
10.00am - 4.00pm

Tel: 01299 896636

Owner: English Heritage   *Contact: The Head Custodian*

This is one of the most spectacular country house ruins in England. Built in the Victorian Italian style, this vast mansion incorporates porticoes by John Nash. It looks out over elaborate gardens with immense fountains. The early Georgian church nearby features a remarkable baroque interior.
Location: 10 miles north west of Worcester on the A443.
Admission: Adults £1.50, OAP/Student/UB40 £1.10, Child 80p.

SPECIAL EVENTS DIARY

Avoncroft Museum of Historic Buildings
- **1st March - 23rd April:** *Exhibition: The Nail Trade.*
- **18th March:** *"Structure This" Demos and workshops for National Science, Engineering & Technology week.*
- **15th - 17th April:** *Steam Rally.*
- **18th - 20th April:** *Holiday workshops for children.*
- **2nd - 5th May:** *1940's week for school.*
- **6th, 7th & 9th May:** *Activity weekend with demonstrations.*
- **8th May:** *Lecture "Making Time" by Mick Aston (tickets from Museum).*
- **27th - 29th May:** *Medieval Building weekend.*
- **11th June:** *B M W Car Club Rally.*
- **17th - 18th June:** *Children's activity weekend.*
- **29th June -1st July:** *Shakespeare's "Much Ado About Nothing" open air theatre; The Bromsgrove Players (tickets from Museum).*
- **2nd July:** *Volvo Car Club Rally.*
- **9th July:** *Armstrong Siddeley Owners Club Rally.*
- **31st July -11th August:** *Childrens Holiday Acitivites (details available June).*
- **5th - 6th August:** *Children's Activity Weekend*
- **26th - 28th August:** *Activity Weekend with Demonstrations*
- **10th September:** *Triumph Sports 6 Car Rally*
- **16th - 17th September:** *"Man, Machine & Beast" including Oil Engine Rally. Living History and demonstrations.*
- **22nd September:** *Lecture and Tasting. An Apple and Cheese evening with Geoff Warren of Westons Cider (tickets from Museum).*
- **3rd - 13th October:** *Fruit Harvesting workshops for Schools*
- **3rd - 29th October:** *Exhibition: The Lawrence Collection of Post Office Model VehicleDisplay.*
- **7th - 8th October:** *Living History Weekend*
- **8th October:** *Exhibition: Model Wheelwright Club of Great Britain*
- **25th - 26th November:** *Craft Show*
- **2nd - 3rd December:** *Christmas Climax*

Hanbury Hall, Worcestershire

BRODSWORTH HALL
Doncaster

1995 sees the opening of Brodsworth Hall, one of the most complete surviving examples of a Victorian country house. The house remains remarkably intact to this day with an abundance of original furnishings, and still holds its original but faded grandeur. The servants' wing gives a fascinating insight into life "below stairs", while the gardens, with their marble statues, croquet lawn and quarry garden, complete a visit to this classical Victorian family home. Coaches must pre-book at this property.

CONTACT

The Head Custodian
Brodsworth Hall
Brodsworth
Doncaster
Yorkshire
DN5 7XJ

Tel: (01302) 722598

LOCATION

6 miles north west of Doncaster on minor road. Access from A1M via A635 or A638

OPENING TIMES

6 July - 15 October
Tuesday- Sunday plus
Bank Holidays
1.00 - 6.00pm

Grounds open 12 Noon.
Last admission 5.00pm

Grounds only
6 July - 15 October
12 Noon - 6.00pm

Closed Mondays except
Bank Holidays

ADMISSION

Adults £4.00
Child* £2.00
OAP/Student/UB40
holders £3.00

15% discount on groups
of 11 or more

* 5 - 15 years.
Under 5's free

EXTRA FACILITIES
Education Centre.

ADVICE TO COURIERS & DRIVERS
Groups must pre-book. Tour leader and Coach driver have free entry. 1 extra place for every 20 additional people.

FACILITIES FOR THE DISABLED
Most of the house accessible for wheelchairs, disabled WC's available.

PARKING FOR COACHES & CARS
Spaces for 220 cars and 3 coaches.

CATERING
Tearoom on site, seating for 70 people.

GUIDED TOURS
The House will be open for pre-booked coach parties from 10.00am - 1.00pm.

GIFT SHOP
Located in the Servants' Hall.

GUIDE BOOKS
Colour guide book and children's guide.

SCHOOL VISIT/CHILDREN
School visits are free if booked in advance.

BROUGHTON HALL
Skipton

BROUGHTON HALL was built in 1597 by Henry Tempest and continues to be the home of the Tempest family, whose ancestry can be traced back 29 generations to Roger Tempest who was established in the area by 1120. This Grade I listed historic building has Elizabethan origins but was extensively added to during the 18th and 19th Centuries, hence its Palladian appearance.

Set in 3,000 acres of beautiful Yorkshire parkland and countryside, the Broughton Hall family home and Estate, is open to the public by prior arrangement and is also available as an exclusive venue for both business and pleasure.

The present design of the grounds owes much to the landscape architecture of Nesfield around 1855. To the east of the Hall is a fine Italianate garden with balustrades and a gazebo. To the rear there are sweeping lawns (ideal for marquee events) enhanced by extensive wooded views and fountains.

The owner likes to make every event unique and highly successful so he is always ready to discuss with clients how he can help them to achieve their objectives by placing his facilities and experience at their disposal. To arrange such a consultation it is only necessary to telephone the Estate Office on 01756 799608.

CONTACT

The Estate Office
Broughton Hall
Skipton
North Yorkshire
BD23 3AE

Tel: (01756) 799608

Fax: (01756) 700357

LOCATION

Skipton A59, 3 miles.
From London M1 to
Leeds and Skipton, A59
to Broughton.

Air: Bradford/Leeds
Airport 40 minutes,
Manchester 1 hour.

Rail: Skipton Station
3 miles.

Bus: Regular service.

OPENING TIMES

Bank Holiday Mondays
11.00am - 4.00pm

Guided Tours can be
arranged by prior
appointment.
The duration of a tour is
approx. 1½ hours.

ADMISSION

HOUSE & GARDEN

Per person £4.00

Guided Tours
Groups*
Per person £4.00

* Minimum payment if
by prior appointment £60.

SUITABILITY FOR EVENTS
Broughton Hall and its grounds are ideal for a wide range of activities; dinners, seminars, corporate entertainment, product launches, clay shoots, archery, fashion shows, equestrian events, firework and laser shows etc. The diversity of the Estate is ideal for filming and still photography. Being a private house your event will have exclusive use of the Hall and Grounds.

EXTRA FACILITIES
Ample parking and an area for light aircraft/helicopters. Lectures on property, contents, garden and history can be held in a lecture room seating 80. Musical evenings are very successful. A grand piano is available. Full size billiard table.

ADVICE TO COURIERS & DRIVERS
When travelling from Skipton on the A59 towards Clitheroe watch for the Bull Inn on left hand side 3 miles from Skipton. Take turning to left approx. 200 yards past Bull Inn. The Hall and entrance gates can then be seen.

FACILITIES FOR THE DISABLED
Disabled and elderly visitors may alight at the front door. The vehicle should then be parked in the allocated area.

PARKING FOR COACHES & CARS
Capacity of the car park - unlimited.

CATERING
This can be provided by prior arrangement. Wide range of options. Buffets and full sit down meals with accent on quality and value. Up to 150 people can be catered for.

GUIDED TOURS
At no additional cost guided tours are conducted for up to 200 people at any one time. Large groups are split up into smaller parties. If requested the owner will meet the group. Average time taken for a tour 1 hour 30 minutes.

LOCAL PLACES OF INTEREST
Broughton is only three miles from the historic market town of Skipton with its roofed castle. The Yorkshire Dales National Park with some of the finest countryside in England is on the doorstep. There are excellent local hotels for overnight accommodation.

CONFERENCE AND FUNCTION FACILITIES
SUBJECT TO PRIOR ARRANGEMENT ALL ROOMS CAN BE MADE AVAILABLE FOR FUNCTIONS.

BURTON AGNES HALL
Driffield

BURTON AGNES HALL, is an outstanding example of late Elizabethan architecture built of the characteristic richly mellowed red brick. Building was begun in the year 1598 when Elizabeth I was Queen and her Royal Arms are carved over the front entrance. Finished in 1610, the Hall has been little altered and is still the home of descendants of the family who built it.

The ceilings and overmantels, wonderfully carved in oak, plaster, stone and alabaster, are unique and world famous.

There are notable paintings by Gainsborough, Reinagle, Cotes, Marlow and others; also a fine collection of modern French paintings by Gaugin, Pissaro, Utrillo, Manet, Lorjou, Courbet, Renoir, Minaux, Maufra, Montane, Vlaminck and others of the Impressionist schools which merge remarkably well into this ancient setting.

GARDENS AND GROUNDS

The Hall is surrounded by lawns with clipped yews, ponds and fountains. The walled garden contains a pôtager of herbs and vegetables, shrub roses, herbaceous borders, a maze with a garden on thymes and a riddle to solve, a jungle garden, campanula, clematis and hardy geranium collections, green houses and coloured 'games' gardens. There are also woodland gardens and a woodland walk. The childrens corner has rabbits and guinea pigs.

❖

SUITABILITY FOR OTHER EVENTS
Fashion shows, garden parties, rallies and filming can all be arranged.

ADVICE TO COURIERS & DRIVERS
Cafe open to visitors not wishing to visit the Hall.

FACILITIES FOR THE DISABLED
Cars and Coaches containing disabled or elderly people may leave them at the entrance to the Hall. The vehicles can then be parked in the allocated areas. Toilets are available. Special entrance for wheelchairs giving access to the ground floor rooms. Tea room accessible. The gardens are especially suitable for wheelchairs with ramps and flag paths.

CATERING
A Restaurant/Tea Room with Table Licence is available for approx 80 people. Groups can book in advance for afternoon tea, buffets and lunches. Menus are available on request. Café open to visitors not wishing to visits the Hall. Available for party bookings outside normal opening hours.

GIFT SHOP
Open at the same time and dates as the Hall. Items include home grown produce and plants. There is also a herb and dried flower shop / display and plant sales.

GUIDE BOOKS
A full colour guide book is available price £1.75. Translation available in French, German and Flemish. Children's guide available.

GUIDED TOURS
Guided tours, at no additional cost, are available for booked parties. Large parties split into smaller groups of 20/30. Average time taken 1¼ hours.

CONTACT

M. E. Wilson
The Estate Office
Burton Agnes
Driffield
East Yorkshire
YO25 OND

Tel: (01262) 490324

Fax: (01262) 490513

LOCATION

From London A1, M18, M62, A166, 4 hours.

Bridlington 6 miles
Hull 25 miles
York 35 miles.

Bus: Regular services from Bridlington, Driffield, Hull, Scarborough, York and Leeds – Stop 300 yards from Hall.

OPENING TIMES

Summer
1 Apr - 31 Oct 1995
Daily 11.00am - 5.00pm

Parties welcome, by appointment outside these times.

Winter
1 Nov - 31 Mar
Open for pre-booked parties of guaranteed minimum numbers.

ADMISSION

All Year

HOUSE & GARDEN
Adult £3.50
Child £2.00
OAP £3.00

Groups (min 30 people)
Adult £3.15
Child £1.80
OAP £2.70

GARDEN ONLY
Adult £1.80
Child £0.80
OAP £1.50
No Group Concessions

Group visits, by appointment outside public opening hours are charged at £3.50 per person. Minimum charge £105.00.

CASTLE HOWARD
York

IN a dramatic setting between two lakes with extensive gardens and impressive fountains, this 18th Century Palace was designed by Sir John Vanbrugh in 1699. Undoubtedly the finest private residence in Yorkshire it was built for Charles Howard, 3rd Earl of Carlisle, whose descendants still live here.

With its painted and gilded dome reaching 80ft into the Yorkshire sky, this impressive house has collections of antique furniture, porcelain and sculpture, while its fabulous collection of paintings is dominated by the famous Holbein portraits of Henry VIII and the Duke of Norfolk.

GARDENS

Designed on a heroic scale covering 1,000 acres. The gardens include memorable sights like The Temple of the Four Winds and the Mausoleum, New River Bridge and the recently restored waterworks of the South Lake, Cascade, Waterfall and Prince of Wales Fountain.

The walled garden has collections of old and modern roses.

Ray Wood has a unique collection of rare trees, shrubs, rhododendrons, magnolias and azaleas.

CONTACT

Mrs. M E Carmichael
Castle Howard
York
North Yorkshire
YO6 7BZ

Tel: (01653) 648444
Fax: (01653) 648462

LOCATION

York 15 miles (20 minutes), A64. From London: M1 exit 32, M18 to A1(M) to A64, York/Scarborough Road, 3½ hours.

Train: London Kings Cross to York 1 hr. 50 mins. York to Malton Station 30 mins.

Bus: Service and tour buses from York station to Castle Howard.

SUITABILITY FOR OTHER EVENTS
Concerts, craft fairs, fashion shows, clay pigeon shooting, equestrian events, garden parties, filming, product launches.

EXTRA FACILITIES
Helicopter Landing, Rose Garden Receptions, Firework Displays. Lectures (by arrangement) covering the House, History, Contents and Gardens.

ADVICE TO COURIERS & DRIVERS
Approaching from the south, A64 to Malton, on entering Malton, take the Castle Howard road via Coneysthorpe Village. Alternative route from A64 following signs to Castle Howard is via the Carrmire Gate 9' wide by 10' high.

FACILITIES FOR THE DISABLED
Disabled toilets. Transport equipped for wheelchairs.

Chairlift in House to main floor.

PARKING FOR COACHES & CARS
Car park capacity - 400 cars and 20 coaches.

CATERING
Cafeterias at the House and Stable Courtyard. The Grecian Hall available for pre-booked private parties - minimum 25. Prices and menus on request. Private dinner, lunches, buffets and functions by arrangement.

GIFT SHOP
Open 10.30am-5pm when House open. Large selection of gifts, souvenirs and books. Plant Centre Shop.

GUIDE BOOKS
Full colour guide book.

GUIDED TOURS
Guides are available throughout the House, no charge. Private tours and Garden Tours by arrangement.

SCHOOL VISITS/CHILDREN
School parties welcome, information pack available. Teacher/pupil ratio required is 1:10. Special interest:18th Century architecture, art, history, wildlife, horticulture.

OPENING TIMES

Summer

17 March - late October

Daily 11.00am - 4.30pm

Last admission 4.30pm

NB Grounds, Rose Gardens, and Plant Centre open 10am.

Winter

November - Mid March

Open by pre-booked appointment and availability.

Grounds open most days November, December and January, telephone for confirmation.

ADMISSION

Summer

HOUSE, GARDEN
Adult £6.00
Child* £3.00
OAP £5.00

Groups (min 12 people)
Adult £5.25
Child* £2.75
OAP £4.75

GARDEN ONLY
Adult £4.00
Child* £2.00

*Age 4-16

Winter
By arrangement

CONFERENCE AND FUNCTION FACILITIES

ROOM	DIMENSIONS	CAPACITY	LAYOUT	POWER POINTS	SUITABLE FOR A/V
Long Gallery	197' x 24'	280	Theatre	20	✓
		280	Buffet/Lunch/Dinner		
Grecian Hall	40' x 40'	160	Various	20	✓
Chinese Room		60	Various	1	✓

DUNCOMBE PARK
Helmsley

The house dates from 1713 and was built for Thomas Duncombe by William Wakefield, a friend of Vanbrugh. A fine forecourt and two pavilions were added by Sir Charles Barry in 1843. Its interiors were remodelled by the First Earl of Feversham after a fire in 1879. The main showrooms are now a fine example of the type of grand interior popular at the turn of the century.

Following the death of the second Earl of Feversham at the Battle of the Somme in 1916, Duncombe Park was leased as a girls school;. In 1985 the present Lord and Lady Feversham decided to restore the house to a family home. After the departure of the school, there was little more than an empty, echoing shell. Today the visitor will see a superb example of the best of British craftsmanship. The restoration is very much a family project and the interior finishes have been deliberately chosen to show visitors a selection of the styles of decoration typical in the 18th and 19th Centuries. There are fine family pictures and Lord Feversham's collection of English and Continental furniture.

The unique 30 acre early 18th Century landscape garden, set in 300 acres of dramatic parkland, has been described as "the supreme masterpiece of the art of the landscape gardener". Its vast expanses of lawn, terraces, temples, woodland walks and fine views across the surrounding North York Moors are something to be explored at leisure.

Visitor Centre, Restaurant, Gift Shop, Picnic Area, Playground. Waymarked Country Walks.

Winner British Tourist Authority Come to Britain Special Award and Yorkshire & Humberside White Rose Awards. Duncombe Park is now a National Nature Reserve.

SUITABILITY FOR OTHER EVENTS
Dinners, receptions, concerts, weddings, conferences, fashion shows, product launches, filming. Also suitable for wide range of outdoor events. Grand piano, tennis court, croquet lawn available.

EVENTS
Year round programme of events in house and park. Details from the Administrator.

PARKING FOR COACHES & CARS
Free parking. Car park at Visitor Centre 400 yards from house. Coach park (Visitors may disembark at front gates).

ADVICE TO COURIERS & DRIVERS
No flash photography in house. Video permits available. Allow 3 hours for group visits.

FACILITIES FOR DISABLED
Disabled toilet. Portable ramps. Parking usually allowed in main forecourt. The House is not particularly suited to those with walking difficulties.

GUIDE BOOK
Full colour guide book available £2.00. Guided tours every day except Sundays and Bank Holiday Mondays.

CATERING
Home made lunches and teas. Maximum 60. Pre-booking recommended for groups.

NOTE
Joint visiting arrangement for groups, in conjunction with Hovingham Hall (£5.75pp).

CONTACT

Duncombe Park Estate
Office
Helmsley
York
YO6 5EB

Tel: (01439) 770213

Fax: (01439) 771114

LOCATION

Entrance just off Helmsley Market Square, signed off A170 Thirsk - Scarborough road.

Taxi: (01439) 770817/771384/770512

OPENING TIMES

Summer

HOUSE AND GARDEN
11.00am - 5.00pm
Last admittance 4.30pm

Easter Weekend
(14 - 19 April) and all bank holidays

April - October
Wed & Sun

May and June
Daily except Mon & Tues

July, August & Sept.
Daily

Days and times may be changed for special events. Please check by phoning (01439) 770213

PARKLAND CENTRE
RESTAURANT & SHOP

As house but also Thur, Fri & Sats April - Oct

ADMISSION

HOUSE, GARDEN & PARK
  Adult £4.50
  Child (10-16) £2.00
  O.A.P. £3.75
  Student £3.75
  Family (2+2) . . .£10.00
  Group £3.75

GARDEN & PARK
  Adult £2.75
  Child £1.50

PARK ONLY £1.00

FAIRFAX HOUSE
York

FAIRFAX HOUSE was acquired and fully restored by the York Civic Trust in 1983/84. The House, described as a classic architectural masterpiece of its age and certainly one of the finest townhouses in England was saved from near collapse after considerable abuse and misuse this century, being converted into a Cinema and Dance Hall.

The richly decorated interior with its plaster-work, wood and wrought iron, is now the home for a unique collection of Georgian furniture, clocks, paintings and porcelain.

The Noel Terry Collection, gift of a former treasurer of the York Civic Trust, has been described by Christie's as one of the finest private collections formed this century. It enhances and complements the House and helps to create that special 'lived-in' feeling, providing the basis for what can be considered a fully furnished Georgian Townhouse.

A 150 page catalogue on the furniture collection available at £19.95, softback £14.95.

SUITABILITY FOR OTHER EVENTS
Fairfax House is suitable for filming.

EXTRA FACILITIES
By prior arrangement the group on a Connoisseur's Tour can be met by one of the trustees. Lectures can be given on the House, its contents and history. The lectures can be given in the hotel in which the group is staying. A screen and projector for such a lecture can be provided by Fairfax House.

For groups of up to 50 people a buffet can be arranged. The Dining Room may be used on certain evenings for special formal dinners. Limited to groups of up to 25 people.

ADVICE TO COURIERS & DRIVERS
Please telephone to arrange for map showing the nearest coach park and approach to the House. No photography inside the House.

FACILITIES FOR THE DISABLED
Disabled and elderly visitors may alight at the door of the property prior to parking in adjacent public car park. No toilet facilities at the House.

PARKING FOR COACHES & CARS
Capacity of the public car park - 300 cars, 50 yards from House. Coach park is ½ mile away, parties are dropped off.

GIFT SHOP
Open every day except Friday from 1 March - 1 January, 11am-5pm. Items include catalogues, tapes, gifts & antiques.

GUIDE BOOKS
Colour guide book, £3.50. Translations in French available.

SCHOOL VISITS/ CHILDREN
A guided tour for school children can be arranged at a cost of £1.00 per head.

GUIDED TOURS
Connoisseur Tour - Guided tour showing secret drawers etc. Wine/sherry to follow tour. Parties split into groups of approx 12 persons, £10.00 per person (Min charge £100).

Evening Guided Tour - Guided tour plus wine/sherry to follow (Secret drawers not included). Parties split into groups of approx 20, £5.00 per person (Min. charge £75).

Evening Guided Tour - Guided Tour only (Does not include secret drawers, wine or sherry). Parties split into groups of approx 20/25, £4.00 per person (Min charge £60).

Daytime Parties - Guided - Accepted only within limits of staff availability/ number involved/other bookings etc. Children admitted only at a ratio of 8 to 1 adult. Adult parties split into groups of 20/25, £4 per person (Min charge £60).

Daytime Parties - Without Guide - To be arranged according to number involved and other bookings. Parties split into smaller groups, special party rate for pre-booked tour of 15 or more persons.

Tours available in French and German. The duration of the tour is approx 1½ hours.

HAREWOOD HOUSE
Leeds

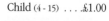

HAREWOOD House, the Yorkshire home of the Earl and Countess of Harewood, is much more than a historic house, it is also the home of one of England's most distinguished families - designed by John Carr in 1759, it has been continually lived in by the Lascelles family ever since. The magnificent interior, created by Robert Adam, has superb ceilings and plasterwork and contains a noteworthy collection of English and Italian paintings. The furniture through all the rooms reflects what many experts have described as 'the richest collection of Chippendale in the world', much of which was made especially for Harewood. New for 1995 is a dedicated Watercolour Gallery.

The Earl of Harewood is the son of the late Princess Mary, daughter of King George V, and is a cousin of Queen Elizabeth II.

Princess Mary lived at Harewood for many years and some of her pictures and possessions are on display in her rooms.

GARDENS
In the grounds, landscaped by "Capability" Brown, are lakeside and woodland walks and Sir Charles Barry's parterre design on the Terrace has recently been restored to its original condition of intricate patterns made with box, bedding and white chippings.

BIRD GARDEN AND TERRACE GALLERY
Harewood Bird Garden has one of the most comprehensive collections in the north of England including exotic species, many endangered, from Africa, America and Australia. The Terrace Gallery was established in 1989 as a venue for exhibitions showing the best of contemporary art.

CONTACT

Gerald Long
The Estate Office
Harewood
Leeds
West Yorkshire
LS17 9LQ

Tel: (0113) 288 6331

Fax: (0113) 288 6467

LOCATION

A1 N or S to Wetherby,

A659 via Collingham, Harewood is on the A61 between Harrogate and Leeds. It is easily reached from A1, M1, M62 and M18 motorways.

Harewood House is 15 mins from the centre of Leeds or Harrogate.

Rail: Leeds Station 7 miles.

Bus: No. 36 from Leeds or Harrogate

CATERING & CORPORATE HOSPITALITY
Harewood House is available for quality corporate entertaining and offers: State Dining Room dinners (50 persons max.), Drinks reception/buffets, Concerts (175 persons max), Wedding receptions, Marquee events, Product launches.
The Courtyard catering complex has recently been completely refurbished, introducing an exciting new theme able to cater for all conferences, exhibitions, product launches and functions held within the Courtyard or the magnificent grounds.
An ideal venue for any gathering, the Courtyard Suite will seat a maximum of 120 theatre style or, conference organisers may wish to also use the Study Centre directly overhead for a meeting then retire to the Courtyard Suite for a meal. The Drawing Room can be incorporated to provide a Reception area, additional dining area or exhibition space. The latest conference equipment is available to suit various requirements.
Large launches etc. can be accommodated by using the full extent of the Courtyard area which can be covered by a 20'x24' marquee. This flexible approach has proven highly successful giving a maximum seating for dinner of 400. Marquees of any size can be completely accommodated within the grounds.

CORPORATE HOSPITALITY
The beautiful grounds of Harewood also provide the ideal setting to incorporate outside activities in your programme, a wide range of options are open from clay shoots to ballooning, jousting to a cricket match on Harewood's private ground - the management team will help make your conference a success.

EXTRA FACILITIES
Grand piano, cricket and football pitch. Subject to availability lectures on the property, its gardens and history for up to 70. Projector and screen can be provided.

ADVICE TO COURIERS & DRIVERS
No unaccompanied children in the Bird Garden. Dogs on leads in grounds but not House (except Guide Dogs) or Bird Garden. Unlimited parking 400 yards from House and an area for 50+ coaches 500 yards from House.

FACILITIES FOR THE DISABLED
Disabled and elderly visitors may alight at entrance to House, before parking in the allocated areas. Guide Dogs allowed in the House. Most facilities are accessible and a wheelchair is available at House and Bird Garden. The toilet is near the car park shop. Special concessions apply to disabled groups.

GIFT SHOP
Gift Shops and Plant Centre are open same time as Park. Items include Leeds pottery, flower pictures, glass, perfume and toys. Full colour guide book price £2.99.

AUDIO TOUR OF HOUSE
Hire charge £1.50.

OPENING TIMES

Summer
25 March - 29 October

BIRD GARDEN & GROUNDS
Daily from 10.00am

HOUSE
From 11.00am

Winter
Nov - Mar   Closed
Certain rooms available for corporate entertaining plus Courtyard Suite for Conferences/ Product launches.

ADMISSION

ALL ATTRACTIONS
Adult £5.95
Child (4 - 15) £3.00
Family £16.50
Groups (min 20 persons)
Adult £4.95
Child (4 - 15) . . . . Free
(If accompanied)

BIRD GARDEN & TERRACE GALLERY
Adult £4.75
Child (4-15) £2.50
Family £12.50

GROUNDS & ADVENTURE PLAYGROUNDS
Adult £3.25
Child (4 - 15) £1.00

NEWBY HALL
Ripon

NEWBY HALL, the Yorkshire home of Mr and Mrs Robin Compton, is a late 17th Century house built in the style of Sir Christopher Wren. William Weddell, an ancestor of Mr Compton, made the Grand Tour in the 1760's and amongst the treasures he acquired were magnificent classical statuary and a superb set of Gobelins Tapestries. To house these treasures, Weddell commissioned Robert Adam to create the splendid domed Sculpture Gallery and Tapestry Room that we see today. The Regency Dining Room and Billiards Room were added later. There is much fine Chippendale furniture and in recent years Mrs Compton has restored the decoration of the house, painstakingly researching colour and decor of the Adam period.

GARDENS

25 acres of glorious gardens contain rare and beautiful shrubs and plants. Newby's famous double herbaceous borders, flanked by great bastions of yew hedges, sweep down to the River Ure. Formal gardens such as the Autumn and Rose Gardens - each with splashing fountains - a Victorian Rock Garden, the tranquillity of Sylvia's Garden, Pergolas and even a Tropical Garden, make Newby a 'Garden for all Seasons'. Newby holds the National Collection of the Genus Cornus and in 1987 won the Christies'/ HHA Garden of the Year Award. The Gardens also incorporate an exciting children's Adventure Garden and Miniature Railway.

CONTACT

The Opening
Administrator
Newby Hall
Ripon
North Yorkshire
HG4 5AE

Tel: (01423) 322583

Fax: (01423) 324452

LOCATION

Midway between London and Edinburgh, 4 miles west of A1, towards Ripon.

Taxi: Ripon Taxi Rank (01765) 601283.

Bus: On Ripon-York route.

SUITABILITY FOR OTHER EVENTS
Individual requests considered. Newby Hall offers filming possibilities and is suitable for special events such as Craft & Country Fairs, Vehicle Rallies etc. The Grantham Room is available for wedding receptions, promotions and lectures.

ADVICE TO COURIERS & DRIVERS
Allow a full day for viewing House and Gardens. Dogs in picnic area only, no photography inside House.

FACILITIES FOR THE DISABLED
5 wheelchairs available on request. Access around ground floor of house and key areas in gardens. Disabled toilet at Restaurant.

PARKING FOR COACHES & CARS
Unlimited parking near House and Gardens.

CATERING
In Garden Restaurant, teas, hot and cold meals. Pre-booked parties in Grantham Room. Menus/rates on request.

THE NEWBY SHOP
Excellent, open from 11am - 5.30pm.

GUIDE BOOKS
Colour guide books of the House and Gardens. Illustrated leaflets for the Gardens and Woodland Discovery Walk can be bought at the shop and plant stall.

SCHOOL VISITS/CHILDREN
School groups welcome. Rates on request. Grantham Room for use as wet weather base subject to availability. Of special interest: Woodland Discovery Walk, Adventure Gardens and train rides on 10¼" gauge railway.

OPENING TIMES

Summer
April - September
HOUSE
Daily exept Mondays
(Bank Hols Mons only)
12 noon - 5.00pm
Last admission 4.30pm.

GARDEN
Daily exept Mondays
(Bank Hols Mons only)
11.00am - 5.30pm
Last admission 5.00pm.

Winter
October - end March
Closed.

ADMISSION

Summer

HOUSE & GARDEN
Adult £5.20
Child* £3.00
OAP £4.50
Disabled £3.00
Group**
Adult £4.50
Child*** £2.80

GARDEN ONLY
Adult £3.50
Child* £2.30
OAP £3.00
Disabled £2.30
Group**
Adult £3.00
Child*** £2.10
Additional charges made for train.

*Age 4-16
**Minimum Number 20 people
***Details from Administrator

CONFERENCE AND FUNCTION FACILITIES

ROOM	DIMENSIONS	CAPACITY	LAYOUT	POWER POINTS	SUITABLE FOR A/V
Grantham Room	200	Theatre 200 100	✓ Reception Lunch/Dinner	✓	

RIPLEY CASTLE
Harrogate

RIPLEY CASTLE has for twenty eight generations been the home of the Ingilby family and it retains that 'much loved and very much alive' feeling of a family home. The guides whilst being very knowledgeable, all have an excellent sense of humour, and the tours which take approximately one hour, are not only informative but great fun. The Castle contains fine portraits, paintings, furnishing and chandeliers and in the old (1555) tower, some splendid armour, books, panelling and a secret hiding place.

The extensive walled gardens have recently been transformed and now house The National Hyacinth Collection and fabulous Ripley tropical plant collection, which includes many rare and exotic species, 85,000 spring flowering bulbs create a blaze of colour in April/May, and are followed by the Bluebells and Rhododendrons, Delphiniums, Roses and Herbaceous Borders. Ripley village, on the Castle's doorstep is also very beautiful, with many interesting shops, an Art Gallery and Farm Museum.

❖

SUITABILITY FOR OTHER EVENTS
Wedding Receptions, Dinners, Dances, Banquets, Outdoor Concerts, Meetings, Activity Days, Medieval Banquets, Management Training Courses.

EXTRA FACILITIES
Conference, Training and Syndicate Rooms, Clay Pigeon Shooting, Archery, Buggies and Hovercraft, Fishing, Cricket, Tennis, Croquet, Infra-Red Combat. Marquee events any size.

ADVICE TO COURIERS & DRIVERS
Dogs prohibited (except Guide Dogs). No photography inside Castle unless prior written consent.

FACILITIES FOR THE DISABLED
5/7 rooms accessible for the disabled. Gardens easily accessible (except Tropical Collection). Disabled toilets at Hotel (100 yards) and in village car park (150 yards). Disabled parking 50 yards from Castle front door.

PARKING FOR COACHES & CARS
Free parking for 290 cars within 300 yards of the Castle entrance. Coach parking 50 yards from Castle entrance.

CATERING
Morning and Afternoon Tea and refreshments at Tea room (seats 80) outside Castle walls. Pub lunches or Dinner at Hotel (100 yards). VIP lunches and dinners (maximum 66) inside Castle, unlimited in Marquees. Parties of 15+ must book in advance in Tea rooms and Hotel.

ACCOMMODATION
At the Boars Head Hotel (RAC****) 100 yards from Castle. Owned and managed by the Estate.

GIFT SHOP
Open daily April to October , weekends only November-March - 10.30am - 5.00pm.

GUIDE BOOKS
Colour guide book, £1.50. Special children's guide book is available price 99p.

GUIDED TOURS
Guided tours standard, and included in price.

SCHOOL VISITS/CHILDREN
Groups are welcome all year round, by prior arrangement, between 10.30am-7.30pm.

EVENTS 1995
22 April to 6 May: Spring Bulb Festival
8 -11 June: Homes & Garden Magazine Grand Summer Fair.
6 August: Performing Arts Orchestra Viennese concert with fireworks.
13 August: Ripley Show.

CONTACT

Tours: Chloe Evans
Meetings/Dinners:
Sheila Fowler
Ripley Castle
Ripley
Harrogate
North Yorkshire
HG3 3AY

Tel: (01423) 770152
Fax: (01423) 771745

LOCATION

Just off A61, 3¹/₂ miles north of Harrogate, 8 miles south of Ripon. M1 18 mls South, M62 20 miles south.

Taxi: Blueline taxis Harrogate 503037

OPENING TIMES

Summer
CASTLE & GARDENS
April, May and October
Sat & Sun
1.30 - 4.30pm

Good Fri. & Bank Hols.
11am - 4.30pm

June and September
Thurs, Fri, Sat & Sun . . .
11.30 - 4.30pm

July and August
Daily   11.30 - 4.30pm

GARDENS ONLY
March
Thurs, Fri, Sat & Sun . . .
11.00 - 4.00pm

April - October
Daily   11am - 5pm

Nov - Dec 23rd
Daily . . . 11am-3.30pm

Winter
Open (except 25 December)
to pre-booked parties of 15+.
10.30 - 7.30pm

ADMISSION

All Year

CASTLE & GARDENS
Adult £3.75
Child* £2.00
OAP £3.00
Groups**
Adult £3.00
Child* £1.75

GARDENS ONLY
Adult £2.25
Child* £1.75
OAP £1.75
Groups**
Adult £1.75
Child* £1.00

*Under 16.
** Min. 25 people.

RIPLEY CASTLE CONTINUED...

CONFERENCE AND FUNCTION FACILITIES

Ripley Castle is well located for Dinners, Banquets, Meetings and Presentations; it enjoys excellent access via road rail and air and is centrally placed for Northern and North Eastern England. Its setting is stunningly beautiful, and the organisation that runs it is efficient, friendly and cheerful. Activity Days can be incorporated into residential meetings or used to entertain clients and staff, and tours can be organised throughout the North of England to incorporate The Yorkshire Dales, The Northumbrian Coast and the Lake District.

Overnight accommodation can be booked at the 25 bedroom (Four Star) Boar's Head Hotel; the Estate-owned and managed Hotel in the Market Square of Ripley Village, 100 yards from the Castle. The standard of cuisine at both the Castle and Hotel is legendary, with a top class team of chefs being employed to work at both establishments.

For charm, character, quality, history, setting and value for money, Ripley is one of the U.K's outstanding Stately Home venues.

Contact Sheila Fowler on (01423) 770152 for further details.

ROOM	DIMENSIONS	CAPACITY	LAYOUT	POWER POINTS	SUITABLE FOR A/V
Morning Room	27' x 22'	35	Schoolroom	6	✓
		32	U-Shape		
		42	Boardroom		
		50	Buffet		
		70	Theatre		
		66	Lunch/Dinner		
Large Drawing Room	30 'x 22'	27	Schoolroom	4	✓
		29	U-Shape		
		36	Boardroom		
		60	Buffet		
		80	Theatre		
		60	Lunch/Dinner		
Library	31 x 19'	27	Schoolroom	3	✓
		26	U-Shape		
		36	Boardroom		
		48	Buffet		
		75	Theatre		
		48	Lunch/Dinner		
Tower Room	33' x 21'	27	Schoolroom	3	✓
		26	U-Shape		
		36	Boardroom		
		48	Buffet		
		75	Theatre		
		48	Lunch/Dinner		
Map Room	19' x 14'	18	Schoolroom	6	✓
		10	U-Shape		
		16	Boardroom		
		15	Buffet		
		24	Theatre		
		16	Lunch/Dinner		
Dining Room	23' 3" x 19' 6"	16	Boardroom	2	✓
		25	Buffet		
		16	Lunch/Dinner		

SPECIAL EVENTS DIARY

- **Shibden Hall** has a busy programme of over 20 events held during the season March - November, including candlelight evenings and adult workshops. Please phone for details.

- **11th - 12th March and 18th - 19th March: Elsham Hall Country & Wildlife Park** *Lambing Weekends - A chance to see the spring lambs born and for children to touch and feel the lambs.*

- **25th - 26th March: Shibden Hall** *Demonstrating Crafts Weekend.*

- **26th March: Harewood House** *Mothers' Day Events.*

- **30th March: Aske Hall**
  Concert with Antony Hopkins and Sian Philipps.

- **15th - 17th April: Harewood House** *Easter Weekend Events.*

- **15th - 17th April: Beningbrough Hall** *Easter Eggstravaganza.*

- **16th April: Nunnington Hall** *Easter Treasure Hunt.*

- **15th April -7th May: Ripley Castle** *Spring Flower Festival.*

- **15th - 17th April: Elsham Hall Country & Wildlife Park**
  Easter Hatching Weekend - see the Easter Chicks in The Hatchery.

- **16th - 17th April: Burton Agnes Hall** *Easter Egg Hunt.*

- **30th April: Newby Hall & Gardens** *Newby Spring Plants Fair.*

- **1st May: Harewood House** *Sports Aid Foundation Fun Run.*

- **5th-7th May: Harewood House** *Zoo Foundation.*

- **7th May: Burton Agnes Hall** *Gala Day.*

- **7th - 8th May: Sion Hill Hall** *Bygone Vehicle Rally in the grounds.*

- **7th - 8th May: Elsham Hall Country & Wildlife Park**
  Children's Festival .

- **19th May: Harewood House** *Closed to Public.*

- **20th - 21st May: Ripley Castle** *Living Crafts Fair.*

- **27th - 30th May: Harewood House**
  Festival of Craft Fashion & Design

- **28th May: Nunnington Hall** *Centenary Spring Fair - music, morris dancing, stalls, plants sales, games.*

- **28th - 29th May:Fountains Abbey and Studley Royal Estate**
  English Civil War Society Muster during the day in the Deer Park.

- **28th - 29th May: Elsham Hall Country & Wildlife Park**
  May Day Festival top magicians perform throughout the festival as well as other entertainers.

- **Weekends in June: Harewood House** *Live music and performances in The Courtyard.*

- **4th June: Harewood House** *Open Air Concert (Dancing Waters).*

- **8th - 11th June: Ripley Castle** *T he Homes & Gardens Magazine "Grand Summer Fair".*

- **10th June: Ormesby Hall** *Festival of Flowers, Food and Drink organised by Women's Institute 11.30am-5.30pm.*

- **10th - 11th June: Newby Hall & Gardens** *Rainbow Craft Fair.*

- **10th - 11th June: Sion Hill Hall** *Flower Festival in the Hall.*

- **10th - 11th June: Burton Agnes Hall** *Gardeners Fair.*

- **11th June: Harewood House**
  Harewood Challenge (Roundhay Rotary) .

- **13th - 18th June: Fountains Abbey and Studley Royal Estate**
  Open Air Shakespeare presented by Illyria Theatre Company 'The Merry Wives of Windsor' and 'A Midsummer Night's Dream' in repertoire 7.30 in the Abbey Cloister.

- **18th June: Newby Hall & Gardens** *Northern Country Fair & Horse Show (in aid of Stoke Mandeville).*

- **18th June: Nunnington Hall** *Yorkshire Music Afternoon - Brass and silver bands & Yorkshire teas.*

- **18th June: Harewood House** *Fathers Day Events.*

- **24th June: Fountains Abbey and Studley Royal Estate**
  Classical Concert with Fireworks in the Water Garden 8pm.

- **25th June: Fountains Abbey and Studley Royal Estate**
  Children's Concert early evening the Water Garden.

- **25th June: Harewood House** *Charity Car Boot Sale.*

- **July to September: Epworth Old Rectory** *'Charles Wesley: Sweet Singer of Methodism" Facsimile exhibition of documents relating to Charles Wesley (on loan from John Rylands University Library, Manchester).*

- **2nd July: Harewood House** *Yorkshire M G Day.*

- **7th - 8th July: Fountains Abbey and Studley Royal Estate**
  Music by Moonlight 7pm-11pm the Abbey.

- **8th - 9th July: Shibden Hall** *Farming Fun Weekend.*

- **9th July: Harewood House** *Jaguar Rally.*

- **16th July: Newby Hall & Gardens** *Historic Vehicle Rally - North East club for Pre-war Austins.*

- **22nd - 23rd July: Ripley Castle** *North Eastern Region Carriage Driving Trials.*

- **22nd -24th July: Harewood House** *Leeds Dog Show.*

- **23rd July: Beningbrough Hall** *Teddy Bears' Centenary Picnic.*

- **23rd July: Fountains Abbey and Studley Royal Estate**
  National Music Day 1pm-6pm at The Abbey, Visitor Centre and Fountains Hall.

- **28th - 30th July: Harewood House** *The National Game Fair.*

- **29th - 30th July: Burton Agnes Hall** *Flower Festival.*

- **6th August: Ripley Castle** *Lakeside Viennese Concert by The Performing Arts Orchestra.*

- **6th August: Harewood House** *BMW Rally . Koi Festival.*

- **8th August: Harewood House** *Harewood Show.*

- **11th - 14th October: Fountains Abbey** *Floodlighting season Weekends dusk-10pm.*

- **12th August: Ripley Castle** *Agricultural & Horticultural Show.*

- **13th August: Beningbrough Hall** *Centenary Family Fun Day.*

- **25th - 28th August: Ripley Castle** *International Citroen 2CV Rally.*

- **26th - 28th August: Harewood House** *Harewood Steam Rally.*
  Yorkshire Dales Country and Western Festival.

- **26th-28th August: Ripley Castle**
  Living Crafts Fair.

- **26th - 28th August: Elsham Hall Country & Wildlife Park**
  Folk Dance Festival.

- **27th - 28th August: Beningbrough Hall**
  Bank Holiday Treasure Hunt.

- **27th - 28th August: Ormesby Hall**
  Teeside Festival of Transport 10am-5.30pm.

- **1st - 3rd September: Ripley Castle**
  Galloway Antiques Fair.

- **3rd September: Harewood House**
  Open Air Concert (Last Night of the Proms).

- **9th - 10th September: Shibden Hall**
  Demonstrating Crafts Weekend.

- **10th September: Beningbrough Hall**
  Great Plant Sale.

- **16th - 17th September: Newby Hall & Gardens**
  Rainbow Craft Fair.

- **23rd September: Harewood House**
  Gardens Open Day.

- **18th - 19th November: Shibden Hall**
  Demonstrating Crafts Weekend.

ABBEY HOUSE MUSEUM

Tel: 01532 755821

Abbey Road, Kirkstall, Leeds, Yorkshire, LS5 3EH.
Owner: Leeds City Council   **Contact:** Mrs J Bridgewater
The house which still includes the Norman Hall, enables visitors to explore the life of the people of Leeds at work and play. Shops and Georgian and Victorian streets recreated.
Location: On A65 3m out of Leeds city centre.
Opening Times: Mon - Sat, 10.00am - 5.00pm. Sun 10.00am - 5.00pm.
Admission: Adult £2.00, Child 50p, Conc/ Groups £1.00.

AMPLEFORTH COLLEGE JUNIOR SCHOOL

Tel: 01439 788238   **Tel:** 01439 788538

The Castle, Gilling East, York, Yorkshire, YO6 4HP.
Owner: Ampleforth Abbey Trustees   **Contact:** Fr Jeremy Sierla
Not suitable for wheelchairs. No public toilets.
Location: 20m N of York on Helmsley Road.
Opening Times: House: term time only, 10.00am - 12.00pm and 2.00pm - 4.00pm. Gardens: open dawn - dusk all year.
Admission: Adult 75p for gardens, house free. Only Great Hall and Entrance Hall open to public.

ASKE

OPEN

April - October
Weekdays only by
appointment
Groups of 15+

Tel: 01748 823222
Fax: 01748 823252

RICHMOND, NORTH YORKSHIRE DL10 5HJ

Owner: The Marquess of Zetland   *Contact:* Sally Anne Lewis

Continuously the seat of the Dundas family since the house and estate were purchased by Sir Lawrence Dundas in 1762. Fine collection of pictures, furniture and porcelain much of which was acquired by Sir Lawrence himself.
Location: 2 miles east of Richmond, on the Gilling West road (B6274).
Admission: House & Grounds: £3.50 per person.

BAYSGARTH HOUSE MUSEUM

Tel: 01652 632318

Caister Road, Barton on Humber, Humberside, DN18 6AH.
Owner: Glanford Borough Council   **Contact:** Mr D J Williams
18th century town house and park. Displays of porcelain and local history.
Location: Caister Road, Barton on Humber.
Opening Times: Thurs Fri, 10.00am - 4.00pm. Sat and Sun, 10.00am - 5.00pm.
Admission: Free.

BENINGBROUGH HALL

Tel: 01904 470666

Shipton-by-Beningbrough, Yorkshire, YO6 1DD.
Owner: The National Trust   **Contact:** The Administrator
This handsome Georgian house has been completely restored and in the principal rooms are one hundred famous portraits on loan from the National Portrait Gallery. Victorian laundry, potting shed and exhibitions. Garden and wilderness play area.
Location: 8m NW of York, 3m W of Shipton A19, 2m SE of Linton-on-Ouse, follow signposted route.
Opening Times: 1 Apr - 31 Oct: Mon, Tues, Wed, Sat, Sun, Good Fri. Also Fris in Jul & Aug. House: 11.00am - 5.00pm. Last admission 4.30pm. Grounds, shop and restaurant: 11.00am - 5.30pm. Last admission 5.00pm.
Admission: House, Gardens and Exhibition: Adult £4.50, Child £2.30, Family £11.30. Parties £3.60, Child £1.80. Garden and Exhibition: Adult £3.00, Child £1.50.

BEVERLEY MINSTER

Tel: 01482 887520

Beverley, Yorkshire, HU17 0DP.
     Contact: Mr R I Shaw
Ancient Medieval Minster dating from 1420. A very fine example of Gothic architecture. Fine set of 68 misericords. Saxon Sanctuary chair, famous Percy tomb canopy.
Location: 8m N of Hull, 30m E of York.
Opening Times: Sept - Mar: 9.00am - 4.00pm, Apr /May: 9.00am - 5.00pm, May - Aug: 9.00am - 8.00pm. Service: 8.00am, 10.30am and 6.30pm, Thurs 7.30pm.
Admission: £1.00 per person.

BISHOPS HOUSE

Tel: 01742 557701

Meersbrook Park, Norton Lees Lane, Sheffield, Yorkshire, S8 9BE.
Owner: Sheffield City Museum   **Contact:** Ms K Streets
Tudor timber framed house with furnished rooms and displays.
Location: A61, 2 m S off Chesterfield Road
Opening Times: Throughout the year; Wed - Sat, 10.00am - 4.30pm, Sun, 11.00am - 4.30pm, Open Bank Hol Mons.
Admission: Adults £1.00, Conc 50p, Family £2.00. Under fives and unemployed free.

BOLTON ABBEY

Tel: 01756 710227   **Fax:** 01756 710535

Skipton, Yorkshire, BD23 6EX.
Owner: Duke of Devonshire   **Contact:** J M Sheard
Location: Off the A59, 5 m E of Skipton, 13 m W of Harrogate.
Opening Times: Every day throughout the year. Car park open 7.30am - 9.00pm.
Admission: Parking is £2.50. Everything else is free.

BOLTON CASTLE

OPEN

March to
end of October
Daily

10.00am - 5.00pm

Tel: 01969 23981
Fax: 01969 23332

LEYBURN, NORTH YORKSHIRE DL8 4ET

Owner: Hon Mr & Mrs Harry Orde-Powlett   *Contact:* Mr & Mrs Harry Orde-Powlett

Medieval castle with fine views over Wensleydale. Home of the Scrope family. Mary Queen of Scots was imprisoned here. Well preserved roof and some furnished rooms. Major restoration work to be completed by spring 1995. Medieval gardens also being developed for 1995. Tea room and well stocked gift shop. Good all weather entertainment.
Location: Approx. 6 mls from market town of Leyburn heading west off the A684.
Admission: Adults £2.50, OAP/Child £1.50.
Guided tours available when pre-booked.

BOWLING HALL MUSEUM

Tel: 01274 723057   **Fax:** 01274 726220

Bowling Hall Road, Bradford, Yorkshire, BD4 7LP.
Owner: City of Bradford Metropolitan District Council   **Contact:** Ms A Bickley
A good example of local, domestic architecture ranging in date from the 15th to 18th century. The rooms are furnished appropriately for this period.
Location: In Bradford.
Opening Times: Jan - 31 Mar, Tues - Sun, 10.00am - 5.00pm, Open on BH Mon. Closed Christmas Day, Boxing Day and Good Fri 1 Apr onwards, Tues - Sun, 10.00am - 6.00pm
Admission: Free.

BRODSWORTH HOUSE

See page 210 for full page entry.

BROUGHTON HALL

See page 211 for full page entry.

BURTON AGNES HALL

See page 212 for full page entry.

BURTON AGNES MANOR HOUSE ⛶

Burton Agnes, Bridlington, Humberside.

Owner: English Heritage   **Contact:** The Administrator

A rare example of a Norman house, altered and encased in brick in the 17th and 18th centuries.

Location: Burton Agnes village, 5m SW of Bridlington on A166.

Opening Times: 1 Apr - 31 Oct daily, 10.00am - 6.00pm. 1 Nov - 31 Mar daily, 10.00am - 4.00pm. Closed 24 - 26 Dec, 1 Jan.

BURTON CONSTABLE HALL

OPEN

Easter Sun to 30 Sept. Suns - Thur. incl. Also Sats. in July & Aug.
Grounds & Coffee Shop open 12 Noon. Hall 1.00 - 4.15pm (Last admission)

Tel: 01964 562400
Fax: 01964 563229

NR. HULL, NORTH HUMBERSIDE HV11 4LN

Owner: Burton Constable Foundation   *Contact:* David Wrench

Burton Constable, a magnificent 16th century house with 18th century additions by Adam, Lightoler and others. The collections include pictures, English furniture and scientific instruments collected in the 18th century by William Constable. With nearly 30 rooms open, a unique insight is possible into the patronage of the Constable family who have lived here since it was built.

Location: 14 miles from Beverley via A165 Bridlington Road, follow Historic House signs. 7 miles from Hull via A1238 to Sproatley then follow Historic House signs.

Admission: Adult £3.50, Senior Citizen £2.75, Child £1.50. Group rates available.

BYLAND ABBEY ⛶   **Tel:** 01347868614

Coxwold, Helmsley, Yorkshire.

Owner: English Heritage   **Contact:** The Administrator

A hauntingly beautiful ruin, set in peaceful meadows in the shadow of the Hambleton Hills. It illustrates later development of Cistercian churches, including a beautiful floor of mosaic tiles.

Location: 2m S of A170 between Thirsk and Helmsley, near Coxwold village.

Opening Times: 1 Apr - 30 Sept, daily 10.00am - 6.00pm, 1 Oct - 31 Oct, daily 10.00am - 4.00pm. 1 Nov - 31 Mar, Wed - Sun, 10.00am - 4.00pm, (Closed 24 - 26 Dec, 1 Jan).

Admission: Adult £1.30, Child 70p, Conc £1.00.

CASTLE HOWARD   See page 213 for full page entry.

CLIFFORD'S TOWER ⛶   **Tel:** 01904 646940

York, Yorkshire.

Owner: English Heritage   **Contact:** The Administrator

A 13th century tower on one of two mottes thrown up by William the Conqueror to hold York. There are panoramic views of the city from the top of the tower.

Location: In Tower Street.

Opening Times: 1 Apr - 30 Sept: daily 10.00am - 6.00pm, 1 Oct - 31 Mar: daily 10.00am - 4.00pm, (Closed 24 - 26 Dec, 1 Jan).

Admission: Adult £1.50, Child 80p, Conc £1.10.

CONISBROUGH CASTLE ⛶

Conisbrough, Yorkshire.

Owner: English Heritage   **Contact:** The Administrator

The spectacular white circular keep of this 12th century castle rises majestically above the River Don. It is the oldest circular keep in England and one of the finest medieval buildings.

Location: NE of Conisbrough Town centre off A630, 4¹/₂ m SW of Doncaster.

Opening Times: 1 Apr - 30th Sept daily, 10.00am - 5.00pm (6.00pm at weekends). 1 Oct - 31 Oct daily, 10.00am - 4.00pm. 1 Nov - 31 Mar daily, 10.00am - 4.00pm. Closed 25 - 26 Dec, 1 Jan.

Admission: Adults £1.80, Child £1.35, Conc 90p.

CONSTABLE BURTON HALL 🏛   **Tel:** 01677 450428   **Fax:** 01677 450626

Leyburn, Yorkshire, DL8 5LJ.

Owner: M C A Wyvill Esq   **Contact:** M C A Wyvill

Extensive borders, large informal garden attached to John Carr house.

Location: 3 m E of Leyburn off the A684.

Opening Times: 9.00am - 6.00pm daily.

Admission: Garden only: 1 Apr - 22 Oct: Adult £1.50, Child 50p, Conc 50p, Group £1.00 per person.

DUNCOMBE PARK   See page 214 for full page entry.

EASBY ABBEY ⛶

Richmond, Yorkshire.

Owner: English Heritage   **Contact:** The Administrator

Substantial remains of the medieval abbey buildings stand in a beautiful setting by the River Swale near Richmond.

Location: 1 m SE of Richmond off B6271.

Opening Times: Any reasonable time.

ELSHAM HALL COUNTRY PARK 🏛   **Tel:** 01652 688698   **Fax:** 01652 688738

Elsham, Brigg, Humberside, DN20 0QZ.

Owner: Capt Jeremy Elwes Esq   **Contact:** Robert Elwes

The Park was founded in 1970, to enable visitors to enjoy natural history and the arts in pleasant surroundings. Attractions include Falconry, the Mini Zoo, Georgian Courtyard, Arboretum and more.

Location: 10 minutes from Junction 5 of the M180, Humber Bridge turnoff.

Opening Times: Easter - mid Sept: 11.00am - 5.00pm every day including Suns and Bank Holidays. Art Gallery: 12.00pm - 5.00pm. Mid-Sept - Easter: Closed.

Admission: Adult £3.95, Child £2.50, OAP £3.00, under 3 years free. Party rates available for groups over 20.

EPWORTH OLD RECTORY   **Tel:** 01427 872268

1 Rectory Street, Epworth, Doncaster, Yorkshire, DN9 1HX.

Owner: World Methodist Council   **Contact:** C J Barton (Warden)

Queen Anne period house, John Wesley's boyhood home. Portraits, period furniture, Methodist memorabilia. Guided tours, garden picnic facilities, toilets, car park. Cinematic presentation.

Location: Epworth lies on A161, 3m South of J7 of M180.

Opening Times: Daily 1 Mar to 31 Oct. Mon - Sat 10.00am - 12.00pm 2.00pm - 4.00pm. Suns 2.00pm - 4.00pm. At other times by appointment.

Admission: Adult £2.00, Child in full-time education £1.00.

FAIRFAX HOUSE   See page 215 for full page entry

FOUNTAINS ABBEY 🦋   **Tel:** 01765 608888 / 601005

Ripon, Yorkshire, HG4 3DY.

Owner: The National Trust   **Contact:** The Group Visits Organiser

Extensive ruins of Cistercian Abbey. Ornamental water gardens laid out by John Aislabie, b.1720. 400 acre deer park with fine Burges church. Awarded World Heritage status in 1987. Visitor Centre.

Location: 2m W of Ripon, 9m W of Harrogate, NW of A61.

Opening Times: Deer Park: open all year during daylight hours. Abbey and gardens: open daily except 24 - 25 Dec and Fris in Jan, Nov and Dec. Jan - Mar: 10.00am - 5, Apr - Sept: 10.00am - 7.00pm, Oct - Dec: 10.00am - 5.00pm (or dusk if earlier). Last admission 1 hour before closing.

Admission: Deer Park: free. Abbey & gardens: Adult £4.00, Child £2.00, Family £10.00. Parties (min 15) £3.50, Child £1.70. Free car parking at Visitor Centre car park. Studley Park, £2.00.

HAREWOOD HOUSE   See page 216 for full page entry.

HARLOW CARR GARDENS   **Tel:** 01423 565418

Crag Lane, Harrogate, Yorkshire, H93 1QB.

Owner: Northern Horticultural Society   **Contact:** B Nuttall Esq

Ornamental and Trial gardens covering 68 acres, include alpines, rock plants, heathers, rose gardens, peat terraces, arboretum, fruit and vegetables.

Location: Crag Lane, Harrogate.

Opening Times: 9.30am - 6.00pm (last admission or dusk if earlier).

Admission: Adult £3.20, Child free, Conc £2.50, Groups of 20 plus £2.50 pp.

HELMSLEY CASTLE ⛫

Tel: 01439 70442

Helmsley, Yorkshire.
Owner: English Heritage   **Contact:** The Administrator
Close to the market square, with a view of the town, is this 12th century castle. Spectacular earthworks surround a great ruined Norman keep. There is an exhibition and tableau on the history of the castle.
Location: Near town centre.
Opening Times: 1 Apr - 30 Sept, daily 10.00am - 6.00pm, 1 Oct - 31 Oct, daily 10.00am - 4.00pm. 1 Nov - 31 Mar, Wed - Sun, 10.00am - 4.00pm (Closed 24 - 26 Dec, 1 Jan).
Admission: Adult £2.00, Child £1.00, Conc £1.50.

HOVINGHAM HALL 🏛

Tel: 01653 628205   **Fax:** 01653 628668

York, Yorkshire, YO6 4LU.
Owner: Sir Marcus Worsley   **Contact:** The Secretary
Palladian house built c.1760 by Thomas Worsley to his own designs. Unique entry by huge riding school. Visitors see family portraits and rooms in everyday use, also the extensive gardens with magnificent yew hedges and dovecot and the private cricket ground, said to be the oldest in England.
Location: In York.
Opening Times: By appointment only. Tues, Wed, Thur 11.00am - 7.00pm.
Admission: Adult £2.50, Child £1.25.

KIRKHAM PRIORY ⛫

Tel: 0165 381768

Kirkham, Whitwell-on-the-Hill, Yorkshire
Owner: English Heritage   **Contact:** The Administrator
The ruins of this Augustinian priory include a magnificent carved gatehouse.
Location: 5 m SW of Malton on minor road off A64.
Opening Times: 1 Apr - 30 Sept daily, 10.00am - 6.00pm. Lunchtime closure 1.00pm - 2.00pm.
Admission: Adults £1.30, Child 70p, Conc £1.00.

KNARESBOROUGH CASTLE ⛫

Tel: 01423 503340   **Fax:** 01423 840026

Royal Pump Room Museum , Crown Place, Harrogate, HG1 2RY.
Owner: Duchy of Lancaster   **Contact:** Mary Kershaw
Ruins of 14th century castle standing high above the town. Local history museum housed in old court. Gallery devoted to the Civil War.
Location: 5m E of Harrogate, off A59.
Opening Times: Easter BH w/e, 1 May - 30 Sept.
Admission: Adult £1.50, Child 75p, Family £3.50, Senior citizen 75p, Group £1.00.

LOTHERTON HALL

Tel: 0113 2813259   **Fax:** 0113 2602285

Aberford, Leeds, Yorkshire, LS25 3EB.
Owner: Leeds City Council   **Contact:** Adam White Esq
Magnificent former home of the Gascoigne family. Fine furniture, paintings and displays of costume.
Location: Just off A1. 12 m NE of Leeds city centre.
Opening Times: Tues - Sun, 10.30am - 12.00pm and 1.00pm - 5.15 or dusk if earlier.
Admission: Adult £2.00, Child £1.00 (50p in organised groups, Leeds schools free), Conc £1.00.

MIDDLEHAM CASTLE ⛫

Tel: 01969 23899

Middleham, Yorkshire.
Owner: English Heritage   **Contact:** The Administrator
This childhood home of Richard III stands controlling the river that winds through Wensleydale. There is a massive 12th century keep with splendid views of the surrounding countryside from the battlements.
Location: At Middleham, 2m S of Leyburn of A6108.
Opening Times: 1 Apr - 30 Sept, daily, 10.00am - 6.00pm. 1 Oct - 31 Oct daily, 10.00am - 4.00pm. Closed 24 - 26 Dec, 1 Jan.
Admission: Adults £1.25, Conc 95p, Child 60p.

MONK BRETTON PRIORY ⛫

Tel: 01226 204089

Barnsley, Yorkshire.
Owner: English Heritage   **Contact:** The Administrator
Grime stained blocks of red sandstone mark the peaceful ruin of this Cluniac monastery founded in 1153. Extensive remains of the fully restored 14th century Gatehouse.
Location: 1 M E of Barnsley town centre off A633.
Opening Times: 1 Apr - 30 Sept daily, 10.00am - 6.00pm. 1 Oct - 31 Oct, daily 10.00am - 4.00pm. 1 Nov - 31 Mar, Wed - Sun, 10.00am - 4.00pm. Closed 24 - 26 Dec, 1 Jan. Lunchtime closure 1.00pm - 2.00pm.
Admission: Adult £1.00, Child 50p, Conc 80p.

MOUNT GRACE PRIORY ⛫

OPEN

1 April - 30 Sept
Open daily
10.00am - 6.00pm
Last admission 5.30pm

1 Oct - 31 - Oct
Daily
10.00am - 4.00pm

1 Nov - 31 Mar
Wed - Sun
10.00am - 4.00pm

Tel: 01609 883494

SADDLE BRIDGE, NORTH YORKSHIRE DL6

Owner: English Heritage   *Contact: The Head Custodian*

The wooded countryside surrounding the ruins of Mount Grace Priory provides an idyllic setting for this, the best preserved Carthusian monastery in England. Unlike other monks, the Carthusian lived as hermits, speaking to no-one and seldom emerging from their individual cells. The remains of these cells and gardens, including one which has been fully restored and furnished, give a fascinating insight into the lives of the monks who once lived there.
Location: 12 miles north of Thirsk, 7 miles north-east of Northallerton on A19.
Admission: Adults £2.20, OAP/UB40/Student £1.70. Children £1.10.
15% discount on parties of 11 or more.

MERCHANT ADVENTURERS' HALL

OPEN

19 Mar - 11 Nov
Daily
8.30am - 5.00pm

12 Nov - 8 Mar 1996
Except Sundays
8.30am - 3.30pm

Closed Christmas/
New Year week

Tel: 01904 654818

FOSSGATE, YORK YO1 2XD

Owner: The Company of Merchant Adventurers   *Contact: Ivison S Wheatley*

The finest medieval guild hall in Europe, built in 1357/61 and substantially unaltered. In it the Merchants transacted their business, as their successors still do today. On the ground floor was their hospice where they cared for the poor, and their private chapel, a unique survival in England. There are good collections of early portraits, furniture, silver and other objects used by the Merchants over the centuries when their wealth and influence helped to make York the second city in England, after London.
Location: On Piccadilly. Main entrance in Piccadilly, other entrance on Fossgate.
Admission: Adult £1.80, OAP £1.50, Child 60p.

NEWBURGH PRIORY

Tel: 01347 868435

Coxwold, Yorkshire, YO6 4AS.
Owner: Sir George Wombwell Bt   **Contact:** Sir George Wombwell
Augustian priory founded in 1145 converted into Tudor mansion, and again later in 18th century. Beautiful water garden.
Location: 7m SE Thirsk.
Opening Times: Apr - end Jun, Wed, Sun & Bank Hols, 2.30pm - 4.45pm. (Best to check first) Guided tours approx 60 mins.

NEWBY HALL

See page 217 for full page entry.

NORMANBY HALL COUNTRY PARK

Tel: 01724 720588   **Fax:** 01724 721248

Scunthorpe, Humberside, DN15 9HU.
     Contact: Mr N Jacques
Regency mansion with rooms decorated in period style. Many activities in surrounding 350 acres of grounds.
Location: 4 m N of Scunthorpe off B1430.
Opening Times: Apr - Sept, daily, 1.00pm - 5.00pm. Park is open all year, 9.00am - 5.00pm (later in summer).
Admission: Apr - Sept per car: weekdays; £1.00, Sat £1.70, Sun and Bank Hol Mon £2.30 Coach parties £12.00 per coach Oct - Mar: £1.00.

NORTON CONYERS

Tel: 01765 640333 / 640601

Ripon, Yorkshire, HG4 5EH.

Owner: Sir James Graham Bt.   **Contact:** Lady Graham

Charming manor house, seat of the Grahams since 1624 and probably the inspiration for Thornfield Hall in Charlotte Bronte's "Jane Eyre". Pictures and furniture reflect 370 years of occupation by the same family.

Location: 4m NW of Ripon. 3m from the A1.

Opening Times: Bank Hol Sun and Mon. Sun: 28 May - 10 Sept. Daily 24 - 29 Jul 2.00pm - 5.00pm.

Admission: Adult £2.95, Child (10 - 16) £2.50, OAP/Student £2.00. Parties (20 or over) by arrangement.

NOSTELL PRIORY

Tel: 01924 863892

Doncaster Road, Nostell, Wakefield, Yorkshire, WF4 1QE.

Owner: National Trust   **Contact:** Jill Hodgson

Built for Sir Rowland Winn by Paine, a wing added in 1766 by Robert Adam. State rooms contain pictures and famous Chippendale furniture made especially for the house.

Location: 6m SE of Wakefield on N side of A638.

Opening Times: 1 Apr - 31 Oct: Apr, May, Jun, Sept & Oct, Sats 12.00pm - 5.00pm, Suns 11.00am - 5.00pm. Jul & Aug: daily except Fri, 12.00pm - 5.00pm. Sun 11.00am - 5.00pm. BHs (not Good Fri). Guided tours on weekdays only. Last tour, 4.00pm.

Admission: House and Grounds: Adult £3.50, Child £1.80. Parties: £3.00, Child £1.50. Grounds: Adult £2.20, Child £1.10. Free parking.

NUNNINGTON HALL

Tel: 01439 748283

Nunnington, Yorkshire, Y06 5UY.

Owner: National Trust   **Contact:** The Administrator

16th Century manor house with fine panelled hall and staircase. Carlisle collection of miniature rooms on display.

Location: In Ryedale, 4¹/2m SE of Helmsley, 11/2m S of B1257.

Opening Times: 1 Apr - 31 Oct: Tues, Wed, Thur, Sat, Sun and Good Fri, 2.00pm - 6.00pm. BHs, 12.00pm - 6.00pm Jul & Aug also Fri, 2.00pm - 6.00pm. Sat & Sun 12.00pm - 6.00pm Last admission 5.00pm Shop and tea-room open as house.

Admission: House and Garden: Adult £3.50, Child £1.50. Parties £3.00, Child £1.30. Garden: Adult £1.00, Child free.

ORMESBY HALL

Tel: 01642 324188

Church Lane, Ormesby, Middlesborough, Yorkshire, TS7 9AS.

Owner: National Trust   **Contact:** The Administrator

A mid 18th century house with opulent decoration inside, including fine plasterwork by contemporary craftsmen. A Jacobean doorway with a carved family crest survives from the earlier house on the site. The stable block, attributed to Carr of York, is a particularly fine mid 18th century building with an attractive courtyard leased to the Mounted Police, also an attractive 5 acre garden with holly walk.

Location: 3m SE of Middlesborough.

Opening Times: 1 Apr - 31 Oct: Wed, Thur, Sat, Sun, BH Mon & Good Fri, 2.00pm - 5.30pm. Last admission 5.00pm.

Admission: House and Gardens: Adult £2.00, Child £1.00, family £4.00. Garden: Adult £1.00, Child 50p.

PICKERING CASTLE

Tel: 01751 74989

Pickering, Yorkshire.

Owner: English Heritage   **Contact:** The Administrator

A splendid motte and bailey castle, once a royal ranch. It is well preserved, with much of the original walls, towers and keep, and there are spectacular views over the surrounding countryside. There is an exhibition on the castle's history.

Location: In Pickering, 15m SW of Scarborough.

Opening Times: 1 Apr - 30 Sept, daily 10.00am - 6.00pm, 1 Oct - 31 Oct, daily 10.00am - 4.00pm. 1 Nov - 31 Mar, Wed - Sun, 10.00am - 4.00pm (Closed 24 - 26 Dec, 1 Jan).

Admission: Adult £2.00, Child £1.00, Conc £1.50.

RICHMOND CASTLE

Tel: 01748 822493

Richmond, Yorkshire.

Owner: English Heritage   **Contact:** The Administrator

A splendid medieval fortress, with a fine 12th century keep and 11th century remains of the curtain wall and domestic buildings. There are magnificent views from the 100 feet high keep.

Location: In Richmond.

Opening Times: 1 Apr - 30 Sept, daily 10.00am - 6.00pm, 1 Oct - 31 Mar, daily 10.00am - 4.00pm. (Closed 24 - 26 Dec, 1 Jan).

Admission: Adult £1.80, Child 90p, Conc £1.40.

RIEVAULX ABBEY

Tel: 01439 798228

Rievaulx, Yorkshire.

Owner: English Heritage   **Contact:** The Administrator

In a deeply wooded valley by the River Rye you can see some of the most spectacular monastic ruins in England, dating from the 12th century. The church has the earliest large Cistercian nave in Britain. A fascinating exhibition shows how successfully the Cistercians at Rievaulx ran their many businesses and explains the part played by Abbot Ailred, who ruled for twenty years.

Location: 2¹/4m W of Helmsley on minor road off B1257.

Opening Times: 1 Apr - 30 Sept, daily 10.00am - 6.00pm, 1 Oct - 31 Mar, daily 10.00am - 4.00pm. (Closed 24 - 26 Dec, 1 Jan).

Admission: Adult £2.40, Child £1.20, Conc £1.80.

RIEVAULX TERRACE AND TEMPLES

Tel: 01439 798340

Rievaulx, Helmsley, Yorkshire, YO6 5LJ.

Owner: The National Trust   **Contact:** The Administrator

A ¹/2m long grass-covered terrace and adjoining woodlands with vistas over Rievaulx Abbey and Rye valley to Ryedale and the Hambleton Hills. There are two mid 18th century temples: the Ionic Temple has elaborate ceiling paintings and fine 18th century furniture. A permanent exhibition in the basement is on English landscape design in the 18th century.

Location: 2¹/2m NW of Helmsley on B1257.

Opening Times: 1 Apr - 31 Oct: daily 10.30am - 6.00pm or dusk if earlier. Last admission 5.00pm.

Admission: Adult £2.50, Child £1.00, Family £5.00, party rates available.

RIPLEY CASTLE

See page 218-219 for full page entry.

RIPON CATHEDRAL

Tel: 01765 604108

Ripon, Yorkshire, HG4 1QR.

Contact: Canon D G Ford

One of the oldest crypts in Europe (672). Marvellous choir stalls and misericords (500 years old). Almost every type of architecture. Treasury.

Location: 5m W signposted off A1, 12m N of Harrogate.

Opening Times: 8.00am - 6.00pm all year.

Admission: Donation.

ROCHE ABBEY

Tel: 01709 812739

Maltby, Yorkshire.

Owner: English Heritage.   **Contact:** The Administrator

This Cistercian monastery, founded in 1147, lies in a secluded landscaped valley sheltered by limestone cliffs and trees. Some of the walls still stand to their full height and excavation has revealed the complete layout of the abbey.

Location: 1¹/2 m S of Maltby off A634.

Opening Times: 1 Apr - 30 Sept, Daily 10.00am - 6.00pm. 1 Oct - 31 Oct, Daily, 10.00am - 4.00pm.

Admission: Adults £1.30, Child £1.00, Conc 70p.

SCARBOROUGH CASTLE

Tel: 01723 372451

Scarborough, Yorkshire.

Owner: English Heritage.   **Contact:** The Administrator

From the walls of this enormous 12th century castle you will have spectacular coastal views. The buttressed castle walls stretch out along the cliff edge and the remains of the great rectangular stone keep still stand to over three storeys high. There is also the site of a 4th century Roman signal station. The castle was frequently attacked, but despite being blasted by cannons of the Civil War and bombarded from the sea during World War I, it is still a spectacular place to visit.

Location: Castle Road, E of town centre.

Opening Times: 1 Apr - 30 Sept, Daily, 10.00am - 6.00pm. 1 Oct - 31 Mar Daily, 10.00am - 4.00pm. (Closed 24 - 26 Dec, 1 Jan).

Admission: Adults £1.50, Child £1.10, Conc 75p.

SEWERBY HALL

Tel: 01262 677874   **Fax:** 01262 674265

Bridlington, Humberside, Y15 1EA.

Owner: Borough of East Yorkshire   **Contact:** The Administrator

Early 18th century house, now an art gallery. Large gardens of some interest.

Location: 2m N of Bridlington.

Opening Times: Summer; 10.00am - 6.00pm. Winter; Sat - Tues, 11.00am - 4.00pm. Closed 10 Jan - 3 Mar.

Admission: Adult £2.50, Child £1.00, Senior citizens £2.00, Groups over 10 50% discount.

SHERIFF HUTTON PARK 🏛

Tel: 01347 878442   **Fax:** 01347 878442

Sheriff Hutton, York, Yorkshire, YO6 1RH.
Owner: East Fifteen Acting School   **Contact:** Mrs Catherine Feakins
Red-brick mansion in Queen Anne style from the outside. Jacobean and early-Georgian rooms within. The garden also displays Jacobean features.
Location: A64 to 5m N of York; Sheriff Hutton exit to left. Rail; York station 10m.
Opening Times: Mon - Fri (except BHs) 10.00am - 4.30pm. Closed mid-Dec - mid-Jan.
Admission: Adult £2.35, Child £1.20 Family £6, Conc £1.75. Party reductions.

SHIBDEN HALL

Tel: 01422 352246   **Fax:** 01422 348440

Listers Road, Shibden, Halifax, Yorkshire, HX3 6XG.
Owner: Calderdale MBC   **Contact:** Ms R Westwood
A half-timbered Manor House, the home of Anne Lister set in a landscaped park. Oak furniture, carriage and an array of objects make Shibden an intriguing place to visit. Cafe and Shop.
Location: 1 ¹/₂m East of Halifax off A58.
Opening Times: 1 Mar - 30 Nov, Mon - Sat 10.00am - 5.00pm. Sun 12.00pm - 5.00pm. Last Admission 4.30pm. For Winter opening please telephone.
Admission: Adult £1.50, Child/OAP/conc 75p, Family £4.50.

SION HILL HALL 🏛

OPEN

26 Mar - 29 Oct
Hall: 12.30 to 4.30pm
(except Mon & Tues)
Grounds, Birds of Prey,
Tearooms:
10.30 - 5.30pm
(except Mons)
All open Bank Hol Mons
Groups anytime Jan -
Nov by arrangement

Tel: 01845 587206
Fax: 01845 587486

KIRBY WISKE, NORTH YORKSHIRE YO7 4EU

Owner: H.W. Mawer Trust   *Contact: John D. Bridges*

Charming Edwardian Mansion designed by Brierley – the 'Lutyens of the North' - has RIBA accolade for outstanding architectural merit. This Award Winning mansion now houses the Mawer Antique Collection of furniture, porcelain & clocks and period costume displays - the most comprehensive in the North. Falconry in the Victorian Walled Garden - daily flying displays. Granary Tearoom. *Support the Mawer Trust Registered Charity No. 502772.*
Location: Off A167. 6m South of Northallerton, 4 miles west of Thirsk, 8 miles East of A1 via A61.
Admission: Hall: Adult £3.50, Child £1.50, Concessions £3.00.
Birds: Adult £3.50, Child & Concessions £2.50. Grounds only: £1.00
Group discounts for 10 or more.

SPOFFORTH CASTLE ⚎

Harrogate, Yorkshire.
Owner: English Heritage   **Contact:** The Administrator
This manor house has some fascinating features including an undercroft built into the rock. It was once owned by the Percy family.
Location: 3¹/₂ m SE of Harrogate on minor road off A661 at Spofforth.
Opening Times: 1 Apr - 31 Oct, daily, 10.00am - 6.00pm. 1 Nov - 31 Mar, daily, 10.00am - 4.00pm. Closed 24 - 26 Dec, 1 Jan.

Harewood House, West Yorkshire.

STOCKELD PARK 🏛

OPEN

6 April - 12 Oct
inclusive

Thursdays only.
2.00 - 5.00pm

Tel: 01937 586101
Fax: 01937 580084

WETHERBY, YORKSHIRE LS22 4AH

Owner: Mr and Mrs. P.G. F. Grant   *Contact: Mrs. L. A. Saunders*

Stockeld is a small and beautifully proportioned Palladian Villa designed for Middletons by James Paine in 1763. The present family have lived at Stockeld for over a century and it is still very much a home, housing a good collection of 18th and 19th century furniture and paintings. Stockeld is set in beautiful parkland and has well established gardens and woodland.
Location: York 12 miles, Harrogate 5 miles, Leeds 12 miles.
Admission: Adult £2.00, Child £1.00, OAP £1.50.

ST WILLIAM'S COLLEGE ⚎

Tel: 01904 637134   **Fax:** 01904 654604

5 College Street, York, Yorkshire, YO1 2JF.
Owner: The Dean and Chapter of York   **Contact:** Miss A S Clarke
Location: College Street, York.
Opening Times: 10.00am - 5.00pm.
Admission: College: Adult 60p, Child 30p. Museum: Adult £2.00, Child £1.00, Family £5.00, Conc £1.50.

STUDLEY ROYAL: ST MARY'S CHURCH ⚎

Tel: 01765 608888

Ripon, Yorkshire.
Owner: English Heritage.   **Contact:** The Administrator
A magnificent Victorian church, designed by William Burges in the 1870s with a highly decorated interior. Coloured glass stained marble, stained glass, gilded and painted figures and a splendid organ.
Location: 2¹/₂ m W of Ripon off B6265, in grounds of Studley Royal estate.
Opening Times: 1 Apr - 30 Sept daily, 1.00pm - 5.00pm.

SUTTON PARK 🏛

Tel: 01347 810249

Sutton on the Forest, York, Yorkshire, YO6 1DP.
Owner: Mrs Sheffield.   **Contact:** Mrs M Wilson
Charming example of early Georgian architecture with rich collection of furniture and paintings put together with great style..
Location: 8m N of York on B1363 Helmsley Road.
Opening Times: House: Easter Sun And Mon and BHs, 1.30pm - 5.30pm. Private parties for house any day except Sat by prior arrangement. Gardens open daily Easter - Oct.
Admission: Adult £3.50, Child £2.00, Senior citizen £3.00, Groups £3.00. Verify with administrator.

TEMPLE NEWSHAM HOUSE

Tel: 0113 2647321   **Fax:** 0113 2602285

Leeds, Yorkshire, LS15 0AE.
Owner: Leeds City Council   **Contact:** Ms C Stokes
Tudor and Jacobean mansion with extensive collections of decorative arts in their original room settings, including incomparable Chippendale collection.
Location: 5m E of city centre, off A63 Leeds/ Selby Road
Opening Times: Throughout the year, Tues - Sun & BH Mons, 10.30am - 5.30pm.
Admission: Adult £2.00, Child 50p, Conc £1.00, Pre-booked groups £1.00.

THE GEORGIAN THEATRE ROYAL

Tel: 01748 823710   **Fax:** 01748 823710

Richmond, Yorkshire, DL10 4DW.
Owner: Georgian Theatre Royal Trust   **Contact:** Bill Sellars
Brochure on request. Built in 1788, this is the country's oldest theatre in original form.
Location: 6m from Scotch Corner
Opening Times: Museum:1 Apr - 31 Oct, Mon - Sat, 11am - 4.45pm. Sun 2.30pm - 4.45pm. Theatre performances; Apr - Dec.
Admission: Museum: Adult £1.00, Child 50p, Conc 70p, Groups by arrangement. Theatre: £1.00 - £3.00.

THE OLD GRAMMAR SCHOOL

Tel: 01482 593902   **Fax:** 01482 593710

83 Alfred Gelder Street, Hull, Yorkshire, HU1 1EP.

Owner: Hull City Council   **Contact:** S R Green

Hull's oldest secular building now houses the social history exhibition "The Story of Hull and its People", an exploration of the fascinating lives of the people of Hull through the centuries. This history is explored using the themes common to all of us such as childhood, education, courtship, marriage and work. Visitors can participate by playing the 'game of life', following fictional characters make their way from birth to death. Various temporary exhibitions are displayed in the museum.

Location: 83 Alfred Gelder St, Hull.

Opening Times: Mon - Sat: 10.00am - 5.00pm, Sun: 1.30pm - 4.30pm (Last admission 15 minutes prior).

THORNTON ABBEY ⛶

Scunthorpe, Humberside.

Owner: English Heritage   **Contact:** The Administrator

The magnificent brick gatehouse of this ruined Augustine priory stands three storeys high, with a facade ornamented with finely carved details including some surviving 14th century statues.

Location: 18 m NE of Scunthorpe on minor road N of A160. 7 m SE of Humber Bridge on minor road E of A1077.

Opening Times: 1 Apr - 30 Sept, 10.00am - 6.00pm, daily. 1 Oct - 31 Mar, 10.00am - 4.00pm, daily, or dusk if earlier. Gatehouse: summer season, 1st & 3rd Sun of every month. 1.00pm - 5.00pm or dusk if earlier. Gatehouse: winter season 3rd Sun of every month, 1.00pm - 4.00pm or dusk if earlier.

THORP PERROW ARBORETUM 🏛

BEDALE, NORTH YORKSHIRE

Owner: Sir John Ropner
Contact: Mr. P Robinson

Tel: 01677 425323
Fax: 01677 422710

The Arboretum comprises over 1,000 wonderful (many rare) trees and shrubs set in 85 acres woodland walks, tree trails, nature trail, lake, picnic area, tearoom, information centre and plant centre. Ample free parking. Disabled visitors welcome: Electric wheelchair available. Coach parties welcome; tours must be pre-booked. Spectacular Autumn colour with thousands of spring flowers and wild flowers.

Location: South of Bedale, N. Yorkshire on Well-Ripon road, 4 miles from Leeming Bar on A1.

Admission: Adult £2.75, OAP £1.50, Child £1.50.

OPEN

All year round from
Dawn to Dusk

TREASURER'S HOUSE

Tel: 01904 624247

Chapter House Street, York, Yorkshire, YO1 2JD.

Owner: The National Trust   **Contact:** The Administrator

A large 17th Century house of great interest. Fine furniture and paintings. Exhibition. In Minster Yard on N side of Minster.

Location: In Minster Yard on N side of Minster.

Opening Times: 1 Apr - 31 Oct: daily 10.30am - 5.00pm. Last admission 4.30pm. Guided tours by arrangement.

Admission: Adult £3.00, Child £1.50. Parties £2.50, Child £1.20.

WAKEFIELD CATHEDRAL

Tel: 01924 373923

Northgate, Wakefield, Yorkshire, WF1 1HG.

Contact: The Very Rev John Allen

Location: Centre of Wakefield shopping area.

Opening Times: Mon - Sat 8.00am - 5.30pm. Closed Bank Hols. Only open for services on Suns ie. 8.00am, 9.15am, 11.00am, 4.00pm (Winter) 6.30pm (Summer).

Admission: Free Admission.

WHITBY ABBEY ⛶

Tel: 01947 603568

Whitby, Yorkshire.

Owner: English Heritage   **Contact:** The Administrator

This in an ancient holy place, once a burial place of kings and an inspiration for saints. A religious community was first established at Whitby in 657 by Abbess Hilda and was the home of Caedmon, the first English poet. The remains we can see today are of a Benedictine church built in the 13th and 14th centuries, and include a magnificent three-tiered choir and north transept. It is perched high above the picturesque harbour town of Whitby.

Location: On cliff top E of Whitby town centre.

Opening Times: 1 Apr - 30 Sept: daily 10.00am - 6.00pm, 1 Oct - 31 Mar: daily 10.00am - 4.00pm (Closed 24 - 26 Dec, 1 Jan).

Admission: Adult £1.50, Child 80p, Conc £1.10.

WILBERFORCE HOUSE

Tel: 01482 593902   **Fax:** 01482 593710

High Street, Hull, Yorkshire, HU1 1EP.

Owner: Hull City Council   **Contact:** S R Green

Built c1656 the house has been a museum to the memory of William Wilberforce, slavery abolitionist, since 1906. The main display tells the horrific story of slavery and Wilberforce's struggle to abolish it. The house also holds many other fascinating displays such as the Victorian parlour, the famous Hull Silver and Georgian rooms.

Location: High Street, Hull.

Opening Times: Mon - Sat, 10.00am - 5.00pm. Sun 1.30pm - 4.30pm. Closed Good Friday and Christmas Day.

Admission: Free.

Burton Agnes Hall, Yorkshire.

BOWHILL
Selkirk

SCOTTISH Borders home of the Duke and Duchess of Buccleuch, dating mainly from 1812 and christened 'Sweet Bowhill' by Sir Walter Scott in his 'Lay of the Last Minstrel'.

Many of the works of art were collected by earlier Montagus, Douglases and Scotts or given by Charles II to his natural son James Duke of Monmouth and Buccleuch. Paintings include Canaletto's "Whitehall", works by Guardi, Claude, Ruysdael, Gainsborough, Raeburn, Reynolds, Van Dyck and Wilkie. Superb French furniture, Meissen and Sévres porcelain, silver and tapestries.

Historical relics include Monmouth's saddle and execution shirt, Sir Walter Scott's plaid and some proof editions, Queen Victoria's letters and gifts to successive Duchesses of Buccleuch, her Mistresses of the Robes.

Completely restored Victorian Kitchen, 19th Century horse-drawn fire engine, 'Bowhill Little Theatre', a lively centre for the performing arts and where, prior to touring the house, visitors can see 'The Quest for Bowhill', a twenty minute audio-visual by Dr Colin Thompson.

Conference Centre, Arts Courses, Education Service, Mountain Bike hire, Visitor Centre. Shop, Tearoom, Adventure Playground, Woodland Walks, Nature Trails, Picnic Areas. Garden and landscape designed by John Gilpin.

SUITABILITY FOR OTHER EVENTS
Fashion shows, air displays, archery, clay pigeon shooting, equestrian events, charity garden parties, shows, rallies, filming, all requests considered. By prior arrangement.

EXTRA FACILITIES
As "education" is the prime function of the Buccleuch Heritage Trust, with emphasis on outstanding works of art and their relationship to their historic associations, the House is opened specially by appointment, outside the scheduled public hours to groups of any age led by officials of a recognised museum, gallery or educational establishment. Lecture theatre and equipment available on request.

ADVICE TO COURIERS & DRIVERS
Photography prohibited inside the House. Free parking for 60 cars and 6 coaches within 50yds of House.

FACILITIES FOR THE DISABLED
Disabled and elderly visitors may alight at the House entrance. Special toilet facilities in the Stables Courtyard. Wheelchair visitors admitted Free of Charge.

CATERING
Restaurant (seating 72). Parties can be booked in advance for tea and other meals. Inside caterers normally used but outside caterers considered. Special rates for groups, menus on request.

GUIDED TOURS
Available for groups. Average time taken to see the House 1 hour 15 minutes.

GIFT SHOP
Open at the same time as the House, or by appointment. Mini shop open when grounds only open.

SCHOOL VISITS/CHILDREN
Groups are welcome, £1.00 per child. The services of Education Officers are provided free and a schoolroom is available. Areas of interest include: projects in Bowhill House and Victorian Kitchen, Ranger-led Nature Walks. Adventure Playground. Please telephone to discuss requirements.

CONTACT

Mrs M Carter
Buccleuch Heritage Trust
Bowhill House & Country Park
Bowhill
Selkirk
Scotland
TD7 5ET

Tel: (01750) 20732

LOCATION

3 mls W of Selkirk off A708 Moffat Road, A68 from Newcastle, A7 from Carlisle or Edinburgh.

Bus: 3 miles Selkirk.

Taxi: (01750) 20354

OPENING TIMES

Summer
30 Apr. to late Summer Bank Hol (UK)

COUNTRY PARK
Daily except Fridays
(open Fridays in July)
12 noon - 5.00pm

HOUSE
July only. Daily
1.00 - 4.30pm

Winter
By appointment only, for educational groups.

ADMISSION

Summer

HOUSE AND
COUNTRY PARK
Adult £4.00
Child* £1.00
OAP/Student . . .£3.50
Group** £3.50

COUNTRY PARK ONLY
All ages £1.00

* 5 - 16yrs.
** Min. 20 persons

Winter

HOUSE AND
COUNTRY PARK
Adult £4.50
Child* £1.00

Pre-booked educational groups over 20 persons welcomed.

CONFERENCE AND FUNCTION FACILITIES

ROOM	DIMENSIONS	CAPACITY	LAYOUT	POWER POINTS	SUITABLE FOR A/V
Bowhill Little Theatre		72	Theatre	✓	✓
		72	Buffet		
		72	Lunch/Dinner		

FLOORS CASTLE
Kelso

FlOORS CASTLE, home of the Roxburghe family is situated in the heart of the Scottish Border Country. It is the largest inhabited Castle in Scotland. Designed by William Adam, who was both masterbuilder and architect, for the first Duke of Roxburghe, building started in 1721.

It was the present Duke's great, great grandfather, James the 6th Duke, who embellished the plain Adam features of the building. In about 1849 Playfair, letting his imagination and talent run riot, transformed the Castle creating a multitude of spires and domes.

Externally the Castle has not been altered since the 6th Duke's time, but internally, several of the rooms, including the Dining Room and Ballroom were remodelled at the turn of the century. These apartments now display the outstanding collection of French 17th and 18th Century furniture, magnificent tapestries, Chinese and European porcelain and the many other fine works of art. Many of the treasures in the Castle today were collected by Duchess May, American wife of the 8th Duke.

The Castle has been seen on cinema screens worldwide in the film 'Greystoke', as the home of Tarzan, the Earl of Greystoke.

GARDENS

The extensive parkland and gardens overlooking the Tweed provides a variety of wooded walks. The Walled Garden contains splendid herbaceous borders and in the outer walled garden a summerhouse built for Queen Victoria's visit in 1867 can still be seen. An excellent children's playground and picnic area is very close to the Castle.

CONTACT

Frances Brown
Roxburghe Estates Office
Kelso
Scotland
TD5 7SF

Tel: (01573) 223333

Fax: (01573) 226056

LOCATION

From South A68, A698.

From North A68, A697/9. In Kelso follow signs.

Bus: Kelso Bus Stn 1 mile

Rail: Berwick 20 miles.

OPENING TIMES

Summer

Easter - September
Daily
10.30am - 5.30pm

October
Sunday & Wednesday
10.30am - 4.30pm

Winter

November to March
Closed to the general public.

ADMISSION

Summer

Adults	£3.80
OAPs	£3.00
Children*	£1.90
Family	£10.00

Groups

Adults	£3.00
OAPs	£2.80
Child*	£1.70

* Aged 5-15

SUITABILITY FOR OTHER EVENTS
Gala dinners, conferences, product launches, incentive groups, 4 x 4 driving, highland games and other promotional events.

EXTRA FACILITIES
Include: extensive park, helicopter pad, fishing, clay pigeon shooting and pheasant shooting.

ADVICE TO COURIERS & DRIVERS
Coaches can be driven to the front door of the Castle, there is a waiting area close to the Restaurant exit. Coach drivers are offered a choice of lunch or tea. No photography inside the Castle. No dogs. Unlimited parking for cars, 100 yards away from the Castle, coach park situated 50 yards from the Castle. Guide book in French, German and Italian £1.50.

FACILITIES FOR THE DISABLED
Disabled and elderly visitors may alight at the entrance to the property, before parking in the allocated areas. Toilets for the disabled.

CATERING
There is a self-service, licensed restaurant seating 125 open from 10.30am, where coffee, lunch and tea are served. Groups can book in advance.

GIFT SHOP
Same hours as the Castle. Wide range of quality goods.

GUIDED TOURS
Tours lasting 1¼ hrs available on request for up to 100.

SCHOOL VISITS/CHILDREN
School visits are welcome and a guide will be provided. Cost per child £1.70. Playground facilities.

CONFERENCE AND FUNCTION FACILITIES

ROOM	DIMENSIONS	CAPACITY	LAYOUT	POWER POINTS	SUITABLE FOR A/V
Dining Room	18.3mx7.3m	150	Theatre	✓	✓
		90	Lunch/Dinner		
		50	Boardroom		
Ballroom	21.1mx7.9m	150	Theatre	✓	✓
		50	Boardroom		
Roxburghe Room (In Sunlaws House Hotel)		25	Boardroom	✓	✓

MANDERSTON
Duns

MANDERSTON, together with its magnificent stables, stunning marble dairy and 56 acres of immaculate garden, forms an ensemble which must be unique in Britain today.

The House was completely rebuilt between 1903 and 1905, with no expense spared.

Visitors are able to see not only the sumptuous State Rooms and bedrooms, decorated in the Adam manner, but also all the original domestic offices, in a truly 'Upstairs Downstairs' atmosphere. Manderston boasts a unique and recently restored silver staircase.

There is a special museum with a nostalgic display of valuable tins made by Huntley and Palmers from 1868 to the present day. *Winner of the AA/NPI Bronze Award UK 1994.*

GARDENS

Outside, the magnificence continues and the combination of formal gardens and picturesque landscapes is a major attraction: unique amongst Scottish houses.

The stables, still in use, have been described by 'Horse and Hound' as "probably the finest in all the wide world."

❖

SUITABILITY FOR OTHER EVENTS
Fashion shows, air displays, archery, clay pigeon shooting, equestrian events, garden parties, shows, rallies, filming, wedding receptions, product launches and marathons. Almost anything is possible by arrangement.

EXTRA FACILITIES
Two airstrips for light aircraft, approx 5 mls. Grand Piano, Full-size Billiard Table. Fox hunting, pheasant shoots (up to 600 birds per day). Sea Angling on coast, salmon on River Tweed. Stabling for 20 horses, cricket pitch, tennis court, lake. Nearby: 9 hole golf course, indoor swimming pool, squash court.

ACCOMMODATION
Manderston offers : 5 twin, 4 doubles and 1 single.

ADVICE TO COURIERS & DRIVERS
It is appreciated and helpful if party fees can be paid by one person on arrival. Dogs (grounds only) on leads. No photography inside House. Please allow plenty of time as there is so much to see. Parking for 400 cars, 125 yds from House, 30 coaches 5 yds from the House.

FACILITIES FOR THE DISABLED
Cars containing disabled visitors can park outside the House. No special toilet facilities.

CATERING
Tea Room (capacity 80) open during day, waitress service. Afternoon Tea from £2.30, £10-£35 other meals. Meals can be booked in advance. menus upon request. Menu can

include local smoked trout pate, pheasant in mushroom and red wine sauce and strawberry mousse, prices include pre-meal cocktails and wines. For special functions/ conferences, buffets, lunches and dinners can be arranged.

GIFT SHOP
Open same time as House, other times by arrangement. Colour guide book, £2.00.

GUIDED TOURS
At no additional cost tours available in French and English. When House open, guides posted in most rooms. If requested the owner may meet groups. Average time for tour 1 1/4 hours.

SCHOOL VISITS / CHILDREN
Groups welcome, £1.50 per child, min. £45. A guide can be provided. The Biscuit Tin Museum is of particular interest.

CONTACT

The Lord or Lady Palmer
Manderston
Duns
Berwickshire
Scotland
TD11 3PP

Tel: (01361) 883450

Fax: (01361) 882010

LOCATION

From Edinburgh
47 miles, 1 hour

Bus: 400 yards

Rail: Berwick Station
12 miles

3 1/2 hrs, from London

Taxi: Chirnside 818216

Air: Edinburgh or Newcastle Airport both 60 miles

OPENING TIMES

Summer
11 May - 28 September

Thurdays & Sundays
2.00 - 5.30pm

Mon Bank Holidays
29 May, 28 Aug
2.00 - 5.30pm

Group visits at other times by arrangement.

Winter
September - May
Visits by arrangement.

ADMISSION

HOUSE & GROUNDS
Adult £5.00
Child £1.00
Groups (min 20 people on open days)
Per person £3.00
School child . . .£1.50
(Min Student group £45.00)

GROUNDS ONLY
Including Stables & Marble Dairy
Adult £2.50
Child £0.50
Groups (min 20 people)
Per person £2.00

On days when the House is closed to the public, parties viewing by appointment will have personally conducted tours of the House and the Gift Shop will be Open. On these occasions however, the above reduced party rates (except for school-children) will not apply. Groups isits other than open days is £5.00 per person (min £100.00). Cream teas on open days only.

CONFERENCE AND FUNCTION FACILITIES

ROOM	DIMENSIONS	CAPACITY	LAYOUT	POWER POINTS	SUITABLE FOR A/V
Dining Room	22'x35'	22	Boardroom	✓	✓
		100	Buffet		
		40	Lunch/Dinner		
Ballroom	34'x21'	150	Theatre	✓	✓
Hall	22'x38'	130	Theatre	✓	✓
Drawing Room	35'x21'	150	Theatre	✓	✓

TRAQUAIR
Peeblesshire

TRAQUAIR, situated amidst beautiful scenery and close by the River Tweed, is the oldest inhabited house in Scotland - visited by twenty-seven kings. Originally a Royal Hunting Lodge it was owned by the Scottish Crown until 1478 when it passed to a branch of the Royal Stuart family whose descendants still live in the house today.

From a single tower block the building grew reflecting the growth and importance of the Stuarts of Traquair and no exterior alterations were made after the end of the 17th Century. At the end of the tree lined avenue leading to the House are the famous Bear Gates, still closed since 1745 when the last person to pass through them was Bonnie Prince Charlie (not to be opened again until the restoration of the Stuarts).

Nearly ten centuries of Scottish political and domestic life can be traced from the collection of treasurers in the House. It is particularly rich in associations with the Catholic Church in Scotland, Mary Queen of Scots and the Jacobite Risings.

GARDEN
70 acres of grounds with peacocks, ducks and other wild life. In spring there is a profusion of daffodils followed by rhododendrons, wild flowers and herbaceous plants. A maze in Beech/Leylandi Cyprus is behind the House.

SUITABILITY FOR OTHER EVENTS
Garden parties, Weddings, receptions, product launches, filming, archery clay pigeon shooting, theatre, son et lumiére.

EXTRA FACILITIES
18th Century fully operational Brewhouse, ale tasting every Friday between 3pm-4pm. 17th Century harpsichord in Drawing Room, croquet (mallets can be hired) Lectures provided on the property, contents , history and grounds.

ADVICE TO COURIERS & DRIVERS
Coaches preferably booked in advance. Drivers please apply for vouchers on arrival. Dogs on leads in grounds. No photography in House. Introductory talks can be given to groups. Out of hours visits with meals and refreshments by prior arrangement.

GIFT SHOP
Open as House, selling Traquair House Ale, wine and crafts.

CATERING
Licensed self-service 1745 Cottage Tearoom. On fine days lunches and teas can be taken outdoors. Marquee (lined and floored) available for receptions, weddings, etc., in the gardens or the courtyard. Parties up to 45 can be served in the Bear Cottage. Lunches and dinners in the house dining room from £25 by special arrangement

ACCOMMODATION
Traquair offers 2 fourposter suites with bathroom. 1 self-catering flat with double bedroom.

FACILITIES FOR THE DISABLED
Disabled and elderly visitors may alight at the entrance to the property, before parking in the allocated area. Toilets for the disabled.

PARKING FOR COACHES & CARS
Capacity of car park: 200 cars and 5 coaches 85 yards from the House. (Advance booking requested for coaches).

GUIDE BOOKS
Colour guide book, £2.00. Translations in French, Spanish, German, Dutch, Swedish, Japanese and Italian. Childrens guide books and quiz sheets.

GUIDED TOURS
Tours only outside opening hours £4.00 per person (£80 min).

CONTACT
Ms C Maxwell Stuart
Traquair House
Innerleithen
Peeblesshire
EH44 6PW

Tel: (01896)830323

LOCATION
From Edinburgh 1 hour, Glasgow1^1/2 hours, Carlisle 1^1/2 hours, Newcastle 2^1/2 hours. On B709 near Junction with A72.

Rail: Edinburgh Waverley 30 miles.

Bus: Hourly bus service from Edinburgh to Innerleithen. Enquiries Eastern Scottish (031) 558 1616.

Taxi: Leithen Valley Taxis. Innerleithen 830486.

OPENING TIMES
Summer
15 April - 30 Sept
Daily   12.30 - 5.30pm

July & August
open 10.30am - 5.30pm
Last admission 5.00pm

October
Fridays - Sundays
2.00pm - 5.00pm

Restaurant open 12 noon
11.00am in July & Aug.

Winter
1 November - Easter
Open by arrangement.

ADMISSION

Summer
HOUSE & GARDEN
  Adult £3.75
  Child* £1.75
Groups**
  Adult £3.00
  Child* £1.50

GARDEN ONLY
  Adult £1.50
  Child* £1.00

* Under 15 years.
** Minimum payment £60.00 when House open £80.00 when closed.

Winter
£6.00 per person.
Includes glass of wine/whisky/ Traquair Ale and shortbread. Minimum charge £100.

CONFERENCE AND FUNCTION FACILITIES

ROOM	DIMENSIONS	CAPACITY	LAYOUT	POWER POINTS	SUITABLE FOR A/V
Dining Room	33' x 18'	22	Lunches	3	✓
		16	Schoolroom		
		30	Buffet		
			Lunch/Dinner		
Drawing Room (with Harpsichord)	27' x 24'	50/60	Drinks	3	✓
		50/60	Music Recitals		

ABBOTSFORD HOUSE   **Tel:** 01896 2043

Melrose, Roxburghshire, TD6 9BQ.
Owner: Mrs P Maxwell-Scott OBE   **Contact:** Mrs P Maxwell-Scott
Sir Walter Scott purchased the Cartley Hall farmhouse on the banks of the Tweed in 1812. Together with his family and servants he moved into the farm which he renamed Abbotsford.   Scott had the old house demolished in 1822 and replaced it with the main block of Abbotsford as it is today. Scott was a passionate collector of historic relics including an impressive collection of armour and weapons and over 9,000 rare volumes in his library.
Location: 3m N of Melrose off B6360.
Opening Times: 19 Mar - 31 Oct; 10.00am - 5.00pm Weekdays. 2.00pm - 5.00pm Suns.
Admission: Adult £3.00, Child £1.50. Party rates: Adult £2.20, Child £1.10.

AYTON CASTLE

OPEN

7 May - 10 Sept
2.00 - 5.00pm
or by appointment

Tel: 018907 81212
Tel: 018907 81550

AYTON, BERWICKSHIRE TD14 5RD
Contact: The Curator

Built in 1846 by the Mitchell-Innes family and designed by the architect James Gillespie Graham. Over the last ten years it has been fully restored and is now a family home. It is a unique restoration project and the quality of the original and restored workmanship is outstanding. The Castle stands on an escarpment surrounded by mature woodlands containing many interesting trees and has been a film-making venue due to this magnificent setting.
Location: 7 miles north of Berwick-on-Tweed on Route A1.
Admission: Adult £2.00, Children under 5 Free.

BOWHILL   **See Page 227 for full page entry.**

DAYWYCK BOTANIC GARDEN   **Tel:** 01721 760254   **Fax:** 01721 760214

Stobo, Peebles, EH45 9JU.
                                            Contact: Assistant Curator
Rare Trees including very fine conifers. In the woods is Dawyck Chapel, designed by William Burn.
Location: 8m SW of Peebles on B712.
Opening Times: 15 Mar - 22 Oct, daily, 10.00am - 6.00pm.
Admission: Adult £2.00, Child 50p, Family £4.50, Conc £1.50, Groups of 11 plus 10% discount.

DRYBURGH ABBEY   **Tel:** 01835 822381

St Boswells, Melrose.
Owner: Historic Scotland   **Contact:** Assistant Curator
The ruins of Dryburgh Abbey are remarkably complete. The burial place of Sir Walter Scott and Field Marshal Earl Haig. Perhaps the most beautiful of all the Border Abbeys.
Location: 8m SW of Peebles on B712.
Opening Times: Summer Hours: 1 Apr - 30 Sept, Mon - Sat, 9.30am - 6.30pm (last admission 6.00pm). Winter Hours: Mon - Sat, 2.00pm - 4.30pm (last Admission 4.00pm).
Admission: 9.30am - 4.30pm (last admission 4.00pm). Sun.

DUNS CASTLE

OPEN

Not open to the public except by arrangement and for individuals, groups and companies for day or residential stays. Available all year.

Tel: 01361 883211
Tel: 01361 882015

DUNS, BERWICKSHIRE TD11 3NW
Owner: Alexander Hay of Duns   Contact: Mrs Aline Hay

This historical 1320 peel tower has been home to the Hay family since 1696, and the current owners Alexander and Aline Hay offer it as a welcoming venue for individuals, groups and corporate guests to enjoy. They have renovated it to produce highest standards of comfort while retaining all the character of its rich period interiors. Wonderful lakeside and parkland setting.
Location: 10 miles off the A4. Rail: Berwick station 16 miles.
            Airports: Newcastle & Edinburgh, 1 hour.
Admission: Rates for private & corporate visits, weddings, filming by arrangement.

FLOORS CASTLE   **See Page 228 for full page entry.**

HERMITAGE CASTLE   **Tel:** 013873 76222

Liddesdale, Newcastleton.
Owner: Historic Scotland   **Contact:** The Earl Of Bothwell
Eerie fortress at the heart of the bloodiest events in the history of the Borders. Mary Queen of Scots made her famous ride here to visit her future husband. Consists of four towers and connecting walls outwardly almost perfect.
Opening Times: Summer Hours: 1 Apr - 30 Sept, Mon - Sat, 9.30am - 6.30pm (last admission 6.00pm). Winter: closed Mon - Fri. Sat 9.30am - 4.30pm (last admission 4.00pm). Sun 2.00pm - 4.30pm (last admission 4.00pm).
Admission: Adult £1.20, Conc £75p, Child 75p.

JEDBURGH ABBEY   **Tel:** 01835 63925

Jedburgh.
Owner: Historic Scotland   **Contact:** The Administrator
A majestic building founded by David I and The Bishop Of Glasgow in 1138. West front has fine rose window known as St Catherine's Wheel. Richly carved Norman doorway.
Location: In Liddesdale. 5¹/2m NE of Newcastleton.
Opening Times: Summer: 1 Apr - 30 Sept, Mon - Sat, 9.30am - 6.30pm (last admission 6.00pm). Sun 2.00pm - 4.30pm (last Admission 4.00pm). Winter: 1 Oct - 31 Mar, Mon - Sat, 9.30am - 4.30pm (last admission 4.00pm). Sun 2.00pm - 4.30pm (last admission 4.00pm).
Admission: Adult £2.50, Conc £1.50, Child £1.00.

MANDERSTON   **See Page 229 for full page entry.**

Traquair, Peeblesshire

MELLERSTAIN HOUSE

OPEN

Easter weekend
(Fri - Mon)

May, June and Sept
Wednesdays,
Fridays, and
Sundays only.

July and August
Daily except
Saturdays

12.30 - 5.00pm

Tel: 01573 410225

MELLERSTAIN, GORDON, BERWICKSHIRE TD3 6L9
Owner: The Earl Haddington   *Contact:* Mrs. F. Turnbull

One of Scotland's great Georgian houses and a unique example of the work of the Adam family; the two wings built in 1725 by William Adam, the large central block by his son, Robert 1770-78. Rooms contain fine plasterwork, colourful ceilings and marble fireplaces. The Library is considered as Robert Adam's finest creation. Many fine paintings and period furniture.

Location: From Edinburgh A68 to Earlston, turn left 5 miles, signposted.
Admission: Adult £3.50, OAP £3.00, Child £1.50. Groups (Min. 20) £3.00.

MELROSE ABBEY
Tel: 01896 822562

Melrose.
Owner: Historic Scotland   **Contact:** The Administrator
Its 14th to 16th century remains retain a unique elegance. Said to be the burial place of Robert The Bruce's Heart. Founded around 1136 as a Cistercian Abbey by David I.
Location: Melrose.
Opening Times: Summer Hours: 1 Apr - 30 Sept, Mon - Sat, 9.30am - 6.30pm (last admission 6.00pm). Winter Hours: Mon - Sat, 2.00pm - 4.30pm (last Admission 4.00pm).
Admission: Adult £2.50, Conc £1.50, Child £1.00. Prices include audio tour.

MERTOUN GARDENS
Tel: 01835 823236   **Fax:** 01835 822474

St Boswells, Melrose, Roxburgh, TD6 OEA.
Owner: The Duke of Sutherland   **Contact:** Miss Miller
20 acres of beautiful grounds. Walled garden and well preserved circular dovecote.
Location: Entrance off B6404 2m NE of St Boswells.
Opening Times: Summer Hours: 1 Apr - 30 Sept, Mon - Sat, 9.30am - 6.30pm (last admission 6.00pm). Winter Hours: Mon - Sat, 2.00pm - 4.30pm (last Admission 4.00pm).
Admission: Adult £1.00, Child 50p, Groups by arrangement.

PRIORWOOD GARDEN
Tel: 0189 682 2493

Melrose, TD6 9PX.
Owner: National Trust for Scotland   **Contact:** Catherine Ross
A garden which specialises in flowers suitable for drying.
Location: Off A6091, in Melrose, adjacent to Abbey.
Opening Times: 1 Apr - 24 Dec, Mon - Sat, 10.00am - 5.30pm, Sun 1.30pm - 5.30pm. NTS Shop: 9 Jan - 31 Mar, Mon - Sat, 12.00pm - 4.00pm; 1 Apr - 24 Dec, Mon - Sat, 10.00am - 5.30pm, Sun 1.30pm - 5.30pm (closed 30 Oct - 6 Nov for stocktaking).
Admission: £1.00 (honesty box).

ROBERT SMAIL'S PRINTING WORKS
Tel: 01896 830206

7/9 High Street, Innerleithen, EH44 6HA.
Owner: National Trust for Scotland   **Contact:** Edward Nicol
Location: High Street, Innerleithen, 30m S of Edinburgh.
Opening Times: Good Fri (14 Apr) - 22 Oct, Mon - Sat, 10.00am - 1.00pm and 2 - 5.00pm, Sun 2 - 5.00pm (last admission 45 mins before closing, morning and afternoon).
Admission: Adult £2.00, Child £1.00, Adult party £1.60, school 80p. Groups by prior appointment only.

SMAILHOLM TOWER
Tel: 01573 460365

Smailholm, Kelso.
Owner: Historic Scotland   **Contact:** The Administrator
Set on a high rocky knoll this well preserved 16th century tower houses an exhibition of tapestries and costume dolls depicting characters from Sir Walter Scott's 'Minstrelsy of the Scottish Borders'.
Location: Smailholm, Kelso.
Opening Times: Summer: 1 Apr - 30 Sept, Mon - Sat, 9.30am - 6.30pm (last Admission 6.00pm). Sun 2.00pm - 6.30pm (last Admission 6.00pm). Winter: Closed.
Admission: Adult £1.50, Conc £1.00, Child 75p.

TRAQUAIR
See Page 230 for full page entry.

THE HIRSEL GARDENS
Tel: 01890 882965   **Fax:** 01890 882834

Coldstream, Berwickshire, TD12 4LP.
Owner: Lord Home of the Hirsel   **Contact:** Hirsel Estate Office
Wonderful spring flowers and rhododendrons. Homestead museum.
Location: Immediately W of Coldstream off A697.
Opening Times: Grounds open every day of the year, daylight hours. Museum and Craft Shop open 10.00am - 5.00pm weekdays, 12.00pm - 5.00pm w/e.
Admission: Adult £1.00, Child free, Groups 75p pp.

PAXTON HOUSE

OPEN

Good Fri - 31 Oct.

Daily

Noon - 5.00pm

Last tour of
House
4.15pm.

Tel: 01289 386291
Fax: 01289 386660

BERWICK-UPON-TWEED TD15 1SZ
Owner: Paxton Trust   *Contact:* Kenneth Scotland

Built in 1756 by John and James Adam for Patrick Home of Billie, Paxton House is a fine example of an 18th century Neo-Palladian mansion. A later picture gallery has been completely restored and is now exhibiting pictures on loan from the National Galleries of Scotland. The House and Picture Gallery were furnished respectively by Chippendale and Trotter and many examples of their furniture are on display.
Location: 5 miles west of Berwick-upon-Tweed on B6461, situated on the north bank of the River Tweed.
Admission: Adult £3.50, Child £1.75.

THIRLESTANE CASTLE

OPEN

Easter 12 - 19 April

1 May - 30 Sept
Sun, Mon, Wed, Thur
afternoons
from 2.00pm
Last Admission
4.30pm

July & Aug.
every afternoon
except Sat.

Tel: 01578 722430
Fax: 01578 722761

THIRLESTANE, LAUDER, BERWICKSHIRE TD2 6RU
Owner: Thirlestane Castle Trust   *Contact:* Peter Jarvis

One of Scotland's oldest and finest castles standing in lovely Border countryside. Thirlestane was the seat of the Earls and Dukes of Lauderdale and is still home to the Maitland family. Unsurpassed 17th century ceilings, fine portrait collection, large collection of historic toys, country life exhibitions. Tearoom, gift shop, woodland walks. ASVA commended. MGC Registered. State rooms available for functions.
Location: Off A68 at Lauder, 28 miles south of Edinburgh.
Admission: Adult £3.50, Family £9.00. Party £3.00. Grounds only £1.00

ARBIGLAND GARDENS

OPEN

1 May - 30 Sept.

Tues - Sun
plus Bank Holiday
Mondays
2.00 - 6.00pm

House open
Sat 20 May -
Mon 29 May
and by
appointment.

Tel: 01387 88283

KIRKBEAN, DUMFRIES & GALLOWAY DG3 4DX

Owner: Capt. and Mrs Beauchamp Blackett   *Contact: Capt. and Mrs Beauchamp Blackett*

Formal wooded and water gardens which have evolved through three centuries. The ideal family outing garden as the gardens run down to a sheltered sandy bay where the younger members (and dogs) can let off steam. 400 yards from the John Paul Jones Birthplace Museum, whose father created the gardens circa 1750.

Location: 15 miles from Dumfries off A710 'Solway Coast Road'.

Admission: Adult £2.00, OAP £1.50, Youngsters 50p, Toddlers Free.

BROUGHTON HOUSE   **Tel:** 01557 30437

12 High Street, Kirkcudbright, DG6 4JX

Owner: National Trust for Scotland   **Contact:** Mrs F Scott

Georgian town mansion, former home of the artist, Edward Hornel. Today a museum and art gallery.

Location: A711 / A75 in Kirkcudbright.

Opening Times: 1 Apr - 22 Oct, 1.00pm - 5.30pm. Last admission 4.45pm.

Admission: Adult £2.00, Child £1.00, Conc £1.00, Pre-booked groups of 20 plus £1.60, Schools 80p.

CAERLAVEROCK CASTLE   **Tel:** 01387 77244

Dumfries.

Owner: Historic Scotland   **Contact:** The Administrator

Caerlaverock (Lark's Nest) is everyone's idea of a medieval fortress. Its most remarkable features are the twin-towered Gatehouse and the Nithsdale Lodging. A splendid Renaissance Range dating from 1638. The scene of two famous sieges. This moated castle has a children's adventure park and model siege engine in its grounds.

Opening Times: Summer: 1 Apr - 30 Sept, Mon - Sat, 9.30am - 6.30pm (last admission 6.00pm). Sun 2.00pm - 6.30pm (last Admission 6.00pm). Winter: 1 Oct - 31 Mar, Mon - Sat, 9.30am - 4.30pm (last admission 4.00pm). Sun 2.00pm - 4.30pm (last admission 4.00pm).

Admission: Adult £2.00, Conc £1.25, Child 75p.

CARDONESS CASTLE   **Tel:** 01387 77244

Gatehouse of Fleet.

Owner: Historic Scotland   **Contact:** The Administrator

The well preserved ruin of a four storey tower house of 15th century date standing on a rocky platform above the Water of Fleet. It is the ancient home of the McCullochs. Very fine fire places.

Opening Times: Summer: 1 Apr - 30 Sept, Mon - Sat, 9.30am - 6.30pm (last admission 6.00pm). Sun 2.00pm - 6.30pm (last admission 6.00pm). Winter: Closed Mon - Fri. Sat 9.30am - 4.30pm. Sun 2.00pm - 4.30pm. Last admission 4.00pm.

Admission: Adult £1.20, Conc 75p, Child 75p.

CARLYLE'S BIRTHPLACE   **Tel:** 01576 300666

The Arched House, Ecclefechan, Lockerbie, DG11 3DG.

Owner: National Trust for Scotland   **Contact:** Mr Ross Walters

The 18th century arched house in which Thomas Carlyle, famous writer and philosopher, was born in 1795. Contains personal possessions and manuscript letters. (Bi-centenary commemoration in December 1995).

Location: Off M74, on A74, in Ecclefechan, 5^1/2m SE of Lockerbie.

Opening Times: Good Fri (14 Apr) - 30 Sept, for opening times ring 01576 300666. Other times by appointment.

Admission: Adult £1.50, Child 80p, Party £1.20, School 60p.

CARSLUITH CASTLE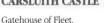

Gatehouse of Fleet.

Owner: Historic Scotland   **Contact:** The Administrator

The delightful and well-preserved ruin of a Tower House of 16th century date with 18th century ranges of out-houses reminding the visitor that such houses were originally linked to out-buildings. One of its owners was the last Abbot of Sweetheart Abbey.

CASTLE KENNEDY GARDENS

OPEN

1 April - 30 Sept.

Daily
10.00am - 5.00pm

Gardens only

Tel: 01776 702024
Fax: 01776 706248

STAIR ESTATES, REPHAD, STANRAER, DUMFRIES & GALLOWAY DG9 8BX

Owner: Lochinch Heritage Estate   *Contact: Estate Office*

Outstanding garden in south west Scotland. Set between two lochs in beautiful countryside. These extensively landscaped gardens extend over 70 acres between the ruined Castle Kennedy and Lochinch Castle, the home of the Earl of Stair. Famous for Rhododendrons, Embothriums and Azaleas, many from original stock. Terraces and mounds built by man and horse provide spectacular views above gardens and water.

Location: 5 miles east of Stranraer on A75 Dumfries-Stranraer road.

Admission: Adult £2.00, OAP £1.50, Child. £1.00. 20% reduction for groups of 20+

DRUMLANRIG CASTLE   **Tel:** 01848 330248/331555

Thornhill, Dumfrieshire, DG3 4AQ.

Owner: The Duke of Buccleuch and Queensbury   **Contact:** A Fisher

Unique example of late 17th century Renaissance architecture in pink sandstone. Louis XIV furniture and paintings by Rembrandt, Leonardo da Vinci, Holbein, Murillo and many others.

Location: 18m N of Dumfries on A76.

Opening Times: May - Aug. Castle closed Thur. Verify times with administrator.

DUNDRENNAN ABBEY   **Tel:** 01557 5262

Kirkcudbright.

Owner: Historic Scotland   **Contact:** The Administrator

Mary Queen Of Scott's spent her last night on Scottish soil in this Cistercian Abbey founded by David I. The Abbey stands in a small and secluded valley. Built in the second half of the 12th century.

Opening Times: Summer: 1 Apr - 30 Sept, Mon - Wed, 9.30am - 6.30pm. Thur 9.30am - 12.00pm. Fri Closed. Sat 9.30am - 6.30pm. Sun 2.00pm - 6.30pm. Last admission half an hour before closing. Winter: closed.

Admission: Adult £1.20, Conc 75p, Child 75p.

GALLOWAY HOUSE GARDENS   **Tel:** 01988 600680

Garlieston, Newton Stewart, Wigtownshire, DG8 8HF.

Owner: Galloway House Gardens Trust   **Contact:** D Marshall

Location: 15m S of Newton Stewart on B7004.

Opening Times: 1 Mar - 31 Oct: 9.00am - 5.00pm.

Admission: Adult £1.00, Child 50p, Family £2.50, Conc 50p.

GLENLUCE ABBEY   **Tel:** 01581 3541

Glenluce.

Owner: Historic Scotland   **Contact:** The Administrator

A Cistercian Abbey Founded In 1190. The remains include a handsome 15th century Chapter House.

Opening Times: Summer: 1 Apr - 30 Sept, Mon - Sat, 9.30am - 6.30pm. Sun 2.00pm - 6.30pm. Winter: Closed Mon - Fri. Sat 9.30am - 4.30pm. Sun 2.00pm - 4.30pm. Last admission half an hour before closing.

Admission: Adult £1.20, Conc 75p, Child 75p.

 HISTORIC HOUSES ASSOCIATION   THE NATIONAL TRUST FOR SCOTLAND   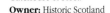 HISTORIC SCOTLAND

LOGAN BOTANIC GARDEN

Tel: 01776 860333   **Fax:** 01776 8602313

Port Logan, Stranraer, Wigtonshire, DG9 9ND.

Owner: Royal Botanic Gardens, Edinburgh.   **Contact:** B Unwin

A Cistercian Abbey Founded In 1190. The remains include a handsome 15th century Chapter House.

Opening Times: 15 Mar - 31 Oct, daily, 10.00am - 6.00pm.

Admission: Adult £2, Child 50p, Family £4.50, Conc £1.50, Groups 11 + 10% discount.

MACLELLAN'S CASTLE

Tel: 01557 31856

Kirkcudbright.

Owner: Historic Scotland   **Contact:** The Administrator

A handsome castellated mansion, built in 1577 using stone from an adjoining ruined monastery by the then Provost. Elaborately planned with fine architectural details it has been a ruin since 1752.

Opening Times: Summer: 1 Apr - 30 Sept, Mon - Sat, 9.30am - 6.30pm. Sun 2.00pm - 6.30pm. Winter: 1 Oct - 31 Mar, Mon - Fri, closed. Sat 9.30am - 4.30pm. Sun 2.00pm - 4.30pm. Last admission half an hour before closing.

Admission: Adult £1.20, Conc 75p, Child 75p.

MAXWELTON HOUSE

MONIAIVE, THORNHILL, DUMFRIES & GALLOWAY DG3 4DX

Owner: Maxwelton House Trust

Contact: Roderick Stenhouse

Tel: 018482 384 or 018482 385

The birthplace of Annie Laurie made famous by the well loved ballad. Glencairn Castle now Maxwelton House dates back to 1370, the home of the Earls of Glencairn. Stephen Laurie bought Glencairn Castle in 1611 and changed the name to Maxwelton. Annie Laurie was born here in 1682. The Laurie family remained in possession until 1968 when Mr and Mrs Hugh Stenhouse bought it and carried out one of the largest restorations to a private house within Scotland. The restoration took three years and the continuing labour of no less than 65 men. It was completed in 1972. House, Museum, Chapel, Garden Tearoom, Gift Shop. Free parking.

Location: Entrances on B729 near Wallaceton or A702 near Penpont.

OPEN

Easter - end Sept: Daily 10.30am - 5.30pm
Group Bookings Welcome

SWEETHEART ABBEY

Tel: 01387 85397

New Abbey Village.

Owner: Historic Scotland   **Contact:** The Administrator

Cistercian abbey founded in 1273 by Devorgilla, in memory of her husband John Balliol. The principal feature is the well preserved precinct wall enclosing 30 acres. She also founded Balliol College, Oxford.

Opening Times: Summer: 1 Apr - 30 Sept, Mon - Sat, 9.30am - 6.30pm. Sun 2.00pm - 6.30pm. Winter: 1 Oct - 31 Mar, Mon - Wed, 9.30am - 4.30pm. Thur 9.30am - 12.00pm. Fri closed. Sat 9.30am - 4.30pm. Sun 2.00pm - 4.30pm. Last admissions half an hour before closing time.

Admission: Adult £1.50, Conc £1.00, Child 75p.

THREAVE CASTLE

Tel: 01831 168512

River Dee.

Owner: Historic Scotland   **Contact:** The Administrator

Built by Archibald the Grim in the late 14th century, early stronghold of the Black Douglases. Round its base is an artillery fortification built before 1455 when the castle was besieged by James II. Ring the bell and the custodian will come to ferry you over. Long walk to property.

Location: Situated on an island on the River Dee.

Opening Times: Summer: 1 Apr - 30 Sept, Mon - Sat, 9.30am - 6.30pm. Sun 2.00pm - 6.30pm. Last admission half an hour before closing. Winter: closed.

Admission: Adult £1.50, Conc £1.00, Child 75p. Charges include ferry trip.

THREAVE GARDEN & ESTATE

OPEN

All Year. Daily
Garden:
9.30am - Sunset
Walled Garden &
Glasshouses:
9.30am - 5.00pm

1 Apr - 22 Oct
Daily
Visitor Centre, Shop
and Display:
9.30 - 5.30pm
Restaurant:
10.00am - 5.00pm

Tel: 01556 502575
Fax: 01556 502683

CASTLE DOUGLAS, DUMFRIES & GALLOWAY DG7 1RX

Owner: National Trust for Scotland   *Contact:* Bill Hean, Administrator

Extensive garden provides interest and colour throughout the year, with special spectacle of over 200 varieties of daffodil in spring. Exhibition on international plant collectors, video programme, visitors centre, shop, plant sales and restaurant.

Location: 1 mile west of Castle Douglas, off A75.

Admission: Adult £3.50, Concession £1.80, Parties £2.80, Schools £1.40.

WHITHORN PRIORY

Tel: 01988 500700

Whithorn.

Owner: Historic Scotland   **Contact:** The Administrator

The site of the first Christian church in Scotland. Founded as 'Candida Casa' by St Ninian in the early 5th century it later became the cathedral church of Galloway. In the museum is a fine collection of early Christian stones including the Monreith Cross.

Opening Times: Summer: 1 Apr - 30 Sept, Mon - Sat, 9.30am - 6.30pm. Sun 2.00pm - 6.30pm. Winter: Closed Mon - Fri. Sat 9.30am - 4.30pm. Sun 2.00pm - 4.30pm. Last admission half an hour before closing.

Admission: Adult £2.70, Conc £1.70, Family £7.50. Reduced charge to Priory and Museum at weekends.

ABERDOUR CASTLE

Tel: 01383 860519

Aberdour, Fife.

Owner: Historic Scotland   **Contact:** The Administrator

A 14th century castle built by the Douglas family. The gallery on the first floor gives an idea of how it was furnished at the time. The castle has a 14th century tower extended in the 16th and 17th centuries, and a delightful walled garden and a circular dovecote.

Location: Aberdour.

Opening Times: Summer: 1 Apr - 30 Sept, Mon - Sat, 9.30am - 6.30pm. Sun 2.00pm - 6.30pm. Winter: 1 Oct - 31 Mar, Mon, Tues, Wed, and Sat, 9.30am - 4.30pm. Thur 9.30am - 12.00pm. Fri closed. Sun 2.00pm - 4.30pm. Last admission half an hour before closing.

Admission: Adult £1.50, Conc £1.00, Child 75p.

CALLENDAR HOUSE

OPEN

Jan - Dec
Mon - Sat
10.00am - 5.00pm

April - Sept.
Sundays
2.00 - 5.00pm

Open on
public holidays
Apr - Sept.

Tel: 01324 612134

CALLENDAR PARK, FALKIRK FK1 1YR

Owner: *Falkirk District Council*   **Contact:** *Mrs L. Anderson*

Imposing mansion within attractive parkland with a 900 year history. Facilities include a working kitchen of 1825 where costumed interpreters carry out daily chores including cooking based on 1820's recipes. Exhibition area, "Story of Callendar House" plus two contemporary galleries with regularly changing exhibitions. There is also a history research centre, gift shop and Georgian Teashop at the Stables.

Location: To the east of Falkirk Town Centre on Callendar Road (A803).

Admission: Adult £1.60, OAP's and Children 80p.

CAMBO GARDENS

Tel: 01333 450313   **Fax:** 01333 450987

Cambo Estate, Kingsbarns, St Andrews, Fife, KY16 8QD.

Owner: Peter Erskine Esq   **Contact:** Peter Erskine

Enchanting traditional walled garden in bloom from snowdrops to Autumn crocus. Blossoms, bulbs, lilies and 200 varieties of roses are a speciality. Gardened with joy to make it more fun than fossilised.

Location: 3m N of Crail.

Opening Times: All year - 10.00am - 4.00pm exc. Christmas and New Year.

Admission: Adult £2.00, Child free.

CASTLE CAMPBELL

Tel: 01259 42408

Dollar Glen, Fife And Central.

Owner: Historic Scotland   **Contact:** The Administrator

Known as 'Castle Gloom' this spectacularly sited 15th century fortress was the lowland stronghold of the Campbells. Stunning views from the parapet walk.

Location: At head of Dollar Glen.

Opening Times: Summer: 1 Apr - 30 Sept, Mon - Sat, 9.30am - 6.30pm. Sun 2.00pm - 6.30pm. Winter: 1 Oct - 31 Mar, Mon, Tues, 9.30am - 4.30pm. Thurs 9.30am - 12 noon. Fri closed. Sun 2.00pm - 6.30pm. Last admissions half an hour before closing.

CHARLETON HOUSE

Tel: 01333 340249   **Fax:** 01333 340583

Colinsburgh, KY9 1HG.

Owner: Baron St Clair Bonde

1740s house reputedly by William Adam. 1833 addition of dining room by William Burn. 1905 - 07, addition of saloon and plasterwork by Sir Robert Lorimer.

Location: Colinsburgh.

Opening Times: Sept, 12.00pm - 3.00pm. Admission every 1/2 hour with guided tours only.

Admission: Standard £5.00.

CULROSS PALACE

Tel: 01383 880359

Culross, Kirkcaldy, KY12 8JH.

Owner: National Trust for Scotland   **Contact:** Mrs G Murray

Location: Off A985. 12m W of Forth Bridge.

Opening Times: Palace: Good Fri (14 Apr) - 1 Oct, 11.00am - 5.00pm daily (last admission 4.00pm).Town House & Study: dates as above, 1.30pm - 5.00pm. Groups at other times by appointment. Tea Room (in Bessie Bar Hall), dates as above, 10.30am - 4.30pm.

Admission: Combined ticket (Palace, Study & Town House, including Walkman tour): Adult £3.50, Child £1.80, Adult parties £2.80, Schools £1.40.

DOUNE CASTLE

Tel: 01786 841742

Doune, Fife And Central.

Owner: Earl of Moray (leased to Historic Scotland)

The formidable 14th century courtyard castle was built for the Regent Albany. The striking keep-gatehouse also combines domestic quarters including the splendid Lord's Hall with its carved oak screen, musicians' gallery and double fireplace.

Location: Off A84 at Doune. 8m NW of Stirling.

Opening Times: Summer: 1 Apr - 30 Sept, Mon - Sat, 9.30am - 6.30pm. Sun 2.00pm - 6.30pm. Winter: 1 Oct - 31 Mar, Mon, Tues, 9.30am - 4.30pm. Thurs 9.30am - 12.00pm. Fri closed. Sun 2.00pm - 4.30pm. Last admissions half an hour before closing.

DUNBLANE CATHEDRAL

Tel: 01786 823388

Dunblane, Fife And Central.

Contact: The Administrator

One of Scotland's noblest medieval churches. The lower part of the tower is Romanesque but the larger part of the building is of the 13th century. It was restored in 1889 - 93 by Sir Rowand Anderson.

Location: In Dunblane.

Admission: Free.

DUNFERMLINE ABBEY

Tel: (not shown)

Dunfermline, Fife And Central.

Owner: Historic Scotland   **Contact:** The Administrator

The remains of the Benedictine abbey founded by Queen Margaret in the 11th century. The foundations of her church are under the 12th century Romanesque style nave. Robert the Bruce was buried in the choir. Substantial parts of the Abbey buildings remain including the vast refectory.

Location: In Dunfermline.

Opening Times: Summer: 1 Apr - 30 Sept, Mon - Sat, 9.30am - 6.30pm. Sun 2.00pm - 6.30pm. Winter: 1 Oct - 31 Mar, Mon, Tues, 9.30am - 4.30pm. Thur 9.30am - 12 noon. Fri closed. Sun 2.00pm - 4.30pm. Last admission half an hour before closing.

FALKLAND PALACE AND GARDEN

Tel: 01337 857397

Falkland, Fife, KY7 7BU.

Owner: HM The Queen   **Contact:** Veronica Woodman

Location: A912, 11m N of Kirkcaldy.

Opening Times: Palace/garden: 1 Apr - 22 Oct, Mon - Sat, 11.00am - 5.30pm., Sun 1.30pm - 5.30pm (last admission to Palace 4.30pm, garden 5.00pm). Groups at other times by appointment. Town Hall, by appointment only.

Admission: Palace & Garden only: Adult £4.00, Child £2.00, Adult parties £3.20, Schools £1.60 (these charges include entrance to Town Hall Exhibition). Garden only: Adult £2.00, Child £1.00. Scots Guards and members of the Scots Guards' Association (wearing the Association's badge) admitted free.

HILL OF TARVIT MANSION HOUSE

Tel: 01334 53127

Cupar, Fife, KY15 5PB.

Owner: National Trust for Scotland   **Contact:** Angela Henderson

House, remodelled in 1906 by Lorimer. Notable collection of pictures and furniture.

Location: Off A916, 2$\frac{1}{2}$m S of Cupar.

Opening Times: Good Fri (14 Apr) - 22 Oct, daily 1.30pm - 5.30pm (last admission 4.45pm). Garden & Grounds: all year, daily 9.30am - sunset.

Admission: House/Garden: Adult £3.00, Child £1.50, Adult party (20+) £2.40, School £1.20. Garden only: £1.00 (honesty box).

INCHCOLM ABBEY

Tel: 01383 823332

Aberdour, Fife And Central.

Owner: Historic Scotland   **Contact:** The Administrator

Known as the 'Iona of the East'. This is the best preserved group of monastic buildings in Scotland, founded in 1123. Includes 13th century octagonal chapter house.

Location: On Island in Firth of Forth. Opposite Aberdour.

Opening Times: Summer: 1 Apr - 30 Sept, Mon - Sat, 9.30am - 6.30pm. Sun 2.00pm - 6.30pm. Last admissions half an hour before closing. Winter: Closed.

Admission: Adults £2.00, Conc £1.25, Child £1.00. Additional charge for ferry.

INCHMAHOME PRIORY

Tel: 01877 385294

Lake of Menteith, Port of Menteith, Fife And Central.

Owner: Historic Scotland   **Contact:** The Administrator

A beautifully situated Augustian priory on an island in the Lake of Menteith founded in 1238 with much of the building surviving. The five year old Mary Queen of Scots was sent here for safety in 1547.

Location: 4 m E of Aberfoyle.

Opening Times: Summer: 1 Apr - 30 Sept, Mon - Sat, 9.30am - 6.30pm. Sun 2.00pm - 6.30pm. Winter: closed.

Admission: Adult £2.00, Conc £1.25, Child 75p. Charge includes ferry trip.

KELLIE CASTLE

Tel: 01330 720271

Pittenweem, Fife, KY10 2RF.

Owner: National Trust for Scotland   **Contact:** The Administrator

Good example of Scottish 16th and 17th century domestic architecture. Victorian walled garden.

Location: On B9171, 3m NW of Pittenweem

Opening Times: Castle: Good Fri (14 Apr) - 22 Oct, daily 1.30pm - 5.30pm (last admission 4.45pm). Garden/Grounds: all year, daily 9.30am - sunset.

Admission: Castle/Garden: Adult £3.00, Child £1.50, Adult party (20+) £2.40, School £1.20. Garden only: £1.00 (honesty box).

SCOTLAND'S SECRET BUNKER

Tel: 01333 310301   **Fax:** 01333 312040

Troywood, St Andrews, KY16 8QH.

     Contact: Dr J Fox

Set 100ft under ground is the secret bunker where the Government would have gone in the event of a nuclear war. Operations room. Cinemas. Restaurants. An unique day out for the family.

Location: Off the B940, 6m S of St Andrews. Thistle signs.

Opening Times: Good Fri to 31 Oct, 11.00am - 6.00pm. Last admissions at 5.00pm.

Admission: Adult £4.00, Conc £3.00, Family £11.00, Tours £5.00, Evening curator's tours by arrangement £5.00 per person.

ST ANDREW'S CASTLE

Tel: 01334 77196

St Andrews, Fife And Central.

Owner: Historic Scotland   **Contact:** The Administrator

The ruins of the castle of the Archbishops of St Andrews. An exhibition in the visitor centre brings the history of the castle and the cathedral to life.

Opening Times: Summer: 1 Apr - 30 Sept, Mon - Sat, 9.30am - 6.30pm. Sun 2.00pm - 6.30pm. Winter: 1 Oct - 31 Mar, Mon - Sat, 9.30am - 4.30pm. Sun 2.00pm - 4.30pm. Last admissions half an hour before closing.

Admission: Adult £2.00, Conc £1.25, Child 75p. Joint entry ticket for St Andrews Castle with St Andrews Cathedral: Adult £3.00, Conc £1.75, Child £1.00.

ST ANDREW'S CATHEDRAL

Tel: 01334 72563

St Andrews, Fife And Central.

     Contact: The Administrator

The remains still give a vivid impression of the scale of what was once the largest cathedral in Scotland along with the associated domestic ranges of the priory. The precinct walls are particularly well preserved. Climb St Rule's Tower for a magnificent view of the town and visit the Cathedral's collection of Celtic and medieval carved stones and other relics found on the site.

Opening Times: Summer: 1 Apr - 30 Sept, Mon - Sat, 9.30am - 6.30pm. Sun 2.00pm - 6.30pm. Winter: 1 Oct - 31 Mar, Mon - Sat, 9.30am - 4.30pm. Sun 2.00pm - 4.30pm. Last admissions half an hour before closing.

Admission: Adult £1.50, Conc £1.00, Child 75p. Joint entry ticket available for St Andrews Cathedral and St Andrews Castle: Adult £3.00, Conc £1.75, Child £1.00.

STIRLING CASTLE

Tel: 01786 450000

Stirling, Fife And Central.

Owner: Historic Scotland   **Contact:** The Administrator

Considered by many as the grandest of all Scotland's castles. The Castle has strong links with Mary Queen of Scots. She was crowned in the Chapel in 1543 and narrowly escaped death by fire in 1561.

Opening Times: Summer: 1 Apr - 30 Sept, all week, 9.30am - 6.00pm. Winter: 1 Oct - 31 Mar, all week, 9.30am - 5.00pm. Last admission 45 minutes before closing time.

Admission: Adult £3.50, Conc £2.00, Child under 16 £1.00. Parking up to 3 hours, cars £1.00 coaches £1.50.

Leith Hall, Aberdeenshire, Grampian.

BALLINDALLOCH CASTLE
Grantown-on-Spey

CONTACT

Mrs. Clare Russell
Ballindalloch Castle
Grantown-on-Spey
Banffshire
AB37 9AX

Tel: (01807) 500206

Fax: (01807) 500210

LOCATION

14 miles north
of Grantown-on-Spey
on A95
22 miles south of
Elgin on A95

BALLINDALLOCH is one of the most beautiful and romantic castles in Scotland. It is first and foremost a much loved family home and has been lived in continuously by its original family, the Macpherson-Grants since 1546. It is set in the magnificent surroundings of the Spey valley and lies in the heart of whisky country with the distilleries of Glenlivet, Glenfarclas and Glenfiddich within ten miles.

Known as the "Pearl of the North" it is a warm and welcoming castle. It exemplifies the transition from the stark Tower house, necessary for survival in 16th century Scotland, to the elegant and comfortable country house so beloved of Victorians in the Highlands. The Castle is filled with family memorabilia and houses a fine collection of 17th century Spanish paintings built up by Sir John Macpherson-Grant in 1850.

Ballindalloch is also the home of the famous Aberdeen-Angus herd of cattle founded by Sir George Macpherson-Grant in 1860 and is the oldest herd in the world.

GARDENS
The Castle is surrounded by beautiful trees and parkland with wonderful walks by the rivers Spey and Avon which run through the grounds. Visitors can relax in the delightful rock garden or walk to the newly renovated walled garden which has been landscaped into a 'Rose and water garden'.

❖

SUITABILITY FOR OTHER EVENTS
Dinners, receptions, filming, product launches, rallies and whisky tasting.

EXTRA FACILITIES
Audio-visual, woodturner, artist/cartoonist, salmon fishing on rivers Spey and Avon, Pheasant and Grouse shooting, Roe stalking.

ADVICE TO COURIERS & DRIVERS
Pre-book if possible. Coach drivers and couriers free. Refreshments in tea shop. No photography/videos inside. Dogs in dog walking area only.

FACILITIES FOR THE DISABLED
Disabled visitors may alight at entrance to castle. Audio visual and 4 rooms in castle. Disabled toilets.

PARKING FOR COACHES AND CARS
200 cars and 4 coaches.

CATERING
Tea room / Light lunches. All home-cooking and baking.

GIFT SHOP
Open at same time as castle selling products from the estate and a range of Scottish goods.

GUIDED TOURS
On request and pre-booked. Room notes in four languages.

GUIDE BOOKS
Colour guide books available.

SCHOOL VISITS / CHILDREN
School visits welcome. Playground and magic drawer for small children.

OPENING TIMES

Summer
Easter - 30th Sept.
Daily
10.00am - 5.30pm.
Last admission 4.45pm.

Winter
Closed.

ADMISSION

Summer

CASTLE & GARDENS
Adult £3.95
Child (5 & under) . . FREE
Child (6 - 16yrs.) . . . £2.00
Disabled £1.50

Groups (min. 12 persons)
Adult £3.50
OAP £3.00

Season Tickets
Per person £5.00

GARDENS ONLY
Per person £1.50

CONFERENCE AND FUNCTION FACILITIES

ROOM	DIMENSIONS	CAPACITY	LAYOUT	POWER POINTS	SUITABLE FOR A/V
Dining Room	30' x 14'	24			

BALMORAL CASTLE (GROUNDS & EXHIBITION)

Tel: 013397 42334   **Fax:** 013397 42471

Balmoral, Ballater, Aberdeenshire, AB35 5TB.

Owner: HM The Queen   **Contact:** Capt J R Wilson

Family holiday home of the Royal Family, bought by Prince Albert in 1852. Grounds and exhibition of paintings and works of art in the Ballroom.

Location: Off A93 between Ballater and Braemar.

Opening Times: 1 May - 31 Jul, Mon - Sat, 10.00am - 5.00pm.

Admission: Adult £2.50, OAPs £2.00, Child under 16 free.

BALLINDALLOCH CASTLE

See page 237 for full page entry.

BALVENIE CASTLE

Tel: 01340 20121

Dufftown.

Owner: Historic Scotland   **Contact:** The Administrator

Picturesque ruins of 13th century moated stronghold originally owned by the Comyns. Visited by Edward I in 1304 and by Mary Queen of Scots in 1562. Occupied by Cumberland in 1746.

Location: Off A93 between Ballater and Braemar.

Opening Times: Summer: 1 Apr - 30 Sept, Mon - Sat, 9.30am - 6.30pm. Sun 2.00pm - 6.30pm. Last admissions half an hour before closing. Winter: closed.

Admission: Adult £1.20, Conc 75p, Child 75p.

BRAEMAR CASTLE

Tel: 03397 41224

Braemar, Aberdeenshire, AB5 4EX.

Owner: Capt A A C Farquharson of Invercauld   **Contact:** Capt Farquharson

Turreted stronghold built in 1628 by the Earl of Mar and burnt by Farquharson of Inverey in 1689. Rebuilt in 1748 when garrisoned by Hanoverian troops. Now a fully furnished family residence.

Location: 1/2 m NE of Braemar.

Opening Times: Easter - Oct, Sat - Thur, 10.00am - 6.00pm.

Admission: Adult £1.90, OAPs/coaches £1.50, Child 90p.

BRODIE CASTLE

Tel: 01309 641371   **Fax:** 01309 641600

Brodie, Forres, Moray, IV36 0TE.

Owner: National Trust for Scotland   **Contact:** Dr S Blackden

Early seat of the Brodies, damaged in 1645 and rebuilt in 17th and 19th centuries. Good French furniture and major collection of paintings.

Location: Off A96, 4¹/₂m W of Forres and 24m E of Inverness.

Opening Times: 14 Apr - 30 Sept, Mon - Sat, 11.00am - 5.30pm. Sun 1.30pm - 5.30pm. 1 - 22 Oct, Sat, 11.00am - 5.30pm. Sun 1.30pm - 5.30pm (last admission 4.30pm). Grounds; All year, 9.30am - sunset.

Admission: Adult £3.50, Child £1.80, Adult parties £2.80, Schools £1.40. Grounds: £1.00 (honesty box).

CASTLE FRASER AND GARDEN

OPEN

Castle:
14 Apr - 30 Jun
1 Sept - 30 Sept
Daily: 1.30 - 5.30
1 Jul - 31 Aug
Daily, 11 am - 5.30pm
1 Oct - 22 Oct
Sat/Sun 1.30 - 5.30
last adm: 4.45pm
Tea room as castle:
but opens 12.15 in Sept

Gardens: All year
Daily, 9.30 - Sunset

Tel: 01330 833463

SAUCHEN, INVERURIE AB51 7LD

Owner: The National Trust for Scotland   *Contact: The Administrator*

One of the 'Castle of Mar' dates from 1575 and incorporates earlier building. The castle comprises a wealth of historic furnishings, paintings and fine embroidery. The Great Hall is regularly used for concerts and other events. The Castle is surrounded by extensive Parkland and has adequate parking. Castle and Grounds available for corporate or private functions.

Location: Off B993, 3 miles south of Kemnay and 16 miles west of Aberdeen.

Admission: Castle: Adult £3.50, Child £1.80, Adult Parties £2.80, Schools £1.40. Garden & Grounds: out with summer season's published opening times), £1.00 (honesty box).

CRATHES CASTLE AND GARDEN

OPEN

Castle, Visitor Centre, Shop, Licensed Restaurant and Plant Sales
1 Apr - 22 Oct
Daily
11.00am - 5.30pm
Last Admission to Castle: 4.45pm
Other times by appointment only.
Gardens & Grounds
All year
Daily 9.30 - Sunset

Tel: 01330 844525

BANCHORY AB31 3QJ

Owner: The National Trust for Scotland   *Contact: The Administrator*

One of the best preserved 16th Century Castles in Scotland with charming furnishings and period painted ceilings. Extensive gardens which cover 3³/₄ acres, noted for unusual plants and considered amongst the finest in Britain. 60 acres of grounds, Adventure Playground and trails are available within the Castle for corporate and private functions. Adequate parking. Tea room, gift shop.

Location: On A93, 3 miles east of Banchory and 15 miles west of Aberdeen.

Admission: Castle, Gardens, Grounds: Adult £4.00, Child £2.00,
Adult Parties £3.20, and Child Parties £1.60.
Grounds only: Adult £1.80, Child 90p.

CORGARFF CASTLE

Tel: 019756 51460

Strathdon.

Owner: Historic Scotland   **Contact:** The Administrator

A 16th century tower house converted into a barracks for Hanoverian troops in 1748. Its last military use was to control the smuggling of illicit whisky between 1827 and 1831. Still complete and with star shaped fortification.

Location: 8m W of Strathdon village.

Opening Times: Summer: 1 Apr - 30 Sept, Mon - Sat, 9.30am - 6.30pm. Sun 2.00pm - 6.30pm. Last admissions half an hour before closing. Winter: closed.

Admission: Adult £2.00, Conc £1.25, Child 75p.

CRAIGIEVAR CASTLE

Tel: 013398 83635

Alford, AB33 8JF.

Owner: National Trust for Scotland   **Contact:** David Mackay

Location: On A980, 6m S of Alford and 26m of Aberdeen.

Opening Times: Castle: 28 Apr - 1 Oct, daily 1.30pm - 5.30pm (last admission 4.45pm). Grounds, all year, daily 9.30am - sunset.

Admission: Castle:Adult £5, Child £2.50, no groups. Grounds: all year, daily 9.30am - Sunset.

CRUICKSHANK BOTANIC GARDEN

Tel: 01224 272704   **Fax:** 01224 272703

St Machar Drive, Aberdeen, Aberdeenshire, AB9 2UD.

Owner: University of Aberdeen   **Contact:** R B Rutherford

Extensive collection of shrubs, herbaceous and alpine plants and trees. Rock and water gardens.

Location: In old arboretum.

Opening Times: All year, Mon - Fri, 9.00am - 4.30pm. May - Sept, Sat and Sun only 2.00pm - 5.00pm.

Admission: Free.

Ballindalloch Castle, Grantown-on Spey, Banffshire.

DELGATIE CASTLE

OPEN

Apr - Oct

11.00am - 5.00pm

Tel: 01888 563479

TURRIFF, ABERDEENSHIRE AB53 8ED

Owner: *Captain Hay of Delgatie*   ***Contact:*** *Mrs. Joan Johnson*

11th century castle. Painted ceilings dated 1592 and 1597. Widest turnpike stair of its kind in Scotland. Lake and woodland walks. Tearoom and shop.

Location: Off A947 Aberdeen to Banff Road.

Admission: Adults £2.50, OAP's & children £1.50

FYVIE CASTLE

OPEN

Castle:
1 Apr - 30 Jun
1 Sept - 30 Sept
Daily, 1.30 - 5.30pm

1 Jul - 31 Aug
Daily, 11 am - 5.30pm

1 - 22 Oct, Sat/Sun
1.30 - 5.30pm
Last adm: 4.45pm
Tearoom as castle, but
open 12.30 when
castle opens 1.30.
Grounds:All year
Daily, 9.30 - sunset

Tel: 01651 891266

FYVIE, NR. TURRIFF AB53 8JS

Owner: *The National Trust for Scotland*   ***Contact:*** *The Administrator*

The five towers of Fyvie Castle enshrine five centuries of Scottish history. The magnificent interior reflects the opulence of the Edwardian era; there is a very important collection of portraits. Two unusual features are a restored American Racquets Court and bowling alley; the Court, Castle and Grounds are available for private and corporate functions. Fully equipped catering kitchen and adequate parking. Tea rom, gift shop.

Location: Off A947, 8 miles SE of Turriff and 25 miles NW of Aberdeen.

Admission: Castle: Adult £3.50. Child £1.80. Grounds: £1.00 (honesty box).
Adult Parties: £2.80, Schools £1.40

DRUM CASTLE

OPEN

Castle:
14 Apr - 30 Jun
1 Sept - 30 Sept
Daily, 1.30 - 5.30

1 Jul - 31 Aug
Daily, 11 am - 5.30pm

1 Oct - 22 Oct
Sat/Sun 1.30 - 5.30
last adm: 4.45pm

Garden:
Good Fri - 22 Oct
Daily , 10am - 6.00pm

Grounds: All year
Daily, 9.30 - Sunset

Tel: 01330 811204

DRUMOAK, BY BANCHORY AB31 3EY

Owner: *The National Trust for Scotland*   ***Contact:*** *The Property Manager*

The most beautiful Castle of Royal Deeside combining a medieval keep, a Jacobean mansion house and a Victorian extension; with a fine collection of paintings and furniture. The grounds contain the walled Garden of Historic Roses and adequate parking. Situated close to Aberdeen the Castle and Grounds are available for corporate and private functions. Tea room, gift shop.

Location: Off A93, 10 miles west of Aberdeen.

Admission: Castle, Garden, Grounds:Adult £3.50, Child £1.80, Adult Parties £2.80, and Schools £1.40. Garden & Grounds: Adult £1.50, Child £80p.
Groups visits must be pre-booked.

HADDO HOUSE

OPEN

14 Apr - 30 Jun
1 Sept - 30 Sept
Daily: 1.30 - 5.30

1 Jul - 31 Aug
Daily, 11am - 5.30pm

1 Oct - 22 Oct
Sat/Sun 1.30 - 5.30
last adm: 4.45pm

Shop, Stables & Restaurant:
1 Apr - 30 Sept
Daily, 11am - 5.30pm

1 Oct - 22 Oct
Sat/Sun 1.30 - 5.30

Garden & Country Park:
All year
Daily, 9.30 - Sunset

Tel: 01651 851440

TARVES, ELLON AB41 0ER

Owner: *The National Trust for Scotland*   ***Contact:*** *The Administrator*

Designed by William Adam in 1731, Haddo House combines Victorian comfort with Georgian elegance. Much of the interior is 'Adam Revival' with fine furniture and ornate plasterwork. The House is bordered by Rose gardens, a country park and has adequate parking. The House and Haddo Hall are available for corporate and private functions; fully equipped catering kitchen.

Location: Off B999, 19 miles N of Aberdeen and 10 miles NW of Ellon.

Admission: Adult £3.50, Child £1.80, Adult Parties £2.80, and Schools £1.40.
Garden (out with summer season's published opening times) £1.00.

DUNNOTTAR CASTLE   **Tel:** 01569 762173

The Lodge, Stonehaven, AB3 2TL.

Contact: P McKenzie

Impressive ruined fortress on rock cliff 160 feet above the sea.

Location: Just off A92.

Opening Times: Easter - Oct, Mon - Sat, 9.00am - 6.00pm. Sun 2.00pm - 5.00pm. Nov - Easter, Mon - Fri, 9.00am - sunset. Closed weekends. Last adm: 30 mins before closing.

Admission: Adult £2.00, Child £1.00. Prices only confirmed up to mid-March.

ELGIN CATHEDRAL   **Tel:** 01343 547171

Elgin.

Owner: Historic Scotland   **Contact:** The Administrator

When entire this was perhaps the most beautiful of Scottish cathedrals, known as the Lantern of the North. 13th century, much modified after almost being destroyed in 1390 by Alexander Stewart, the infamous 'Wolf of Badenoch'. The octagonal chapterhouse is the finest in Scotland. You can see the Bishop's home at Spynie Palace.

Location: 2 m N of the town.

Opening Times: Summer: 1 Apr - 30 Sept, Mon - Sat, 9.30am - 6.30pm. Sun 2.00pm - 6.30pm. Winter: 1 Oct - 31 Mar, Mon, Tues, Wed and Sat, 9.30am - 4.30pm. Thur 9.30am - 12.00pm. Fri closed. Sun 2.00pm - 4.30pm. Last admissions half an hour before closing.

HUNTLY CASTLE   **Tel:** 01466 793191

Huntly.

Owner: Historic Scotland   **Contact:** The Administrator

Known also as Strathbogie Castle, this glorious ruin stands in a beautiful setting on the banks of the River Deveron. Famed for the fine heraldic sculpture and inscribed stone friezes. Beautiful setting.

Location: In Huntly.

Opening Times: Summer: 1 Apr - 30 Sept, Mon - Sat, 9.30am - 6.30pm. Sun 2.00pm - 6.30pm. Winter: 1 Oct - 31 Mar, Mon - Sat, 9.30am - 4.30pm. Thur 9.30am - 12.00pm. Friday closed. Sun 2.00pm - 4.30pm. Last admission half an hour before closing.

Admission: Adult £2.00, Conc £1.25, Child 75p.

KILDRUMMY CASTLE   **Tel:** 019755 71331

Alford, Aberdeenshire, AB33 8RA.

Owner: Historic Scotland   **Contact:** The Administrator

Though ruined, the best example in Scotland of a 13th century castle with a curtain wall, four round towers hall and chapel of that date. The seat of the Earls of Mar, it was dismantled after the first Jacobite rising in 1715.

Location: 10m W of Alford.

Opening Times: Summer: 1 Apr - 30 Sept, Mon - Sat, 9.30am - 6.30pm. Sun 2.00pm - 6.30pm. Winter: 1 Oct - 31 Mar, Mon - Fri closed. Sat 9.30am - 4.30pm. Sun 2.00pm - 4.30pm. Last admissions half an hour before closing.

Admission: Adult £1.50, Conc £1.00, Child 75p.

KILDRUMMY CASTLE GARDEN

Tel: 019755 71203/71277

Kildrummy, Aberdeenshire, AB33 8RA.

Contact: Alastair J Laing

Ancient quarry shrub and alpine gardens renowned for their interest and variety. Water gardens below ruined castle.
Location: On A97 off A944 10m W of Alford.
Opening Times: Apr - Oct, daily, 10.00am - 5.00pm.
Admission: Adult £1.70, Child 50p.

MONYMUSK WALLED GARDEN

Tel: 01467 651 543

Home Farm, Monymusk, Aberdeen, AB51 7HL.
Owner: Mrs M Colman   **Contact:** Mrs M Colman
Mainly herbaceous plants in walled garden setting.
Opening Times: Mar - Oct, Mon - Sat, 10.00am - 5.00pm. Sun 2.00pm - 5.00pm. Nov - Mar, Tues - Fri, 10.00am - 3.00pm.
Admission: Donations welcome.

LEITH HALL

OPEN

House & Tea Room:
Good Fri - 1 Oct
Daily
1.30 - 5.30pm
Last adm: 4.45pm

Garden & Grounds:
All Year
Daily
9.30am - sunset

Tel: 01464 831216

HUNTLY AB54 4HQ

Owner: The National Trust for Scotland   *Contact: The Property Manager*

The mansion house of Leith Hall is at the centre of a 286 acre estate which was the home of the Leith family from 1650, most of whom followed a tradition of military service. There is an outstanding Military Exhibition. With charming Walled Gardens, two lochs and extensive parkland, the Hall and Grounds are available for corporate and private functions. Adequate parking.
Location: Off B9002 1 ml west of Kennethmont & 34 mls north west of Aberdeen.
Admission: House & Grounds: Adult £3.00, Child £1.50, Adult Parties £2.40
Schools £1.20. Gardens and Grounds £1.00 (honesty box).

PITMEDDEN GARDEN

OPEN

Garden, Visitor Centre,
Museum, Grounds and
other facilities
28 Apr - 1 Oct
Daily
10.00am - 5.30pm
Last Adm: 5.00pm

Tel: 01651 872352

ELLON AB41 0PD

Owner: The National Trust for Scotland   *Contact: The Administrator*

A reconstructed 17th Century Garden with floral designs, fountains and sundials. There is also a display of the evolution of the formal garden as well as the Museum of Farming Life.
Location: 14 miles north of Aberdeen on A920 1 mile W of Pitmedden Village.
Admission: Garden & Museum: Adult £3.00, Child £1.50,
Adult Parties £2.40, Schools £1.20.

Batoni's Col Wm. Gordon of Fyvie Castle, Turriff, Aberdeenshire.

SPYNIE PALACE

Tel: 01467 651 543

Elgin.
Owner: Historic Scotland   **Contact:** The Administrator
Spynie Palace was the residence of the bishops of Moray from the 14th century to 1686. The site is dominated by the massive tower built by Bishop David Stewart (1461-77) and affords spectacular views across Spynie Loch.
Location: 2 m N of Elgin off the A941.
Opening Times: Summer: 1 Apr - 30 Sept, Mon - Sat, 9.30am - 6.30pm. Sun 2.00pm - 6.30pm. Winter: 1 Oct - 31 Mar. Mon - Fri closed. Sat 9.30am - 4.30pm. Sun 2.00pm - 4.30pm. Last admissions half an hour before closing.
Admission: Adult £1.20, Conc 75p, Child 75p.

ST MACHAR'S CATHEDRAL

Tel: 01224 485988

Old Aberdeen.   **Contact:** The Administrator
Founded in 1131 on an earlier site, although the main part of this granite building dates from the early 15th century. The West front with its twin towers is notable as is the painted wooden heraldic nave ceiling.
Location: In old Aberdeen.

TOLQUHON CASTLE

Tel: 01651 5286

Aberdeen.
Owner: Historic Scotland   **Contact:** The Administrator
Tolquhon was built for the Forbes family. The early 15th century tower was enlarged between 1584 and 1589 with a large mansion round the courtyard. Noted for its highly ornamented gatehouse and pleasance.
Location: 15 m from Aberdeen off the Pitmedden - Tarves road.
Opening Times: Summer: 1 Apr - 30 Sept, Mon - Sat, 9.30am - 6.30pm. Sun 2.00pm - 6.30pm. Winter: 1 Oct - 31 Mar, Mon - Fri closed. Sat 9.30am - 4.30pm. Sun 2.00pm - 4.30pm. Last admissions half an hour before closing.
Admission: Adult £1.50, Conc £1.00, Child 75p.

CAWDOR CASTLE
Nairn

This splendid romantic castle dating from the late 14th Century was built as a private fortress by the Thanes of Cawdor, and remains the home of the Cawdor family to this day. The ancient medieval tower was built around the legendary holly-tree.

Although the house has evolved over 600 years, later additions mainly of the 17th Century were all built in the Scottish vernacular style with slated roofs over walls and crow-stepped gables of mellow local stone. This style gives Cawdor a strong sense of unity, and the massive, severe exterior belies an intimate interior that gives the place a surprisingly personal friendly atmosphere.

Good furniture, fine portraits and pictures, interesting objects and outstanding tapestries are arranged to please the family rather than to echo fashion or impress. Memories of Shakespeare's 'Macbeth' give Cawdor an elusive, evocative quality that delights visitors.

GARDENS
The Flower Garden has again a family feel to it, where plants are chosen out of affection rather than affectation. This is a lovely spot between spring and late summer. The Wild Garden beside its stream leads into beautiful trails through a spectacular mature mixed woodland, through which paths are helpfully marked and colour-coded.

❖

SUITABILITY FOR OTHER EVENTS
Conferences and day functions

EXTRA FACILITIES
9 hole golf course, putting green, golf clubs for hire. Special arrangements can be made for groups to include lunches, sherry or champagne receptions, whisky tasting, musical entertainments. Specialised garden visits.

ADVICE TO COURIERS & DRIVERS
Two weeks advance notice for group catering. Coach drivers/couriers free. Refreshments or lunch in restaurant. Drivers entered in monthly prize draw. No photography, video photography or tripods inside. No dogs. Parking for 250 cars and 25 coaches.

FACILITIES FOR THE DISABLED
Disabled and elderly visitors may alight at the entrance to the Castle, before parking in the allocated areas. Disabled toilets.

CATERING
The licensed Castle Buttery provides hot meals, snacks and home baking from May to October, capacity 50. Groups should book in advance, Tel: (01667) 404615. Menus on request.

GIFT SHOP
There are three shops open at the same time as Castle. The Gift Shop items include: cashmere, china, leather goods, children's toys, sweets and a wide selection of products made in Scotland, many exclusively for Cawdor Castle. The Book Shop sells a wide and unusual selection of books, prints, stationery and cards. The Wool Shop: the best of

Scottish cashmere, capes, ponchos and a large collection of sweaters and children's clothes including tartans.

GUIDE BOOKS
Colour guide book and room notes. French, German and Japanese translations available,

SCHOOL VISITS/CHILDREN
School groups are welcome £2.50 per child. Room notes, quiz and answer sheet can be provided. Of particular interest: Ranger service and nature trails.

CONTACT

The Secretary
Cawdor Castle
Nairn
Scotland
IV12 5RD

Tel: (01667) 404615

Fax: (01667) 404674

LOCATION

From Edinburgh
A9 3¹/₂ hours,
Inverness 20 minutes,
Nairn 10 minutes.

Main road: A9 14 miles.

Rail: Nairn Station
5 miles.

Bus: Inverness to Nairn
bus route 200 yards.

Taxi: Piperhill Taxis
(01667) 404680.

Air: Inverness Airport
5 miles.

OPENING TIMES

Summer
1 May - 1 October

Daily 10am - 5.30pm

Last admission 5pm.

Winter
2 October - 30 April
Closed

ADMISSION

Summer
HOUSE & GARDEN

Adult £4.50
Child* £2.50
OAP £3.50
Family (2+5) £12.50

Groups (Min 20 people)
Adult £4.00
Child* £2.50

GARDEN ONLY

Adult £2.50
Child* £2.50
OAP £2.50

*Age 5 - 15

CONFERENCE AND FUNCTION FACILITIES

ROOM	DIMENSIONS	CAPACITY	LAYOUT	POWER POINTS	SUITABLE FOR A/V
Cawdor Hall		40 Lunch/Dinner	Boardroom	✓	✓

DUNVEGAN CASTLE
Isle of Skye

DUNVEGAN is unique. It is the only Great House in the Western Isles of Scotland to have retained its family and its roof. It is the oldest home in the whole of Scotland continuously inhabited by the same family - the Chiefs of the Clan Macleod. A Castle placed on a rock by the sea - the curtain wall is dated before 1200 A.D. - its superb location recalls the Norse Empire of the Vikings, the ancestors of the Chiefs.

Dunvegan's continuing importance as a custodian of the Clan spirit is epitomised by the famous Fairy Flag, whose origins are shrouded in mystery but whose ability to protect both Chief and Clan is unquestioned.

To enter Dunvegan is to arrive at a place whose history combines with legend to make a living reality.

GARDENS
The gardens and grounds extend over some ten acres of woodland walks, peaceful formal lawns and a water garden dominated by two spectacular natural waterfalls. The temperate climate aids in producing a fine show of rhododendrons and azaleas, the chief glory of the garden in spring. Always one is aware of the proximity of the sea and many garden walks finish at the Castle Jetty, from where traditional boats make regular trips to view the delightful Seal Colony.

❖

Paul Tomkins

CONTACT

The Administrator
Dunvegan Castle
Isle of Skye
IV55 8WF

Tel: (01470) 521206
Fax: (01470) 521205

LOCATION

1 mile north of village.

From Inverness A82 to Invermoriston, A887 to Kyle of Lochalsh 82 miles. From Fort William A82 to Invergarry, A87 to Kyle of Lochalsh 76 miles.

Kyle of Lochalsh to Dunvegan 45 miles.

Ferry: to the Isle of Skye, 'roll-on, roll-off'; 4 minute crossing.

Rail: Inverness to Kyle of Lochalsh 3/4 trains per day - 45 miles.

Bus: Portree 25 miles, Kyle of Lochalsh 45 miles.

EXTRA FACILITIES
SEAL COLONY. $1/2$ mile from Castle. Boat trips to see seals at frequent intervals from the Castle Jetty. The Seals are generally undisturbed by people in our small boats and are a joy to study and photograph at close quarters. Loch Cruises on 35 seater motor vessel $1\frac{1}{2}$ hours. cruises throughout the day. Also available for charter and fishing trips. Herd of pedigree Highland Cattle.

ADVICE TO COURIERS & DRIVERS
Please park in Coach Park, 150 metres walk from Castle. DO NOT attempt to take passengers to Castle Jetty, it is a further 50 metres walk. Allow at least 1 hour preferably 2. If possible please book in advance, particularly if it is intended to include the Seal Boat Trip. However, this facility is dependant upon the weather and can not be pre-booked. Dogs allowed in grounds only and must be kept on a leash. No photography within Castle. Parking for 120 cars and 10 coaches 150 yards from the Castle.

FACILITIES FOR THE DISABLED
Disabled and elderly visitors may be left at the entrance to the Castle before parking in the allocated areas. Toilets for the disabled.

CATERING
Licensed restaurant. The Castle Restaurant provides snacks and hot meals throughout the season. Seating 70, special rates are offered to groups, menus upon request. Tel: (01470) 521310. Open late at height of season for evening meals.

GUIDED TOURS
Tours available by appointment in English or Gaelic at no extra charge. If requested the owner may meet groups. Average time for tour is 45 minutes.

GIFT SHOPS
2 Gift and Craft Shops, one in car park, the other in the Castle. Shops open 10am-5.30pm seven days a week.

GUIDE BOOKS
Full colour guide book £1.70. Translations in French, German, Spanish, Italian and Japanese.

SCHOOL VISITS/CHILDREN
Groups of children are welcome by arrangement. If requested a guide can be available.

ACCOMMODATION
Dunvegan offers 4 self-catering units, 3 of which sleep 6 and 1 of which sleeps 7.

OPENING TIMES

Summer

20 March - 31 October

Daily 10.00am - 5.30pm
Last entry 5.00pm

Sundays:
GARDENS, CRAFT SHOP & RESTAURANT 10.00am - 5.30pm
CASTLE: 1.00 - 5.30pm
Last entry 5.00pm

Winter
November-March
By appointment.
No boat trips.

ADMISSION

Summer

CASTLE & GARDENS
Adult £4.00
Child (Under 16) . .£2.20
OAP/Student . . .£3.60
Group £3.60

GARDEN ONLY
Adult £2.50
Child (Under 16) . .£1.50

SEAL BOAT TRIP
Adult £3.50
Child (Under 16) . .£2.50

LOCH CRUISES
Adult £6.50
Concessions . . .£4.50

Winter
By appointment.
No Boat Trips.

BISHOP'S & EARL'S PALACES

Tel: 01856 875461

Kirkwall, Orkney.
Owner: Historic Scotland **Contact:** The Administrator
The Bishop's Palace is a 12th century hall-house with a round tower built by Bishop Reid in 1541-48. The adjacent Earl's Palace built in 1607 has been described as the most mature and accomplished piece of Renaissance architecture left in Scotland.
Location: In Kirkwall.
Opening Times: Summer: 1 Apr - 30 Sept, Mon - Sat, 9.30am - 6.30pm. Sun 2.00pm - 6.30pm. Last admissions half an hour before closing time. Winter: closed.
Admission: Adult £1.20, Conc 75p, Child 75p, Joint entry ticket available for all the Orkney monuments: Adult £6.00, Conc £3.50, Child £2.00.

CAWDOR CASTLE

See page 241 for full page entry.

CLAN DONALD CENTRE & ARMADALE GARDENS

Tel: 01471 844275 **Fax:** 01471 844305

Armadale, Isle of Skye, IV45 8RS.
Owner: Clan Donald Lands Trust **Contact:** R McDonald Parker
Part of Armadale Castle houses a visitor centre telling the story of the Macdonalds and the Lord of the Isles. 40 acres 19th century woodland garden.
Location: 1m from Mallaig - Armadale ferry terminal.
Opening Times: Apr - Oct, daily, 9.30am - 5.30pm.
Admission: Adult £3.20, Child £2.20, Conc £2.20, Groups £2.20.

CROMARTY COURTHOUSE

Tel: 01381 600418 **Fax:** 01381 600408

Church Street, Cromarty, IV11 8XA.
Contact: David Alston
18th century village courthouse, visitor centre and museum.
Location: 25m N of Inverness.
Opening Times: Apr - Oct, daily, 10.00am - 6.00pm. Nov - Mar, daily, 12.00pm - 4.00pm.
Admission: Adult £2.75, Child £1.50, Family £7.50, Conc, £1.50, Groups £2.00.

CULLODEN

Tel: 01463 790607

National Trust for Scotland Visitor Centre, Culloden Moor, Inverness, IV1 2ED.
Owner: National Trust for Scotland. **Contact:** Ross Mackenzie
Site of last battle fought on British mainland in 1746. Visitor centre and old Leanoch cottage, now furnished in style of the period.
Location: B9006, 5m E of Inverness.
Opening Times: Site: all year, daily. Visitor Centre: 4 Feb - 31 Mar and 1 Nov - 30 Dec (except 25/26 Dec), daily 10.00am - 4.00pm. 1 Apr - 31 Oct, daily 9.00am - 6.00pm. Restaurant and audio visual show: same dates, but closes 30 mins earlier, and restaurant opens at 10.00am. Shop closed 30 Oct - 5 Nov for stocktaking.
Admission: Visitor Centre, including audio-visual and Old Leanach Cottage: Adult £1.80, Child 90p, Parties of 20 or more (paying as a group): Adult £1.40, School 70p.

DOCHFOUR GARDENS

Tel: 01463 861218

Inverness.
Owner: The Lord Burton **Contact:** Lord Burton
Victorian terraced garden near Inverness with panoramic views over Loch Dochfour. Magnificent specimen trees, naturalised daffodils, rhododendrons, water garden, yew topiary. Integral nursery selling shrubs, herbaceous, alpines.
Location: 6m SW of Inverness on A82 to Fort William.
Opening Times: Mon - Fri all year, Sat & Sun Apr - Oct. House not open.
Admission: Garden Walk - £1.50.

DUNVEGAN CASTLE

See page 242 for full page entry.

EILEEN DONAN CASTLE

Tel: 01599 555202

Dornie, Kyle, Wester, IV40 8DX.
Contact: The Administrator
Picturesque castle on an islet dating back to 1220.
Location: On A87 8m E of Skye Ferry.
Opening Times: 1 Apr - end Oct, 10.00am - 5.30pm.
Admission: Adult £1.50, Child 75p, Group £1.25.

DUNROBIN CASTLE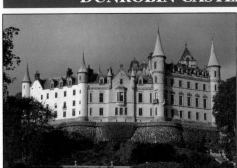

OPEN
14-17 Apr & 1 May
to 15 Oct
Mon - Sat
10.30am -5.30pm
Sun: 1.00 - 5.30pm
(last entry 5.00pm)

Closes 1 hour earlier
in April, May and
October

Tel: 01408 633177
Fax: 01408 634 081

GOLSPIE, SUTHERLAND KW10 6SF
Owner: The Sutherland Trust *Contact: Keith Jones, Curator*
Dates from the 13th century with additions in the 17th, 18th and 19th centuries. Wonderful furniture, paintings, library, ceremonial robes and memorabilia. Tearoom and gift shop. Victorian museum in grounds with a fascinating collection including Pictish stones. Set in fine woodlands overlooking the sea. Magnificent formal gardens, one of few remaining French/Scottish formal parterres.
Location: 50 miles north if Inverness.
Admission: Adult £3.70, OAP £2.30, Child £1.90, Family £9.40.
Groups: Adult £3.50, Child £1.80.

FORT GEORGE

Tel: 01667 462777

Ardersier, Inverness.
Owner: Historic Scotland **Contact:** The Administrator
Completed in 1769 following the Battle of Culloden as a Highland fortress for the army of George II. Fort George is still an active army barracks which houses the Regimental Museum of the Queen's Own Highlanders.
Location: 11m NE of Inverness by the village of Ardersier.
Opening Times: Summer: 1 Apr - 30 Sept, Mon - Sat, 9.30am - 6.30pm. Sun 2.00pm - 6.30pm. Winter: 1 Oct - 31 Mar, Mon - Sat, 9.30am - 4.30pm. Sun 2.00pm - 4.30pm. Last admission 45 minutes before closing time.
Admission: Adult £2.50, Conc £1.50, Child £1.00.

HUGH MILLER'S COTTAGE

Tel: 01381 600245

Cromarty, Rosshire, IV11 8XA.
Owner: National Trust for Scotland **Contact:** Ms Frieda Gostwick
Furnished thatch cottage of c.1711, birthplace of eminent geologist and writer Hugh Miller. Exhibition and video.
Location: Via Kessock Bridge and A832, in Cromarty, 22m NE of Inverness.
Opening Times: 28 Apr - 1 Oct, Mon - Sat, 10am - 1pm and 2 - 5.30pm. Sun 2 - 5.30pm.
Admission: Adult £1.50, Child 80p, Adult party £1.20, School 60p.

INVEREWE GARDEN

Tel: 01445 781200 **Fax:** 01445 781497

Poolewe, Ross-shire, IV22 2LQ.
Owner: National Trust for Scotland **Contact:** Keith Gordon
Plants from many countries flourish in this garden created by Osgood Mackenzie over 130 years ago.
Location: On A832, by Poolewe, 6m NE of Gairloch.
Opening Times: Garden; 1 Apr - 22 Oct, daily, 9.30am - 9.00pm. 23 Oct - 31 Mar, 9.30am - 5.00pm. Visitor Centre & Shop; 1 Apr - 22 Oct, daily, 9.30am - 5.30pm. Licensed Restaurant, same dates, daily 10.00am - 5.00pm. Guided walks with gardener, 1 Apr - 22 Oct, Mon - Fri at 1.30pm.
Admission: Adult £3.50, Child £1.80, Adult party (incl. cruise party) £2.80, School £1.40.

URQUHART CASTLE

Tel: 01456 450551

Loch Ness, Drumnadrochit.
Owner: Historic Scotland **Contact:** The Administrator
The remains of one of the largest castles in Scotland dominate a rocky promontory on Loch Ness. It fell into decay after 1689. Most of the existing buildings date from the 16th century. A popular viewpoint for monster spotting. Splendid views up and down the Loch.
Location: On Loch Ness, nr Drumnadrochit.
Opening Times: Summer: 1 Apr - 30 Sept, Mon - Sat, 9.30am - 6.30pm. Sun 10.00am - 6.30pm. Winter: 1 Oct - 31 Mar, Mon - Sat, 9.30am - 4.30pm. Sun 11.30am - 4.30pm. Last admission sold half an hour before closing.
Admission: Adult £3.00, Conc £2.00, Child £1.00.

DALMENY HOUSE
South Queensferry

DALMENY HOUSE rejoices in one of the most beautiful and unspoilt settings in Great Britain, yet it is only seven miles from Scotland's capital, Edinburgh, fifteen minutes from Edinburgh Airport and less than an hour's drive from Glasgow. It is an eminently suitable venue for group visits, business functions, meetings and special events, including product launches and outdoor activities such as off-road driving.

Dalmeny Estate, the family home of the Earls of Rosebery for over three hundred years, boasts superb collections of porcelain and tapestries, fine paintings by Gainsborough, Raeburn, Reynolds and Lawrence, together with the exquisite Mentmore Rothschild collection of 18th Century French furniture.

There is also the Napoleonic collection, assembled by the Fifth Earl of Rosebery, Prime Minister, historian and owner of three Derby Winners.

The Hall, Library and Dining Room will lend a memorable sense of occasion to corporate receptions, luncheons and dinners. Alternatively, there are the recently-renovated areas of the former kitchen and servants' hall (now named the Rosebery Rooms) and the new Courtyard Restaurant, with facilities specifically designed for business meetings, small conferences, promotions, exhibitions and product launches. A wide range of entertainment can also be provided, from piano recitals to a floodlit pipe band Beating the Retreat.

CONTACT

Mrs Lindsay Morison
Dalmeny House
South Queensferry
West Lothian
EH30 9TQ

Tel: (0131) 331 1888

Fax: (0131) 331 1788

LOCATION

From Edinburgh A90,
B924, 7 mls west.
A90 $^1/_2$ mile.

Bus: From St Andrews
Square to Chapel Gate
1 mile from House.

Rail: Dalmeny Railway
Station 3 miles.

Taxi: Hawes Landing
(0131) 331 1077, Ken
Taylor 031 331 1402.

OPENING TIMES

Summer

May - September

Sundays   1.00 - 5.30pm
Last admission 4.45pm.

Mon, Tues
12 Noon - 5.30pm
Last admission 4.45pm.

Open at other times by
appointment only.

ADMISSION

Summer

Adults £3.50
Students £2.80
Child (10-16) £1.80
OAP £3.00
Groups £2.80
(Min. 20)

SUITABILITY FOR OTHER EVENTS
Fashion shows, product launches, archery, clay pigeon shooting, equestrian events, shows, filming, background photography, small meetings and special events.

EXTRA FACILITIES
Lectures can be arranged on House, contents and family history. Screen and projector can be provided. Helicopter landing area. House is in the centre of a $4^1/_2$ mile shore walk from Forth Rail Bridge at South Queensferry to small foot passenger ferry at Cramond. Walk open throughout the year, ferry 9am - 1pm. 2pm - 7pm summer, 4pm winter and closed Fridays.

ADVICE TO COURIERS & DRIVERS
Fires, picnics, dogs and cameras not permitted.

FACILITIES FOR THE DISABLED
Disabled and elderly visitors may alight at the entrance, before parking in the allocated areas. Disabled toilets.

PARKING FOR COACHES & CARS
Capacity of the car park: 60 cars, 150 yards from the House and 3 coaches, 250 yards from the House. Parking for functions and special groups visits in front of the House.

CATERING
Afternoon tea and light lunches - self service. Cost for catering for functions on application. Groups can book in advance for tea and other meals. Buffets, lunches, dinners can be arranged for conferences and special functions.

GUIDED TOURS
Please apply for details. Guided tours for special interest groups can be arranged outside normal opening hours.

CONFERENCE AND FUNCTION FACILITIES

ROOM	DIMENSIONS	CAPACITY	LAYOUT	POWER POINTS	SUITABLE FOR A/V
Library	10.4 x 7m	20	Informal Meeting		
Dining Room	11.2 x 7.4m	25	Boardroom	4	✓
		30 - 50	Lunch/Dinner		
		80 - 100	Buffet		
Garden Restaurant	12.7 x 9m	120	Theatre	3	✓
		96	Round Tables		
		200	Buffet Receptions		
Rosebery Rooms					
I	9 x 6m	64	Theatre	8	✓
II	6.4 x 6m &	18	Boardroom	8	✓
	4.6 x 3.3m	45	Theatre style or back-projection		
I and II		150	Reception		

HARBURN HOUSE
West Calder

HARBURN HOUSE offers it's guests the perfect alternative to a first class hotel. This privately owned Georgian mansion surrounded by it's own 3000 acre sporting and leisure estate is ideally situated offering unparalleled accessibility.

Harburn is essentially small and very personal. It is therefore frequently taken over exclusively for conferences, incentive travel, training seminars and product launches, etc. In this way guests may enjoy the luxury of a five star hotel, combined with the comfort and privacy of their own home.

A stay at Harburn is essentially a very relaxed and informal affair. The staff are first class and the atmosphere is one of a private house party.

The estate provides the full range of sporting and leisure activities including, golf, game shooting, fishing, clay pigeon shooting, tennis, riding and archery to name but a few. Our guests are automatically members of our local country club and Harburn loch together with "Robinson Island" is a Bar-B-Quer's paradise.

The complete privacy and outstanding scenery, so accessible to the major cities and beauty spots, makes Harburn the ultimate choice for the discerning event or conference organiser.

❖ ─────────────

CONTACT

Rozi Spurway
Harburn House
Harburn
West Calder
West Lothian
EH55 8RN

Tel: (01506) 461818
Fax: (01506) 416591

LOCATION

Almost equidistant between Glasgow and Edinburgh and well within one hour of Perth, Stirling or Dundee and the Border country.

SUITABILITY FOR OTHER EVENTS
Weddings, filming, conferences, activity days, game shooting, product launches.

EXTRA FACILITIES
Any form of leisure facilities available; i.e. Golf, Riding, Fishing, Archery, Buggies, Shooting, Falconry, etc. Also all guests can use the nearby Golf and Country Club.

ACCOMMODATION
Harburn House offers: 8 Double/Twin rooms with bathrooms, 2 Four poster suites and two other units (1 for 8, 1 for 4/6). All with other private facilities.

The House is always exclusive to one party. The grounds are available for almost any leisure pursuit. The bedrooms are available for single or double occupancy. All catering is done by our own staff.

ADVICE TO COURIERS & DRIVERS
Dogs on leads. Follow one way system and 20 mile per hour speed limit. Vehicles should not park on grass verges. Parking for up to 300 cars/coaches 100 yards from house summer, 50 cars/coaches winter.

FACILITIES FOR THE DISABLED.
Ground floor bedroom, dining room and drawing room.

CATERING
High quality in-house catering by our own top chef. Prices and menus on request.

OPENING TIMES

All Year

ADMISSION

The exclusive use of House and Grounds for activity days with no accommodation

Per day £575.00

Accommodation Rates:
   Single with bath . .£78.50

Double with bath . £110.00

Dinner, bed & breakfast
   Single £95.00
   Double (per person) .£78.00

Day Delegate Rate .£27.00

VAT is not included in the above rates

CONFERENCE AND FUNCTION FACILITIES

ROOM	DIMENSIONS	CAPACITY	LAYOUT	POWER POINTS	SUITABLE FOR A/V
Conference Room	30' x 18'	20	Boardroom	6	✓
		20	Lunch/Dinner		
Drawing Room	30' x 18'	30	Schoolroom	10	✓
		20	Boardroom		
		40	Theatre		
Dining Room	30' x 18'	30	Schoolroom	6	✓
		20	Boardroom		
		40	Theatre		
		40	Lunch/Dinner		
Library	14' x 12'	10	Schoolroom	4	✓
		8	Boardroom		
		15	Theatre		
Morning Room	16' x 15'	12	Schoolroom		✓
		12	Boardroom		
		20	Theatre		
WHOLE HOUSE	All above rooms	80	Buffet		
		60	Lunch/Dinner		✓
Marquee	120' x 40' MAX	400	Schoolroom	As required	✓
		500	Buffet		
		500	Theatre		
		400	Lunch/Dinner		

HOPETOUN HOUSE
Edinburgh

HOPETOUN HOUSE, 'Scotland's Finest Stately Home', is a gem of Europe's architectural heritage. Set in a hundred acres of parkland on the shores of the Forth with fine views of the famous Forth bridges to the east.

Hopetoun has been the home of the Hope family since it was built. The head of the family, formerly known as the Earl of Hopetoun was created Marquess of Linlithgow in 1901 after serving as the first Governor General of Australia. The 2nd Marquess served as Viceroy of India from 1936-1943. The present head of the family, Adrian, the 4th Marquess of Linlithgow lives in a private wing of the House.

The original House was designed by Sir William Bruce and built between 1699 and 1702. Enlargements were made by William Adam and his 3 sons John, Robert and James from 1721. Much of the original furniture made for the rooms in the 1760's survives today. Paintings by many famous artists adorn the State Apartments and there is a fine collection of 17th century tapestries and Meissen ornaments.

Separate exhibitions include 'The Building of Hopetoun', 'Horse and Man in Scotland' and 'Wildlife' a seasonal display of particular interest to children. To the west of the House there are magnificent woodland walks, a Red Deer Park, nature trails and a profusion of wild flowers. A Countryside Ranger is in attendance.

CONTACT

Capt R H Fox RN
Hopetoun House
South Queensferry
Edinburgh
EH30 9SL

Tel: (0131) 331 2451

Fax: (0131) 319 1885

LOCATION

2¹/₂ miles west of Forth Road Bridge.

12 miles west of Edinburgh (25 mins. drive).

34 miles east of Glasgow (50 mins. drive).

SUITABILITY FOR OTHER EVENTS
A major venue in Scotland for private functions and special events throughout the year; Receptions, Gala Dinners, Antique Fairs, Concerts, Scottish Gala Evenings, Conferences.

EXTRA FACILITIES
Grand piano in Library. Boules (Petanque), Piste and Croquet Lawn. Helicopter landing.

ADVICE TO COURIERS & DRIVERS
Pre-book if possible. No smoking or flash photography in House. No dogs in house but welcome (on leads) in Grounds. Free parking close to the house.

CATERING
The Tapestry Room licensed Restaurant caters for 50-60 people. Groups (up to 250) can book in advance for lunch, afternoon tea and other meals in the Ballroom. Menus available on request (Tel: Banqueting Dept. 0131 331 4305)

FACILITIES FOR THE DISABLED
Restaurant, toilet facilities and exhibitions all on ground floor and easily accessible.

GIFT SHOP
Daily 10.30am-5.30pm. Wide range of quality Scottish goods.

GUIDED TOURS
Normally visitors tour at leisure but special guided tours can be arranged in advance. Foreign language guides usually available.

SCHOOL VISITS/CHILDREN
Holders of 2 Sandford Awards for Heritage Education. Special tours in House and/or Grounds for different age/interest groups. Of particular interest; Family life in Georgian and Victorian times, Nature trails with Countryside Ranger, Red Deer park. Teachers information pack available. Childrens Guide Book.

OPENING TIMES

Summer

14 April - 1 October

Daily 10.00am - 5.30pm
Last entry 4.45pm

Earlier admission for parties by prior arrangement. Booking for large groups advisable.

Winter

2 October - Easter
Closed except for group visits by prior arrangement.

Open throughout the year for booked functions.

ADMISSION

HOUSE & GROUNDS
  Adult £4.00
  Child * £2.00
  OAP £3.30
  Student £3.30
Groups (min 20 people)
  . . . . £3.30
GROUNDS ONLY
  Adult £2.00
  Child *) £0.60
  OAP £2.00
  Student £2.00
*Age 5-16. Under 5's Free

Guided Tours (Max 20 per guide) £10.00.

Winter

Out of season rates.

CONFERENCE AND FUNCTION FACILITIES

ROOM	DIMENSIONS	CAPACITY	LAYOUT	POWER POINTS	SUITABLE FOR A/V
Ballroom	92' x 35' Height 28'	350	Theatre/Buffet	✓	✓
		250	Dinner/Dance		
		370	Lunch/Dinner		
Tapestry Room (adjacent to	37' x 24' Height 28'	100	Theatre	✓	✓
		50	U-Shape/Boardroom/ Dinner/Dance		
Ballroom)		70	Lunch/Buffet		
*Red Drawing Room	44' x 24' Height 22'	100	Theatre	✓	
		40	U-Shape/Boardroom		
		60	Lunch/Dinner		
*State Dining Room *(In Main House)	39' x 23' 16"	20	Lunch/Dinner	✓	

ARNISTON HOUSE

OPEN

2 July - 14 Sept

Sundays, Tuesdays and Thursdays

2.00 - 5.00pm

Guided tours. Pre-arranged groups 10-50 people accepted throughout the year.

Tel: 01875 830238
Fax: 01875 830573

GOREBRIDGE, MIDLOTHIAN EH23 4RY
Owner: Mrs. A Dundas-Bekker   *Contact:* Mrs. A Dundas-Bekker

Magnificent William Adam Mansion started in 1726. Fine plaster work, Scottish portraiture, period furniture and other fascinating contents. Beautiful country setting beloved by Sir Walter Scott. Home-baked teas are also available.

Location: 11 miles from Edinburgh, off 6372 one mile from A7.
Admission: Adult £3.00, Child under school age free. Pre-arranged groups of 10 to 50 people accepted throughout the open season (2 Jul to 14 Sept.).

BLACKNESS CASTLE   **Tel:** 01506 834807

Linlithgow, Lothian.
Owner: Historic Scotland   **Contact:** The Administrator
One of Scotland's most important strongholds. Built in the 14th century and massively strengthened in the 16th century as an artillery fortress, it has been a royal castle and a prison armaments depot and film location for Hamlet. It was restored by the Office of Works in the 1920s. It stands on a promontory in the Forth estuary.
Location: 4m N of Linlithgow.
Opening Times: Summer: 1 Apr - 30 Sept, Mon - Sat, 9.30am - 6.30pm. Sun 2.00pm - 6.30pm. Winter: 1 Oct - 31 Mar, Mon, Tues, 9.30am - 4.30pm. Thur 9.30am - 12.00pm. Fri closed. Sun 2.00pm - 4.30pm. Last admissions half an hour before closing.

CRAIGMILLAR CASTLE   **Tel:** 0131 661 4445

Edinburgh.
Owner: Historic Scotland   **Contact:** The Administrator
Mary Queen of Scots fled to Craigmillar after the murder of Rizzio and it was here that the plot was hatched for the murder of her husband Lord Darnley. This handsome structure with courtyard and gardens covers an area of one and a quarter acres. Built round an L plan tower house of the early 15th century including a range of private rooms linked to the hall of the old tower.
Location: 2¹/₂ m SE of Edinburgh.
Opening Times: Summer: 1 Apr - 30 Sept, Mon - Sat, 9.30am - 6.30pm. Sun 2.00pm - 6.30pm. Winter: 1 Oct - 31 Mar, Mon - Wed and Sat, 9.30am - 4.30pm. Thur 9.30am - 12.00pm. Fri closed. Sun 2.00pm - 4.30pm. Last admissions half an hour before closing.
Admission: Adult £1.50, Conc £1.00, Child 75p.

CRICHTON CASTLE   **Tel:** 0131 661 4445

Pathhead.
Owner: Historic Scotland   **Contact:** The Administrator
A large and sophisticated castle with a spectacular facade of faceted stonework in an Italian style added by the Earl of Bothwell between 1581 and 1591 following a visit to Italy. Mary Queen of Scots attended a wedding here.
Location: 2¹/₂ m SSW of Pathhead.
Opening Times: Summer: 1 Apr - 30 Sept, Mon - Sat, 9.30am - 6.30pm. Sun 2.00pm - 6.30pm. Last admissions half an hour before closing. Winter: closed.
Admission: Adult £1.20, Conc 75p, Child 75p.

DALMENY HOUSE   See page 244 for full page entry.

DALKEITH PARK   **Tel:** 0131 665 3277

Dalkeith Country Park, Dalkeith, Midlothian, EH22 2NJ.
    Contact: J C Manson
Extensive grounds of Dalkeith Palace. 18th century bridge and orangery.
Location: 7m SE of Edinburgh.
Opening Times: Mar - Oct, 10.00am - 6.00pm.
Admission: Adult £1.50, Child £1.50, Family £4.00, Groups £1.00.

DIRLETON CASTLE AND GARDEN   **Tel:** 01620 85330

Direlton.
Owner: Historic Scotland   **Contact:** The Administrator
Romantic castle besieged by Edward I in 1298, rebuilt, expanded and then destroyed in 1650. The ruins now stand within a good garden established in the 16th century.
Location: In Direlton.
Opening Times: Summer: 1 Apr - 30 Sept, Mon - Sat, 9.30am - 6.30pm. Sun 2.00pm - 6.30pm. Winter: 1 Oct - 31 Mar, Mon - Sat, 9.30am - 4.30pm. Sun 2.00pm - 4.30pm. Last admissions half an hour before closing.
Admission: Adult £2.00, Conc £1.25, Child 75p.

DUNGLASS COLLEGIATE CHURCH   **Tel:** 01620 85330

Cockburnspath.
Owner: Historic Scotland   **Contact:** The Administrator
Founded in 1450 for a college of canons by Sir Alexander Hume. A handsome cross-shaped building with vaulted nave, choir and transepts.
Location: In NW Cockburnspath.

EDINBURGH CASTLE   **Tel:** 0131 2259846

Edinburgh, Lothian.
Owner: Historic Scotland   **Contact:** The Administrator
This most famous of castles dominates Scotland's capital and gives stunning views of the city and countryside. The oldest parts of the castle date from the Norman period. St Margaret's Chapel, the enormous 500 year old siege cannon Mons Meg, the Great Hall built by James IV, the Half Moon Battery built by the Regent Morton in the late 16th century, the royal palace, and the Scottish National War Memorial are here together with the highly acclaimed 'Honours of the Kingdom' exhibition which traces the history of Scotland's Crown Jewels and culminates in a visit to the Crown Room. The Vaults were where foreign prisoners-of-war were held, particularly those captured in the wars with France in the 18th and 19th centuries. Some of the graffiti scrawled by the prisoners can still be seen. Courtesy vehicle can take disabled visitors to the top of the castle (sponsored by the Bank of Scotland). Restaurant offering self and table service.
Location: Edinburgh
Opening Times: Summer: 1 Apr - 30 Sept, all week, 9.30am - 6.00pm. Winter: 1 Oct - 31 Mar, all week, 9.30am - 5.00pm . Last admission 45 minutes before closing. Hours may be altered during the Tattoo or for State and military events.
Admission: Adult £5.00, Conc £3.00, Child under 16 £1.00, parking for up to 2 hours: Cars £1.50, Coaches £2.00. There is no discount for parties. Members of HM Forces will be admitted free on production of their Identity Card. Visitors who want to visit only the Scottish National War Museum are admitted free. Guided tours are normally available but they cannot be reserved in advance.

EDINBURGH CATHEDRAL   **Tel:** 0131 2256293   **Fax:** 0131 2253181

Edinburgh EH12 5AW.
    Contact: Cathedral Secretary
Neo-Gothic grandeur in the classical new town.
Location: ¹/₂m W of west end of Princes Street.
Opening Times: 7.30am - 6.15pm Sun services: 8.00am, 10.30am and 3.30pm. Weekday services: 7.30am, 1.05pm and 5.30pm.

GLADSTONE'S LAND   **Tel:** 0131 2265856

477b Lawnmarket, Edinburgh, EH1 2NT.
Owner: National Trust for Scotland   **Contact:** Alison Butler
Built 1620. Remarkable painted wooden ceilings. Furnished as a typical "Old Town" house of the period.
Location: In the Royal Mile, five minutes walk from Princes Street via The Mound.
Opening Times: 1 Apr - 22 Oct, Mon - Sat, 10.00am - 5.00pm, Sun 2.00pm - 5.00pm (last admission 4.30pm).

GOSFORD HOUSE   **Tel:** 01875 870200

East Lothian, EH32 0PX.
Owner: Lord Wemyss' Trust   **Contact:** The Earl Of Wemyss
Central block of house by Robert Adam. Two wings by William Young 1890. The south wing contains celebrated marble hall. Fine collection of paintings.
Location: On A198 between Aberlady and Longniddry.
Opening Times: Jun & Jul, Wed, Sat, Sun, 2.00pm - 5.00pm.
Admission: Adult £1.00, Child 50p, Senior citizens 75p.

HAILES CASTLE   **Tel:** 01875 870200

East Linton.
Owner: Historic Scotland   **Contact:** The Administrator
Beautifully sited ruin incorporating a fortified manor of 13th century date. It was extended in the 14th and 15th centuries. There are two vaulted pit prisons.
Location: 1¹/₂m SW of East Linton.

HARBURN HOUSE

See page 245 for full page entry.

HOPETOUN HOUSE

See page 246 for full page entry.

HOUSE OF THE BINNS

Tel: 01506 834255

Linlithgow, West Lothian, EH49 7NA.
Owner: National Trust for Scotland   **Contact:** Kathleen Dalyell
Historic home of the Dalyell family. Reflects early 17th century transition in Scottish architecture from fortified stronghold to spacious mansion. Magnificent plaster ceilings added in 1630.
Location: Off A904, 15m W of Edinburgh.
Opening Times: House: 29 Apr - 1 Oct, daily except Fri, 1.30pm - 5.30pm (last admission 5.00pm). Parkland, all year, daily 10.00am - 7.00pm (last admission 6.30pm).
Admission: Adult £3.00, Child £1.50, Adult party £2.40, School £1.20. Visits by guided tours only. Parties to book beforehand. Members of They Royal Scots Dragoon Guards, successors of 'The Greys", in uniform, are admitted free.

INVERESK LODGE GARDEN ☻

Tel: 01592 266566

24 Inveresk Village, Musselburgh, East Lothian, EH21 7TE.
Owner: National Trust for Scotland   **Contact:** Kathleen Dalyell
Small garden in grounds of 17th century house, with large selection of plants. (House not open).
Location: A6124, S of Musselburgh, 6m E of Edinburgh.
Opening Times: 1 Apr - 30 Sept, Mon - Fri, 10.00am - 4.30pm, Sat/ Sun, 2.00pm - 5.00pm. 1 Oct - 31 Mar, Mon - Fri, 10.00am - 4.30pm, Sun 2.00pm - 5.00pm.
Admission: £1.00 (honesty box).

LAURISTON CASTLE

Tel: 0131 336 2060

Cramond Road South, Edinburgh, EH4 5QD.
Owner: City of Edinburgh District Council   **Contact:** R Barnes
16th century tower house with extensive 19th century additions. Edwardian interior, well furnished.
Location: At Davidson's Mains 10 mins NW of Edinburgh city centre.
Opening Times: 1 Apr - 31 Oct, daily except Fri, 11.00am - 4.20pm. 1 Nov - 31 Mar 2.00pm - 3.20pm.
Admission: Adult £2.00, Child £1.00, Senior citizens/UB40s £1.00.

LENNOXLOVE HOUSE

Tel: 01620 823720   **Fax:** 01620 825112

Haddington, East Lothian, EH41 4NZ.
Owner: His Grace The Duke of Hamilton   **Contact:** House Opening Administrator
Originally called Lethington Tower, and for centuries belonged to the Maitlands. Of interest because of its architecture, association of its proprietors with the Royal House of Stewart, and the Hamilton Palace collection of portraits, furniture and porcelain.
Location: 1¹/₂m S of Haddington on B6369, 18 m E of Edinburgh off A1.
Opening Times: Easter weekend and May - Sept, Sat, Sun and Wed 2.00pm - 5.00pm.
Admission: Adult £3.00, Child £1.50, Groups £2.00 pp (min 30).

LINLITHGOW PALACE ⟨img⟩

Linlithgow.
Owner: Historic Scotland   **Contact:** The Administrator
Magnificent ruin of a great Royal Palace, set in its own park. All the Stewart Kings lived here. In 1542 Mary Queen of Scots was born at Linlithgow while her father James V lay dying at Falkland Palace.
Location: In Edinburgh, two minutes from west end of Princes Street.
Opening Times: Summer: 1 Apr - 30 Sept, Mon - Sat, 9.30am - 6.30pm. Sun 2.00pm - 6.30pm. Winter: 1 Oct - 31 Mar, Mon - Sat, 9.30am - 4.30pm. Sun 2.00pm - 6.30pm. Last admission half an hour before closing.
Admission: Adult £2.00, Conc £1.25, Child 75p.

NEIDPATH CASTLE

Tel: 01721 720333

Peebles, EH45 8NW.
Owner: The Lord Neidpath   **Contact:** The Administrator
Medieval castle dramatically situated above the River Tweed. Good example of how such a fortress could be adapted to more civilised living conditions of the 17th century.
Location: 1m W of Peebles on A72.
Opening Times: Easter - 30 Sept, Mon - Sat, 11.00am - 5.00pm. Sun 1.00pm - 5.00pm.

NEWLISTON

Tel: 0131 3333231   **Fax:** 0131 3353596

Kirkliston, West Lothian, EH29 9EB.
Owner: J S Findlay Esq   **Contact:** J S Findlay
Late Robert Adam house. Costumes on display. 18th century designed landscape, rhododendrons and azaleas.
Location: 8m W of Edinburgh, off B800
Opening Times: 3 May - 4 Jun, Wed - Sun, 2.00pm - 6.00pm.
Admission: Adult £1.00, Child 50p, Senior citizens 50p.

PRESTON MILL & PHANTASSIE DOOCOT ☻

Tel: 01620 860426

East Linton, East Lothian, EH40 3DS.
Owner: National Trust for Scotland   **Contact:** Frances Scott
Picturesque 16th century water driven meal mill in commercial production until 1957.
Location: Off A1, in East Linton, 23, E of Edinburgh.
Opening Times: Good Fri (14 Apr) - 30 Sept, Mon - Sat 11.00am - 1.00pm and 2.00pm - 5.30pm, Sun 1.30pm - 5.30pm. 1 - 22 Oct, Sat/ Sun 1.30pm - 4.00pm (last admission 20 mins before closing, morning and afternoon).
Admission: Adult £1.50, Child 80p, School 60p. Groups by prior arrangement.

ROYAL BOTANIC GARDEN

Tel: 0131 552 7171   **Fax:** 0131 552 0382

Inverleith Row, Edinburgh, EH3 5LR.

    Contact: Ms J Roberts
One of the world's finest Botanic Gardens and an internationally renowned centre for the scientific study and conservation of plants.
Location: Off A1, in East Linton, 23, E of Edinburgh.
Opening Times: Nov - Feb, 10.00am - 4.00pm (not 25 Dec /1 Jan). Mar - Apr, 10.00am - 6.00pm. May - Aug, 10.00am - 8.00pm. Sept - Oct, 10.00am - 6.00pm.
Admission: Free. Donations welcome.

TANTALLON CASTLE ☻

Tel: 01620 2727

North Berwick.
Owner: Historic Scotland   **Contact:** The Administrator
Set on the edge of the cliffs looking out to the Bass Rock this formidable castle was a stronghold of the Douglas family. It features earthwork defences and a massive 50 foot high 14th century curtain wall with towers. During the 16th century the castle was strengthened to resist artillery.
Location: 3m E of North Berwick.
Opening Times: Summer: 1 Apr - 30 Sept, Mon - Sat, 9.30am - 6.30pm. Sun 2.00pm - 6.30pm. Winter: 1 Oct - 31 Mar, Mon,Tues, Wed, and Sat, 9.30am - 4.30pm. Thur 9.30am - 12.00pm. Fri closed. Sun 2.00pm - 4.30pm. Last admission half an hour before closing.
Admission: Adult £2.00, Conc £1.25, Child 75p.

THE DRUM

Tel: 01316 647215   **Fax:** 01316 581944

Gilmerton, Edinburgh, EH17 8RX.
Owner: G A More-Nisbett Esq   **Contact:** Mrs More-Nisbett
William Adams' most sumptuous villa, superb high relief plasterwork by Thomas Clayton and Samuel Calderwood, attached to 15th century Tower house.
Location: ¹/₂m N of city bypass between A7 and A722.
Opening Times: By arrangement only.

THE GEORGIAN HOUSE ☻

Tel: 0131 225 2160

7 Charlotte Square, Edinburgh, EH2 4DR.
Owner: National Trust for Scotland   **Contact:** Shelagh Kennedy
Part of Robert Adams splendid North side of Charlotte Square. Lower floors of this house have been furnished in style of 1800. Audio visual show.
Location: In Edinburgh, two minutes from west end of Princes Street.
Opening Times: 1 Apr - 22 Oct, Mon - Sat 10-5.00pm, Sun 2.00pm - 5.00pm (last admission 4.30pm).
Admission: Adult £3.50, Child £1.80, Adult party £2.80, School £1.40.

WINTON HOUSE

Tel: 01875 340357

Pencaitland, Tranent, East Lothian, EH34 5AT.
Owner: Lady Ogilvy of Inverquharity   **Contact:** Mrs B Hewitt
Built 1620. Famous twisted stone chimneys and beautiful plaster ceilings in honour of Charles I's visit. Enlarged 1800. Fine pictures and furniture. Terraced gardens.
Location: Wrought-iron gates and lodges in Pencaitland (A6093) and New Winton Village B6355.
Opening Times: Restricted to groups of 10 or more (and other very specially interested) at any time by prior arrangement with the owner.
Admission: £3.50.

BLAIRQUHAN CASTLE
Maybole

BLAIRQUHAN is the home of James Hunter Blair, the great great grandson of Sir David Hunter Blair, 3rd Baronet for whom it was designed by William Burn and built in 1821-24.

All the Regency furniture bought for the house remains and the house has not been altered except discreetly to bring it up to date. There are 10 double bedrooms, including 4-posters, with bathrooms en suite, five singles and many public rooms which can be used for conferences and every sort of occasion.

The Castle is approached by a 3 mile private drive along the River Girvan and it is situated in one of the most charming parts of South West Scotland. There is a well-known collection of pictures. The River Girvan runs through the Estate and five miles of it is available for fishing for salmon and sea trout.

Blairquhan is only 50 miles from Glasgow and Glasgow Airport. It is within about half an hour's driving distance of the famous golf courses of Prestwick, Troon and Turnberry - the last two of which are venues for the British Open Golf Championships.

❖

SUITABILITY FOR OTHER EVENTS
Fashion shows, air displays, archery, clay pigeon shooting, equestrian events, garden parties, shows, rallies, filming, wedding receptions.

EXTRA FACILITIES
Grand piano, snooker, tennis, fishing, shooting. Slide projector, overhead projector, screen, and secretarial assistance available for meetings.

ACCOMMODATION
Blairquhan offers. 10 Doubles (4 4-posters) with bathrooms en suite, 5 Singles. The Dower House at Milton has 8 Doubles, 2 singles, 5 bathrooms. 6 holidays cottages on the Estate.

ADVICE TO COURIERS & DRIVERS
No photography within the Castle. Unlimited parking.

FACILITIES FOR THE DISABLED
Disabled and elderly visitors may alight at the entrance to the Castle. Toilets for the disabled.

CATERING
Restaurant: Afternoon teas, lunches, buffets and dinners.

Groups can book in advance for tea and other meals. Special rates for groups. Prices start at £1.70 per person.

GIFT SHOP
The small shop is open when required.

GUIDED TOURS
Can be arranged at no extra charge for up to 100 people – duration 1 hour. Also available in French.

SCHOOL VISITS/CHILDREN
School visits are welcome. A guide and schoolroom can be provided. Cost negotiable.

CONTACT

James Hunter Blair
Blairquhan Castle
Straiton
Maybole
Ayrshire
KA19 7LZ
Tel: (01655) 770239
Fax: (01655) 770278

LOCATION

From London M6 to Carlisle, A76 to Dumfries, A75 to Crocketford, A712 to A71 near New Galloway, B741 to Straiton on B7045 to Ayr. Turn left.

Rail: Maybole 7 miles.

Taxi: Watson (01655) 631

OPENING TIMES

Summer

16 July -13 August

Open daily except Mondays

Open at all other times by appointment.

Winter
Open by pre-booked appointment.

ADMISSION

Summer & Winter

HOUSE & GARDEN
Adult £3.00
Child** £2.00
OAP £2.00

Groups*
Negotiable

* Minimum payment £20.
** Age 5 - 14

CONFERENCE AND FUNCTION FACILITIES

ROOM	DIMENSIONS	CAPACITY	LAYOUT	POWER POINTS	SUITABLE FOR A/V
Drawing Rooms (2 rooms)	1200 sq ft	100	Theatre	4	3
		50	Schoolroom		
		30	U-Shape		
		20	Boardroom		
		100	Dinner/Dance		
		100	Buffet/Lunch/Dinner		
		50	Seated Lunch/Dinner		
Dining Room	750 sq ft	100	Dinner/Dance	4	3
		100	Buffet/Lunch/Dinner		
		50	Seated Lunch/Dinner		
Library	400 sq ft	25 up to 100	(Using other rooms 100)		
Saloon	600 sq ft	100	Dinner Dance		
		100	Buffet/Lunch/Dinner		
		50	Seated Lunch/Dinner		
Meeting Room	255 sq ft	50	Buffet/Lunch/Dinner		

INVERARAY CASTLE
Argyll

The Duke of Argyll's family have lived in Inveraray since the early 15th Century. The present Castle was built between 1740 and 1790.

The ancient Royal Burgh of Inveraray lies about 60 miles north west of Glasgow by Loch Fyne in an area of spectacular natural beauty combining the ruggedness of highland scenery with the sheltered tidal loch 90 miles from the open sea.

The Castle is the home of the Duke and Duchess of Argyll. Its fairy tale exterior belies the grandeur of its gracious interior. The building was designed by Roger Morris and decorated by Robert Mylne, the clerk of works being William Adam, father of Robert and John, who did much of the laying out of the present Royal Burgh, an unrivalled example of an early planned town.

Visitors to the Castle may see the famous Armoury Hall containing some 1300 pieces, French tapestries made especially for the Castle, fine examples of Scottish, English and French furniture together with a wealth of other works of art including China, Silver and family artifacts, all of which form a unique collection spanning the generations which are identified by a magnificent genealogical display in the Clan Room.

ADVICE TO COURIERS & DRIVERS
It is preferable that party bookings are made in advance. No dogs and no photography.

FACILITIES FOR THE DISABLED
Disabled and elderly visitors may alight at the entrance to the castle before parking in the car park close by. There is a wheelchair ramp to the Castle plus two steps. All main public rooms may be visited by the infirm and those in wheelchairs, but there are two long flights of stairs to the smaller rooms upstairs. Toilet facilities are suitable for disabled visitors although not specially adapted.

PARKING FOR COACHES & CARS
Parking for approximately 100 cars. Separate coach park close to Castle.

CATERING
The Tea Room seats up to 50 people for afternoon tea and other meals. Menus are available on request and groups can book in advance. Telephone (01499) 302112.

GIFT SHOP
Open at the same time as the Castle.

GUIDE BOOKS
Colour guide book, £1.50. French, Italian, Japanese and German translations available.

GUIDED TOURS
Tours can be arranged for up to 100 people at no additional cost. Average time taken 1 hour.

SCHOOL VISITS/CHILDREN
School parties are welcome. £1.25 per child in organised party. If requested a guide can be provided. Areas of interest include a nature walk, special school project, wild life park (nearby) and War Museum.

CONTACT

The Factor
Dept HHD
Argyll Estates Office
Cherry Park
Inveraray
Argyll
PA32 8XE

Tel: (01499) 302203

Fax: (01499) 302421

LOCATION

From Edinburgh 2¹/₂ - 3 hours via Glasgow.

Bus: Bus route stopping point within ¹/₂ mile.

OPENING TIMES

Summer

1 April - 8 October
April, May, June, Sept. Oct.
Mon, Tues, Wed, Thurs & Sats 10.00am - 1.00pm and 2.00pm - 5.30pm
Fridays Closed
Sundays   1.00 - 5.30pm

July - August
Open   10am - 5.30pm (inc. Fridays)
Sundays   1.00 - 5.30pm

Last admissions
12.30pm & 5.00pm

ADMISSION

Summer

HOUSE ONLY
Adult £3.50
Child* £1.75
OAP £2.50
Family (2+2) £9.00
Groups (Min 20 people)
20% Discount

*Under 16

Winter
Closed

CONFERENCE AND FUNCTION FACILITIES

ROOM	DIMENSIONS	CAPACITY	LAYOUT	POWER POINTS	SUITABLE FOR A/V
State Dining Room	30' x 22'	50	Lunch/Dinner	3	
Tapestry Drawing Room	45' x 21'	200 / 90	Lecture Room Lunch/Dinner	4	✓
Armoury Hall	23' x 31'	120	Assembly	2	✓
Saloon	24' x 44'	200	Lecture	2	✓

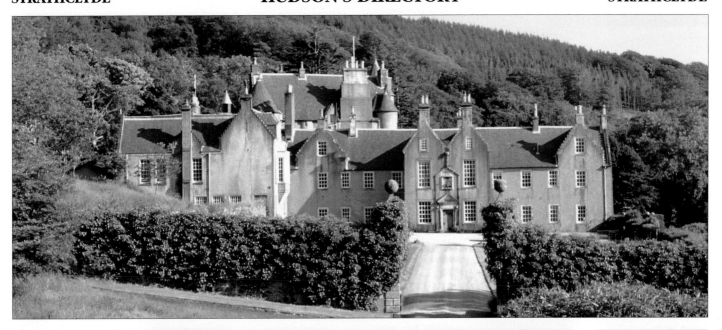

KELBURN CASTLE
Fairlie

The historic home of the Boyle family, later Earls of Glasgow, Kelburn is situated on the picturesque north Ayrshire coast. Kelburn Castle dates from the 13th Century and is thought to be the oldest Castle in Scotland to be inhabited by the same family throughout its history. The original 1200 Norman Keep was extended in 1580 by a Tower House, and an elegant William and Mary Mansion House was added in 1700 by David Boyle, who was created 1st Earl of Glasgow by Queen Anne in 1703 for his role in persuading reluctant Jacobite nobles to sign the Act of Union. A Victorian wing was built in 1879. Kelburn's essential charm is its informal family atmosphere, varied interior decor, and stunning location.

The grounds at Kelburn are quite lovely. Romantic Kelburn Glen with winding woodland trails, waterfalls and deep gorges.

Featured gardens are the Plaisance, a formal walled garden dominated by two magnificent 1,000 year old Yew trees, and the Children's Garden which is planted in the shape and colours of the Saltire. An extraordinary mutant Weeping Larch, Scotland's oldest and tallest Monterey Pine, a Robert Adam Monument, 18th Century Sundial and Ice House are among Kelburn's featured natural and historical attractions.

Within the Country Centre there is The Kelburn Story Cartoon Exhibition, a family Museum, Horse Riding, Adventure Play Areas, Commando Assault Course, Soft Play Room, Pets Corner, Nature Centre, Activity Workshop, Information Centre, Ranger Service, and Picnic Areas. Kelburn's newest attraction, THE SECRET FOREST, features The Maze of Green Man, The Mysterious Grotto and Crocodile Swamp.

SUITABILITY FOR OTHER EVENTS
The property is suitable for a variety of indoor and outdoor events. Consideration given to all enquiries, rates negotiable.

EXTRA FACILITIES
Gardens, Grounds. Golf Club adjacent. The pavilion is available for buffets, exhibitions, nature activities and barbecues.

ADVICE TO COURIERS & DRIVERS
Coach passengers can alight at the Castle forecourt. The coach must then leave and return via the estate exit and use Country Centre car park. This is approx 5/10 mins walk from the Castle, next to the Country Centre buildings.

PARKING FOR COACHES & CARS
Ample parking for coaches and cars.

CATERING
There is a licensed restaurant and a cafe at the country centre. Groups can book in advance. Special rates offered to groups. Full catering facilities available for special functions/conferences in the Castle, outside caterers may also be used.

FACILITIES FOR THE DISABLED
Elderly/disabled visitors may alight at the entrance to the Castle before vehicles are parked. Toilets for the disabled.

GIFT SHOP
The gift shop in the country centre carries souvenirs, craft items etc. Open throughout the summer season.

GUIDED TOURS
Maximum party size of 25 at no additional cost. Average time for a tour is 45 minutes. With prior notice lectures can be provided on the Castle, grounds, history etc.

SCHOOL VISITS/CHILDREN
Groups welcome £1.10 per child. Teachers free at ratio of 1:10 pupils, thereafter £1.50 ea. Countryside Ranger Service available for Guided Walks and Nature Activities, also Worksheets, Pets Corner, Pony Rides/Treks, Adventure Play Areas.

CONTACT

Earl of Glasgow
Kelburn Castle &
Country Centre
South Offices
Fairlie
Ayrshire
KA29 OBE

Tel: (01475) 568685

Fax: (01475) 568328

LOCATION

M8 Edinburgh to Glasgow, M8 Glasgow to Greenock, A78 to Largs, A78 main coastal trunk road.

Rail: Largs station 2 miles.

Bus: A78 main bus route to Ayr, stop adjacent to property.

Taxis: A2B taxis (01475) 673976.

CONFERENCE AND FUNCTION FACILITIES

ROOM	DIMENSIONS	CAPACITY	LAYOUT	POWER POINTS	SUITABLE FOR A/V
Drawing Room	33'x24'	60	Lunch/Dinner		
Dining Room		53	Seated Dinner		
		120	Buffet		
PRESENTLY THERE ARE NO FORMAL CONFERENCE FACILITIES.					

OPENING TIMES

Summer

CASTLE
July and August
Tours: 1.45, 3.00 and 4.15pm. (Except when there are afternoon functions)

Tours can be arranged at other times of the year.

COUNTRY CENTRE & GARDENS
Easter - end of October
Daily 10.00am - 6.00pm.

Winter

CASTLE
By special arrangement only.

COUNTRY CENTRE
End of October - Easter
11.00am - 5.00pm
Grounds only.

ADMISSION

Summer

CASTLE ONLY
Per person £1.50
Student £1.20
Per person £1.20
(These prices do not include entry fee to Centre)

COUNTRY CENTRE . . .
Adult £3.50
Child* £2.00
OAP £2.00
Student £2.00
Groups (min 12 people)
Adult £2.00
Child* £1.50
OAP £1.50
Student £1.50

Winter
CASTLE ONLY
As Summer rates

COUNTRY CENTRE
Adult £1.50
Child* £1.00

*Accompanied children 2 - school age.

ACHAMORE HOUSE

Tel: 01583 5267

Isle of Gigha, Argyll, PA41 7AD.

Contact: Ms Linda Oswald

Gardens only open. Sub-tropical gardens created by Sir James Horlick who bought Gigha in 1944.
Location: Off the Mull of Kintyre. Ferry from Tayinloch
Opening Times: Dawn until dusk every day.
Admission: Adults £2.00, Child £1.00.

ARDCHATTON PRIORY

Tel: 01631 75274

Oban, Argyll, PA37 1RQ.

Contact: Lt Col R Campbell Preston

The oldest inhabited house in Scotland. 3 acre garden, wild garden to west of house, formal garden in front, two herbaceous borders, 3 shrub borders, 1 rose garden. Fine variety of shrubs, trees and roses. Tea and light lunch room, gift shop.
Location: 5m E Connel Bridge, North side.
Opening Times: 1 Apr - 31 Oct, dawn - dusk (9.00am - 9.00pm).
Admission: Adult £1.00, Child free, OAP £1.00.

ARDNAISEIG GARDENS

Tel: 01866 3333   **Fax:** 01866 3222

Oban, Argyll, PA37 1RQ.
Owner: Nigel Liston Esq   **Contact:** Nigel Liston
Woodland garden with fine trees and a great variety of rhododendrons, azaleas and other flowering shrubs surrounding one acre walled garden with large herbaceous border.
Location: 9 m S of Taynuilt on B845.
Opening Times: 30 Mar - mid Oct, 9.00am - 9.00pm.
Admission: Adult £1.00, Child free, Conc 50% groups by arrangement.

ARDUAINE GARDEN

Tel: 01852 2366

Arduaine, by Oban, Argyll, PA34 4XQ.
Owner: National Trust for Scotland   **Contact:** Maurice Wilkins
Outstanding 18 acre woodland garden on sound of Jura/Loch Melfort and nationally noted for rhododendrons and azalea species, magnolias and other rare trees and shrubs. Climatically favoured by gulf stream.
Location: A816, 20m S of Oban and 17m N of Lochgilphead.
Opening Times: All year, daily 9.30am - sunset.
Admission: Adult £2.00, Child £1.00, Adult party £1.60, School 80p.

BACHELOR'S CLUB

Tel: 01292 541940

Sandgate Street, Tarbolton, KA5 5RB.
Owner: National Trust for Scotland   **Contact:** Yule Lithgow
17th century thatched house in which poet Robert Burns and friends formed a debating society in 1780. Burns' mementos and relics, period furnishings.
Location: In Tarbolton, B744, 7¹/₂m NE of Ayr, off B743.
Opening Times: Good Fri (14 Apr) - 30 Sept, daily 1.30pm - 5.30pm; 1 - 22 Oct, Sat/Sun 1.30pm - 5.30pm. Other times by appointment.
Admission: Adult £1.50, Conc 80p, Adult party £1.20, School 60p.

BLAIRQUHAN CASTLE

See page 249 for full page entry.

BONAWE IRON FURNACE

Tel: 01866 2432

Taynuilt, Argyll And Bute And Arran.
Owner: Historic Scotland   **Contact:** The Administrator
Founded in 1753 by Cumbrian iron masters this is the most complete remaining charcoal fuelled ironworks in Britain. Displays show how iron was once made here.
Location: Close to village of Taynuilt.
Opening Times: Summer: 1 Apr - 30 Sept, Mon - Sat, 9.30am - 6.30pm. Sun 2.00pm - 6.30pm. Last admissions half an hour before closing. Winter: closed.
Admission: Adult £2.00, Conc £1.25, Child 75p.

BOTHWELL CASTLE

Tel: 01698 816894

Bothwell, UddingstoneSouth Strathclyde.
Owner: Historic Scotland   **Contact:** The Administrator
The largest and finest 13th century stone castle in Scotland, much fought over during the Wars of Independence. Part of the original circular keep survives, but most of the castle dates from the 14th and 15th centuries. In a beautiful setting overlooking the Clyde.
Location: Bothwell.
Opening Times: Summer: 1 Apr - 30 Sept, Mon - Sat, 9.30am - 6.30pm. Sun 9.30am - 4.30pm. Winter: 1 Oct - 31 Mar, Mon, Tues, 9.30am - 4.30pm. Thur 9.30am - 12.00pm, Fri closed. Sun 2.00pm - 4.30pm. Last admissions half an hour before closing.

BRODICK CASTLE & COUNTRY PARK

OPEN
Castle:
14 Apr - 30 Sept
Daily
11.30am - 5.00pm
1 Oct - 22 Oct
Sat & Sun
11.30am - 5.00pm
Last Adm: 4.30pm
Reception Centre,
Restaurant, & Shop
Dates as castle
10.00am - 5.00pm
Garden & Park
All year - Daily
9.30am - Sunset

Tel: 01770 302202
Fax: 01770 302312

ISLE OF ARRAN, STRATHCLYDE KA2Y 8HY
Owner:National Trust for Scotland   *Contact:Mrs Olive Raymond, Admin.*

Ancient seat of Dukes of Hamilton dating from 13th century, contents include superb collections of silver, porcelain and paintings. Rhododendron garden, one of Europe's finest, and Victorian garden are backed by Goatfell and neighbouring mountains.
Location: 2 miles (bus service) from Brodick terminal of ferry from Ardrossan.
Admission: Castle & Gdn: Adult £4.00/Parties £3.20, Concession £2.00/Parties £1.60.
Garden only: Adult £2.00/Parties £2.00, Concession £1.00/Parties £1.00.

BURNS COTTAGE

Tel: 01292 441215

Alloway, Ayrshire, KA7 4PY.

Contact: J Manson

Thatched cottage, birthplace of Robert Burns in 1759. Now a museum.
Location: 2m SW of Ayr.
Opening Times: Spring: Apr - May, Mon - Sat, 10.00am - 5.00pm. Sun 1.00pm - 5.00pm Summer: Jun - Aug, Mon - Sat, 10.00am - 5.00pm. Sun 1.00pm - 5.00pm. Winter: Nov - Mar, 9.00am - 4.00pm. Sun 10.00am - 6.00pm. Autumn: Sept - Oct, 10.00am - 4.00pm. Closed Sun.
Adminssion: Adult £2.50, Child £1.25, Family £6.00, Senior citizens £1.85. Admission charge includes entry to Burns Monument and Gardens.

CHATELHERAULT COUNTRY PARK

OPEN
All Year round
except Christmas
and New Year
Holidays
Lodgehouse:
Summer:
11.00am - 4.30pm
Winter:
11.00am - 4.00pm
The lodgehouse is
occasionally closed
for functions.

Tel: 01698 426213
Fax: 01698 421532

FERNIEGAIR, BY HAMILTON, ML3 7UE
Owner: Hamilton District Council   *Contact: Jim Brockie, Sites Manager*

Built for James, 5th Duke of Hamilton, designed by William Adam, completed around 1744. Built to provide dog kennels, but pavilions also contain a banqueting room and other ornate apartments. Gardens, terraced walkway, herbaceous borders and parterre design. The plant species are generally herbal or medicinal in origin, indigenous or pre date 1750. Set in 500 acre country park.
Location: Situated on A72, Tourist route, 1¹/₂ miles south east of Hamilton.

COLZIUM HOUSE & WALLED GARDEN

Tel: 01236 823281   **Fax:** 01236 823281

Colzium - Lennox Estate, Off Stirling Road, Kilsyth, G65 0RZ.
Owner: Cumbernauld & Kilsyth District Council   **Contact:** A C Spiers Esq
A walled garden with an extensive collection of conifers, rare shrubs and trees, Kilsyth heritage museum, curling pond, tea room, picnic tables, pitch and putt, woodland walks.
Location: Off A803 Bank Knock to Kirkintilloch Road.
Opening Times: Walled garden - 1.00am to dusk Easter to Sept. House museum 2.00pm - 5.00pm Wed. Apr to Sept or by appointment.
Admission: Free. Charge for pitch and putt.

CRAIGNETHAN CASTLE

Tel: 01555 86364

Lanark, South Strathclyde.

Owner: Historic Scotland   **Contact:** The Administrator

In a picturesque setting overlooking the River Nethan and by a wide and deep ditch with an unusual caponier, a stone vaulted artillery chamber, unique in Britain

Location: $5^1/_2$ m WNW of Lanark.

Opening Times: Summer: 1 Apr - 30 Sept, Mon - Sat, 9.30am - 6.30pm. Sun 2.00pm - 6.30pm. Winter: 1 Oct - 1 Nov and 28 Feb - 31 Mar, Mon - Sat, 9.30am - 4.30pm. Sun 2.00pm - 4.30pm. Last admission half an hour before closing.

Admission: Adult £1.50, Conc £1.00, Child 75p.

CRARAE GLEN GARDEN

Tel: 01546 86614/86388

Crarae, Inveraray, Argyll, PA32 8YA.

Owner: Crarae Garden Trust   **Contact:** Mrs F Sinclair

One of the loveliest gardens open to the public in Scotland, set in a Highland Glen beside Loch Fyne.

Location: 10m SW of Inveraray on A84..

Opening Times: All year; Summer: 9.00am - 6.00pm Winter; daylight hours.

Admission: Adult £2.50, Child £1.50, Family £7.00, Group discount of 10% if paid in advance.

CROSSRAGUEL ABBEY

Tel: 01555 86364

Maybole, South Strathclyde.

Owner: Historic Scotland   **Contact:** The Administrator

Founded in the early 13th century by the Earl of Carrick. Remarkably complete remains include church, cloister, chapter house and much of the domestic premises.

Location: 2m S of Maybole.

Opening Times: Summer: 1 Apr - 30 Sept, Mon, Tues, Wed and Sat, 9.30am - 6.30pm. Thur 9.30am - 12.00pm. Fri closed. Sun 2.00pm - 4.30pm. Last admissions half an hour before closing. Winter: closed.

Admission: Adult £1.20, Conc 75p, Child 75p.

CULZEAN CASTLE & COUNTRY PARK

OPEN

1 Apr - 22 Oct
Daily
Castle, Shop,
Visitor Centre,
and Licensed
Restaurant:
10.30am - 5.30pm
Last adm: 5.00pm
Country Park
All Year. Daily
9.30am - Sunset

Tel: 01655 760274
Fax: 01655 760615

MAYBOLE, AYRSHIRE KA19 8LE

***Owner:** National Trust for Scotland*   ***Contact:** Jonathan Cardale, Administrator*

Robert Adam's masterpiece, one of Scotland's most visited tourist attractions, provides a perfect day out for the family. Only 45 miles from Glasgow. Facilities include exhibitions, a/v programmes, shops and restaurant.

Location: 12 miles south of Ayr on A719/ 4 miles west of Maybole off A77.

Admission: Castle & Park: Adult £5.50/Parties £4.50, Concession £3.00/Parties £2.50.
Castle: Adult £3.50, Concession £1.80.
Country Park: Adult £3.00/Parties £2.50, Concession £1.50/Parties £1.25.

Culzean Castle, a bedroom in the castle apartment which is available to let.

DUART CASTLE

OPEN

1 May - 14 Oct.

10.30am - 6.00pm

Tel: 01680 812309

ISLE OF MULL, ARGYLL PA64 6AP

***Owner:** Sir Lachlan Maclean Bt.*   ***Contact:** Sir Lachlan Maclean Bt.*

Duart Castle has been a Maclean stronghold since the 12th century. The keep was built by Lachlan Lubanach, 5th Chief, in 1360. Burnt by the English in 1758, the castle was restored in 1912 and today is still the home of the Chief of the Clan Maclean. It has a spectacular position overlooking the Sound of Mull.

Location: Off A849 on the east point of the Isle of Mull.

Admission: Adult £3.00, OAP £2.00, Child £1.50. Family Ticket £7.50.

DUMBARTON CASTLE

Tel: 01389 32828

Dumbarton, South Strathclyde.

Owner: Historic Scotland   **Contact:** The Administrator

Site of the ancient capital of Strathclyde. Mary Queen of Scots sailed to France from here as a child in 1548. The castle is spectacularly sited on a volcanic rock overlooking the River Clyde. The most interesting features are the 18th century artillery fortifications with 19th century guns. Displays in Governor's House.

Location: Dumbarton.

DUNSTAFFNAGE CASTLE AND CHAPEL

Tel: 01631 62465

Oban, Argyll And Bute.

Owner: Historic Scotland   **Contact:** The Administrator

A very fine 13th century castle built on a rock with a great curtain wall. Close by are the remains of a chapel with beautiful architectural detail.

Location: By Loch Etive $3^1/_2$ m from Oban.

Opening Times: Summer: 1 Apr - 30 Sept, Mon - Sat, 9.30am - 6.30pm. Sun 2.00pm - 6.30pm. Last admissions half an hour before closing time. Winter: closed.

Admission: Adult £1.50, Conc £1.00, Child 75p.

FINLAYSTONE HOUSE

Tel: 01475 540285

Langbank, Renfrewshire, PA14 6TJ.

Owner: George MacMillan Esq   **Contact:** George MacMillan Esq

The main attraction is not so much the house but the formal, walled and woodland gardens.

Location: On A8, 10 minutes W of Glasgow Airport.

Opening Times: House: Apr - Aug, weekends. Alternatively, by appointment. Gardens/woodlands, 10.30am - 5.00pm all year.

Admission: Adult £1.50, plus £1.50 for house, Child £1.10, plus £1 for house, Conc £1.00.

GLASGOW CATHEDRAL

Tel: 0141 221 3096

Glasgow.

Contact: The Dean

The only Scottish mainland medieval cathedral to have survived the Reformation complete. Built over the tomb of St Kentigern. Notable features in this splendid building are the elaborately vaulted crypt, the stone screen of the early 15th century and the unfinished Blackadder Aisle.

Location: In Glasgow.

GREENBANK GARDEN

Tel: 0141 639 3281   **Fax:** 0141 616 0550

Flenders Road, Clarkston, Glasgow, G76 8RB.

Owner: National Trust for Scotland   **Contact:** Jim May

Glasgow "Tobacco-Lords" (tobacco merchant) 18th century estate, walled garden ($2^1/_2$ acres) and 13 acres of policies surrounding elegant Georgian house (open by arrangement). Garden relevant to suburban gardeners, gardening classes, special garden and facilities for the disabled.

Location: 1m S of Clarkston Toll off A726, 6m S of Glasgow city centre, off A77.

Opening Times: All year, daily 9.30am - sunset, except 25/26 Dec and 1/2 Jan. Shop & Tea room: 1 Apr - 22 Oct, daily 11.00am - 5.30pm. House open by arrangement (available for small functions).

Admission: Adult £2.00, Conc £1.00, Adult party £1.60, School 80p.

HUTCHESONS' HALL

Tel: 0141 552 8391   **Fax:** 0141 552 7031

158 Ingram Street, Glasgow, G1 1EJ.
Owner: National Trust for Scotland   **Contact:** Mrs Sheila Tandy
Described as one of Glasgow City Centre's most elegant buildings, the hall by David Hamilton, replaced the earlier 1641 hospice founded by George & Thomas Hutcheson. Reconstructed in 1876, the building is now "A-Listed" as being of national importance. Available for functions.
Location: Glasgow City Centre, Ingram Street, near SE corner of George Square.
Opening Times: Visitor Centre/Function Hall: all year (except public holiday and 24 Dec - 3 Jan), Mon - Fri 9.30am - 5.00pm, Sat 10.00am - 4.00pm. (Hall on view subject to functions in progress). Shop: same dates 10.00am - 4.00pm. Glasgow's Merchant City video 1 Jul - 31 Aug, Mon - Sat 11.30am - 3.30pm on hour and half-hour (other times by appointment).
Admission: Free.

INVERARY CASTLE

See page 250 for full page entry.

INVERARAY JAIL

Tel: 01499 302381   **Fax:** 01499 302195

Church Square, Inveraray, Argyll, PA32 8TX.
Owner: J Linley Esq   **Contact:** J Linley
A living 19th century prison! Uniformed prisoners and wardens, life-like figures, imaginative exhibitions, sounds, smells, and trials in progress, bring the 1820 courtroom and former County Prison back to life.
Location: Church Square, Inveraray.
Opening Times: April - Oct, 9.30am - 6.00pm, last admission 5.00pm. Nov - Mar last admission 4.00pm.
Admission: Adult £3.95, Child £2.00, Family £10.00, Senior citizens £2.50, Groups £3.20, Senior citizen groups £2.00.

KELBURN CASTLE

See page 251 for full page entry.

NEWARK CASTLE

Tel: 01475 41858

Port Glasgow, South Strathclyde.
Owner: Historic Scotland   **Contact:** The Administrator
The oldest part of the castle is a tower built soon after 1478 with a detached gatehouse, by George Maxwell. The main part was added in 1597 - 99 in a most elegant style. Enlarged in the 16th century by his descendent, the wicked Patrick Maxwell who murdered two of his neighbours.
Location: In Port Glasgow.
Opening Times: Summer: 1 Apr - 30 Sept, Mon - Sat, 9.30am - 6.30pm. Sun 2.00pm - 6.30pm. Last admissions half an hour before closing. Winter: closed.
Admission: Adult £1.50, Conc £1.00, Child 75p.

POLLOCK HOUSE

Tel: 0141 632 0274   **Fax:** 0141 649 0823

Glasgow, G43 1AT.
Owner: City of Glasgow District Council   **Contact:** The Administrator
Early 18th century house, containing the remarkable Stirling Maxwell collection of Spanish paintings. Nearby in Pollock Park is the Burrell collection.
Location: 2m S of Glasgow city centre.
Opening Times: Mon - Sat, 10.00am - 5.00pm. Sun 11.00am - 5.00pm.
Admission: Free.

ROTHESAY CASTLE

Tel: 01700 502691

Rothesay, Argyll And Bute.
Owner: Historic Scotland   **Contact:** The Administrator
A favourite residence of the Stuart Kings, this is a wonderful example of a 13th century circular castle of enclosure with 16th century forework containing the great hall. Attacked by Vikings in its earlier days.
Location: Rothesay.
Opening Times: Summer: 1 Apr - 30 Sept, Mon - Sat, 9.30am - 6.30pm. Sun 2.00pm - 6.30pm. Winter: 1 Oct - 31 Mar, Mon, Tues, Wed and Sat, 9.30am - 4.30pm. Thur 9.30am - 12.00pm. Fri closed. Sun 2.00pm - 4.30pm. Last admissions half an hour early.

SORN CASTLE

Tel: 0292 268181

Ayrshire, KA5 6HR.
Owner: Mrs R G McIntyre   **Contact:** Mrs R G McIntyre
Originally 14th century castle. James V visited the castle then owned by the Earl of Winton in 1598. The castle has been enlarged several times, most recently in 1908.
Location: 4m E of Mauchline on B743.
Opening Times: By appointment.

SOUTER JOHNNIE'S COTTAGE

Tel: 01655 760274 / 603

Main Road, Kirkoswald, KA19 8HY.
Owner: National Trust for Scotland   **Contact:** Ms Jan Gibson
The home of John Davidson, original "Souter" (cobbler) of Robert Burns famous narrative poem "Tam O' Shanter". Burns' mementos and restored cobbler's workshop. Life-sized stone figures in adjacent "ale-house".
Location: On A77, in Kirkoswald village, 4m SW of Maybole.
Opening Times: Good Fri (14 Apr) - 30 Sept,daily 1.30pm - 5.30pm. 1 - 22 Oct, Sat/Sun 1.30pm - 5.30pm (last admission 5.00pm). Other times by appointment
Admission: Adult £1.50, Conc 80p, Adult party £1.20, School 60p.

ST ANDREW'S CATHEDRAL

Tel: 0141 2042409

Glasgow, G1 4ER.

Contact: Rev H McEwan
The earliest Catholic church (post reformation) in the Glasgow area. Built in 1816.
Location: Clyde Street, central Glasgow on N Bank of Clyde.
Opening Times: 8.00am - 6.00pm all year Sun services: 8.00am, 10.00am, 12.00pm and 5.00pm Weekday services: 8.15am, 1.00pm and 5.15pm.

ST BLANE'S CHURCH

Kingarth, Argyll And Bute.
Owner: Historic Scotland   **Contact:** The Administrator
This 12th century Romanesque chapel stands on the site of a 12th century Celtic Monastery.
Location: At the south end of the Isle of Bute.

ST MARY THE VIRGIN CATHEDRAL

Tel: 0141 3396691   **Fax:** 0141 3574544

300 Great Western Road, Glasgow, G4 9JB.

Contact: The Very Rev P Francis
Fine Gothic Revival church by Sir George Gilbert Scott, with outstanding contemporary murals by Gwyneth Leech.
Location: 1/4m after taking the Dumbarton A82 exit from M8 motorway.
Opening Times: 9.00am - 5.45pm. Sun services: 8.30am, 10.00am, 12.00pm and 6.30pm Weekday services: Tel 0141 3396691.

THE HILL HOUSE

Tel: 01436 673900

Upper Colquhoun Street, Helensburgh, Dumbarton , G84 9AJ.
Owner: National Trust for Scotland   **Contact:** Mrs Anne Ellis
Charles Rennie Mackintosh's domestic masterpiece, built in 1904 for Walter Blackie, Glasgow Publisher, includes his furniture, fittings and decorative schemes, interpretive exhibition, specialist shop, restored garden (parties must be booked in advance)..
Location: Off B832, between A82 and A814, 23 NW of Glasgow.
Opening Times: 1 Apr - 23 Dec, daily 1.30pm - 5.30pm (last admission 5.00pm). Tea Room: 1 Apr - 31 Oct, daily 1.30pm - 4.30pm. Shop: as house (closed 30 Oct - 6 Nov for stocktaking).
Admission: Adult £3.00, Conc £1.50, Adult party £2.40, School £1.20.

WEAVER'S COTTAGE

Tel: 0150 705588

Shuttle Street, Kilbarchan, Renfrew, PA10 2JG.
Owner: National Trust for Scotland   **Contact:** Mrs Irene MacDiamid
Typical cottage of an 18th century handloom weaver contains looms, weaving equipment and domestic utensils. Attractive cottage garden. Occasional weaving demonstrations.
Location: Off A740 (off M8) and A737, at The Cross, Kilbarchan, (nr Johnstone, Paisley) 12m SW of Glasgow.
Opening Times: Good Fri (14 Apr) - 30 Sept, daily 1.30pm - 5.30pm. (Last admission 5.00pm).
Admission: Adult £1.50, Conc 80p, Adult party £1.20, School 60p.

YOUNGER BOTANIC GARDEN

Tel: 01369 706261   **Fax:** 01369 706369

Dunoon, Argyll, PA23 8QU.

Contact: Assistant Curator
Rhododendrons, conifers and Redwood Avenue.
Location: 7m N of Dunoon on A815.
Opening Times: 15 Mar - 31 Oct, daily, 10.00am - 6.00pm.
Admission: Adult £2.00, Child 50p, Family £4.50, Conc £1.50, Groups of 11 plus - 10% discount.

BLAIR CASTLE
Pitlochry

CONTACT

Brian H Nodes
Administrator
Blair Castle
Blair Atholl
Pitlochry
Perthshire
PH18 5TL

Tel: (01796) 481207
Fax: (01796) 481487

LOCATION

From Edinburgh (80 miles), M90 to Perth, A9, follow signs for Blair Castle. 1¹/₂ hours. Trunk Road A9 2 miles

Bus: Bus stop 1 mile in Blair Atholl.

Train: 1 mile, Blair Atholl Euston-Inverness line. FREE Castle minibus from Station to Castle.

Taxi: Elizabeth Yule, (01796) 472290

BLAIR CASTLE has been the ancient home and fortress of the Earls and Dukes of Atholl for over 725 years. Its central location makes it easily accessible from all major Scottish centres in less than two hours.

The Castle has known the splendour of Royal visitations, submitted to occupation by opposing forces on no less than four occasions, suffered siege and changed its architectural appearance to suit the taste of successive generations.

Today 32 rooms of infinite variety display beautiful furniture, fine collections of paintings, arms, armour, china, costumes, lace and embroidery, masonic regalia, Jacobite relics and other unique treasures giving a stirring picture of Scottish life from the 16th to 20th Centuries.

The 10th Duke of Atholl, who still lives at Blair Castle, has the unique distinction of having the only remaining Private Army in Europe - The Atholl Highlanders.

GARDENS

Blair Castle is set in extensive parklands. Near the free car and coach parks, there is a picnic area, a Deer Park and a unique two acre plantation of large trees known as 'Diana's Grove.' It has been said that "it is unlikely that any other two acres in the world contain such a number of different conifers of such heights and of such small age."

❖

SUITABILITY FOR OTHER EVENTS
Fashion shows, archery, clay pigeon shooting, equestrian events, garden parties, shows, rallies, filming, wedding receptions, Highland Balls, Charity Balls, Piping Championships, plus full range of concerts and banquets.

EXTRA FACILITIES
Grand Piano, helicopter pad, cannon firing by Atholl Highlanders, resident piper, parkland, picnic areas. Special arrangements for groups touring House and gardens can include lunches, dinners and entertainment, highland balls, piper, cannon, needlework displays.

ADVICE TO COURIERS & DRIVERS
Coach drivers and couriers free, plus free meal and weekly free prize draw for bottle of whisky. On first visit drivers/couriers receive free information pack. No dogs or smoking. Parking for 200 cars and 20 coaches 100 yards from Castle.

FACILITIES FOR THE DISABLED
Disabled and elderly visitors may alight at the entrance of the Castle, before parking in the allocated areas. Disabled toilets Wheelchair available.

CATERING
Two restaurants, both 'no smoking'. Self-service area seats 112, 'The Old Gun Room' (waitress service) seats 48. Prices from £1.00 - £3.50 for tea, snacks from £3.00, lunches from £6.00. Buffets, Dinners and Banquets for 70-200 can be provided. Details on application.

GIFT SHOP
Open as for Castle. Over 1,000 items sold, 72% are Scottish made.

GUIDE BOOKS
Colour guide book in English, German, French, Dutch, Italian, Spanish and Japanese, £1.50. Special guide book for children.

GUIDED TOURS
Tours available in English, German and French at no extra cost. Maximum size 25. Average time for tour of house 1¹/₂ hours.

SCHOOL VISITS/CHILDREN
School parties welcome £3.50 each, Primary Schools £3.00 each. Of particular interest: nature walks, deer park, collection of children's games, pony trekking. Special guide book .

OPENING TIMES

Summer
1 April - 27 October

Daily 10.00am - 6.00pm
Last entry 5.00pm.

Winter
Closed from
28 October - 31 March

ADMISSION

HOUSE & GARDEN
Adult £5.00
Child/Student** .£4.00
OAP £4.00
Family £14.00

Groups*
Adult £4.50
Child** £3.50
OAP £3.50
Disabled £2.00

* Minimum payment £200
  out of season.
**Age 5-16

FUNCTION FACILITIES

ROOM	DIMENSIONS	CAPACITY	LAYOUT	POWER POINTS	SUITABLE FOR A/V
Ballroom	89' x 35'	400	Theatre	14	✓
		200	Schoolroom		
		200	Buffet		
		300	Dinner/Dance		
		200	Lunch/Dinner		
State Dining Room (Evenings only)	36' x 25'	200	Receptions only	4	
Library	27' x 15'	40	Theatre	6	

GLAMIS CASTLE
Glamis

GLAMIS CASTLE is the family home of the Earls of Strathmore and Kinghorne and has been a royal residence since 1372. It is the childhood home of Her Majesty Queen Elizabeth The Queen Mother, the birthplace of Her Royal Highness The Princess Margaret and the legendary setting of Shakespeare's play 'Macbeth'. Though the Castle is open to visitors it remains a family home lived in and loved by the Strathmore family.

The Castle, a five-storey 'L' shaped tower block, was originally a royal hunting lodge. It was remodelled in the 17th Century and is built of pink sandstone. It contains the Great Hall, with its magnificent plasterwork ceiling dated 1621, a beautiful family Chapel constructed inside the Castle in 1688, an 18th Century Billiard Room housing what is left of the extensive library once at Glamis, a 19th century Dining Room containing family portraits and the Royal Apartments which have been used by Her Majesty Queen Elizabeth The Queen Mother. The Castle stands in an extensive park, landscaped towards the end of the 18th Century, and contains the beautiful Italian Garden which reflects the peace and serenity of the Castle and grounds.

❖

SUITABILITY FOR OTHER EVENTS
Grand dinners, receptions, fashion shows, archery, clay pigeon shooting, equestrian events, garden parties, shows, rallies, filming, product launches, highland games and wedding receptions.

EXTRA FACILITIES
Grand piano in the Great Drawing Room.

ADVICE TO COURIERS & DRIVERS
Coach drivers and couriers are admitted free of charge. No photography within the Castle. Beware the narrow gates, they are wide enough to take buses.

FACILITIES FOR THE DISABLED
Disabled toilet available. Disabled visitors may alight at the Castle entrance. Those in wheelchairs will be unable to tour the Castle but may visit the Coach House Exhibition.

PARKING FOR COACHES & CARS
Capacity of the car park - 500 cars, 30 yards from Castle, 20 coaches 50 yards from Castle.

CATERING
Self-service, licensed restaurant serving morning coffees, light lunches and afternoon teas. Seating for 100 in old Castle Kitchen. The State Rooms are also available for Grand Dinners.

GIFT SHOP
Open when Castle is open to visitors. Items include: glass, china, clothing, pictures and tea towels. The Garden Shop is open at the same time.

GUIDE BOOKS
Full colour guide book in English, Dutch, French, German, Italian, Spanish and Japanese £2.50.

GUIDED TOURS
All visits are guided - average time 50/60 minutes. Tours can be conducted by prior arrangement in French, German, Italian, Spanish and Portuguese.

SCHOOL VISITS/CHILDREN
School groups are welcome with one teacher admitted free for every 10 children. Facilities include a nature trail, family exhibition room, Estate exhibition in Coach House, dolls house and play area.

CONTACT

Lt Col. P J Cardwell Moore
Estates Office
Glamis Castle
Glamis
By Forfar
Angus
DD8 1RJ

Tel: (01307) 840242
Fax: (01307) 840257

LOCATION

From Edinburgh M90, A94, 81 miles.
From Forfar A94, 6 miles.
From Glasgow 101 miles.

Motorway: M90.

Rail: Dundee Station 12 miles.

Air: Dundee Airport 12 miles.

Taxi: C M Walker, Glamis 840270.

CONFERENCE AND FUNCTION FACILITIES

ROOM	DIMENSIONS	CAPACITY	LAYOUT	POWER POINTS	SUITABLE FOR A/V
Dining Room	84 sq.m.	120	Buffet	✓	✓
		120	Theatre		
Restaurant	140 sq.m.	100	Buffet	✓	✓
		100	Theatre		

SCONE PALACE
Perth

SCONE PALACE, just outside Perth is the home of the Earls of Mansfield. Here Kenneth MacAlpine united Scotland and in 838AD, placed the stone of Scone upon the Moot Hill which became the Crowning Place of Scottish kings, including Macbeth and Robert the Bruce. Edward I moved the Coronation Stone to Westminster in 1296.

The Abbey of Scone and the Bishops' Palace were ransacked and burned in 1559. The Gowries built a new Palace in 1580, which was enlarged and embellished around 1804 by the Third Earl and houses a fabulous collection of French furniture, clocks, 16th Century needlework (including bed hangings, worked by Mary Queen of Scots), ivories, objets d'art and Vernis Martin and one of the finest collections of Porcelain in the country.

GARDENS

Scone's famous Pinetum is a unique collection of rare pines, some of which are over 150 feet high and still growing. There are pleasant walks through 100 acres of Wild Garden which offer the visitor magnificent displays of daffodils, rhododendrons and azaleas.

There is a fine picnic area, adventure playground and a collection of veteran machinery. A cricket pitch and pavilion in an attractive setting is ideal for a variety of outdoor functions.

❖

SUITABILITY FOR OTHER EVENTS
Grand dinners, receptions, fashion shows, war games, archery, clay pigeon shooting, equestrian events, garden parties, shows, rallies, filming, shooting and fishing, floodlit tattoos, weddings, product launches, highland games.

EXTRA FACILITIES
Including organ, parkland, cricket pitch, airfield, helicopter landing and croquet. Speciality lectures can be arranged. Race course, polo field, firework displays, adventure playground.

ADVICE TO COURIERS & DRIVERS
Please advise in advance, especially if catering required. Couriers and drivers admitted free to all facilities, free meal available. Advisable to pre-book especially groups over 60. Advise ticket seller at coach park if handicapped visitors require transport to Palace. Couriers of booked parties receive token on last visit of season, value dependent on visits.

FACILITIES FOR THE DISABLED
All the State Rooms on one level. Special wheelchair access to Restaurants. Disabled and elderly visitors may alight at entrance. Toilet facilities for the disabled.

PARKING FOR COACHES & CARS
500 cars and 15 coaches 100 yards from the Palace.

CATERING
Two Restaurants/Tea Rooms capacity 54 and 66. Teas from £1.75, lunches from £5, dinners from £18. All meals can be pre-booked, menus upon request, special rates for groups. Large numbers can be accepted for buffets and grand dinners in State Rooms a speciality. Receptions, weddings, cocktail parties etc., all prepared by the Palace's own chef.

GIFT SHOP
Produce Shop and Gift Shop open as Palace. Guide book, £2.50, in seven languages. 1 page introduction available in 10 languages.

GUIDED TOURS
Free. English speaking guides in all rooms. Out of hours parties have 1 guide per tour. Average time for tour 45 minutes. Personal French and German guides usually available by appointment for a £30.00 charge.

CONTACT

Lt Cdr. A R Robinson
Scone Palace
Perth
PH2 6BD

Tel: (01738) 552300

Fax: (01738) 552588

LOCATION

From Edinburgh Forth Bridge M90, A93 1 hour.

Bus: 2 buses a day from Perth.

Rail: Perth Station 3 miles.

Motorway: M90 from Edinburgh.

Taxi: Perth Radio Cabs (01738) 628171.

OPENING TIMES

Summer
14 April - 9 October

Daily 9.30am - 5.00pm

Evening tours by appointment.

Winter
10 October - 13 April
By appointment only.

ADMISSION

Summer

HOUSE & GARDEN
Adult £4.50
Child* £2.50
OAP £3.70
Family £13.00
Groups (min 20 people)
Adult £4.00
Child* £2.25
OAP £3.40

GARDEN ONLY
Groups
Adult £2.25
Child* £1.25
OAP £2.25

*Age 5 - 16

Winter
Per person £8.00
(£160 min. payment)

CONFERENCE AND FUNCTION FACILITIES

ROOM	DIMENSIONS	CAPACITY	LAYOUT	POWER POINTS	SUITABLE FOR A/V
Long Gallery	140' x 20'	250	Theatre/Buffet	8	✓
		90	Lunch/Dinner		
Queen Victoria's Room	20' x 20'	35	Theatre\Buffet	4	✓
		20	Schoolroom		
		24	U-Shape		
		18	Boardroom		
		16	Lunch/Dinner		
Drawing Room	50' x 24'	90	Theatre	20	✓

ANGUS FOLK MUSEUM

Tel: 01307 840288

Kirkwynd, Glamis, Forfar, Angus, DD8 1RT.
Owner: National Trust for Scotland **Contact:** Valerie McAlister
Row of 19th century cottages adapted to display the Angus Folk collection.
Location: off A94, in Glamis, 5m SW of Forfar.
Opening Times: Good Fri (14 Apr) - 2 Oct, daily 11.00am - 5.00pm: 3 - 22 Oct, Sat/Sun 11.00am - 5.00pm (last admission 4.30pm).
Admission: Adult £2.00, Child £2.00, Adult party £1.60, School 80p.

ARBROATH ABBEY

Tel: 01241 78756

Arbroath, Tayside.
Owner: Historic Scotland **Contact:** The Administrator
The substantial ruins of a Tironensian monastery, notably the gate house range and the abbot's house. Arbroath Abbey holds a very special place in Scottish history. It was here in 1320 that Scotland's nobles swore their independence from England in the famous 'Declaration of Arbroath'. Introductory display.
Location: In Arbroath.
Opening Times: Summer: Mon - Sat, 9.30am - 6.30pm. Sun 2.00pm - 6.30pm. Winter: Mon - Sat, 9.30am - 4.30pm. Sun 2.00pm - 4.30pm. Last admissions half an hour before closing time.
Admission: Adult £1.20, Conc 75p, Child 75p.

BARRIE'S BIRTHPLACE

Tel: 01575 572646

9 Brechin Road, Kirriemuir, Angus, DD8 4BX.
Owner: National Trust for Scotland **Contact:** Karen Gilmour
Birthplace of Sir James Barry (1860 - 1937), creator of Peter Pan. Part is furnished as it might have been when Barry lived there. The neighbouring house has an exhibition on his works.
Location: A926/A928, in Kirriemuir, 6m NW of Forfar.
Opening Times: Good Fri (14 Apr) - 30 Sept, Mon - Sat 11.00am - 5.30pm, Sun 1.30pm - 5.30pm, 1 - 22 Oct, Sat 11.00am - 5.30pm, Sun 1.30am - 5.30pm (last admission 5.00pm).
Admission: Adult £1.50, Child 80p, Adult party £1.20, School 60p.

BARRY MILL

Tel: 01241 56761

Barry, Carnoustie, Angus, DD7 7RJ.
Owner: National Trust for Scotland **Contact:** The Administrator
18th century mill. Demonstrations and displays.
Location: N of Barry village between A92 and A930, 2m W of Carnoustie.
Opening Times: Good Fri (14 Apr) to 30 Sept, daily 11.00am - 5.00pm. 1 to 22 Oct, Sat/Sun, 11.00am - 5.00pm.
Admission: Adult £1.50, Child 80p, Adult parties £1.20, Schools 60p.

BLAIR CASTLE

See page 255 for full page entry.

BRANKLYN GARDEN

Tel: 01738 625535

116 Dundee Road, Perth, PH2 7BB.
Owner: National Trust for Scotland **Contact:** Bob & Felicity Mitchell
Location: A85, Dundee Road, Perth.
Opening Times: 1 Mar - 31 Oct, daily 9.30am - sunset.
Admission: Adult £2.00, Child £1.00, Adult party £1.60, School 80p.

CASTLE MENZIES

Tel: 01887 820982

Weem, Aberfeldy, Perth, PH15 2JD.
Owner: Menzies Charitable Trust **Contact:** R A Adam
Seat of Chiefs of Clan Menzies. 16th century fortified house. Bonnie Prince Charlie rested here en route for Culloden in 1746.
Location: 1$^{1}/_{2}$ m from Aberfeldy on B846.
Opening Times: 1 Apr - 14 Oct 1995.
Admission: Adult £2.50, Child £1.00, Conc £2.00, Groups: Adults £2.25.

CLAYPOTTS CASTLE

Tel: 01382 736420

Broughty Ferry
Owner: Historic Scotland **Contact:** The Administrator
An unusually complete tower house with circular towers on diagonally opposite corners corbelled out to form overhanging cap-houses. Built in the late 16th century for the Strachan family and later the property of 'Bonnie Dundee', John Graham of Claverhouse.
Location: Nr Broughty Ferry.

CLUNY HOUSE GARDENS

Tel: 01887 820795

Aberfeldy, Perthshire, PH15 2JT.
Contact: W Mattingley
Good Woodland garden including many rare Himalayan species.
Location: 3$^{1}/_{2}$ m from Aberfeldy on the Uleem to Strathtay Road.
Opening Times: 1 Mar - 31 Oct, 10.00am - 6.00pm.
Admission: Adults £2.00, Child under 16 free, Groups £2.00 per person (guided tour).

DAMSIDE HERB GARDEN

Tel: 01561 361496

Montrose, Angus, Kincardine, DD10 0HY.
Owner: Ian Cruickshank Esq **Contact:** Ian Cruickshank
Location: Signposted on A92 halfway between Stonehaven and Montrose.
Opening Times: Daily 10.00am - 5.00pm. Closed Jan & Feb.
Admission: Adult £1.00, Child 80p, Conc 80p, Accompanied child under 12 free. Groups by arrangement.

DRUMMOND CASTLE GARDENS

Tel: 01764 681257

Drummond Estate Office, Muthill, Crieff, Perthshire, PH5 2AA.
Owner: Grimsthorpe & Drummond Castle Trust **Contact:** J Buchanan
One of the finest formal gardens in Europe, first laid out in the 17th century. From the terrace by the castle you can look over a large parterre in the form of St Andrews Cross at the centre of which is a notable multi-faceted sundial dating from 1630.
Location: 2m S of Crieff off A822.
Opening Times: 1 May - 31 Oct, daily, 2.00pm - 6.00pm. Last entry 5.00pm.
Admission: Adult £3.00, Child £1.50, Senior citizens £2.00, Groups by prior arrangement.

EDZELL CASTLE AND GARDEN

Tel: 01356 648631

Edzell, Brechin.
Owner: Historic Scotland **Contact:** The Administrator
The beautiful pleasance, a walled garden, was built by Sir David Lindsay in 1604, the heraldic and symbolic sculptures are unique in Scotland, and the flower filled recesses in the walls add to the outstanding formal garden, which also has a turreted garden house.
Location: 6m N of Brechin.
Opening Times: Summer: 1 Apr - 30 Sept, Mon - Sat, 9.30am - 6.30pm. Sun 2.00pm - 6.30pm. Winter: Mon, Tues, Wed and Sat 9.30am - 4.30pm. Thur 9.30am - 4.30pm. Fri closed. Sun 2.00pm - 4.30pm. Last admission half an hour before closing time.
Admission: Adult £2.00, Conc £1.25, Child 75p.

ELCHO CASTLE

Tel: 01738 23437

Perth.
Owner: Historic Scotland **Contact:** The Administrator
This handsome and complete fortified mansion of 16th century date has four projecting towers. The original wrought-iron grills to protect the windows are still in place.
Location: On the Tay, 3m SE of Perth.
Opening Times: April - Sept, Mon - Sat 9.30am - 6.30pm. Sun 2.00pm - 6.30pm.

GLAMIS CASTLE

See page 256 for full page entry.

HOUSE OF DUN

OPEN

Good Fri - 30 June
& 1 - 30 September
Daily
1.30pm - 5.30pm
1 July - 31 August
Daily
11.00am - 5.30pm
1- 22 October
Sat/Sun
1.30pm - 5.30pm
Restaurant opens
12noon when house
opens at 1.30pm
Tel: 01674 810264

BY MONTROSE, ANGUS DD10 9LQ
Owner: National Trust For Scotland *Contact: Mrs June Pratt*
Georgian house overlooking the Montrose Basin, designed and built by William Adam in 1730 for David Erskine, Lord Dun. Superb contemporary plasterwork by Joshep Enzer. The house contains royal mementos and woolwork and embroidery by Lady Augusta Kennedy-Erskine, daughter of William IV and Mrs Jordanand a collection of portrait, furniture and porcelain. Miniature theatre display and video. Courtyard buildings and displays including handloom weaving workshop. Shop, restaurant, walled garden and woodland walks with a dog walk.
Location: On A935, 3 miles west of Montrose.
Admission: Adult £3.00, Concessions £1.50. Group rates available.

HUNTING TOWER CASTLE

Tel: 01738 27231

Perth.

Owner: Historic Scotland   **Contact:** The Administrator

The splendid painted ceilings are especially noteworthy in this castle, once owned by the Ruthven family. Scene of a famous leap between two towers by a daughter of the house who was nearly caught in her lover's room. The two towers are still complete, one of 15th -16th century date, the other of 16th century origin. Now linked by a 17th century range.

Location: 2m W of Perth.

Opening Times: Summer: 1 Apr - 30 Sept, Mon - Sat, 9.30am - 6.30pm. Sun 2.00pm - 6.30pm. Winter: 1 Oct - 31 Mar, Mon, Tues 9.30am - 4.30pm. Thur 9.30am - 12.00pm. Fri closed. Sun 2.00pm - 4.30pm. Last admissions half an hour before closing.

LOCHLEVEN CASTLE

Tel: 01738 627231

Loch Leven, Kinross.

Owner: Historic Scotland   **Contact:** The Administrator

Mary Queen of Scots endured nearly a year of imprisonment in this 14th century tower before her dramatic escape in May 1568. During the First War of Independence it was held by the English, stormed by Wallace and visited by Bruce.

Location: By boat from Kinross.

Opening Times: Summer: 1 Apr - 30 Sept, Mon - Sat, 9.30am - 6.30pm. Sun 2.00pm - 6.30pm. Last admissions half an hour before closing. Winter: closed.

Admission: Adult £2.00, Conc £1.25, Child 75p, Prices include ferry trip.

MEGGINCH CASTLE GARDENS

Tel: 01821 642222   **Fax:** 01821 642708

Errol Perthshire, PH2 7SW.

Owner: Captain Drummond of Megginch

15th century castle, 1,000 year old yews, flowered parterre, double walled kitchen garden, topiary, astrological garden, pagoda dovecote in courtyard. Part used as a location for the film "Rob Roy" to be released in 1995.

Location: 8m E of Perth on A90.

Opening Times: Apr - Oct Wed, Aug every day 2.30pm - 6.00pm.

Admission: Adult £2.00, Child £1.00.

MEIGLE SCULPTURES STONE MUSEUM

Tel: 01828 4612

Meigle.

Owner: Historic Scotland   **Contact:** The Administrator

A remarkable collection of 25 sculptured monuments of the Celtic Christian period. This is one of the finest collections of Dark Age sculpture in Western Europe.

Location: Meigle.

Opening Times: Summer: 1 Apr - 30 Sept, Mon - Sat, 9.30am - 6.30pm. Sun 2.00pm - 6.30pm. Winter: closed. Last admissions half an hour before closing.

Admission: Adult £1.20, Conc 75p, Child 75p.

SCONE PALACE

See page 257 for full page entry.

THE HOUSE OF PITMUIES

Tel: 01241 828245

By Forfar, Angus, DD8 2SN.

Owner: Mrs Farquhar Ogilvie

Adjacent to 18th century house, walled gardens with long borders, massed delphiniums and old fashioned roses.

Location: A932 - 7m from Forfar, 1m from Friockheim.

Opening Times: Gardens only: 1 Apr - 31 Oct, 10.00am - 5.00pm.

Admission: Adult £2.00, Child free.

The Courtyard at Megginch Castle, transformed for the film Rob Roy, September 1994.

Photograph Humphrey Drummond.

SPECIAL EVENTS DIARY

- **29th-30th April: Scone Palace**
  Horse Trials.

- **29th-30th April: Kelburn Castle and Country Centre**
  Woodcraft and Forestry Fair.

- **1st May: Kelburn Castle and Country Centre**
  Woodcraft and Forestry Fair.

- **1st May - 30th June: Cawdor Castle**
  Newly restored paradise garden, knot garden and maze open daily 10am - 5.30pm.

- **13th-14th May: Kelburn Castle and Country Centre**
  West of Scotland Field Sports Fair.

- **21st May: Glamis Castle**
  Lochside Bowmen Archery Tournament.

- **21st May: Kelburn Castle and Country Centre**
  Noah's Ark Festival.

- **27th May: Blair Castle**
  Atholl Highlanders Parade 3.00pm.

- **27th - 28th May: Traquair**
  Scottish Beer Festival.

- **28th May: Blair Castle**
  Atholl Gathering & Highland Games 1.30pm.

- **28th May: Mellerstain**
  Fete in aid of the R.N.L.I.

- **4th June: Mellerstain**
  Borders Vintage Automobile Club annual display. Over 500 vintage and veteran vehicles.

- **25th June: Scone Palace**
  Coronation Pageant.

- **1st - 2nd July: Scone Palace**
  Game Fair.

- **4th-29th July: Dunvegan Castle**
  15th Annual Music and Arts Festival

- **12th July: Colzium House, Walled Garden & Estate**
  Display of Model Trains and Boats within the grounds.

- **16th July: Glamis Castle**
  Strathmore Vintage Vehicle Club Extravaganza - Vintage vehicles, side shows, exhibitions etc.

- **22nd July: Glamis Castle**
  Glamis Castle Prom (Classical Concert & firework display in grounds).

- **22nd-24th July: Mellerstain**
  Craft Festival.

- **23rd July: Ardchatton Priory**
  Ardchatton Fête - Garden and house open, light lunches, teas, stalls, produce, etc.

- **30th July: Traquair**
  Sheep and Wool Day.

- **2nd August: Dunvegan Castle**
  The Silver Chanter Piping Recital.

- **5th-6th August: Traquair**
  Traquair Fair.

- **12th-13th August: Thirlestane Castle**
  Kite flying festival.

- **13th August: Megginch Castle**
  Garden opening for Scotland's Garden Scheme.

- **19th - 20th August: Kelburn Castle and Country Centre**
  New Zealand Festival.

- **20th August: Dunrobin Castle**
  Vintage Car Rally.

- **26th - 27th August: Glamis Castle**
  Glamis Castle Craft Fair.

- **3rd September: Kelburn Castle and Country Centre**
  Viking Day - Viking battle display, fun and games.

- **10th September: Scone Palace**
  Farming of Yesteryear.

- **16th - 17th September: Traquair**
  Traquair Needlework weekend.

- **23rd - 24th September: Scone Palace**
  Horse Trials.

Sealed Knot at Fyvie Castle, Aberdeenshire.

TREDEGAR HOUSE
Newport

South Wales' finest country house, ancestral home of the Morgan dynasty for over 500 years.

Parts of a mediaeval house in stone remain, but Tredegar owes its reputation to lavish rebuilding in brick at the end of the 17th Century. The new house was built on an exceptionally grand scale and included a glittering series of State Rooms complemented by a more intimate family wing, although the mediaeval courtyard plan was retained. The service wing was built in the 19th Century.

The house and contents were sold in 1951 and for 23 years served as a school. Purchased by Newport Borough Council in 1974, it has been carefully restored and refurnished, often with original pieces. Visitors have a lively and entertaining tour through 40 rooms in a variety of historical decorative styles. Exquisite carving, plasterwork and decorations, fine painting and tapestries, and special attention to the accurate use of recreated fabrics, textiles and floor coverings are features of rooms above stairs, while a host of domestic bygones capture the visitor's imagination in the Great Kitchen, Housekeeper's Room, Servants' Hall and other rooms 'below stairs'.

GARDENS

The basic mediaeval garden plan survives on two sides of the house in a series of Walled Gardens currently undergoing restoration. Late 18th Century landscaping by Mickle swept away all but one of the avenues of oak and chestnut radiating from the house. Ninety acres of parkland. The Sunken Garden has now been restored with an early 20th Century planting scheme.

SUITABILITY FOR OTHER EVENTS
Press launches, concerts, lectures, filming and wedding receptions.

EXTRA FACILITIES
Park and gardens. Carriage rides, boating, adventure playground as well as craft workshops.

ADVICE FOR COURIERS & DRIVERS
Please book in advance and allow at least three hours at the house for tours and refreshments. No dogs, unaccompanied children, photography, stilettos or smoking allowed in house.

FACILITIES FOR THE DISABLED
Disabled access to ground floor and toilets Free wheelchair loan. Please give advance warning.

PARKING FOR COACHES & CARS
Parking for 1800 cars and 10 coaches 150 yards from the house.

CATERING
The Restaurant/Tea Room can cater for up to 80 people. Prices from £1.80 (tea), £5 (2 course lunch), £16 (3 course dinner). Groups can book in advance; menus available. Catering facilities available for special functions/conferences.

GIFT SHOP
Country Park Shop open daily 10.30am - 6.00pm. Housekeeper's Shop open as house. Including souvenirs, Welsh crafts, books, spices, toiletries and souvenirs.

GUIDED TOURS
Parties of 40 people can be taken round the house at no additional cost. Average time for tour 1$^{1}/_{4}$ hours.

SCHOOL VISITS/CHILDREN
Groups welcome and guide available. £2 per child (house only). Areas of interest include: 'Below Stairs', boating, carriage rides, woodland walk, craft workshops and adventure play farm.

CONTACT

The Curator
Tredegar House & Park
Newport
Gwent
NP1 9YW

Tel: (01633) 815880

LOCATION

From London M4, signposted Junction 28 2$^{1}/_{2}$ hours. Newport 2 miles

Rail: London to Newport station.

Bus: Bus within 300 yards of entrance.

Taxi: Dragon (01633) 216216.

OPENING TIMES

Summer
Good Friday - 30 Sept.

Bank Hol. Mons
11.00am - 5.00pm

Tues School Summer Hols only
11.30am - 4.00pm

Wed, Thur, Fri, Sat, Sun Tours 11.30am - 4.00pm.

NB Country Park open. Daily 8.00am - Dusk Evening Tours by appointment only.

Winter
October only - weekend opening as Summer.

Day & Evening tours by appointment only. Christmas opening: Details from September

ADMISSION

HOUSE & GARDEN
Adult £3.80
Child £3.00
OAP £3.00
Student £3.00
Family £10.00

Prices correct at time of going to press.

CONFERENCE AND FUNCTION FACILITIES

ROOM	DIMENSIONS	CAPACITY	LAYOUT	POWER POINTS	SUITABLE FOR A/V
Morgan Room	58' x 20' x 8'	40 - 120	Various	4	✓
Tea Room & Bar	50' x 20' x 8'	30-80	Various	4	✓

CLWYD

BODELWYDDAN CASTLE

OPEN

8 Apr - 30 Jun
8 Sept - 31 Oct
Daily except Fridays
10.00am - 5.00pm

1 Jul - 7 Sept
Daily 10.00am - 5.00pm

1 Nov - 30 Mar 1996
Daily except Mon - Fris
11.00am - 4.00pm

Last Adm: 1 hour
before closing

• Castle galleries open
at 10.30am

Tel: 01745 584060

ST. ASAPH, CLWYD

Owner: Clwyd County Council   *Contact: Karen Short*
Managed by Bodelwyddan Castle Trust - a Registered Charity

This magnificently restored Victorian mansion set in rolling parkland displays extensive collections from the National Portrait Gallery, furniture from the Victoria and Albert Museum, and John Gibson sculpture from the Royal Academy. Exhibitions of Victorian amusements and inventions and a programme of large and small indoor and outdoor events throughout the year. Winner of the Museum of the Year Award.
Location: Follow signs off A55 Expressway Nr. St Asaph, opposite Marble Church.
Admission: Castle & Grounds: Adult £4.00, OAP/Unemployed £3.50, Child Student/Disabled £2.50, Family (2+2) £10.00. Grounds only: Adult £1.50, OAP/Unemployed £1.50, Child/Student/Disabled £1.50, Family (2+2) £5.00.

BODNANT GARDEN

Tel: 01492 650460

Tal-y-Cafn, Colwyn Bay, Clwyd, LL28 5RE.
Owner: The National Trust   **Contact:** The Secretary
Begun in 1875 by Henry Pochin. Amongst the finest gardens in the country. Magnificent collections of rhododendrons, camellias, magnolias and conifers.
Location: 18 Mar - 31 Oct: daily 10.00am - 5.00pm. Last admission 4.30pm.
Opening Times: Mar 1 to following Jan 31 – Daily (except Mon and Fri but open Bank Hol Mon) 1 - 6pm. Last Admin 5.30. Adm. £1.20. Chd 30p, OAP's 60p. Closed Dec 24 - 26.
Admission: Adult £3.90, Child £1.90. Parties (20 or more) £3.50.

BODRHYDDAN HALL

OPEN

8 Apr - 30 Jun
8 Sept - 31 Oct
Daily except Fridays
10.00am - 5.00pm

1 Jul - 7 Sept
Daily 10.00am - 5.00pm

1 Nov - 30 Mar 1996
Daily except Mon - Fris
11.00am - 4.00pm

Last Adm: 1 hour
before closing

• Castle galleries open
at 10.30am

Tel: 01745 590414

NR. RHUDDLAN, CLWYD LL18 5SB

Owner: Colonel The Lord Langford OBE   *Contact: Colonel The Lord Langford*
Basically a 17th century house with 19th century additions by the famous architect, Nesfield, although traces of an earlier building exist. The house has been in the hands of the same family since it was originally built over 500 years ago. There are notable pieces of armour, pictures, period furniture and a 3000 year old Egyptian Mummy. There is a formal French Garden and attractive picnic areas. Teas are available. Bodrhyddan has recently been upgraded by CADW to a Grade I listing making one of few in Wales to be in private hands.
Location: On the A5151 midway between Dyserth and Rhuddlan.
Admission: Adult £2.00, Child £1.00. Free car park. Coaches by appointment only.

CHIRK CASTLE

Tel: 01691 777701

Chirk, Wrexham, Clwyd, LL14 5AF.
Owner: The National Trust   **Contact:** The Administrator
Built 1310, a unique example of a border castle of Edward I's time. Interesting portraits, tapestries etc. Gardens.
Location: 5m from Chirk on A5, then 1.5m private driveway. 20m NW of Shrewsbury, 7m SE of Llangollen.
Opening Times: 2 Apr - 29 Sept: daily except Mon and Sat but open BH Mon. Jul & Aug: daily except Sat. 1 Oct - 29 Oct open Sat & Sun. Castle: 12.00pm - 5.00pm, Gardens: 11.00am - 6.00pm. Last admission 4.30pm.
Admission: Adult £4.00, Child £2.00, Parties (20 or more) £3.20. Family ticket £10.00.

DENBIGH CASTLE

Tel: 01745 813979

Denbigh, Clwyd.
Owner: CADW: Welsh Historic Monuments   **Contact:** The Administrator
Crowning the summit of a prominent outcrop dominating the Vale of Clwyd, the principal feature of this spectacular site is the great gatehouse dating back to the 11th century. Some of the walls can still be walked by visitors.
Location: Denbigh via A525 or B5382.
Opening Times: 1 May - 30 Sept: Daily 10.00am - 5.00pm 1 Oct - 30 Apr: Open at all times Closed Christmas Eve, Christmas Day, Boxing Day, New Year's Day.
Admission: Castle: Adult £1.70, Reduced £1.20, Family: £4 (2 adults & up to 3 children).

ERDIGG

Tel: 01978 313333

Wrexham, Clwyd, LL13 0YT.
Owner: The National Trust   **Contact:** The Administrator
Late 17th Century house with 18th Century additions and containing much of the original furniture. Range of domestic outbuildings including laundry, bakehouse, sawmill and smithy all in working order. Fine walks in extensive woods and parkland.
Location: 2m S of Wrexham off A525 or A483.
Opening Times: 14 Apr (Good Fri) -1 Oct daily, except Thur and Fri. House: 12.00pm - 5.00pm Gardens 11.00am - 6.00pm Last admission 4.00pm, 2 Oct - 29 Oct: whole house Sat and Sun only. Below stairs on Mon, Tue and Wed. House 12.00pm - 4.00pm, gardens 11.00am - 5.00pm. Last admission 3.00pm.
Admission: Downstairs: Adult £3.20, Child £1.60. Family £8.00. Pre-booked parties £2.50. Downstairs & Upstairs: Adult £5.00, Child £2.50. Pre-booked parties £4.00 Mid-week discount Mon (not BH Mons), Tue, Wed except Jul & Aug. Family rooms: Adult £4.50. Below stairs: Adult £2.70.

ST ASAPH CATHEDRAL

Tel: 01745 583597

St Asaph, Clwyd, LL17 0RL.

    Contact: The Dean
Smallest ancient cathedral in Great Britain. Founded 560AD. Present building dates from 13th century.
Location: Just off A55.
Opening Times: Summer: 7.30am - 6.30pm Winter: 7.30am - dusk Sun services: 8.00am, 11.00am, 3.30pm.

VALLE CRUCIS ABBEY

Tel: 01978 860326

Llangollen, Clwyd.
Owner: CADW: Welsh Historic Monuments   **Contact:** The Administrator
The lovely ruins of the 13th century Abbey are set at the foot of the Horseshoe Pass beside a stream.
Location: B5103 from A5, W of Llangollen, or A542 from Ruthin.
Opening Times: 28 Mar - 22 Oct: Daily 9.30am - 6.30pm 23 Oct - 26 Mar: Mon - Sat 9.30am to 4.00pm Sun 2.00am - 4.00pm Closed Christmas, Boxing Day, New Year's Eve.
Admission: Adult £1.70, Reduced Rate: £1.20, Family: £4.00 (2 adults & up to 3 children).

DYFED

CILGERRAN CASTLE

Tel: 01239 615136

Cardigan, Dyfed.
Owner: CADW: Welsh Historic Monuments   **Contact:** The Administrator
Perched high up on a rugged spur above the River Teifi, Cilgerran Castle is one of the most spectacularly sited fortresses in Wales. It dates from the 11th - 13th centuries.
Location: Main roads to Cilgerran from A478 and A484.
Opening Times: 28 Mar - 22 Oct: Daily 9.30am - 6.30pm 23 Oct - 26 Mar: Mon - Sat 9.30am to 4.00pm Sun 2.00pm - 4.00pm Closed Christmas Eve, Christmas Day, Boxing Day, New Year's Day.
Admission: Adult £1.70, Reduced Rate £1.20, Family: £4.00 (2 adults & up to 3 children).

COLBY WOODLAND GARDEN

Tel: 01558 822800 / 811885

Colby Bothy, Amroth, Narbeth, Dyfed, SA67 8PP.
Owner: The National Trust   **Contact:** The Centre Manager
An attractive woodland garden with walks through secluded valleys along open and wooded pathways, one of which links the property with the nearby coastal resort of Amroth.
Location: NE of Tenby off A477, E of jn A477/A478.
Opening Times: 1 Apr - 3 Nov: daily 10.00am - 5.00pm. 1 Apr - 30 Oct: Walled Garden 11.00am - 5.00pm.
Admission: Adult £2.60, Child £1.10. Parties £2.10, Child 90p.

CYMER ABBEY

Tel: 01341 422854

Dolgellau, Dyfed.

Owner: CADW: Welsh Historic Monuments   **Contact:** The Administrator
This remote and tranquil setting is typical of locations sought by the austere Cistercian monks. It suffered badly during the Welsh wars and was finally closed during the reign of Henry VIII. However, it is still impressive and gives wonderful insight into Cistercian life.
Location: 2 m NW of DolgellauDollgellau on A494.
Opening Times: 28 Mar - 22 Oct: Daily 9.30am - 6.30pm 23 Oct - 26 Mar: Mon - Sat 9.30am - 4pm, Sun 2pm - 4.00pm Closed Christmas. Boxing Day and New Year's Day.
Admission: Adult £1.20, Reduced rate £1.00.

DYFI FURNACE

Tel: 01222 465511

Aberdyfi, Dyfed.

Owner: CADW: Welsh Historic Monuments   **Contact:** The Administrator
This was built around 1755 and probably the best preserved charcoal furnace in Britain. Set in beautiful woodland it also has a grand external water wheel in working order.
Location: On the A487 near Eglwsfach, 6 m from Machynlleth.
Opening Times: 1 May - 30 Sept: Daily 9.30am - 6.30pm 1 Oct - 30 Apr: Open all times Closed Christmas Eve, Day, Boxing Day and New Year's Day.
Admission: Adult £1.70, Reduced rate £1.20, Family : £4.00 (2 Adults & up to 3Children).

LAMPHEY BISHOP'S PALACE

Tel: 01646 672224

Lamphey, Dyfed.

Owner: CADW: Welsh Historic Monuments   **Contact:** The Administrator
Lamphey marks the place of the spectacular Bishop's Palace but it reached its height of greatness under Bishop Henry de Gower who raised the new great hall. Today the ruins of this comfortable retreat reflect the power enjoyed by the medieval bishops.
Location: A4139 from Pembroke or Tenby.
Opening Times: 28 May - 30 Sept: Daily 10.00am - 5.30pm, Oct - 30 Apr : Open all times. Closed Christmas, Boxing Day, New Year's Day.
Admission: Adult £1.70, Reduced rate £1.20, Family : £4.00 (2 Adults & up to 3 Children).

ST DAVID'S BISHOPS PALACE

Tel: 01437 720517

Pembroke, Dyfed.

Owner: CADW: Welsh Historic Monuments   **Contact:** The Administrator
St. David's Bishop's Palace was a grand and richly decorated building and one of the medieval buildings unique to Wales. The architecture includes superb arcaded parapets and sculpted heads. Exhibition: "Life in the Palace of a Prince of the Church".
Location: A487 to St. David's, minor road past the Cathedral.
Opening Times: 28 Mar - 22 Oct: Daily 9.30am - 6.30pm 23 Oct - 26 Mar: Mon - Sat 9.30am - 4pm Sun: 11am - 4pm Closed Christmas, Boxing Day and New Year's Day.
Admission: Adult £1.70, Reduced Rate: £1.20, Family : £4.00 (2 Adults & up to 3 Children).

ST DAVID'S CATHEDRAL

Tel: 01437 720691   **Fax:** 01437 721885

St David's, Dyfed, SA62 6QW.

Contact: Mr R G Tarr
St David's is Britain's smallest city by Royal Charter March 1994. Premier cathedral of church in Wales. Over eight centuries old. Many unique and "odd" features. Resited to be on site of St David's 6th century monastery.
Location: 5 - 10 minutes walk from car/coach parks signposted for pedestrians.
Opening Times: 7.30am - 7.00pm Sun: 12.30am - 5.30pm May be closed when services are in progress. Sun services: 8.00am, 9.30am, 11.00am and 6.00pm. Weekday services: 7.30am, 8.00am and 6.00pm.
Admission: Donations.Guided tours (Adult £2.00, Child 75p) must be booked in advance.

STRATA FLORIDA ABBEY

Dyfed.

Owner: CADW: Welsh Historic Monuments   **Contact:** The Administrator
The Abbey was founded in the 12th century when the Norman baron Robert Fitz Stephen drew a colony of 13 monks from the Cistercian abbey Whitland and set up a new house in this tranquil location.
Location: Minor road from Pontrhydfendigaid reached from the B4340.
Opening Times: 1 May - 30 Sept: Daily 10am - 5.30pm. 1 Oct - 30 Apr: Open all times.
Admission: Adult £1.70, Reduced Rate: £1.20, Family : £4.00 (2 Adults & up to 3 Children).

 CADW

 THE NATIONAL TRUST

HISTORIC HOUSES ASSOCIATION

TUDOR MERCHANTS HOUSE

Tel: 01834 842279

Quay Hill, Tenby, Dyfed, SA70 7BX.

Owner: The National Trust   **Contact:** The Administrator
A late 15th century town house, characteristic of the building tradition of south-west Wales. The ground-floor chimney at the rear of the house is a fine vernacular example, and the original scarfed roof trusses survive. The remains of early frescos can be seen on three interior walls. Access to small herb garden, weather permitting. Furniture and fittings re-create the atmosphere from the time when a Tudor family was in residence.
Location: Quay Hill.
Opening Times: 2 Apr - 31 Oct: Mon-Fri, 10.30am - 5.30pm: Sun, 1.30 - 5.30pm, Sat, closed.
Admission: Adult £1.60, Child 80p, Groups £1.30, Child 60p. One child (-16) free with 1 full paying adult 25 Jul - 4 Sept.

MID GLAMORGAN

CAERPHILLY CASTLE

Tel: 01222 833143

Caerphilly, Mid Glamorgan.

Owner: CADW: Welsh Historic Monuments   **Contact:** The Administrator
This vast fortress is one of the great surviving castles of the medieval western world. It covers a massive 30 acres. Restoration began in the late 19th century and was completed in 1939 so that much of its magnificence remains today.
Location: A468 (from Newport) A469 (from Cardiff).
Opening Times: 28 Mar - 22 Oct . Daily 9.30am - 6.30am 23 Oct - 26 Mar. Mon - Sat 9.30am - 4pm, Sun 11am - 4pm Closed Christmas Day, Boxing Day, New Year's Day.
Admission: Adult £2.20, Reduced rates £1.70, Family : £6.00 (2 Adults & up to 3 Children).

SOUTH GLAMORGAN

CARDIFF CASTLE

Tel: 01222 822083   **Fax:** 01222 231417

Castle Street, Cardiff, South Glamorgan, CF1 2RB.

Owner: Cardiff City Council   **Contact:** Mrs J Brown
Location: Cardiff city centre.
Opening Times: Castle Green, Roman Wall, Norman Keep;1 May - 30 Sept, 10am - 6pm Mar, Apr and Oct, 10am - 5pm Nov - Feb, 10.00am - 4.30pm Conducted tour of Castle interior; Mar, Apr and Oct, daily at 30 min intervals, 10am - 12.30pm and 2 - 4pm. May - Sept, daily at 20 min intervals, 10.00am -12.40pm and 2.00pm - 5.00pm. Nov - Feb, daily, 10.30am, 11.45am, 2pm, 3.15pm. The Castle is closed on Christmas and New Year BHs.
Admission: Conducted tour of Castle including admission to Military Museum, Green, Roman Wall and Norman Keep: Adult £3.50, Child/senior citizen £1.70, Short tour of Castle including admission to Military Museum, Green, Roman Wall and Norman Keep: Adult £2.90, Child £1.50. Green, Roman Wall, Norman Keep and Military Museum: Adult £2.20, Child/senior citizen £1.10, 10% discount for groups of 20 plus. For further details contact administrator.

CASTELL COCH

Tel: 01222 810101

Taff Wells, Cardiff, South Glamorgan.

Owner: CADW: Welsh Historic Monuments   **Contact:** The Administrator
This breath-takingly decorated 19th century castle was the creation of the fabulously wealthy Lord Bute on the site of a medieval castle, set in the beech woods to the North of Cardiff. Wonderful murals of Aesop's fables.
Location: M4 (Jct 32), A470 then signposted Taff Wells.
Opening Times: 28 Mar-22 Oct: Daily 9.30am-6.30pm, 23 Oct -26 Mar:Mon-Sat 9.30am - 4pm Suns 11am - 4pm Closed Christmas Eve, Christmas Day, Boxing Day, New Year's Day.
Admission: Adult £2.20, Reduced Rate £1.70, Family : £6.00 (2 Adults & up to 3Children).

DYFFRYN GARDENS

Tel: 01222 593328   **Fax:** 01222 591966

St Nicholas, Cardiff, South Glamorgan, CF5 6SU.

Owner: Mid & South Glamorgan County Council   **Contact:** Ms N Walby
55 acres of landscaped gardens, beautiful at most times of year. Numerous small theme gardens, heather bank, arboretum and glass houses.
Location: Exit junction 33/M4 - signposted Barry.
Opening Times: Mar weekends only, 10.30am - 4.30pm. Apr - Oct, daily, 10.am - 5.30pm.
Admission: Adult £2.00, Child £1.50, Family £6.00, Conc £1.50, Groups £1.50.

WELSH FOLK MUSEUM

Tel: 01222 569441

St Fagans, Cardiff, South Glamorgan.

Contact: The Administrator
St Fagans Castle, a 16th century building built within the walls of a 13th century castle. The grounds have numerous reconstructed old farmhouses, cottages and other buildings which together with the museum building represent the life and culture of Wales.
Location: All year daily 10.00am - 5.00pm.
Opening Times: All year daily 10.00am - 5.00pm.
Admission: Adult £4.00, Child £2.00, Parties £3.00, Family £10.00.

WEST GLAMORGAN

ABERDULAIS FALLS
Tel: 01639 636674

Aberdulais, Neath, West Glamorgan, SA10 8EU.

Owner: The National Trust   **Contact:** The Administrator

For over 300 years this famous waterfall has provided the energy to drive the wheels of industry. Nestling amongst the site's historic remains, a unique hydro-electric scheme has been developed to harness this great natural resource. The Turbine House provides visitor access to the top of the falls, with views of equipment, fish pass and displays. Nearby, in the restored Victorian tinplate works' wheel pit, Britain's largest electricity generating water wheel makes Aberdulais Falls self-sufficient in environmentally friendly energy.

Location: On A465, 3m NE of Neath.

Opening Times: 1 Apr - 3 Nov: Mon - Fri, 10am - 5pm , Sat, Sun & BHs 11am - 6pm. Last admission ¹/₂ hour beforehand.

Admission: Adult £2.80, Child £1.20, Party £2.20, Child £1.00.

CARREG CENNEN CASTLE
Tel: 01558 822291

Brecon Beacons National Park, Llandeilo, West Glamorgan.

Owner: CADW: Welsh Historic Monuments   **Contact:** The Administrator

Carreg Cennen Castle occupies a spectacular defensive location and is one of the earliest stone-built castles and is a marvellous example of how a sophisticated castle was built despite the obstacles of such rugged terrain.

Location: Minor roads from A483(T) to Trapp village.

Opening Times: 28 Mar - 22 Oct: Daily 9.30am - 7.30pm 23 Oct - 26 Mar: Daily 9.30am - 4.00pm Closed Christmas Eve, Christmas Day, Boxing Day, New Year's Day.

Admission: Adult £2.20, Reduced £1.70, Family £6.00 (up to 2 adults and 3 children).

KIDWELLY CASTLE
Tel: 01554 890104

Kidwelly, West Glamorgan.

Owner: CADW: Welsh Historic Monuments   **Contact:** The Administrator

Kidwelly Castle is built in a magnificent sweeping crescent set high above the River Gwendraeth making full use of the huge earthwork stronghold built in 1106. Outstanding example of later 13th century castle design.

Location: Kidwelly via A484: Kidwelly Rail Station 1 m.

Opening Times: 28 Mar - 22 Oct : Daily 9.30am - 6.30pm 23 Oct - 26 Mar: Weekdays 9.30am - 4pm Sun 11am - 4pm. Closed Christmas. Boxing Day and New Year's Day.

Admission: Adult £2.20, Reduced £1.70, Family £6.00 (2 Adults and up to 3 Children).

WEOBLEY CASTLE
Tel: 01792 390012

Gower, West Glamorgan.

Owner: CADW: Welsh Historic Monuments   **Contact:** The Administrator

Weobly Castle is as much a medieval fortified manor house as a true castle. Visitors to Weobly can enjoy a fascinating exhibition about the castle high above the stark northern shore of the Gower Peninsula.

Location: B4271 or B4295 to Llanrhidian Village, then minor road.

Opening Times: 28 Mar - 22 Oct: Daily 9.30am - 6.30pm, 23 Oct - 26 Mar: Mon - Sat 9.30am - 4.00pm Sun 2 - 4pm, Closed Christmas, Boxing Day and New Year's Day.

Admission: Adult £1.70, Reduced Rates £1.20, Family: £4.00 (2 Adults & up to 3 Children).

GWENT

BLAENAVON IRONWORKS
Tel: 01495 792615

Near Brecon Beacons National Park, Blaenavon, Gwent.

Owner: CADW: Welsh Historic Monuments   **Contact:** The Administrator

Blaenavon Ironworks is one of the most complete works to survive in the country and dates back to the 18th century. Furnaces can be viewed and are in varying stages of preservation.

Location: Via A4043 follow signs to Big Pit Mining Museum and Blaenavon Ironworks. Abergavenny 8m. Pontypool 8m.

Opening Times: 1 May - 30 Sept: Mon - Sat 11.00am - 5.00pm, Sun 2.00pm - 5.00pm Winter by appointment only.

Admission: Adult £1.20. Reduced Rate £1.00.

CHEPSTOW CASTLE
Tel: 01291 624065

Chepstow, Gwent.

Owner: CADW: Welsh Historic Monuments   **Contact:** The Administrator

Chepstow Castle is magnificently situated on the cliffs above the River Wye guarding one of the main crossings from England to Wales.

Location: Chepstow via A465, B4235. A48 or M4 (Jct 22).

Opening Times: 28 Mar - 22 Oct: Daily 9.30am - 6.30pm 23 Oct - 26 Mar: Mon - Sat 9.30am - 4pm Sun 11am - 4pm Closed Christmas, Boxing Day and New Year's Day.

Admission: Adult £2.50, Reduced Rate: £1.50,Family : £4.00 (2 Adults & up to 3 Children).

RAGLAN CASTLE
Tel: 01291690228

Raglan, Gwent.

Owner: CADW: Welsh Historic Monuments   **Contact:** The Administrator

Situated on the Borders. Raglan Castle is famed for its striking hexagonal Great Tower. It is also unique as part of it is constructed of brick, probably the earliest use of this material in Wales. It was as much a product of social grandeur as it was of military necessity.

Location: Raglan, Gwent.

Opening Times: 28 Mar - 22 Oct: Daily 9.30am - 6.30pm 23 Oct - 26 Mar: Mon - Sat: 9.30am - 4pm, Sun 11am - 4pm Closed Christmas, Boxing Day and New Year's Day.

Admission: Adult £2.20, Reduced Rate £1.70, Family : £4.00 (2 Adults & up to 3 Children).

TINTERN ABBEY
Tel: 01291 689251

Tintern, Gwent.

Owner: CADW: Welsh Historic Monuments   **Contact:** The Administrator

Originally founded in 1131 for the Cistercian monks and by 1536 was the richest Abbey in Wales. The great church is still gloriously intact and visitors will find the views both beautiful and unforgettable.

Location: Tintern via A466, from M4 (Jct 22). Chepstow 6 m.

Opening Times: 28 Mar - 22 Oct: Daily 9.30am - 6.30pm 23 Oct - 26 Mar: Mon - Sat 9.30am - 4pm Sun: 11am - 4pm Closed Christmas, Boxing Day and New Year's Day.

Admission: Adult £2.20, Reduced Rate: £1.70, Family : £4.00 (2 Adults & up to 3 Children).

TREDEGAR HOUSE
See page 261 for full page entry.

WHITE CASTLE
Tel: 01606 85380

Brecon Beacons National Park, Gwent.

Owner: CADW: Welsh Historic Monuments   **Contact:** The Administrator

Situated on a low hill about a mile from the village of Llantilio Crossenny, White Castle was built in the 11th century to control the southern March. It was given the name "White Castle" because of the rendering, traces of which can be seen today.

Location: By minor roads from B4233 near Llantilio Crossenny. Abergavenny 8m.

Opening Times: 28 Mar - 22 Oct: Daily 9.30am - 6.30pm 23 Oct - 26 Mar: Open all times Closed Christmas, Boxing Day, New Year's Day.

Admission: Adult £1.70, Reduced Rate £1.20, Family : £4.00 (2 Adults & up to 3 Children).

GWYNEDD

ABERCONWY HOUSE
Tel: 01492 592246

Castle Street, Conwy, Gwynedd, LL32 8AY.

Owner: The National Trust   **Contact:** The Administrator

Dating from the 14th century, this is the only medieval merchant's house in Conwy to have survived the turbulent history of this walled town for nearly six centuries. Furnished rooms and an audio-visual presentation show daily life from different periods in its history. At junction of Castle Street and High Street

Location: At junction of Castle Street and High Street

Opening Times: 31 Mar - 30 Oct, daily except Tues, 10am - 5pm, last admission 4.30pm.

Admission: Adult £1.80, Child 90p, Pre-booked Parties £1.60, Family £4.50.

BEAUMARIS CASTLE
Tel: 01248 810361

Beaumaris, Anglesey, Gwynedd, WL58 8AP.

Owner: CADW : Welsh Historic Monuments   **Contact:** The Administrator

Baumaris is a World Heritage Listed Site. Built by Edward I in his conquest of Wales, it is the most sophisticated example of medieval military architecture.

Location: A545 (Menai Bridge), A5 (Bangor).

Opening Times: 28 Mar - 22 Oct: Daily 9.30am - 6.30am 23 Oct - 26 Mar: Mon - Sat 9.30am - 4.00pm, Sun 11.00am - 4.00pm, Closed Christmas Eve, Christmas Day, Boxing Day, New Year's Day.

Admission: Adult £1.70, Reduced Child under 16 (under 5 Free of charge) Over 60s and students with student cards £1.20, Family, up to 2 adults and 3 children: £4.00.

BRYN BRAS CASTLE
Tel: 01286 870210   **Fax:** 01286 870210

Llanrug, Caernarfon, Gwynedd, LL55 4RE.

Owner: Mrs M Gray Parry   **Contact:** Mrs M Gray Parry

Built 1830 in Romanesque style on earlier structure. Family home with richly carved furniture. Gardens over 32 acres have streams, statuary and knot garden.

Location: 4¹/₂ miles E of Caernarfon.

Opening Times: Spring Bank Hol weekend - mid Sept; Tue, Wed, Thu, Fri 1.00pm - 5.00pm. From mid Jul - end Aug open 11.00am.

Admission: Adult £3.50, Child £1.75, Groups 10% discount by prior arrangement.

CAERNARFON CASTLE ✤
Tel: 01286 677617

Caernarfon, Gwynedd, LL55 2AY.
Owner: CADW: Welsh Historic Monuments   **Contact:** The Administrator
Caernarfon Castle is a mighty medieval fortress built by Edward I and is undoubtedly one of Europe's finest. It became famous in modern times as the setting for the Prince of Wales investiture.
Location: In Caernarfon.
Opening Times: 28 Mar - 22 Oct : 9.30am - 6.30pm daily 23 Oct - 26 Mar: weekdays: 9.30am - 4.00pm. Sunday 11.00am - 4.00pm Closed: Christmas Eve, Christmas Day, Boxing Day, New Year's Day.
Admission: Adults £3.80. Reduced £2.80 Family (up to 2 adults & 3 children) £10.00.

CONWAY CASTLE ✤
Tel: 01492 592358

Conwy, Gwynedd.
Owner: CADW: Welsh Historic Monuments   **Contact:** The Administrator
Conwy Castle is a masterpiece of medieval military architecture. Built between 1238 and 1289 by Edward I, it helped to complete the conquest of the Welsh princes in North Wales. World Heritage Listed site.
Location: Conwy by A55 or B5106.
Opening Times: 28 Mar - 22 Oct: Daily 9.30am - 6.30pm 23 Oct - 26 Mar: Mon - Sat 9.30am - 4.00pm Sun: 11.00am - 4.00pm Closed Christmas, Boxing Day and New Year's Days.
Admission: Adults: £3.00, Reduced Rate £2.00, Family: £8.00 (2 adults & up to 3 children).

CRICCIETH CASTLE ✤
Tel: 01766 522227

Criccieth, Gwynedd.
Owner: CADW: Welsh Historic Monuments   **Contact:** The Administrator
Criccieth is made impressive by the natural sea cliff defence and the construction of the earthworks. Overlooking Cardigan Bay its ruins are testament to Welsh castle building.
Location: A497 to Criccieth from Portmadoc or Pwelleli.
Opening Times: 28 Mar - 22 Oct: Daily 9.30am - 6.30pm 23 Oct - 26 Mar: Mon - Sat 9.30am - 4pm Sun 11am - 4pm. Closed Christmas, Boxing Day and New Year's Day.
Admission: Adult £2.20, Reduced Rate £1.70, Family £6.00 (2 adults & up to 3 children).

DOLWYDDELAN CASTLE ✤
Tel: 01690 6366

Blaenau Ffestiniog, Gwynedd.
Owner: CADW: Welsh Historic Monuments   **Contact:** The Administrator
Standing proudly on a ridge, this stern building remains remarkably intact and visitors cannot fail to be impressed with the great solitary square tower, built by Llewelyn the Great in the early 13th century.
Location: A470(T) Blaenau Festiniog to Betws-y-Coed.
Opening Times: 28 Mar - 22 Oct: Daily 9.30am - 6.30pm 23 Oct - 26 Mar: Mon - Sat 9.30am - 4pm Sun 2pm - 4pm Closed Christmas Eve, Day, Boxing Day & New Year's Day.
Admission: Adult £1.70, Reduced Rate £1.20, Family £4.00 (2 adults & up to 3 children).

HARLECH CASTLE ✤
Tel: 01766 780552

Harlech, Gwynedd.
Owner: CADW: Welsh Historic Monuments   **Contact:** The Administrator
Set against the backdrop of Snowdonia, visitors will be struck by the awe-inspiring and majestic fortress of Harlech Castle which is now deservedly a World Heritage Listed site. It was impregnable until captured by Owain Glyndwr during the Welsh uprising in 1404.
Location: Harlech, Gwynedd.
Opening Times: 28 Mar - 22 Oct: Daily 9.30am - 6.30pm 23 Oct - 26 Mar: Mon - Sat : 9.30am - 4pm Sun: 11am - 4pm Closed Christmas. Boxing Day and New Year's Day.
Admission: Adult £3.00, Reduced Rate: £2.00, Family £8.00 (2 adults & up to 3 children).

PENRHYN CASTLE ✤
Tel: 01248 353084

Bangor, Gwynedd, LL57 4HN.
Owner: The National Trust   **Contact:** The Administrator
The 19th Century castle is a unique and outstanding example of Neo-Norman architecture. The grounds have exotic and rare trees and shrubs. There is an industrial railway museum, Victorian formal garden, superb views of mountains and Menai strait. Audio tour.
Location: 1m E of Bangor on A5122.
Opening Times: 29 Mar - 30 Oct: daily except Tue. Castle: 12.00pm - 5.00pm, Grounds 11.00am - 6.00pm, Jul & Aug: Castle: 11.00am - 5.00pm Grounds: 11.00am - 6. 00pm. Last admission 4.30pm. Last audio tour, 4.00pm.
Admission: Adult £4.40, Child £2.20, Parties (20 or more) £3.50. Family ticket £11.00.

PLAS BRONDANW GARDENS
Tel: 01766 770484 / 770814

Menna Angharad, Plas Brondanw, Llanfrothen, Gwynedd, LL48 6SW.
Owner: The Trustees of the Second Portmeirion Foundation
Location: 3m N of Penrhyndeudraeth off A40A5, on Croesor Road.
Opening Times: Daily, 9.00am - 5.00pm.
Admission: Adult £1.50, Child 25p, Group £1.00 (if pre-booked).

PLAS NEWYDD ✤
Tel: 01248 714795

Llanfairpwll, Anglesey, Gwynedd, LL61 6EQ.
Owner: The National Trust   **Contact:** The Administrator
18th Century house by James Wyatt in unspoilt position adjacent to Menai Strait. Magnificent views to Snowdonia. Fine spring garden. Rex Whistler exhibition and mural painting. Military museum.
Location: 1m SW of Llanfairpwll on A4080 to Brynsiencyn; turn off A5 to Llanfairpwll at W end of Britannia bridge.
Opening Times: 31 Mar - 29 Sept: daily except Sat. 1 Oct - 29 Oct: Fri and Sun only. House 12.00pm - 5.00pm, Garden 11.00am - 500pm. Last admission 4.30pm.
Admission: Adult £3.80, Child £1.90, Family £9.50. Pre-booked parties (20 or more) £3.00.

PLAS YN RHIW ✤
Tel: 01758 780219

Rhiw, Pwllheli, Gwynedd, LL53 8AB.
Owner: The National Trust   **Contact:** The Administrator
A small manor house, with garden and woodlands, overlooking the west shore of Porth Neigwl (Hell's Mouth Bay) on the Llyn Peninsula. The house is part medieval, with Tudor and Georgian additions, and the ornamental gardens have flowering trees and shrubs, divided by box hedges and grass paths, rising behind to the snowdrop wood.
Location: 12m from Pwllheli on S coast road to Aberdaron.
Opening Times: 2 Apr - 29 Sept, daily (except Sat), 12pm - 5pm, last admission 4.30pm.
Admission: Adult £2.30, Child £1.15, Family £6.00. Pre-booked parties evenings only £3.00.

PORTMEIRION
Tel: 01766 770228 **Fax:** 01766 771331

Portmeirion, Gwynedd, LL48 6ET.

          Contact: Mr R Llewellyn
Fairy tale Italianate village on shores of Cardigan Bay built by the architect Sir Clough Williams Ellis.
Location: Off A487 at Minffordd between Penrhyndeudraeth and Porthmadog.
Admission: Adult £3.00. Child £1.30, Family £8.60, Conc £2.40, Group £2.40.

POWYS

POWIS CASTLE ✤
Tel: 01938 554336

Welshpool, Powys, SY21 8RF.
Owner: The National Trust   **Contact:** The Administrator
The medieval stronghold of the Welsh princes of Upper Powys. The home of the Herbert family since 1587. Clive of India Museum. Fine plasterwork, murals, furniture, paintings and tapestry. Historic terraced garden. Herbaceous borders. Rare trees and shrubs.
1m S of Welshpool, off A483. Pedestrian access from High Street A490.
Location: 1m S of Welshpool, off A483. Pedestrian access from High Street A490.
Opening Times: 1 Apr - 30 Jun and 1 Sept - 29 Oct: daily except Mon and Tue. Jul & Aug: daily except Mon but open BH Mon. Castle and Clive Museum: 12.00pm - 5.00pm. Garden 11.00am - 6.00pm Last admission 30 minutes prior to closing. Winter opening: Sun only until Christmas. Tea room and shop 2.00pm - 4.00pm.
Admission: Garden: Adult £3.80, Child £1.90. Family £9.50. Parties £3.00. All-in ticket: Adult £5.80, Child £2.90,Family £14.50.

TREBINSHUN HOUSE
Tel: 01874 730653 **Fax:** 01874 700843

Brecon, Powys, LD3 7PX.
Owner: R Watson Esq   **Contact:** R Watson
A medium sized 16th century manor house which underwent extensive restoration in 1800. Fine courtyard and walled garden.
Location: 7m SE of Brecon 1 $^1/_2$m from Bwlch A40.
Opening Times: 1 May - 31 Aug, Mon -Tue 10.00am - 5.00pm.

TRETOWER COURT AND CASTLE ✤
Tel: 01874 730279

Brecon Beacons National Park, Crickhowell, Powys.
Owner: CADW: Welsh Historic Monuments   **Contact:** The Administrator
Tretower Court is a glorious late 15thfifteenth century house made up of a group of medieval buildings. It is memorable for its magnificent roof and timbers as well as the ornamental garden that was created as recently as 1991.
Location: Signposted to Tretower Village, off A479, 3 m NW of Crickhowell.
Opening Times: 28 Mar - 22 Oct: Daily 9.30am - 6.30pm, 23 Oct - 26 Mar: Mon - Sat 9.30am - 4.00pm, Sun 2.00pm - 4.00pm Closed Christmas, Boxing Day, New Year's Day.
Admission: Adult £2.20, Reduced rates £1.70, Family £6.00 (2 Adults & up to 3 Children).

SPECIAL EVENTS DIARY- WALES

- **16th - 17th April: Tredegar House and Park**
  Easter at Tredegar House.

- **8th May: Tredegar House and Park**
  V E Day.

- **12th - 14th May: Tredegar House and Park**
  Folk Festival.

- **13th June: Tredegar House and Park**
  Antiques Evening.

- **30th June: Bodnant Garden**
  *Gala Evening of Entertainment in the Garden.
  Contact 01492 860123.*

- **July/August: Tredegar House and Park**
  Children's Activities.

- **5th - 7th July: Colby Woodland Garden**
  Country Fair.

- **17th July: Tredegar House and Park**
  Opera Evening.

- **18th July: Erddig**
  Outdoor Concert with Fireworks.

- **22nd - 23rd July: Penrhyn Castle**
  Country Fayre with Rare Breeds.

- **23rd July : Chirk Castle**
  *700th Anniversary Outdoor Concert with Fireworks
  Tel: 01691 777701.*

- **24th July: Plas Newydd**
  Midsummer Concert.

- **26th July: Plas Newydd**
  Enterprise Neptune Jazz Concert. For details tel 01248 714795.

- **21st August: Tredegar House and Park**
  Masque with Consort de Danse Baroque.

- **28th August: Tredegar House and Park**
  17th Century Entertainment.

- **2nd-3rd September: Tredegar House and Park**
  Newport Show.

- **3rd September: Erddig**
  Victorian Day.

- **31st October: Tredegar House and Park**
  Hallowe'en Candlelit Tours.

- **10th - 17th December: Tredegar House and Park**
  Christmas at Tredegar House.

SPECIAL EVENTS DIARY - IRELAND

- **7th April: Mount Stewart House**
  Jazz Band Ball.

- **8th April: Mount Stewart House**
  Fashion Show.

- **9th April: Mount Stewart House**
  Craft Fair.

- **16th April: Springhill**
  Easter Children's Event.

- **15th-16th April: Springhill**
  The House of Goodwill.

- **27th-28th May: Florence Court**
  Country Fair and Gun Dog Trials.

- **8th June - 1st July: Castle Ward**
  Castle Ward Opera.

- **11th June: Springhill**
  Teddy Bears' Picnic.

- **17th June: Rowallane Garden**
  Midsummer Jazz Concert.

- **23rd - 24th June: Rowallane Garden**
  Percy French Concerts.

- **25th June: Florence Court**
  Victorian Tea Party.

- **28th July: The Argory**
  Children's Fun Day.

- **2nd - 3rd December: The Argory**
  Victorian Christmas at the Argory.

- **8th - 9th December: Rowallane Garden**
  Yuletide Market.

HUDSON'S DIRECTORY

**If you have a property that you feel should be included
or are interested in display advertising,**

contact the publisher;

Norman Hudson and Company, P.O. Box 16, Banbury, Oxon OX17 1TF
Tel: 01295 750750   Fax: 01295 750800

ARDRESS HOUSE

Tel: 01762 851236

64 Ardress Road, Portadown, Co. Armagh, BT62 1SQ.

Owner: The National Trust   **Contact:** The Administrator

Originally a 17th century farmhouse, the main front and garden facades were added in the 18th century by the owner-architect George Ensor. The house contains some particularly fine neo-Classical plasterwork as well as good furniture and pictures. There is a display of farm implements and livestock in the farmyard, an attractive garden and woodland walks.

Location: 7m from Portadown on Moy road B28, 5m from Moy, 3m from Loughgall intersection 13 on M1, 9m from Armagh.

Opening Times: Apr: weekends & Easter (14 - 18 Apr) 2.00pm - 6.00pm; May, Jun & Sept: Sat, Sun & BH 2.00pm - 6.00pm; Jul to end Aug: daily except Tues 2.00pm - 6.00pm. Farmyard also open weekdays (except Tues) May, Jun & Sept 12.00pm - 4.00pm.

Admission: Adult £2.00, Child £2.00, Party £1.60.

CASTLE COOLE

Tel: 01365 322690

Enniskillen, Co. Fermanagh, BT74 6JX.

Owner: The National Trust   **Contact:** The Administrator

Very fine neo-classical late 18th century house, colonnaded wings, was designed by James Wyatt. It contains original decoration and furniture dating from before 1830, and is set in a landscaped parkland with mature oak woodland. State Bedroom prepared for George IV in 1821. Exterior attractions include servants' tunnel, stables and Lady Dorothy's Walk.

Location: 1.5m SE of Enniskillen on A4, Belfast - Enniskillen road.

Opening Times: Estate: dawn to dusk daily from 1 Apr-30 Sept. House: Easter (14 -18 Apr), Apr, May: weekends and BHs; Jun, Jul, Aug: daily except Thu; Sept: weekends only 2 - 6pm.

Admission: House & grounds: Adult £2.50, Child £1.25. Parties £2.00. After hours £3.00 Estate parking £1.50.

FLORENCE COURT

Tel: 01365 348249

Eniskillen, Co Fermanagh, BT92 1DB.

Owner: The National Trust   **Contact:** The Administrator

One of the most important houses in Ulster, built in the mid 19th century by John Cole, father of 1st Earl of Enniskillen. Contents include fine rococo plasterwork and good examples of 18th century furniture. There are pleasure grounds with an ice house and water-powered sawmill, plus walled garden and fine views over surrounding mountains.

Location: 8m SW of Enniskillen via A4 Sligo road and A32 Swanlinbar road.

Opening Times: Easter daily 1 - 6pm, Apr, May & Sept. Sat, Sun, BH only 1 - 6pm Jun - Aug daily except Tue 1 - 6.pm. Last adm: 5.15pm. Grounds: All year, 10am - 7pm. Closed Dec 25.

Admission: House: £2.50, Child £1.25, Parties £2.00. Parties outside normal opening hours £3.00. Estate: £1.50.

GRAY'S PRINTING PRESS

Tel: 01504 884094

49 Main Street, Strabane, Co Tyrone, BT82 8AU.

Owner: The National Trust   **Contact:** The Administrator

An 18th century printing press, shop and stationers. It may be here that John Dunlap, the printer of the US Declaration of Independence, and James Wilson, grandfather of President Woodrow Wilson, learned their trade. Collection of 19th century hand printing machines.

Location: Strabane centre.

Opening Times: Apr - end Sept: daily, except Thur, Sun & BH, 2.00pm - 5.30pm. Other times by prior arrangement.

Admission: Adult £1.40, Child 70p, Party £1.00.

HEZLETT HOUSE

Tel: 01265 848567

107 Sea Road, Castlerock, Coleraine, Co. Londonderry, BT51 4TW.

Owner: The National Trust   **Contact:** The Administrator

A 17th century thatched house, with an interesting cruck truss roof construction. Furnished in late Victorian style. Small museum of farm implements.

Location: 5m W of Coleraine on Coleraine - Downhill coast road A2.

Opening Times: Easter (14 - 18 Apr); daily 1 - 6pm. Apr, May, Jun & Sept; Sat, Sun & BH only 1 - 6.pm. Jul & Aug; daily, except Tues 1 - 6pm. Pre-arranged parties (max 15).

Admission: Adult £1.50, Child 75p, Party £1.00.

MOUNT STEWART

Tel: 012477 88387 / 88487

Newtownards, Co. Down, BT22 2AD.

Owner: The National Trust   **Contact:** The Administrator

Fascinating 18th century house with 19th century additions, where Lord Castlereagh grew up. Gardens largely created by Edith, wife of 7th Marquess of Londonderry, with an unrivalled collection of plants, colourful parterres and magnificent vistas. The Temple of the Winds, James 'Athenian' Stuart's banqueting hall of 1785 overlooks Strangford Lough.

Location: On E shore of Strangford Lough, 5m SE of Newtownards, 15m E of Belfast on A20.

Opening Times: Apr: weekends and Good Fri - Sun after Easter (14 - 23 Apr). May to Sept: daily except Tue, 1 - 6pm. Oct: weekends only, 1 - 6pm. Garden: 1 Apr - end Sept, daily. Oct: weekends only, 10.30am - 6pm. Temple of the Winds: open as house, 2 - 5pm. Shop & Tea room: Apr: Weekends; Apr 1 -10, May - Sept: daily except Tue 1.30pm - 5.30pm; Oct: weekends only 1.30pm - 5.30.pm

Admission: House, Garden & Temple: Adult £3.30, Child £1.65. Parties £2.60. After hours £4.30. Garden & Temple: Adult £2.70, Child £1.35. Parties £2.00 After hours £3.70. Temple only: 90p.

ROWALLANE GARDEN

Tel: 01238 510131

Saintfield, Ballynahinch, Co. Down, BT24 7LH.

Owner: The National Trust   **Contact:** The Administrator

52 acre garden, with daffodils and rhododendrons in spring, summer-flowering trees and shrubs and herbaceous plants, fuchsias and shrub roses in the Wall Garden. The garden also includes a national collection of penstemons, and the rock garden with primula, meconopsis, heathers and dwarf shrubs is interesting throughout the year. The are several acreas of natural wild flowers to attract butterflies.

Location: 11m SE of Belfast, 1m S of Saintfield on the W of the A7 Downpatrick road.

Opening Times: 1 Apr to end Oct: Mon - Fri, 10.30am - 6.00pm; Sat - Sun, 2.00pm - 6.00pm. Nov - end Mar: Mon - Fri, 10.30am - 5.00pm. Closed 25, 26 Dec and 1 Jan.

Admission: Easter - end Oct: Adult £2.80, Child £1.15. Parties £1.60. After hours £3.00. Nov - end Mar: Adult £1.30. Parties 80p.

SEAFORDE GARDENS 🏛

Tel: 01396 811225   **Fax:** 01396 811370

Seaforde, Co. Down, BF30 8PG.

Owner: Patrick Ford Esq   **Contact:** Patrick Ford Esq

Beautiful gardens and maze containing many rare plants, some tender, huge rhododendrons and the National Collection of eucryphias. Also a tropical butterfly house and nursery garden. Teas.

Location: 20m S of Belfast on the main road to Newcastle.

Opening Times: Easter to end Sept, Mon - Sat 10.00am - 5.00pm, Sun 2.00pm - 6.00pm. Oct - Mar Mon - Fri 10.00am - 5.00pm

Admission: Adult £2.00, Child £1.20.

SPRINGHILL

Tel: 016487 48210

20 Springhill Road, Moneymore, Magherafelt, Co. Londonderry, BT45 7NQ.

Owner: The National Trust   **Contact:** The Administrator

17th century 'Planter' house with 18th and 19th century additions. Springhill was the home of ten generations of a family which arrived from Ayrshire in the 17th century and the house contains family furniture, a refurbished nursery, paintings, ornaments, curios and 18th century hand-blocked wallpaper. Outbuildings house an extensive costume collection and there are walled gardens and woodland walks.

Location: On Moneymore - Coagh road B18, 1m from Moneymore.

Opening Times: Apr: weekends and Good Fri - Easter Tue (14 - 18 Apr); May & Jun: weekends and BHs only; Jul & Aug: daily except Thu; Sept: weekends only, 2.00pm - 6.00pm.

Admission: House: Adult £2.20, Child £1.10. Parties £1.60. After hours £2.80.

TEMPLETOWN MAUSOLEUM

Tel: 01238 510721

Templepatrick, Ballyclare, Co. Antrim.

Owner: The National Trust   **Contact:** The Administrator

Built in 1783 by Robert Adam in memory of the Hon. Arthur Upton.

Location: In Castle Upton graveyard at Templepatrick on Belfast - Antrim road A6.

Opening Times: All year during daylight hours.

THE ARGORY

Tel: 0186 87 84753

Moy, Dungannon, Co. Tyrone, BT71 6NA.

Owner: The National Trust   **Contact:** The Administrator

Set in over 300 acres of woodland, the house dates from 1820 and was substantially changed in the 19th century. Fascinating furniture and contents. Imposing stableyard with coach house and carriages. Interesting sundial garden and extensive walks. NOTE: Certain rooms have no electric light. Visitors wishing to make a close study of the interior and paintings should avoid dull days early and late in the season.

Location: On Derrycaw Road, 4m from Moy , 3m from M1, Exit 13 or 14.

Opening Times: Easter (14 - 18 Apr), Apr, May, Jun: Weekends & BHs only; Jul & Aug daily except Tues 2.00pm - 6.00pm (open from 1.00pm on BHs). Last admission 5.15pm.

Admission: House and grounds: Adult £2.20, Child £1.10, Parties £1.60. After hours £2.80. Car park 50p.

WELLBROOK BEETLING MILL

Tel: 016487 51735

20 Wellbrook Street, Corkhill, Cookstown, Co Tyrone, BT80 9RY.

Owner: The National Trust   **Contact:** The Administrator

Hammer mill powered by water for beetling - the final process in linen manufacture. Original machinery is in working order. The mill is situated in attractive glen, with wooded walks along the Ballinderry river and by the mill race.

Location: 4m W of Cookstown, 1/2 m off Cookstown - Omagh road, from Cookstown turn right at Kildress Parish Church or follow Orritor Road to avoid town centre.

Opening Times: Easter daily 2.00pm - 6.00pm, Apr, May, Jun & Sept. Sat, Sun & BH only 2.00pm - 6.00pm, July & Aug. daily except Tue 2.00pm - 6.00pm.

Admission: Adults £1.40, Child 70p, Parties £1.00. Pre-booked parties outside normal opening hours £1.80.

ACCOMODATION

in Privately Owned Historic Houses

Included are houses where accommodation is provided as an ancillary to the house's function as a family home.

Staying at one of these houses provides visitors with the opportunity to be private guests in comfortable, historic country houses. You will be made to feel at home as personal guests of your host and hostess.

Bedroom and bathroom arrangements are as you would find when staying in any private country residence. Often en-suite bathrooms are available otherwise your bathroom will be close by, probably exclusive to you.

Because these houses are not hotels, visitors should observe usual courtesies as when staying with friends. The visits must be arranged in advance and hostesses will want to know the time of your arrival, which because they may be out and about during the day should not normally be much before 5pm. Meals will be served at normal times rather than on demand and on occasion it may not be possible for the hostess to provide dinner but visitors would be informed beforehand and recommended to a local restaurant if they so wish.

Accommodation is also available in some houses listed in the previous (dark blue titled) section but usually on either a totally exclusive basis or in conjunction with conferences and functions *(see the accommodation index on page 276).*

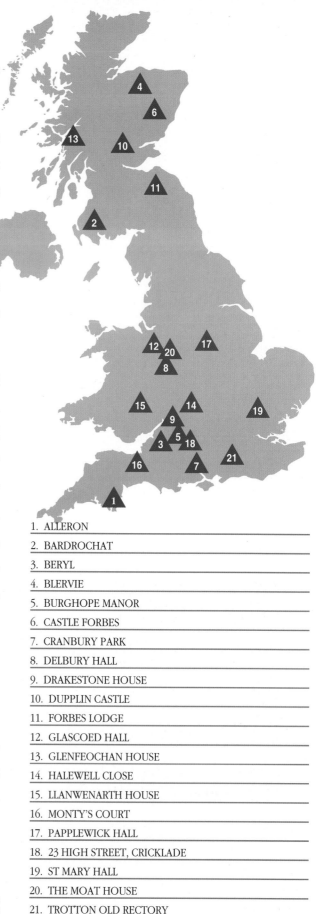

1. ALLERON
2. BARDROCHAT
3. BERYL
4. BLERVIE
5. BURGHOPE MANOR
6. CASTLE FORBES
7. CRANBURY PARK
8. DELBURY HALL
9. DRAKESTONE HOUSE
10. DUPPLIN CASTLE
11. FORBES LODGE
12. GLASCOED HALL
13. GLENFEOCHAN HOUSE
14. HALEWELL CLOSE
15. LLANWENARTH HOUSE
16. MONTY'S COURT
17. PAPPLEWICK HALL
18. 23 HIGH STREET, CRICKLADE
19. ST MARY HALL
20. THE MOAT HOUSE
21. TROTTON OLD RECTORY

ALLERON

PRICES
B & B: £29.00 / £26.00
Dinner: £19.50

OPEN
All year except Xmas.

HOST
Mrs. Lavinia Davies

Tel: 01548 550306

LODDISWELL, KINGSBRIDGE, SOUTH DEVON TQ7 4ED

A very special Regency Country House, beautifully situated in its own peaceful valley surrounded by 40 acres of grass farmland, woods and lakes. Gardens of 3 acres feature a unique circular thatched walled garden, age and origin unknown; also a Butter House with a lily pond fed by a spring. Lavinia makes all the bread and preserves; fresh coffee and spring water complete the delicious meals. An excellent base for enjoying this pretty area, the coast, Dartmoor and East Cornwall.

Location: 4 miles north of Kingsbridge, 6 miles south of the A38 and Dartmoor. Plymouth 18 miles, Exeter 30 miles (approx. distances).

BARDROCHAT

PRICES
B & B: £55.00 /person
Dinner: £45.00
inclusive of all drinks.

OPEN
April - October

HOST
Mr and Mrs. A McEwan

Tel: 01465 88242

GIRVAN, AYRSHIRE

Built by Robert Lorimer in 1893 for the present owner's grandfather, Bardrochat stands high on the south side of the Stinchar Valley. The house sleeps six couples in great comfort with their own bathrooms. The maximum is eighteen. Centrally situated for the great golf courses and gardens with its own tennis court, croquet and salmon fishing. The Walled Garden provides all the vegetables for the house and memorable food. All drinks are included in the price.

Location: Nr. Colmonell, 10 miles south of Girvan.

BERYL

PRICES
B & B: £32.50 - £37.50
Single: £45.00
Dinner: £18.00

OPEN
All year except
24 - 27 Dec.

HOST
Eddie & Holly Nowell

Tel: 01749 678738
Fax: 01749 670508

WELLS, SOMERSET BA5 3JP

A small mansion built in Gothic revival style in its original parkland of 13 acres. The reception rooms and bedrooms are comfortably furnished with antiques and have ensuite facilities and direct dial telephone. Holly enjoys cooking using much of the produce from the 3/4 acre walled vegetable garden. Eddie, a senior member of the B.A.D.A. still keeps shop in Wells. They enjoy dining with their guests and serving local and well selected wines and drinks.

Location: 1 mile North East of Wells Cathedral.

BLERVIE

PRICES
B & B: £22.50 - £25.00
Dinner: £16.50

OPEN
All year.

HOST
Lt. Cdr. and
Mrs I.P.F. Meiklejohn

Tel: 01309 672358

BY FORRES, MORAY IV36 0RH

Built in 1766 from the stone of the ruined Blervie castle, Blervie is strategically situated within an easy day's driving of Strathspey, the Monaliadhs and the spectacular West Highlands. Fiona and Paddy enjoy making their guests feel thoroughly at home among attractive furnishings and antique furniture and acquainting them with the nearby castles and museums which give witness to Scotland's turbulent history and culture. Dinner in the period dining room features game dishes, local produce and fresh garden vegetables.

Location: In the centre of Forres High street turn south by the clocktower; straight across next roundabout and exit town on the B91010 St. Leonards road. Past hospital and two miles sign "Mains of Blervie' on left. Follow sign and turn right at farm.

BURGHOPE MANOR

PRICES
B & B: £35.00/£40.00 ea.
Dinner: by arrangement

OPEN
All year except
Christmas & New Year.

HOST
Elizabeth & John
Denning

Tel: 01225 723557
Fax: 01225 723113

WINSLEY, BRADFORD -ON-AVON, WILTSHIRE BA15 2LA

An historic and beautiful home 5 miles from the Roman-Georgian city of Bath, on the edge of Winsley village which overlooks the glorious Avon valley. Dating from the 13th century it is a fine example of an English Manor House, a living family home with a most relaxed and friendly atmosphere.
Burghope offers the best of both worlds - tradition and elegance combined with every modern comfort and facility. For those seeking an attractive outdoor life it is in the centre of an area which offers superlative sports facilities.

Location: 5 miles Bath off A36 onto B3108, Bradford-on Avon Road.

CASTLE FORBES

PRICES
B & B: £75.00
Dinner: £45.00

OPEN
All year.

HOST
The Hon.
Mrs. Malcolm Forbes.

Tel: 01975 562574
or 01975 562524
Fax: 01975 562898

ALFORD, ABERDEENSHIRE AB33 8DR

Built in 1815 by the 17th Lord Forbes, Castle Forbes occupies a magnificent site in parkland overlooking the Don. It is now owned and occupied by his great-great-great grandson Malcolm, The Master of Forbes, and his wife Jinny. Flowers from the delightful courtyard garden that Jinny created, wonderful dinners based on fresh Estate produce and fine wine complement the warm, friendly and relaxed atmosphere. Outdoor activities including fishing, Roe stalking, tennis and walks, are available on Forbes Estate.

Location: Four miles north of Alford on River Don. Aberdeen 25 miles.

CRANBURY PARK

PRICES
B & B: £70.00 /single
£140.00/couple
Dinner: £30.00 ea.

OPEN
1 April - 30 September

HOST
Penelope
Chamberlayne-
Macdonald

Tel: 01703 252617
Fax: 01703 262692

WINCHESTER, HAMPSHIRE SO21 2HL

Cranbury was built in 1780 by George Dance for his brother and sister-in-law Sir Nathaniel and Lady Dance-Holland. It was left to the Chamberlayne family in the early part of the 19th Century when the pleasure grounds were laid out, and most of the paintings and furiture were acquired.

Location: 5 miles south of Winchester, off exit 12 on M3. Entrance lodge in Hocombe Road Chandlers Ford, 1 mile west of exit 12.

DELBURY HALL

PRICES
B & B: £35.00-50.00
Dinner: £25.00 ea.

OPEN
All year except Xmas.

HOST
Patrick & Lucinda
Wrigley

Tel: 01584 841267
Fax: 01584 841441

LUDLOW, SHROPSHIRE SY7 9DH

Delbury is in a tranquil setting with flower filled gardens, two trout lakes for fly fishing and a hard tennis court. A home farm provides Jersey milk and hand churned butter and a walled garden produces vegetables. Patrick and Lucinda have 2 small children, Jack and Kate and Patrick is an experienced cook (Leith's). Extremely comfortable bedrooms, with private bathroom, colour TV and telephone, guests sitting room, dining room, snooker room and drinks licence.

Location: In Shropshire's Corvedale, between Ludlow and Much Wenlock.

DRAKESTONE HOUSE

PRICES
B & B: £23.00/person
Dinner: £15.00/person

OPEN
April - October.

HOST
Hugh & Crystal
St. John Mildmay

Tel: 01453 542140

DRAKESTONE HOUSE, DURSLEY, GLOUCESTERSHIRE

A fine listed Edwardian country house with links with Arts and Craft Movement. Hugh's grandparents laid out the formal gardens with terraces and yew hedges before the First World War, and Hugh and Crystal since taking over the family home have been engaged in a steady process of restoration. Guests are offered a warm welcome and a relaxing atmosphere at Drakestone. It is ideal centre for touring the Cotswold and within easy reach of Bath and Bristol.

Location: Midway between Dursley and Wotton-under-Edge on B4060.

DUPPLIN CASTLE

PRICES
B & B: £45.00/person
Dinner: £28.00 ea.

OPEN
All year except Xmas
and New Year.

HOST
Derek and Angela
Straker

Tel: 01738 623224
Fax: 01738 444140

BY PERTH, PERTHSHIRE PH2 0PY

Rebuilt on the site of the original castle in 1969 in private parkland. The balustraded terrace and rose garden have stunning views over the lovely Earn valley and the reception and bed rooms are elegantly furnished to a high standard. Ideally situated for the River Tay valley with shooting, roe stalking, fishing and golf (St Andrews, Rosemount at Blairgowrie, Auchterader) available by prior arrangement. Theatres in Perth & Pitlochry, Polo and National Hunt Racing at nearby Scone Palace. Derek and Angela make their guests feel at home and enjoy entertaining providing them with delicious food. Perth 10 mins. Edinburgh & Glasgow 1 hour.

Location: From M90 roundabout, A93 towards Perth for 1 mile; sharp turn right B9112 to Fortevoit & Dunning after 2.7 mls the lodge and ornamental gates are on the right (N) side of the road. From Stirling/Glasgow ornamental gates approx. 3.5 miles S of Perth on the E side of the A9.

FORBES LODGE

PRICES
B & B: £40.00/person
Dinner: £18.00/person

OPEN
All Year.

HOST
Lady Marioth Hay.

Tel: 01620 81212

GIFFORD, HADDINGTON, EAST LOTHIAN, SCOTLAND EH4 14VE

A handsome eighteenth-century house dating from 1763, just 18 miles from Edinburgh. It is a most stylish home with family portraits going back over 200 years. One of the bedrooms is sumptuous, with a bathroom of grand proportions in keeping with the whole house. It is a memorable experience staying with Lady Marioth whose enjoyment of entertaining, music and gardening complements the atmosphere of this delightful house. Castles are plentiful in the area as are golf courses including Muirfield and Gullane. There are also 2 very good restaurants located in the village.

Location: On the edge of Gifford. Four miles from the A1.

GLASCOED HALL

PRICES
B & B: £30.00/person
Dinner: £17.00/person

OPEN
All Year except
Christmas and
New Year.

HOST
Ben & Louise
Howard- Baker.

Tel: 0691 791334

LLANSILIN, NR. OSWESTRY, SHROPSHIRE SY10 9BP

A grade II listed Elizabethan Hall of historical interest, set in the beautiful foothills of the Welsh borders, yet within easy reach of Chester, Shrewbury and numerous historic houses and castles. Ben and Louise enjoy entertaining guests in their home which features magnificent oak beams and staircase open log fires and antique furniture. There is a heated outdoor swimming pool and a hard tennis court within the gardens.

Location: Five miles south west of Oswestry, Shrewsbury 25 miles.

GLENFEOCHAN HOUSE

PRICES
Dble. Room: £128.00
Dinner: £30.00/person

OPEN
1 March - 31 October

HOST
David & Patricia Baber

Tel: 01631 770273
Fax: 01631 770624

KILMORE, BY OBAN, ARGYLLSHIRE PA34 4QR

Glenfeochan House is turreted Victorian Country Mansion built in 1875 and set amidst a 350 acre Estate of Hills, Lochs, Rivers and Pasture. The House is surrounded by one of the Great Gardens of the Highlands. Rare trees, magnificent Rhododendrons, Azaleas, carpets of spring bulbs and spectacular Walled Garden. There, the vegetables, herbs and flowers that decorate the house grow. With three beautifully appointed rooms and the excellent cuisine, this house is an exceptional place to stay.

Location: 5 miles south of Oban on the A816.

HALEWELL CLOSE

PRICES
B & B: £39.50ea. - Dble
B & B: £49.50ea. - Sgl.
Dinner: £19.50/person

OPEN
All Year.

HOST
Mrs E.J Carey-Wilson

Tel: 01242 890238
Fax: 01242 890332

HALEWELL CLOSE, WITHINGTON, CHELTENHAM, GLOS GL54 4BN

Halewell is in the heart of the Cotswolds, on the edge of a quiet and pretty village off the main tourist routes. The main reception rooms were a fifteenth century Monastery. The six double or twin rooms are all ensuite and include two family suites and one especially built for disabled guests. The fifty acre grounds include formal gardens, a secluded children's play area, a landscaped pool and a five acre lake.

Location: 8 miles E of Cheltenham, S of A40. London 90 miles, Oxford 35 miles.

LLANWENARTH HOUSE

PRICES
B & B: £32 - £35ea.Dble
B & B: £48 - £50ea. Sgl.
Dinner: £21.00/person

OPEN
March - Mid January

HOST
Amanda & Bruce
Weatherill

Tel: 01873 830289
Fax: 01873 832199

GOVILON, ABERGAVENNY, GWENT NP7 9SF

The house which predates 1600 was the ancestral home of the Morgans; Privateer, Captain Henry (1635-1688) Governor of Jamaica being the best known. Now restored to something approaching it's former splendour, it is the family home of the Weatherills, who with the children and friendly Lurcher dogs welcome guests. Apertifs in the Georgian Drawing room are followed by dinner, utilising much home grown produce, accompanied by fine wine from the cellar. The history of the area embraces ancient castles and many relics of the Industrial revolution.

Location: From junction of A40 Monmouth, A465 from Hereford and A4042 from Newport, east of Abergavenny follow A465 towards Merthyr Tydfil for 3^{1}/$_{2}$ miles to next roundabout. Take first exit to Govilon, and the ^{1}/$_{2}$ mile drive is 150 yards on right-hand side.

MOAT HOUSE

PRICES
B & B: £32.00/ person
Dinner: from £20.00

OPEN
1 April - 31 October

HOST
Peter & Margaret
Richards

Tel: 01743 718434
Fax: 01743 718434

LONGNOR, NR SHREWSBURY, SHROPSHIRE SY5 7PP

A 15th Century timber framed manor house, set within its 700 year old water filled moat. Dine in the open hall beneath the unique carved timbers with its massive stone fireplace. Enjoy the medieval hospitality and ambience of this peaceful, friendly home. Capture a sense of timelessness in a changing world. En-suite facilities and central heating ensure 20th Century comforts.
The natural grounds harbour many wild herbs, flowers, birds and animals.

Location: 8 miles south of Shrewsbury A49, turn east to Longor, through village, left into lane signed 'No Through Road', lane turns sharp left, Moat House straight ahead.

MONTYS COURT

PRICES
B & B: £30.00 - £25.00
Dinner: £15.00
(if required)

OPEN
All Year

HOST
Major & Mrs A. C. W.
Mitford-Slade

Tel: 01823 432255

TAUNTON, SOMERSET TA4 1BT

Described by one visitor as a house that opens its arms to welcome you. Built in 1838 for the Slade family, the house is set in parkland with views to the Quantock and Blackdown Hills. At the end of a large, well maintained garden are hard tennis courts and a heated swimming pool (May - Sept.). Exmoor, the North Devon coast and numerous National Trust Properties are within easy reach. 18 hole golf course at Oake (2 miles). Children over 12 welcome.

Location: South side of B3227, 1 mile west of Norton Fitzwarren (home of Taunton Cider), 4 miles west of Taunton.

NUMBER TWENTY THREE

PRICES
B & B: £26.00
Dinner: £16.00
(By prior request)

OPEN
All Year except
Christmas
and New Year

HOST
Robin & Patti Shield

Tel: 01793 750205

23 HIGH STREET, CRICKLADE, WILTSHIRE SN6 6AP

Number twenty three is a fine Queen Anne Grade II town house in the historic small town of Cricklade at the Southern edge of the Cotswolds. The house has recently been restored and furnished to the highest standard and has featured in articles in *Country Homes, Interiors* and other magazines. Patti is a trained cordon bleu cook, and in season, meals feature produce from the walled kitchen garden.

Location: Cricklade is just off the A419 Swindon/Cirencester road and is a few minutes from junction 15 of the M4. The house is situated in front of St. Sampson's Church.

PAPPLEWICK HALL

PRICES
B & B: £45.00
Dinner: £25.00

OPEN
All Year

HOST
Dr. & Mrs. Richard
Godwin-Austen

Tel: 0115 9633491

PAPPLEWICK, NOTTINGHAMSHIRE NG15 8FE

This lovely Georgian house, Grade I listed, stands in twelve acres of grounds on the edge of Sherwood Forest, convenient for Newstead Abbey, Thoresby, Chatsworth, Hardwick, Haddon, Calke Abbey, Kedleston, Belton, Sudbury and Belvoir Castles, Southwell and Lincoln Cathedrals. Royal Crown Derby China and Nottingham Lace manufacturers can all be visited. Richard and Jane enjoy entertaining visitors at their beautiful home.
Location: 5 miles off M1 motorway off M1 motorway, exit 27, on B683 between Nottingham and Mansfield.

ST MARY HALL

PRICES
B & B: £24.00 -£28.00
Dinner: £16.00 - £20.00

OPEN
2 Jan - 20 Dec

HOST
Mr & Mrs David Morse

Tel: 01787 237202

BELCHAMP WALTER, SUDBURY, SUFFOLK CO10 7BB

Although houses have stood on the site since Domesday Book and before, the present building dates mainly from the late 15th and early 16th Centuries. Catherine and David have made an attractive garden in the 5 acres surrounding the house which contains a tennis court and heated swimming pool. This is a convenient centre for visiting the "Wool towns' of South Suffolk, as also Bury St Edmunds, Cambridge and Ely. Stansted Airport is less than 40 minutes away, and Harwich Ferry Terminal about an hour.
Location: 5 miles from Sudbury off the minor road through Bulmer and Gestingthorpe leading to Great Yeldham on the A604 1^1/₂ miles SW from cross-roads in Belchamp Walter.

TROTTON OLD RECTORY

PRICES
B & B: £35.00/person
Dinner: £20.00/person

OPEN
All Year.

HOST
Captain & Mrs John
Pilley

Tel: 01730 813612

NEAR PETERSFIELD, HAMPSHIRE GU31 5EN

This attractive Georgian former rectory with its curled slate roof and shutters is reminiscent of France and provides a relaxed, comfortable and peaceful atmosphere in summer and winter. The typical English garden with its rose beds designed by Hazel Le Rougetel, framed in a box and yew, has two levels with beautiful and interesting trees and shrubs running down to the lake and the River Rother. There is also a fruit and vegetable garden which supplies the house.
Location: On the A272. 2 miles form Midhurst and 5 miles from Petersfield. The drive is opposite the Church and just west of the bridge.

AMBERLEY CASTLE
Nr. Arundel, West Sussex

Begun in the early 1100's by Bishop Luffa of Chichester as a country manor house, Amberley Castle's raison d'etre was to provide a peaceful retreat and a setting for lavish entertainment, for half a millennium Amberley Castle has fulfiled this role for a succession of episcopal chatelains.

Its subsequent secular tenants continued the tradition to the highest level in the land, extending hospitality to King Charles II and his Queen, Catherine of Braganza. The 17th century mural in the Queen's Room, Amberley Castle's handsome barrel-vaulted restaurant, commemorates the occasion.

Marauding pirates may have threatened the peace within the mighty 14th century walls which Oliver Cromwell's soldiers tried to reduce to rubble. But Amberley Castle has endured, bringing with it to the present day its tranquillity, its security and the wonderful sense of history that envelopes all who enter beneath the great oaken portcullis.

Since 1989, Amberley Castle's owners, Joy and Martin Cummings, have wrought a miracle in the ancient building, transforming it into a peaceful, luxurious hotel, its 14 superbly appointed rooms, each named after a Sussex castle and boasting an en-suite Jacuzzi bath.

The three lovely lounges, each with its own individual character offer space and comfort conducive to conversation and relaxation. There are two private dining rooms for parties or small business meetings, and the magnificent Great Room for banquets and receptions of every kind.

The magic of Amberley Castle has inspired another unique innovation: Castle Cuisine, the exciting creation of Award-winning Head Chef, Nigel Boschetti. English culinary tradition - the ingredients and cooking methods of our forebears - together with the castle's own history have inspired Nigel to create dishes which draw their origins from the past while pleasing the palates of today.

Just an hour from the clamour of the City, yet steeped in the peace of beautiful Sussex Downland, there is a treat in store for Amberley Castle's guests - friendly service, splendid food, serenity.

The warmth of Amberley Castle's welcome has resulted in an array of prestigious awards including an RAC Blue Ribbon, 2 AA Rosettes and "Best Family Run Hotel in the World Award 1993" (Gallivanter's Guide).

PRICE GUIDES

Day delegate : £35.00

24 hr. delegate: £135.00

Rooms

Single: £95.00 - £225.00

Double: £95.00 - £225.00

Includes breakfast, newspaper and VAT. All rooms have en-Suite Bathrooms. Jacuzzi.

CARTE BLANCHE - 2 DAYS

Sun - Thurs £345.00

Fri - Sun £445.00

Include dinner, breakfast and VAT on both nights.

CONTACT

Resident Proprietors, Joy & Martin Cummings, Amberley Castle Amberley Arundel West Sussex BN18 9ND

Tel: (01798) 831992

Fax: (01798) 831998

LOCATION

Amberley Castle is situated on the B2139 between A29 at Bury Hill and Storrington

Rail: Located 1/2 mile from Amberley station (Direct line service to London Victoria).

ATTRACTIONS

The Castle is surrounded by a wealth of attractions for the discerning traveller including Parham and Petworth House, Goodwood House and Racecourse and only 40 minutes drive from Historic Portsmouth and Brighton.

FACILITIES

◆ 14 Luxury Rooms all with en-suite Jacuzzi
◆ Peace and Tranquility
◆ Award winning Restaurant
◆ Full conference and Private Dining Facilities
◆ All major Credit Cards accepted
◆ Children welcome
◆ Colour T.V. Video & Video Library
◆ Direct dial telephones
◆ Helicopter landing facilities
◆ Horse Riding and croquet
◆ Clay Shooting and Archery by prior arrangement
◆ Ornamental Gardens

CONFERENCE AND FUNCTION FACILITIES

ROOM	DIMENSIONS	CAPACITY	LAYOUT	POWER POINTS	SUITABLE FOR A/V
Great Room	35' 11" x 14' 10"	48	Banquet		✓
		30	Boardroom		
King Charles 1st Room	17' x 13'	12	Boardroom		✓

The Landmark Trust

A CHARITY WHICH RESTORES HISTORIC BUILDINGS AND LETS THEM FOR HOLIDAYS

Over 150 places where you can become, for a short time, the owner of a fine historic building. No membership is required but you do need to buy The Landmark Handbook which illustrates every property with plans, location maps and black and white photographs (£8.50, refundable against your booking).

WARDEN ABBEY

NR. BIGGLESWADE, BEDFORDSHIRE

Landmarks are chosen for their historic interest or architectural importance, because they need our help, and also because many are in surroundings which give unexpected pleasure. Warden Abbey is a fragment of a great Cistercian Abbey and a Tudor House, set in fruitful countryside, once farmed by monks.

Accommodation:
Sleeps up to 5 people.

CULLODEN TOWER

RICHMOND, NORTH YORKSHIRE

The beauty of the Landmark solution is not only that a building is saved and put to good use, but also that the restoration respects its original design. For a short time it is possible to live with rooms in surprising places. At Culloden Tower, there are 68 steps between the bathroom and the main bedroom.

Accommodation:
Sleeps 4 people.

LANGLEY GATEHOUSE

ACTON BURNELL, SHROPSHIRE

Landmarks often lie off the beaten track. Langley is no exception, set in a remote valley with a view to the Wrekin. In our restorations, we prefer to repair the old, and avoid renewal, to preserve the building's texture. When the building is timber framed, this can be like trying to patch a cobweb !

Accommodation:
Sleeps 4 people.

EAST BANQUETING HOUSE

CHIPPING CAMPDEN, GLOUCESTERSHIRE

Some Landmarks, like this one, reflect a way of life from more gracious times and are connected with grand old families. All are furnished as appropriately as possible, with curtains designed and printed for each place, and furniture which is old, simple and good, with occasional extravagant flourishes.
Accommodation: Sleeps 4, a further 2 beds in the North Lodge.

SANDERS

LETTAFORD, NORTH BOVEY, DEVON

We do not favour any one age or style of building. Landmarks range from the humble to the grand and from the eccentric to the purely functional. Sanders is a Dartmoor Longhouse. Inner room, hall, cross-passage and cow-byre are all under one roof, with a porch which once gave entry to both cows and people.
Accommodation: Sleeps 5 people.

KINGSWEAR CASTLE

NR. DARTMOOR, SOUTH DEVON

Landmark cares for many redundant buildings, put up for a specific purpose but no longer needed. Among them are five forts. Kingswear Castle's design was revolutionary in 1500, but was soon outdated. In an idyllic setting at the mouth of the River Dart, you feel from inside as if you are genuinely at sea.
Accommodation: Sleeps 4 with further 2 in the WWII blockhouse, 50 yards from the main fort.

The Landmark Trust, Shottesbrooke, Maidenhead, Berkshire SL6 3SW
Charity Number: 243312   **Telephone (01628) 825925   Facsimilie (01628) 825417**

ST. OSYTH ABBEY
also known as ST. OSYTH PRIORY
ESSEX, DEDHAM 12 MILES, COLCHESTER 12 MILES, FRINTON 8 MILES

St. Osyth Priory was founded in 1191 and remained a priory for 80 years, after which it was raised to the rank of abbey for 400 years unntil the dissolution of the monasteries, and was one of the great Augustinian abbeys of Europe.

Beautiful gardens overlooking a deer park including a rose garden, topiary garden and wide-spreading lawns, surrounded by buildings half as old as England's History, which create an important serenity in the modern world, and where peacocks stroll on shady lawns.

Famous art collection including the world-famous painting of Whistlejacket by George Stubbs, ARA and other paintings by Stubbs, Van Dyck, Lely, etc.

Banqueting Hall with ceiling painted by Edward Ladell 1866

State Drawing Room with famous Oriel window dated 1527 AD with numerous carved escutcheons.

Opening times: Art Collection May to September 30th every day except Saturdays 10.30 to 12.30 and 2.30 to 4.30.
Admission £3.50 adults, £2.50 OAP's Children £1.00   Garden open 10am to 5pm.

ACCOMODATION INDEX

HUDSON'S DIRECTORY INDEX